Solving Problems in Fluid Dynamics

Other titles in the Series

Solving Problems in Vibrations, *J.S. Anderson and M. Bratos-Anderson*

Solving Problems in Fluid Mechanics Volume 1, *J.F. Douglas*

Solving Problems in Fluid Mechanics Volume 2, *J.F. Douglas*

Solving Problems in Soil Mechanics, Second Edition, *B.H.C. Sutton*

Solving Problems in Applied Thermodynamics and Energy Conversion. *G.J. Sharpe*

Solving Problems in Solid Mechanics Volume 1, *S.A. Urry and P.J. Turner*

Solving Problems in Solid Mechanics Volume 2, *S.A. Urry and P.J. Turner*

Solving Problems in Structures Volume 1, *P.C.L. Croxton and L.H. Martin*

Solving Problems in Structures Volume 2, *P.C.L. Croxton and L.H. Martin*

Solving Problems in Electrical Power and Power Electronics, *H.F.G. Gwyther*

Solving Problems in Surveying, *A. Bannister and R. Baker*

Solving Problems in Control, *R.J. Richards*

Solving Problems in Fluid Dynamics

G. J. Sharpe BSc(Eng), BSc, MPhil, CEng, MIMechE, FInstE

Longman Scientific & Technical

Longman Scientific & Technical
Longman Group UK Limited
Longman House, Burnt Mill, Harlow
Essex CM20 2JE, England
and Associated Companies throughout the world

Copublished in the United States with
John Wiley & Sons, Inc., 605 Third Avenue, New York
NY 10158

First published 1994

British Library Cataloguing in Publication Data
A catalogue entry for this title is available from the British Library.

ISBN 0-582-03374-8

Library of Congress Cataloging-in-Publication data
A catalog entry for this title is available from the Library of Congress.

ISBN 0-470-22168-2 (USA only)

Transferred to digital print on demand, 2002
Printed & Bound by Antony Rowe Ltd, Eastbourne

Contents

Preface

This volume contains material associated with BSc courses in Engineering in which a knowledge of fluid dynamics is required. The emphasis is placed on *advanced* aspects of the subject, and a knowledge of the basic principles is assumed. The volume should therefore be appropriate to the final year of study, and some postgraduate areas. Chapters 1-6 cover the theoretical aspects, and Chapters 7-11 applications thereof.

The treatment adopted is the same as that used in the *Solving Problems* series. Each chapter comprises a *summary* of the basic theory or pertinent material, a selection of worked examples, and several examples (with answers) for the reader to attempt. The volume is therefore intended to complement a text book.

The majority of the problems have been devised by the author for use in examinations and tutorial work. Some have been taken from examination papers set by Newcastle-upon-Tyne Polytechnic (now The University of Northumbria in Newcastle), and I am indebted to the University for permission to use them.

Inevitably a few errors may have escaped the scrutiny of the author, publisher and printer. I should be pleased to receive any corrections or constructive criticism.

G. J. Sharpe December 1992

List of symbols

The symbols listed are those which appear throughout the book. Other symbols are stated in the appropriate chapters.

a	acoustic velocity, radius, inflow factor
A	area
b	span
B	buoyancy force $(M^2 - 1)^{1/2}$
c	chord
C	specific heat, coefficient, torque
D	diameter, drag factor
e	internal energy
f	friction coefficient
F	force, influence coefficient, solids/liquid fraction
G	mass flow/unit area, modulus of rigidity
h	enthalpy, width
H	shape factor, height
i	$\sqrt{-1}$, angle of incidence
j	volumetric flux
J	advance ratio
K	bulk modulus, slip ratio
l	mixing length
L	length, mixing length, lift force
m	mass, source/sink strength
M	Mach number, pitching moment
n	speed (rotational)
N	number of particles
p	pressure
P	perimeter, pressure gradient, power
q	flow/unit width
Q	heat, flow rate
r	radius
R	characteristic gas constant, radius, area ratio
s	entropy, relative density, pitch
t	thickness
T	temperature, thrust, torque

u	velocity, phase velocity
U	velocity, superficial velocity
v	velocity, superficial velocity, blade velocity
w	velocity, complex potential function, downwash
W	work, weight
x	mass flow fraction
X	force
y	depth
Y	force
z	complex number

Greek letters

α	voidage fraction, flow ratio, angle of incidence (attack)
β	angle
γ	specific heat ratio
Γ	circulation
δ	deviation angle
Δ	boundary layer thickness
ε	eddy viscosity, surface roughness, porosity
ζ	vorticity, loss coefficient
η	efficiency, boundary layer thickness ratio y/Δ
θ	momentum thickness, blade angle
Λ	Pohlhausen parameter
μ	absolute (dynamic) viscosity, Mach angle, doublet strength
ν	kinematic viscosity, Prandtl-Meyer function
ξ	stagger angle
ρ	density
σ	solidity
τ	shear stress
ϕ	potential function
ψ	stream function, sphericity
Ω	angular velocity

1

Isentropic flow: incompressible flow

The flow and behaviour of a fluid can be described by certain basic equations and, though small in number, can be expressed in many forms. These basic equations are detailed as follows.

State equation

The relationship between pressure p, density ρ and temperature T, for an *ideal* gas is

$$p = \rho RT \tag{1.1}$$

where R = characteristic gas constant.

The specific volume ν_s can be used instead of density, or the volume ν. The state equation is then

$$p\nu_s = RT \text{ or } p\nu = mRT$$

However it is more convenient to use density ρ rather than specific volume and this will be done in this book.

The gas constant and molecular mass (weight) are related by the expression

$$MR = R_0 = 8314 \text{ J/kmol K} \tag{1.2}$$

where M = molecular mass

R_0 = universal gas constant

Real gases diverge from this simple law, especially in the neighbourhood of critical points, or at high pressures, or extreme temperatures; and it does not apply to vapours, such as steam.

A modified form of the state equation is that due to Van der Waals:

$$\left(p + \frac{a}{\nu^2}\right)\left(\nu - b\right) = mRT$$

or

$$\left(p + a\rho^2\right)\left(\frac{1}{\rho} - b\right) = RT$$

where a, b are constants.

Equation of continuity

This equation states the principle of mass conservation, that in a fluid flowing between two stations the mass flow rate is the same at each station. This clearly does not apply if fluid is withdrawn or added between the stations.

In the simplest case of steady, one dimensional flow (Fig. 1.1) the equation is

$$\dot{m} = \rho_1 A_1 u_1 = \rho_2 A_2 u_2 \tag{1.3}$$

where A= cross-sectional area, u= velocity.

In unsteady flow (where the conditions vary with time) the equation becomes

$$\frac{\partial(\rho u)}{\partial x} = -\frac{\partial \rho}{\partial t} \qquad (1.4)$$

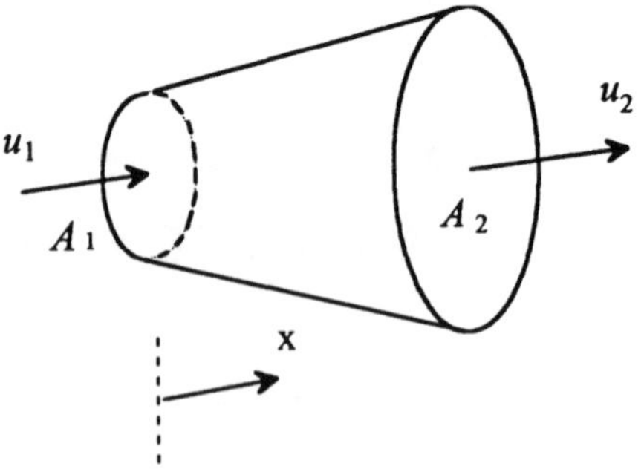

Figure 1.1

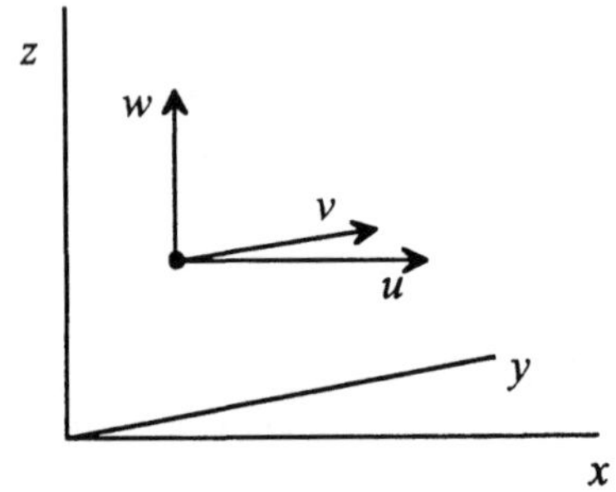

Figure 1.2

The velocity of a fluid may be two or three dimensional. If the velocity components are u, v, w in the directions of the x, y, z axes respectively (Fig. 1.2), the *continuity equation* takes the form

$$\frac{\partial(\rho u)}{\partial x} + \frac{\partial(\rho v)}{\partial y} + \frac{\partial(\rho w)}{\partial z} = -\frac{\partial \rho}{\partial t} \qquad (1.5)$$

and for an incompressible (constant density) fluid

$$\frac{\partial u}{\partial x} + \frac{\partial v}{\partial y} + \frac{\partial w}{\partial z} = 0 \qquad (1.6)$$

Energy equation

This equation expresses the principle of the conservation of energy, that energy cannot be created or destroyed. Thus energy can be converted from one form to another, but the *total* energy content of a fluid remains constant.

The energy in a fluid can take several forms, such as:

(a) pressure energy $\frac{p}{\rho}$ (J/kg)

(b) kinetic energy $\frac{1}{2}v^2$ (J/kg)

(c) potential energy gz (J/kg)

(d) internal energy $e = C_V T$ (J/kg)

(e) enthalpy $h = C_P T$ (J/kg) $= e + \frac{p}{\rho}$

where v = velocity of the fluid.

The steady flow energy equation is

$$Q - W_s = \Delta(h + gz + \tfrac{1}{2}v^2) \tag{1.7}$$

or, in differential form:

$$Q - W_s = dh + gdz + vdv \tag{1.8}$$

where Q = heat added to, or rejected by, the fluid

W_s = external (shaft) work done by or on the fluid.

In many cases the fluid flow does not involve any external work, and if the flow is adiabatic (no heat transfer into or out of the fluid) the equation becomes

$$dh + gdz + vdv = 0$$

or

$$h + gz + \tfrac{1}{2}v^2 = \text{constant} \tag{1.9}$$

The alternative form is

$$dp + \rho gdz + \rho vdv = 0 \tag{1.10}$$

or

$$p + \rho qz + \tfrac{1}{2}\rho v^2 = \text{constant} \tag{1.11}$$

This form is known as the *Bernoulli* equation.

In the flow of a fluid in a pipe or duct, for example, work is done by the fluid in overcoming frictional effects at the duct walls. In this case the Bernoulli equation takes the form

$$dp + \rho gdz + \rho vdv + dp_f = 0 \tag{1.12}$$

or

$$p + \rho gz + \tfrac{1}{2}\rho v^2 + \Delta p_f = \text{constant} \tag{1.13}$$

where Δp_f denotes the pressure drop due to friction.

The equations can also be expressed in terms of the *stagnation* enthalpy h_o or pressure p_o. These are defined as

$$h_0 = h + \tfrac{1}{2}v^2 \text{ or } dh_0 = dh + vdv$$

$$dp_0 = dp + \rho vdv$$

Thus the stagnation pressure is the static pressure that would be attained by the fluid if the fluid was brought to rest isentropically, i.e. all the kinetic energy was completely converted into pressure energy.

Momentum equation

This equation expresses Newton's law of the Conservation of Momentum. Considering linear momentum (mass $\times$ velocity), the general form is given by the Navier-Stokes equations:

$$\rho\left(\frac{\partial v}{\partial t} + v.\nabla v\right) = \rho\mathbf{B} - \nabla p + \mu\nabla^2 v + \tfrac{1}{3}\nabla(v.\nabla v) \tag{1.14}$$

where $\nabla = \mathbf{i}\frac{\partial}{\partial x} + \mathbf{j}\frac{\partial}{\partial y} + \mathbf{k}\frac{\partial}{\partial z}$

$v = \mathbf{i}u + \mathbf{j}v + \mathbf{k}w$

i, **j**, **k** are the unit vectors in the x, y, z directions (Fig. 1.3)

B = body force/unit mass = $-\nabla(gz)$

μ = absolute (dynamic) viscosity

u, v, w are the velocity components in the x, y, z directions.

This general form can be considerably simplified for use in fluid dynamics problems. For *viscous incompressible* fluid the equations become

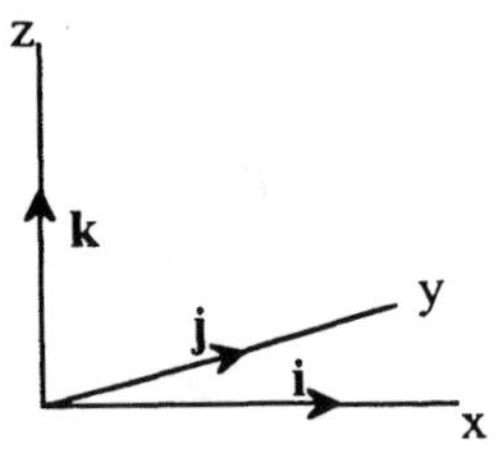

Figure 1.3

$$\frac{\partial \mathbf{v}}{\partial t} + \mathbf{v}.\nabla\mathbf{v} = \mathbf{B} - \frac{\nabla p}{\rho} + \nu.\nabla^2\mathbf{v} = 0 \qquad (1.15)$$

If the fluid is inviscid (negligible viscosity) they become

$$\frac{\partial \mathbf{v}}{\partial t} + \mathbf{v}.\nabla\mathbf{v} = \mathbf{B} - \frac{\nabla p}{\rho} \qquad (1.16)$$

which is known as the *Euler* equation. Taking $\mathbf{B} = -\nabla(gz)$ and integrating gives, for *steady* flow,

$$\frac{1}{2}\mathbf{v}^2 = -gz - \frac{p}{\rho} + \text{constant}$$

which is the *Bernoulli* equation.

For compressible fluid flow the one-dimensional form of the momentum equation is

$$pdA - d(\dot{m}u) - d(pA) - \tau_0 s = 0 \qquad (1.17)$$

where τ_0 = shear stress at the surface, s.

Friction in ducts

The pressure energy of a fluid can be reduced by the work done against frictional effects. The basic law is that due to *Fanning*:

$$\Delta p_f = \frac{4\rho f \mathbf{v}^2 L}{2D_e} \qquad (1.18)$$

where Δp_f = pressure drop due to friction
f = friction coefficient
L = pipe or duct length
D_e = equivalent diameter

The *equivalent diameter* is used for non-circular sections, and is given by the expression

$$D_e = \frac{4 \times \text{area filled by the fluid}}{\text{perimeter in contact with the fluid}}$$

Thus for a circular pipe 'running full' or completely filled by the fluid

$$D_e = 4\left(\frac{\pi D^2}{4}\right)/\pi D = D$$

where D= pipe diameter.

Isentropic flow

The pressure and density are related by the expression

$$p = c\rho^\gamma$$

where c = constant, γ = specific heat ratio, $\frac{C_p}{C_v}$

The stagnation conditions are constant in isentropic flow. Neglecting changes in potential energy, and considering flow only (i.e. no work input/output), the energy equation is

$$h + \frac{1}{2}\mathbf{v}^2 = \text{constant}$$

or $\quad h_o = \text{constant}$

Also, the Bernoulli equation (Ex. 1.3) is

$$\frac{\gamma}{\gamma - 1}\left(\frac{p}{\rho}\right) + \frac{1}{2}\mathbf{v}^2 = \text{constant}$$

$$= \frac{\gamma}{\gamma - 1}\left(\frac{p_0}{\rho_0}\right)$$

and the stagnation pressure is constant. The important aspect of isentropic flow is that both the stagnation pressure and temperature are constant.

Prandtl-Meyer flow

This flow type is particular to *supersonic* regimes, where an isentropic flow is accelerated by expansion round a corner. A fan of Mach waves is generated at the corner to produce a deflection of the supersonic stream. The flow is two-dimensional.

Mach waves are discussed in Ex. 1.10 and Prandtl-Meyer flow in Ex. 1.11. The flow can also be analysed by linearised flow equations, in which first order effects only are considered. This is illustrated in Ex. 1.12.

1.1 Incompressible flow in a pipe

A gas flows along a circular pipe, 20 cm diameter, at a rate of 2.0 kg/s (Fig. 1.4). The density is constant and equal to 1.2 kg/m^3. The friction coefficient is constant and equal to 0.005. Calculate the pressure drop over a length of 20 m.

Solution. The continuity equation for one-dimensional flow is

$$\dot{m} = \rho A u = \text{constant}$$

and, since the density and area are constant, the velocity is constant.

$$u = \frac{\dot{m}}{\rho A} = \frac{2.0}{1.2 \times \frac{\pi}{4}(0.2)^2} = 53.05 \text{ m/s}$$

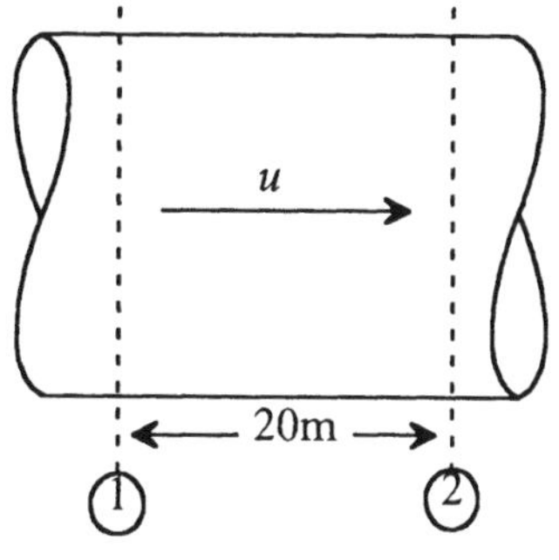

Figure 1.4

The pressure drop is given by the Fanning equation 1.18,

$$\Delta p_f = \frac{4\rho f L u^2}{2D}$$

$$= \frac{4(1.2)(0.005)(20)(53.05)^2}{2(0.2)}$$

$$= \mathbf{3377\ N/m^2}$$

The Fanning equation is not given in the problem, and will therefore be derived. Consider a short element of the pipe, length dx (Fig. 1.5). The application of the momentum equation, viz rate of change of momentum = net force acting on the element, gives

$$pA - (p - dp)A - \tau_0 s = \dot{m}(u_2 - u_1)$$

$$A.dp - \tau_0 s = 0$$

since the velocity is constant.

Hence $dp = \dfrac{\tau_0 s}{A}$

The perimeter of the pipe in contact with the gas is $\pi D dx$, and

$$\frac{s}{A} = \frac{\pi D\,dx}{\frac{1}{4}\pi D^2} = \frac{4dx}{D}$$

Hence $\Delta p_f = \dfrac{4\tau_0\,dx}{D}$

The shear stress at the wall, τ_0, can be expressed in terms of a friction coefficient f

$$\tau_0 = f(\tfrac{1}{2}\rho u^2)$$

Hence $\Delta p_f = \dfrac{4f}{D}(\dfrac{1}{2}\rho u^2)\,dx$

$$= \frac{4\rho f u^2}{2D}dx$$

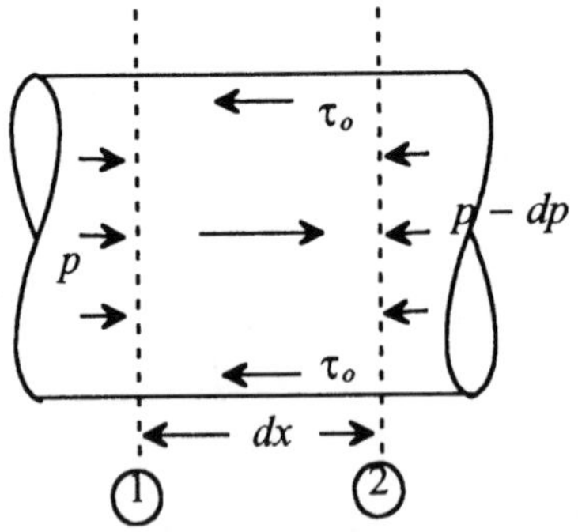

Figure 1.5

Note. The friction coefficient depends upon the fluid properties and the surface roughness. The effect of the fluid properties appears in the Reynolds number $R_e = \rho Du/\mu$, and the type of flow. In a circular pipe the flow is laminar at a Reynolds number less than about 2000, and $f = 16/R_e$. At a Reynolds number greater than about 3000 the flow becomes turbulent, and the relationship between f and Re is more complex: typically of the form $f = a/R_e^n$ where a is a constant, and n an index of value 0.20 to 0.25.

The flow is described as incompressible. It could be more accurately described as constant density flow, since all fluids are compressible (including liquids).

1.2 Incompressible flow in a nozzle

> A convergent nozzle passes water, as shown in Fig. 1.6. At the inlet the static pressure is 3 bar, area = 0.2 m^2 and the water velocity = 5 m/s. The area at exit = 0.1 m^2. Ambient air pressure is 1.0 bar. Neglecting frictional effects calculate the force on the nozzle.

Solution. The fluid flow can be taken as incompressible, with a constant density of 1000 kg/m³.

The continuity equation gives

$$\dot{m} = \rho A_1 u_1 = \rho A_2 u_2 = 1000 \text{ kg/s}$$
$$(0.2)(5) = (0.1)u_2$$
$$u_2 = 10 \text{ m/s}$$

Let F = force exerted by the water on the nozzle. Then the momentum equation gives

$$F + p_1 A_1 - p_2 A_2 - p_a(A_1 - A_2) = \dot{m}(u_2 - u_1)$$

where p_a is the external ambient pressure.

The force can then be determined provided that the static pressure at the exit, p_2, is known. This can be obtained by application of the energy equation 1.11 (Bernoulli). Taking the nozzle as horizontal there is no change in potential energy, and

$$p_1 + \tfrac{1}{2}\rho u_1^2 = p_2 + \tfrac{1}{2}\rho u_2^2$$

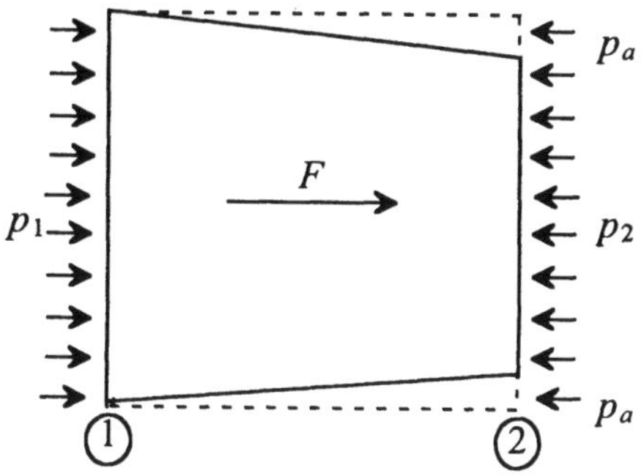

Figure 1.6

$$p_1 - p_2 = \tfrac{1}{2}\rho(u_2^2 - u_1^2)$$
$$= \tfrac{1}{2}(1000)(100 - 25) = 37.5 \text{ kN/m}^3$$

and $\quad p_2 = 300 - 37.5 = 262.5 \text{ kN/m}^3$

Substituting in the momentum equation

$$F = \dot{m}(u_2 - u_1) + p_a(A_1 - A_2) + p_2 A_2 - p_1 A_1$$
$$= 1000(10 - 5) + 10^5(0.2 - 0.1)$$
$$+262.5(1000)(0.1) - 300(1000)(0.2)$$
$$= \mathbf{-18750} \text{ N}$$

Note. A negative sign indicates that the force on the nozzle is in the opposite direction to that assumed in Fig. 1.6 and is to the left.

1.3 Bernoulli equation for compressible flow

> Derive a form of the Bernoulli equation for compressible flow which is (a) isothermal, (b) isentropic. Neglect frictional effects, and potential energy changes.

Solution. The differential form of the equation is

$$dp + \rho g dz + \rho u du + dp_f = 0 \qquad (1.12)$$

In the absence of frictional effects and changes in potential energy this becomes

$$dp + \rho u du = 0$$

If the flow was incompressible the equation can be integrated directly, giving

$$p + \tfrac{1}{2}\rho u^2 = \text{constant}$$

In this case the density is not constant, and depends upon the pressure. The equation can therefore only be integrated if the relationship between pressure and density is known.

(a) An isothermal process is one in which the static temperature is constant.

Hence $p = \rho RT = k\rho$ (say using the state equation).

Substituting in

$$\frac{dp}{\rho} + u du = 0$$

gives

$$k\frac{dp}{p} + u du = 0$$

$$k \ln p + \tfrac{1}{2}u^2 = \text{constant}$$

or, between two points or stations,

$$RT \ln\frac{p_2}{p_1} = \frac{1}{2}(u_1^2 - u_2^2)$$

(b) The necessary relationship in an isentropic process is

$$p = c\rho^\gamma$$

Substituting

$$dp = \gamma c\rho^{\gamma-1}\, d\rho$$

$$\frac{\gamma c\rho^{\gamma-1}}{\rho} d\rho + u\, du = 0$$

$$\gamma c \int \rho^{\gamma-2}\, d\rho + \frac{1}{2}u^2 = \text{constant}$$

$$\frac{\gamma c\rho^{\gamma-1}}{\gamma - 1} + \frac{1}{2}u^2 = \text{constant}$$

Using the relationship $c = p/\rho^\gamma$ gives

$$\frac{\gamma}{\gamma-1}\left(\frac{p_1}{\rho_1} - \frac{p_2}{\rho_2}\right) = \frac{1}{2}\left(u_2^2 - u_1^2\right)$$

1.4 Venturi meter

> A Venturi meter conveys a gas at a rate of 1 kg/s. The gas constant R = 290 J/kg K. Specific heat ratio $\gamma = 1.40$.
>
> The static pressure and temperature in the pipe are 3 bar, 60 °C, the pipe diameter is 125 mm and the throat diameter is 100 mm. Assuming isentropic flow calculate the static pressure and temperature at the throat.
>
> Neglect the potential energy of the fluid.

Solution. A Venturi meter is a device that is used to measure the flow of fluid in a pipe. The reduction in the cross-sectional area produces pressure decrease between the stations 1 and 2 in the pipe and throat, respectively (Fig. 1.7). Measurement of the pressure difference enables the flow rate to be determined.

The energy equation for isentropic flow is

$$\frac{\gamma}{\gamma-1}\left(\frac{p_1}{\rho_1} - \frac{p_2}{\rho_2}\right) = \frac{1}{2}\left(u_2^2 - u_1^2\right)$$

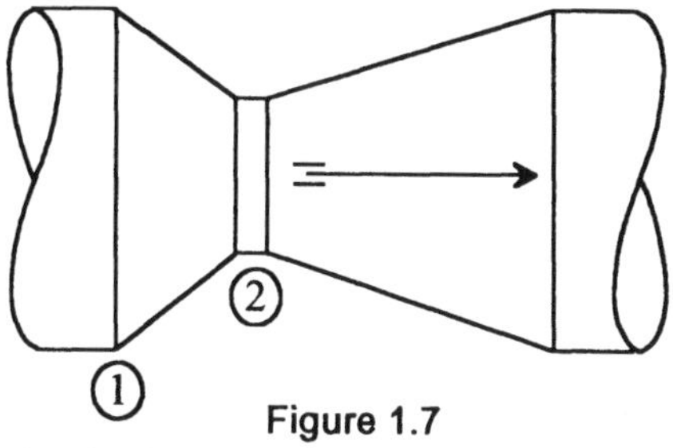

Figure 1.7

At the upstream station in the pipe,

$$\rho_1 = \frac{p_1}{RT_1} = \frac{3(10^5)}{290(333)} = 3.107 \text{ kg/m}^3$$

Using the continuity equation

$$\dot{m} = 1.0 \text{ kg/s} = \rho_1 A_1 u_1 = \rho_2 A_2 u_2$$

$$u_1 = \frac{1.0}{3.107(\frac{\pi}{4})(0.125)^2} = 26.23 \text{ m/s}$$

and $$\rho_2 u_2 = \frac{1}{\frac{\pi}{4}(0.1)^2} = 127.3 \text{ kg/m}^2\text{s}$$

The density at the throat depends upon the static conditions p_2 and T_2. Also the isentropic law gives

$$\frac{p_2}{p_1} = \left(\frac{\rho_2}{\rho_1}\right)^{\gamma}$$

or $$\rho_2 = \rho_1 r^{1/\gamma}$$

where $r = p_2/p_1$

Substituting into the energy equation

$$\frac{\gamma}{\gamma - 1}\left(\frac{p_1}{\rho_1}\right)\left(1 - \frac{r}{r^{1/\gamma}}\right) = \frac{1}{2}\left(\left(\frac{127.3}{\rho_1 r^{1/\gamma}}\right)^2 - (26.23)^2\right)$$

$$\frac{1.4}{0.4}\left(\frac{3 \times 10^5}{3.107}\right)(1 - r^{1-1/\gamma}) = \frac{1}{2}\left(\frac{1678.7}{r^{2/\gamma}} - 688.0\right)$$

$$337947(1 - r^{0.286}) = \frac{839.3}{r^{1.429}} - 344$$

or $$\frac{839.3}{r^{1.429}} + 337947 r^{0.286} = 338291$$

$$r^{1/1.429} + 402.7 r^{0.286} = 403.1$$

Solving by trial and error gives

$$r = 0.995$$

$$p_2 = r p_1 = \mathbf{2.985} \text{ bar}$$

$$\rho_2 = \rho_1 r^{1/\gamma} = 3.107(0.995)^{0.714} = 3.096 \text{ kg/m}^3$$

$$T_2 = \frac{p_2}{\rho_2 R} = \frac{2.985(10^5)}{3.096(290)} = \mathbf{332} \text{ K}$$

1.5 Acoustic velocity: Mach number

Show that the velocity of sound, a, in a gas is given by the equation

$$a = \sqrt{\gamma RT}.$$

State the equation for the velocity in a liquid. Define the Mach number M. Hence derive relationships between the stagnation and static pressure in terms of the Mach number and specific heat ratio γ.

Solution. Consider a plane pressure wave moving through a gas, initially at rest, with a velocity a. The unsteady conditions so produced can be converted into steady state conditions by superimposing a velocity a to the left, as shown in Fig. 1.8.

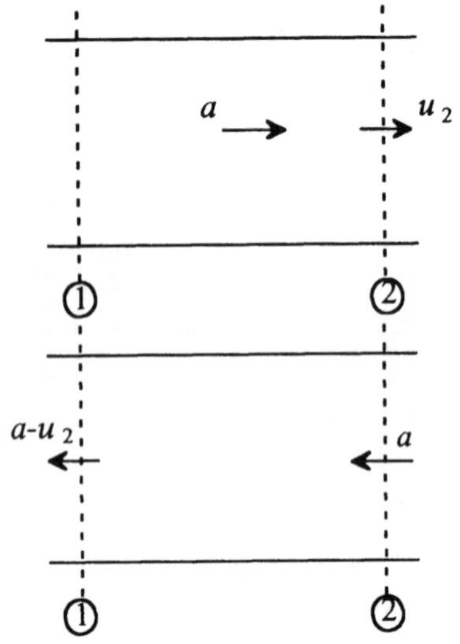

Figure 1.8

The continuity equation gives

$$\rho_1 a = \rho_2(a - u_2)$$

and the momentum equation is

$$p_1 + \rho_1 a^2 = p_2 + \rho_2(a - u_2)^2$$

Combining the equation gives

$$a^2 = \frac{p_1}{\rho_1}\left(\frac{p_2}{p_1} - 1\right)\Big/\left(1 - \frac{\rho_1}{\rho_2}\right) = \frac{\rho_2}{\rho_1}\frac{\Delta p}{\Delta \rho} \quad \text{say}$$

The energy equation is

$$\frac{\gamma}{\gamma - 1}\frac{p_1}{\rho_1} + \frac{1}{2}a^2 = \frac{\gamma}{\gamma - 1}\frac{p_2}{\rho_2} + \frac{1}{2}(a - u_2)^2$$

and this can be rearranged to give

$$a^2 = \frac{\gamma - 1}{2}\frac{p_1}{\rho_1} + \frac{\gamma + 1}{2}\frac{p_1}{\rho_1}\frac{p_2}{p_1}$$

Finally for a small disturbance (weak wave) the wave velocity is

$$a = \text{Lim}\left(\frac{\rho_2}{\rho_1}\frac{\Delta p}{\Delta \rho}\right)^{\frac{1}{2}}$$

as Δp, $\Delta \rho$ approach zero, that is

$$a = \left(\frac{dp}{d\rho}\right)^{\frac{1}{2}}$$

In the case of a sound wave the compression is isentropic, and $p = c\rho^{\gamma}$. Hence the acoustic velocity is

$$a = \left(\frac{\gamma c \rho^{\gamma-1}\, d\rho}{d\rho}\right)^{\frac{1}{2}} = \left(\gamma c \rho^{\gamma-1}\right)^{\frac{1}{2}}$$

or $$a = \left(\frac{\gamma p}{\rho}\right) = \sqrt{(\gamma RT)}$$

In the case of a liquid the velocity of sound is given by the equation

$$a = \sqrt{\frac{K}{\rho}}$$

where K = bulk modulus.

Note. The velocity of sound is much higher in a dense fluid such as water than in a gas. For example,

in air at 1 bar, 15°C, $a = \sqrt{1.4(287)(288)} = 340$ m/s

in water, $K = 2 \times 10^9 \text{N/m}^2$, $a = \sqrt{2 \times 10^9/1000} = 1414$ m/s

The Mach number, M, is defined as the ratio of the velocity of the *gas* to the acoustic velocity at the same local conditions,

$$M = \frac{u}{a} = \frac{u}{\sqrt{\gamma RT}}$$

It is not used for sound waves in liquids. As will be seen in later text it is an important parameter in the study of gas flow.

The types of flow can be classified as follows:

M<1 subsonic flow
M>1 supersonic flow
M>5 hypersonic flow

The stagnation enthalpy h_0 is the sum of the static enthalpy h and the enthalpy equivalent of the kinetic energy,

$$h_0 = h + \tfrac{1}{2}u^2$$

For an ideal gas $h = C_P T$ and the specific heat is constant:

$$C_P = \frac{\gamma R}{\gamma - 1}.$$

Hence $$T_0 = T + \frac{u^2}{2C_P}$$

$$\frac{T_0}{T} = 1 + \frac{u^2}{2\frac{\gamma R}{\gamma-1}T} = 1 + \frac{(\gamma - 1)u^2}{2\gamma RT}$$

Introducing the acoustic velocity $a^2 = \gamma RT$ gives

$$\frac{T_0}{T} = 1 + \frac{(\gamma - 1)u^2}{2a^2} = 1 + \left(\frac{\gamma - 1}{2}\right)M^2$$

Finally, for an isentropic process,

$$\frac{p_0}{p} = \left(\frac{T_0}{T}\right)^{\frac{\gamma}{\gamma-1}} = \left[1 + \frac{1}{2}(\gamma - 1)M^2\right]^{\frac{\gamma}{\gamma-1}}$$

Note. The stagnation/static pressure ratio increases rapidly with the Mach number of the flow. For many gases $\gamma = 1.4$, and the values of the ratios are tabled as follows:

M	0.5	1.0	2.0	3.0	4.0	5.0
T_0/T	1.05	1.20	1.8	2.8	4.2	6.0
p_0/p	1.186	1.893	7.82	36.73	151.8	529.0

1.6 Convergent-divergent nozzle: critical conditions

An ideal gas flows through a convergent-divergent nozzle (see Fig. 1.9). Assuming steady, one-dimensional, isentropic flow show the mass flow rate, $\dot{m}$, is given by the equation

$$\dot{m} = Ak^{1/\gamma}\sqrt{\frac{2\gamma p_0\rho_0}{\gamma - 1}(1 - k^{1-1/\gamma})} \quad \text{where } k = p/p_0 .$$

Define the critical pressure ratio and show that it is equal to

$$\left(\frac{2}{\gamma + 1}\right)^{\frac{\gamma}{\gamma-1}} .$$

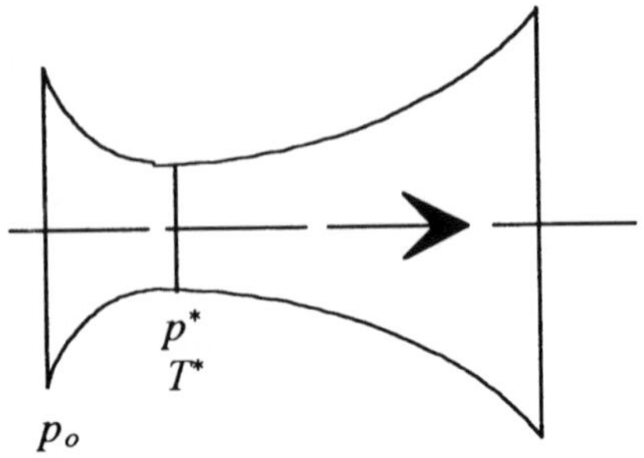

Figure 1.9

Solution. The continuity and momentum equations are

$$\dot{m} = \rho A u = \text{constant} \tag{1.3}$$

$$h_0 = h + \tfrac{1}{2}u^2 = \text{constant}.$$

The flow is isentropic and the law $p/\rho^\gamma = \text{constant}$ is applicable.

$$\dot{m} = \rho A u = \left(\frac{\rho}{\rho_0}\right)\rho_0 A u = \rho_0 A u\left(\frac{p}{p_0}\right)^{1/\gamma}$$

and $$T_0 = T + \frac{u^2}{2C_P} = T + \left(\frac{\gamma - 1}{2\gamma R}\right)u^2 \tag{Ex. 1.5}$$

$$u^2 = \frac{2\gamma R}{\gamma - 1}\left(T_0 - T\right)$$

Substituting into the momentum equation

$$\dot{m} = \rho_0 A k^{\frac{1}{\gamma}}\sqrt{\frac{2\gamma R}{\gamma - 1}\left(T_0 - T\right)}$$

Using the relationship

$$\frac{T}{T_0} = \left(\frac{p}{p_0}\right)^{1-\frac{1}{\gamma}}$$

gives $$\dot{m} = \rho_0 A k^{\frac{1}{\gamma}}\sqrt{\frac{2\gamma R T_0}{\gamma - 1}\left(1 - k^{1-\frac{1}{\gamma}}\right)} = A k^{\frac{1}{\gamma}}\sqrt{\frac{2\gamma p_0\rho_0}{\gamma - 1}\left(1 - k^{1-\frac{1}{\gamma}}\right)}$$

The mass flow rate can be seen to depend on the pressure ratio p/p_0, for given (fixed) stagnation conditions. The flow through a fixed throat area A is therefore proportional to

$$k^{1/\gamma}\sqrt{1 - k^{1-1/\gamma}}$$

The flow rate varies with the pressure ratio and, as an illustration, the variation is shown for $\gamma = 1.40$:

k	1	0.9	0.8	0.7	0.6	0.5	0.4	0.3
flow	0	0.16	0.21	0.24	0.24	0.26	0.25	0.23

The flow rate increases to a *maximum* at a particular pressure ratio. Under these conditions the nozzle is said to be choked and the conditions at the throat are said to be *critical*. The critical pressure ratio can be determined by differentiation and equating to zero (maximum value of $\dot{m}$).

Hence $\dot{m} \propto k^{1/\gamma}\sqrt{1 - k^{1-1/\gamma}}$

$$\dot{m}^2 \propto k^{2/\gamma}(1 - k^{1-1/\gamma})$$

$$\frac{d\dot{m}^2}{dk} \propto k^{2/\gamma}\left(-\left(1 - \frac{1}{\gamma}\right)k^{1-1/\gamma-1}\right) + \frac{2}{\gamma}k^{2/\gamma-1}(1 - k^{1-1/\gamma})$$

$$\propto -\left(1 - \frac{1}{\gamma}\right)k^{2/\gamma}k^{-1/\gamma} + \frac{2}{\gamma}k^{2/\gamma-1}(1 - k^{1-1/\gamma})$$

and equating to zero gives

$$k^{2/\gamma} = 0 \text{ and } k = 0$$

or $\quad k^{-1/\gamma}\left(1 - \frac{1}{\gamma}\right) = \frac{2}{\gamma}k^{-1}(1 - k^{1-1/\gamma})$

which reduces to

$$k = \left(\frac{2}{\gamma + 1}\right)^{\frac{\gamma}{\gamma-1}}$$

The value $k = 0$ simply means a no flow situation (the minimum!), where $p = p_0$. The latter value gives the critical pressure ratio for the maximum flow rate. The critical conditions are denoted by the superscript *.

Thus $\quad \dfrac{p^*}{p_0} = \left(\dfrac{2}{\gamma + 1}\right)^{\frac{\gamma}{\gamma-1}}$

Note. The importance of this result lies in the choking condition. As the pressure at the throat is reduced below the stagnation pressure p_0, the mass flow rate increases to a maximum value at $p = p^*$. If the throat pressure continues to decrease the mass flow remains the same, whatever the pressure conditions downstream of the throat become.

The static temperature, at critical conditions, T^*, is easily determined from this result. The flow is isentropic, hence

$$\frac{p^*}{p_0} = \left(\frac{T^*}{T_0}\right)^{\frac{\gamma}{\gamma-1}}$$

and it follows that

$$\frac{T^*}{T_0} = \frac{2}{\gamma + 1}$$

An interesting corollary follows from this equation. Since

$$T_0 = T\left(1 + \frac{\gamma - 1}{2}M^2\right)$$

then $\quad \dfrac{T_0}{T} = 1 + \dfrac{1}{2}(\gamma - 1)M^{*2} = \dfrac{\gamma + 1}{2}$

giving $M^* = 1$.

Thus, at the critical conditions the Mach number has the specific value

$M = 1$.

1.7 Isentropic flow in a variable area duct

An ideal gas flows along a duct of varying cross-sectional area A (Fig. 1.10). The flow is steady, one-dimensional, and isentropic. Show that at any section the area and Mach number of the flow are related by the equation

$$\frac{A}{A^*} = \frac{1}{M}\left(\frac{2+(\gamma-1)M^2}{\gamma+1}\right)^k$$

where $k = \dfrac{\gamma+1}{2(\gamma-1)}$.

Discuss the result.

Solution. The isentropic law p/ρ^γ = constant and the relationship

$$\frac{T_0}{T} = 1 + \frac{1}{2}\left(\gamma - 1\right)M^2$$

can be used in the continuity equation, $\dot{m} = \rho A u$ to give,

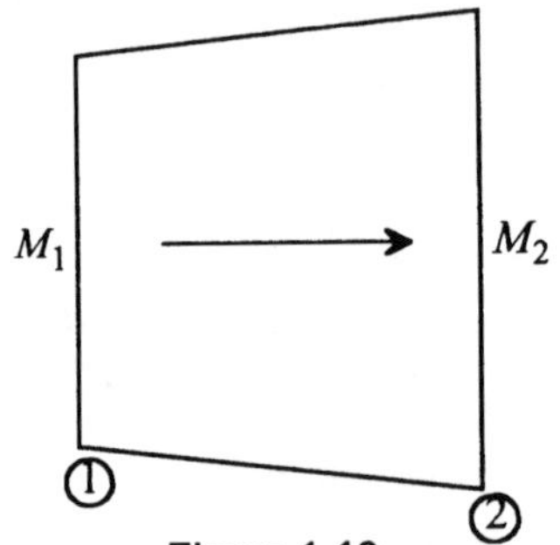

Figure 1.10

$$\dot{m} = \rho_0 A u\left(\frac{p}{p_0}\right)^{\frac{1}{\gamma}} = \rho_0 A^* u^*\left(\frac{p^*}{p_0}\right)^{\frac{1}{\gamma}}$$

Hence $$\frac{A}{A^*} = \frac{u^*}{u}\left(\frac{p^*}{p_0}\right)^{\frac{1}{\gamma}}\left(\frac{p_0}{p}\right)^{\frac{1}{\gamma}}$$

Since $$\frac{p_0}{p} = \left(\frac{T_0}{T}\right)^{\frac{\gamma}{\gamma-1}} = \left(1 + \frac{1}{2}\left(\gamma - 1\right)M^2\right)^{\frac{\gamma}{\gamma-1}}$$

and $$\frac{p^*}{p_0} = \left(\frac{2}{\gamma+1}\right)^{\frac{\gamma}{\gamma-1}}$$

then $$\frac{A}{A^*} = \frac{u^*}{u}\left(\frac{2}{\gamma+1}\right)^{\frac{1}{\gamma-1}}\left(1 + \frac{1}{2}\left(\gamma - 1\right)M^2\right)^{\frac{\gamma}{\gamma-1}}$$

Finally $$\frac{u^*}{u} = \frac{M^* a^*}{Ma} = \frac{\sqrt{\gamma R T^*}}{M\sqrt{\gamma R T}} = \frac{1}{M}\sqrt{\frac{T^*}{T}}$$

$$= \frac{1}{M}\sqrt{\frac{T^*}{T_0}\frac{T_0}{T}} = \frac{1}{M}\sqrt{\frac{2}{\gamma+1}\left(1 + \frac{1}{2}\left(\gamma - 1\right)M^2\right)}$$

Substituting into the continuity equation then gives the desired result.

Consider a gas flowing through the duct, with a given set of conditions at some upstream starting point, that is a given value of the Mach number, M_1.

Corresponding to this particular value of M_1 and A there will be one value, and *only* one, for the critical area A^*. At any section downstream where the area $= A_2$ say, the equation still applies and from the known values of A_2, A^* the Mach number at this section, M_2 can be determined.

For example, suppose the area = 1.0 m² at section 1, where $M_1 = 0.5$. Taking $\gamma = 1.4$ gives

$$\frac{A_1}{A^*} = \frac{1}{M_1}\left(\frac{2 + 0.4M_1^2}{2.4}\right)^3 = \frac{1}{M_1}\left(\frac{5 + M_1^2}{6}\right)^3$$

$$A^* = 1.0(0.5)\left(\frac{6}{5.25}\right)^3 = 0.746 \text{ m}^2$$

Suppose the area at section 2 is $A_2 = 2.0 \text{ m}^2$. Then substituting into the equation

$$\frac{2}{0.746} = \frac{1}{M_2}\left(\frac{5 + M_2^2}{6}\right)^3$$

and solving gives *two* possible values of M_2, 0.22 or 2.52. This result is a general one, in that there are normally two possible flows. Clearly, in practice, only one actually arises, depending on the physical situation. In this example, the duct area gradually and continuously increases from section 1 to section 2, and the area nowhere reduces to the critical value. Hence, since the flow is subsonic ($M_1 < 1$) at the upstream section it will be subsonic at section 2, and $M_2 = 0.22$.

An interesting relationship between area, velocity and Mach number can be derived as follows. The continuity equation, in the differential form, can be combined with the energy equation, also in differential form:

$$\rho A u = \text{constant}$$

$$\ln \rho + \ln A + \ln u = \text{constant}$$

$$\frac{d\rho}{\rho} + \frac{dA}{A} + \frac{du}{u} = 0$$

and $\quad dp + \rho u du = 0$

Combining and introducing the Mach number gives the relationship

$$\frac{dA}{A} = (M^2 - 1)\frac{du}{u}$$

Several important points can be observed from this equation:

(a) Comparing it with the corresponding equation for incompressible flow

$$\frac{dA}{A} = -\frac{du}{u}$$

it can be seen that in compressible flow the factor $1 - M^2$ appears. This emphasises the importance of the Mach number.

(b) At the particular value of $M = 1$, $dA/A = 0$ or $dA = 0$, indicating that the area is a minimum.

(c) At subsonic velocities, $M < 1$ and hence $dA/A = -du/u$. Hence as the area decreases the velocity increases: a subsonic nozzle requires a decreasing area. However at supersonic velocities $M > 1$ and $dA/A = +du/u$. The situation is now reversed: a supersonic nozzle requires an increasing area.

1.8 Nozzles in series

> Two nozzles, of throat areas A_1 and A_2, are in series (Fig. 1.11). There is a stagnation pressure drop (due to friction) Δp_o between the nozzles. Show that for both nozzles to choke simultaneously
>
> $$p_{01}A_1 = p_{02}A_2.$$
>
> A stagnation temperature drop (due to energy extraction) Δp_0 occurs between the nozzles. Show that for both nozzles to be choked
>
> $$\frac{A_2}{A_1} = \frac{T_{01}}{(T_{01} - \Delta T_0)^3}$$
>
> Take $\gamma = 1.40$.

Solution. At choking conditions in the nozzle

$$\frac{\dot{m}}{A} = \rho^* u^* = \left(\frac{p^*}{RT^*}\right)u^* = p^*\sqrt{\frac{\gamma}{RT^*}}$$

since $u^* = a^* = \sqrt{\gamma RT^*}$

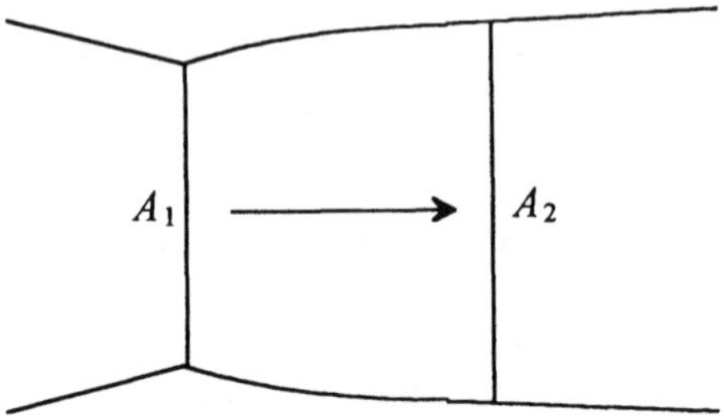

Figure 1.11

Now $\dfrac{T^*}{T_0} = \dfrac{2}{\gamma+1}$, $\dfrac{p^*}{p_0} = \left(\dfrac{2}{\gamma+1}\right)^{\frac{\gamma}{\gamma-1}}$

hence $\dfrac{\dot{m}}{A} = \left(\dfrac{2}{\gamma+1}\right)^{\frac{\gamma}{\gamma-1}} p_0\sqrt{\dfrac{\gamma}{R}}\sqrt{\dfrac{\gamma+1}{2T_0}} = \dfrac{kp_0}{\sqrt{T_0}}$ say

Now there is no fluid extraction between the nozzles and *both* nozzles are choked, so that

$$\dot{m} = \frac{kp_{01}A_1}{\sqrt{T_{01}}} = \frac{kp_{02}A_2}{\sqrt{T_{02}}}$$

and for no stagnation temperature drop it follows that

$$p_{01}A_1 = p_{02}A_2$$

In the second situation energy is extracted, causing a decrease in the stagnation temperature. This accords with the steady flow energy equation: 1.7 (in the absence of gravitational forces).

$$Q - W_s = \Delta\left(h + \frac{1}{2}v^2\right) = \Delta h_0 = Cp\Delta T_0$$

Now $T_{02} = T_{01} - \Delta T_0$

and $\dfrac{p_{02}}{p_{01}} = \left(\dfrac{T_{02}}{T_{01}}\right)^{\frac{\gamma}{\gamma-1}} = \left(1 - \dfrac{\Delta T_0}{T_{01}}\right)^{3.5}$

The flow rate is constant, and

$$\dot{m} = \rho_1^* A_1^* u_1^* = \rho_2^* A_2^* u_2^*$$

Hence $\dfrac{A_2^*}{A_1^*} = \dfrac{\rho_1^* u_1^*}{\rho_2^* u_2^*}$

Further $\rho^* = \dfrac{p^*}{RT^*} = \dfrac{p_0\left(\frac{2}{\gamma+1}\right)^{\frac{\gamma}{\gamma-1}}}{RT_0\left(\frac{2}{\gamma+1}\right)} = \left(\dfrac{2}{2.4}\right)^{2.5}\dfrac{p_0}{RT_0}$

and $\quad u^* = \sqrt{\gamma RT^*} = \sqrt{\gamma RT_0\left(\dfrac{2}{\gamma+1}\right)}$

Hence $\dfrac{A_2^*}{A_1^*} = \dfrac{p_{01}T_{02}}{T_{01}p_{02}}\sqrt{\dfrac{T_{01}}{T_{02}}} = \left(\dfrac{p_{01}}{p_{02}}\right)\left(\dfrac{T_{02}}{T_{01}}\right)^{\frac{1}{2}}$

$$= \left(1 - \frac{\Delta T_0}{T_{01}}\right)^{-3.5}\left(1 - \frac{\Delta T_0}{T_{01}}\right)^{0.5} = \frac{1}{\left(1 - \frac{\Delta T_0}{T_{01}}\right)^3}$$

$$= \frac{T_{01}^3}{(T_{01} - \Delta T_0)^3}$$

1.9 Rocket motor

A rocket motor discharges the combustion products through a convergent-divergent nozzle (Fig. 1.12). The stagnation conditions are 50 bar, 3500K. Mass flow rate = 300 kg/s. The exit plane area = 0.32 m^2. Ambient pressure = 1 bar. Assuming isentropic flow calculate the throat area; static pressure and temperature, and Mach number at the exit plane; and thrust developed.

Take $\gamma = \frac{4}{3}$, $C_p = 1.15$ kJ/kg K.

Solution. The stagnation and exit plane conditions are denoted by the subscripts $_0$ and $_e$ respectively, and critical conditions at the throat by the subscript $_*$.

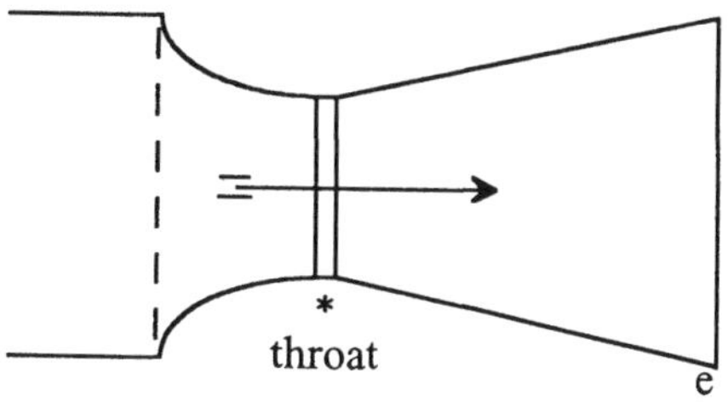

Figure 1.12

At the throat

$$T^* = T_0\left(\frac{2}{\gamma+1}\right) = 3500\left(\frac{2}{2\frac{1}{3}}\right) = 3000$$

$$p^* = p_0\left(\frac{T^*}{T_0}\right)^{\frac{\gamma}{\gamma-1}} = 50\left(\frac{3000}{35000}\right)^4 = 27.0 \text{ bar}$$

For an ideal gas

$$R = \frac{\gamma - 1}{\gamma} C_p = \frac{1}{4}(1150) = 288 \text{ J/kg K}$$

hence $\rho^* = \dfrac{p^*}{RT^*} = \dfrac{27.0(10^5)}{288(3000)} = 3.125 \text{ kg/m}^3$

$$u^* = \sqrt{\gamma R T^*} = \sqrt{\tfrac{4}{3}(288)(3000)} = 1073 \text{ m/s}$$

throat area

$$A^* = \frac{\dot{m}}{\rho^* u^*} = \frac{300}{3.125(1073)} = \mathbf{0.089} \text{ m}^2$$

Considering the exit plane, the flow is isentropic and the stagnation enthalpy is constant,

$$C_p T_o = C_p T_e + \tfrac{1}{2} u_e^2$$

$$u_e^2 = 2C_p(T_o - T_e)$$

Now $\dfrac{T_2}{T_o} = \left(\dfrac{p_2}{p_o}\right)^{\frac{\gamma-1}{\gamma}} = x^{0.25}$ where $x = \dfrac{p_e}{p_o}$

Hence $u_e^2 = 2C_p To(1 - x^{0.25}) = 8.05(10^6)(1 - x^{0.25})$

The continuity equation $\dot{m} = \rho_e A_e u_e$ can be used to determine the value of x, since the exit area is known; u_e, ρ_e can be expressed in terms of x; and the mass flow rate is known.

$$\rho_e = \rho_o \left(\frac{p_e}{p_o}\right)^{\frac{1}{\gamma}} = \frac{50(10^5)}{288(3500)} x^{0.75} = 4.960 x^{0.75}$$

Substituting

$$\dot{m} = 300 = 4.960 x^{0.75}(0.32)\sqrt{(8.05)(10^6)(1 - x^{0.25})}$$

$$0.0666 = x^{0.75}\sqrt{1 - x^{0.25}}$$

Solving by trial and error gives $x = 0.04$.

Hence $T_e = T_o x^{0.25} = 3500(0.04)^{0.25} = \mathbf{1565}$ **K**

$$p_e = x p_o = 0.04(50) = \mathbf{2.0} \text{ bar}$$

$$u_e^2 = 8.05(10^6)(1 - x^{0.25}) \quad \text{and} \quad u_e = 2110 \text{ m/s}$$

The acoustic velocity at the exit plane is

$$a_e = \sqrt{\gamma R T_e} = \sqrt{\tfrac{4}{3}(288)(1565)} = 775 \text{ m/s}$$

and $M_e = \dfrac{u_e}{a_e} = \dfrac{2110}{775} = \mathbf{2.72}$

The thrust developed by the exhaust stream of gas is made up of the momentum thrust $\dot{m}u_e$ and the pressure thrust $(p_e - p_a)A_e$, where p_a = ambient pressure outside the rocket

$$F = \dot{m}u_e + (p_e - p_a)A_e$$

$$= 300(2110) + 10^5(2.0 - 1.0)(0.32)$$

$$= 633\,000 + 32\,000 \text{ N} \quad = \mathbf{665 \text{ kN}}$$

Note. The performance of a rocket can be measured by the parameters:

specific impulse $= \dfrac{F}{\dot{m}}$

thrust coefficient $C_F = \dfrac{F}{p_o A^*}$

propulsive efficiency $\dfrac{F_u}{F_u + \frac{1}{2}\dot{m}_p(c - u)^2}$

where $\dot{m}_p$ = consumption rate of propellant

u = velocity of the rocket

c = effective exit velocity

$$= u_e + \frac{(p_e - p_a)A_e}{\dot{m}_p}$$

In this problem the values are:

$$\text{specific impulse} = \frac{665\,000}{300} = 2217 \text{ Ns/kg}$$

$$\text{or} \quad \frac{2217}{g} = \frac{2217}{9.81} = 226 \text{ s}$$

$$\text{thrust coefficient} = \frac{665\,000}{50(10^5)(0.089)} = 1.49$$

Use of flow tables

This problem can be solved more easily with the convenience of flow tables: and numerical values of various parameters read directly from flow tables are indicated by the symbol T.

Thus, at the *throat* M=1 and

T $\quad \frac{T_o}{T} = 1.1665, \quad \frac{p_o}{p} = 1.8524, \quad \frac{u}{\sqrt{T_o}} = 18.11$

giving $T = 3000$ K, $p = 27.0$ bar, $u = 1073$ m/s

T $\quad$ Flow parameter $\frac{\dot{m}\sqrt{T_o}}{Ap_o} = 0.0397$

$$\text{giving } A = \frac{300\sqrt{3500}}{0.0397(50)(10^5)} = \mathbf{0.089} \text{ m}^2$$

At the *exit* plane,

$$A_e = 0.32 \text{ m}^2 \text{ and } \frac{A_e}{A^*} = \frac{0.32}{0.089} = 3.5$$

and this corresponds to a Mach number of

T $\quad M_e = \mathbf{2.72}$

At this value the tables give

T $\quad \frac{T_o}{T_e} = 2.236, \quad \frac{p_o}{p_e} = 25.00$

and $\quad T_e = 1565$ K, $p_e = 2.0$ bar.

1.10 Supersonic flow: Mach waves

> Briefly outline the von Karman rules for small disturbances arising from the supersonic velocity of a body in a stationary fluid.
>
> Explain what is meant by a Mach wave, and Mach angle. Discuss the behaviour of Mach waves, including the reflections and interference of waves.

Solution. When a body moves through a stationary fluid a disturbance is created, and pressure (acoustic) waves are formed. The wave pattern which arises depends upon the velocity of the body, and the manner in which the pattern changes is illustrated in Fig, 1.13.

A 'point' disturbance moves, from left to right, at a steady velocity u. Starting from the position marked 0, the positions of the source (the point body) are marked at intervals of 1, 2, 3, ... time intervals. The motion of the pressure wave created is shown at the same time intervals; the wave being spread in a circular path for the one-dimensional flow considered.

The pattern changes significantly as the Mach number increases, i.e. as the body velocity increases. At subsonic velocities the body signals its approach to the upstream fluid, whereas at supersonic velocities the body arrives before the signal. The effect of the pressure waves, in supersonic velocities, is confined to a conical region, as shown.

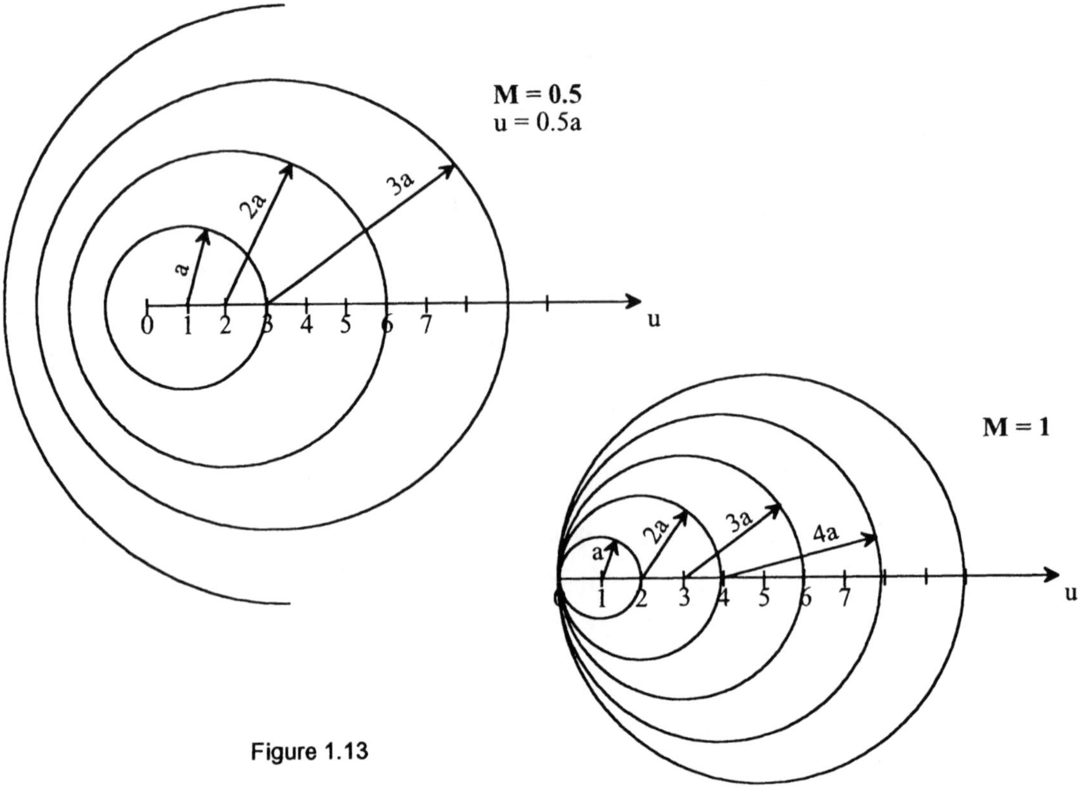

Figure 1.13

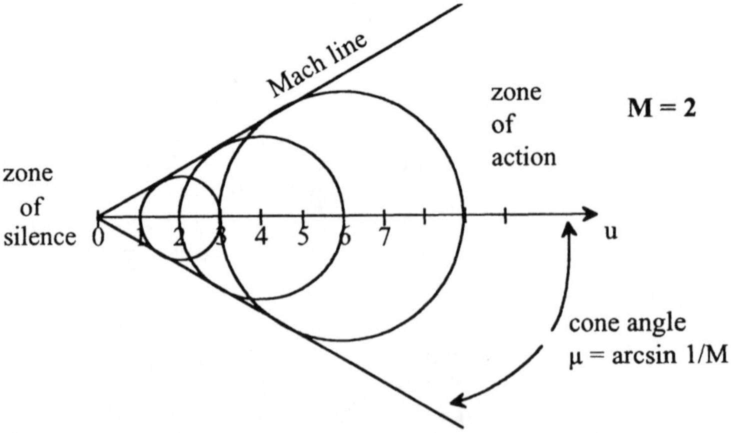

The von Karman rules are as follows:

(a) forbidden signals—the small pressure changes produced by the motion of the body cannot reach points ahead of the body. In the reverse situation of supersonic flow of a fluid past a stationary body the pressure changes cannot reach points upstream of the body.

(b) zones of silence and action—the conditions at any point in the fluid can only be influenced if the body is within or on the Mach cone, extending upstream from that point.
(c) concentrated action—the closer the circles (wave fronts) are together the greater the wave strength.

A Mach wave is the envelope of the circular pressure wave fronts, and the two Mach waves formed enclose a Mach wedge.

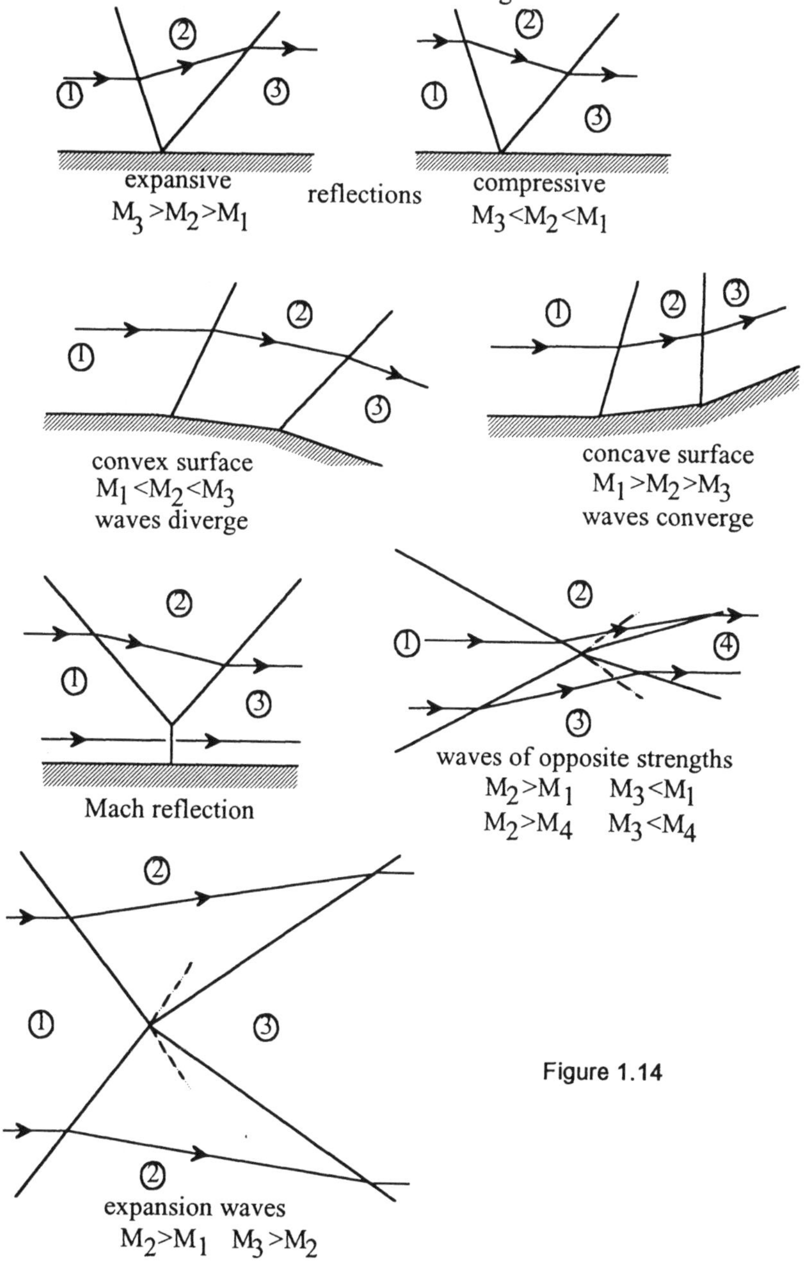

Figure 1.14

In the case of three-dimensional flow the circles would be replaced by spheres, and a Mach cone would result. The angle of the cone is known as the *Mach angle*

$$\mu = \arcsin\frac{a}{u} = \arcsin\frac{1}{M}.$$

Mach waves can, in general, be reflected from a surface as a simple or Y (Mach) reflection (as shown in Fig. 1.14). The latter type arises when a compression wave impinges on a surface and the upstream conditions cannot support supersonic flow after two compressions (incident and reflected waves).

Waves which intersect each other suffer a change of direction and strength, as shown in Fig. 1.14.

1.11 Prandtl-Meyer flow

> State the meaning of the term Prandtl-Meyer flow, and outline the situation to which it applies.
>
> Derive an expression for the Prandtl-Meyer function.
>
> An air stream approaches a convex corner at a Mach number of 1.5, and static conditions of 1 bar, 300 K. The stream is deflected through an angle of 5°.
>
> Determine the conditions after expansion, and sketch the fan showing the initial and final Mach lines.
>
> Flow tables should be used. ($\gamma = 1.40$)

Solution. Prandtl-Meyer (P-M) flow is the supersonic, two-dimensional flow accelerated by expansion round a corner. The fluid is taken as inviscid (zero viscosity), so that the analysis gives an exact solution. The analysis can be applied to concave corners where a compression is produced, but only to small angles of deflection. The analysis gives a good approximation to real flow situations since the effect of viscous flow (vorticity) is often small and localised. The situation is shown in Fig. 1.15.

The fluid velocity, u, can be resolved into two components, parallel and perpendicular to the Mach line. The Mach line is the envelope of wave fronts so that the pressure gradient is normal to the Mach line. Hence the parallel component, t, is constant. Also the fronts are acoustic wave fronts and the normal component, n, is equal to the acoustic velocity a.

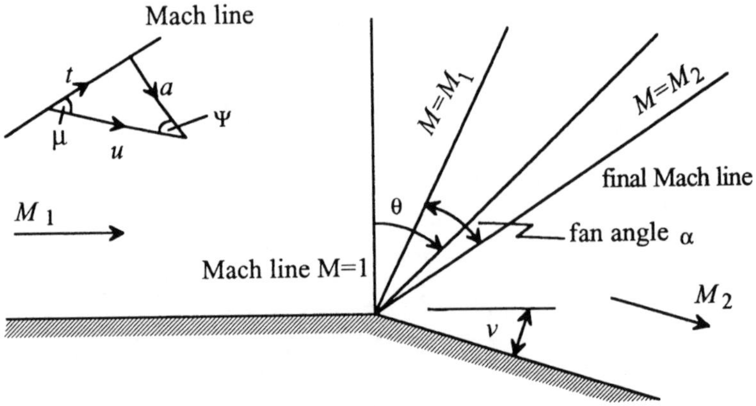

Figure 1.15

Consider a Mach line, as shown in Fig. 1.16.
From the velocity triangles (downstream)

$$u + n' \sin\mu = (u + du)\cos d\nu$$
$$n' \cos\mu = (u + du)\sin d\nu$$

If $d\nu$ is small, $\sin d\nu \cong d\nu$ and $\cos d\nu \cong 1$, hence neglecting second order terms

$$n' \sin\mu = du$$

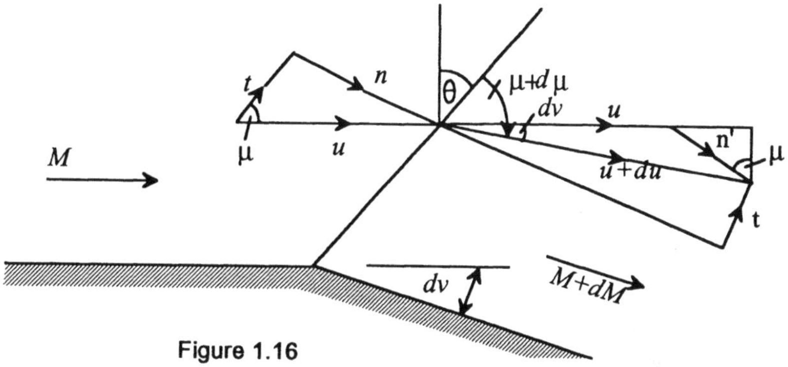

Figure 1.16

$$n' \cos\mu = u\,d\nu$$

Thus $\tan\mu = \dfrac{du}{u\,d\nu}$

Introducing the Mach number,

$$\mu = \arcsin\left(\frac{1}{M}\right)$$

and $\quad \tan\mu = (M^2 - 1)^{-\frac{1}{2}}.$

This gives

$$d\nu = (M^2 - 1)^{\frac{1}{2}}\left(\frac{du}{u}\right)$$

Since the flow is isentropic

$$C_pT_o = C_pT + \tfrac{1}{2}u^2$$

Using the relationship

$$a^2 = \gamma RT = (\gamma - 1)C_pT$$

gives $\quad \dfrac{a^2}{\gamma - 1} + \dfrac{1}{2}u^2 = \text{constant} = k, \text{ say}$

or $\quad \dfrac{1}{(\gamma - 1)M^2} + \dfrac{1}{2} = \dfrac{k}{u^2}$

and $\quad \dfrac{u^2}{k} = \dfrac{2(\gamma - 1)M^2}{2 + (\gamma - 1)M^2}$

Differentiating

$$\frac{1}{\gamma - 1}\left(-\frac{dM^2}{M^4}\right) = -\frac{2kdu}{u^3}$$

or $\quad \dfrac{du}{u} = \dfrac{u^2}{2k}\cdot\dfrac{dM^2}{(\gamma - 1)M^4}$

Substituting in the previous equation

$$d\gamma = (M^2 - 1)\left(\frac{1}{2k}\right)\frac{dM^2}{(\gamma - 1)M^4}\,\frac{2k(\gamma - 1)M^2}{2 + (\gamma - 1)M^2}$$

$$= \frac{(M^2 - 1)^{\frac{1}{2}} dM^2}{M^2(2 + (\gamma - 1)M^2)}$$

This equation can be integrated, and taking $\nu = 0$ at $M = 1$ as datum, the result is

$$\nu = b \arctan \sqrt{\frac{M^2 - 1}{b}} - \arctan \sqrt{M^2 - 1}$$

$$\text{where} \quad b = \sqrt{\frac{\gamma + 1}{\gamma - 1}}$$

and ν is known as the *Prandtl-Meyer function*.

This now enables the change in flow properties between two points to be determined as is shown in the calculation which follows. It should be noted that the change depends *only* on the *upstream* conditions and the change in flow *direction* between them.

The specific example can now be considered. Referring to Fig. 1.17,

$M_1 = 1.5$ and from isentropic flow tables,

T $\quad \nu_1 = 11.88, \quad \mu_1 = 41.81, \quad \theta_1 = 60.07°$

$$\frac{p_o}{p_1} = 3.675, \quad \frac{T_o}{T_1} = 1.453$$

Hence $p_o = 3.675$ bar, $T_o = 436$ K

$$a_1 = \sqrt{\gamma R T_1} = 347 \text{ m/s}$$

$$u_1 = M_1 a_1 = 520 \text{ m/s}$$

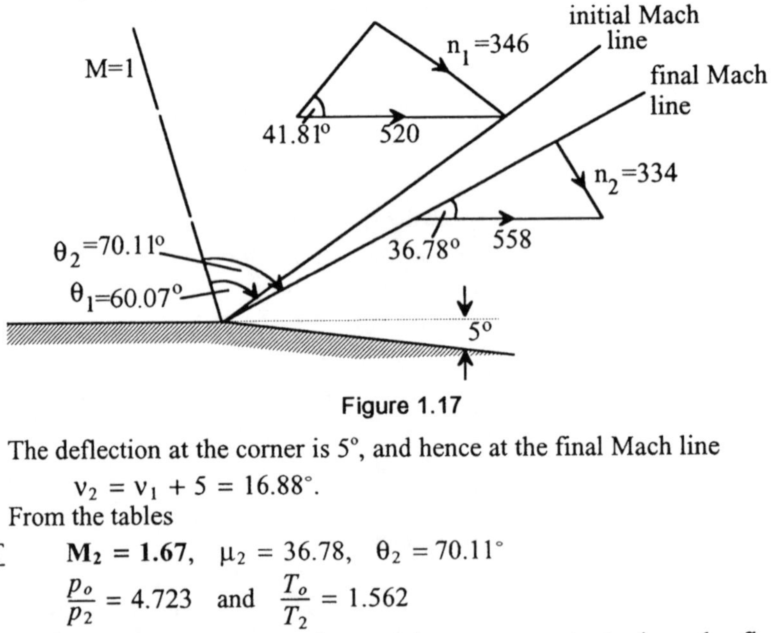

Figure 1.17

The deflection at the corner is 5°, and hence at the final Mach line

$$\nu_2 = \nu_1 + 5 = 16.88°.$$

From the tables

T $\quad$ **$M_2 = 1.67$**, $\quad \mu_2 = 36.78, \quad \theta_2 = 70.11°$

$$\frac{p_o}{p_2} = 4.723 \quad \text{and} \quad \frac{T_o}{T_2} = 1.562$$

The *stagnation* pressure and temperature are constant, since the flow is isentropic. Hence

$$p_2 = \mathbf{0.78} \text{ bar}, \quad T_2 = \mathbf{279}$$

$$a_2 = \mathbf{334} \text{ m/s}, \quad u_2 = 1.67 a_2 = \mathbf{558} \text{ m/s}$$

It is sometimes convenient to use polar coordinates, as shown in Fig. 1.18.

The velocity components at a point P on the Mach line are v_r in the radial direction (along the Mach line), and v_θ in the direction normal to the Mach line.

The component v_θ (or component n) (Fig. 1.16) is again equal to the acoustic velocity.

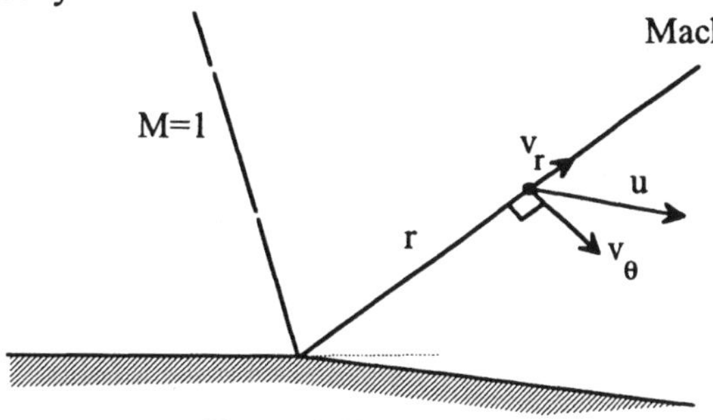

Figure 1.18

1.12 Linearised flow

A two-dimensional supersonic flow occurs over a convex corner. Show, by linearised flow equations, that

$$\frac{p}{\bar{p}} = 1 - \frac{\gamma \bar{M}^2 u'}{\bar{u}}, \quad \frac{T}{\bar{T}} = 1 - \frac{(\gamma - 1)\bar{M}^2 u'}{\bar{u}}$$

where $\bar{p}, \bar{u}, \bar{M}, \bar{T}$ refer to the upstream conditions and u' is the perturbation velocity.

Solution. The changes in flow properties across the wave front are represented by small quantities (perturbations), the fluid velocity changing from $\bar{u}$ to **v** (components $\bar{u} + u', v'$) as shown in Fig. 1.19.

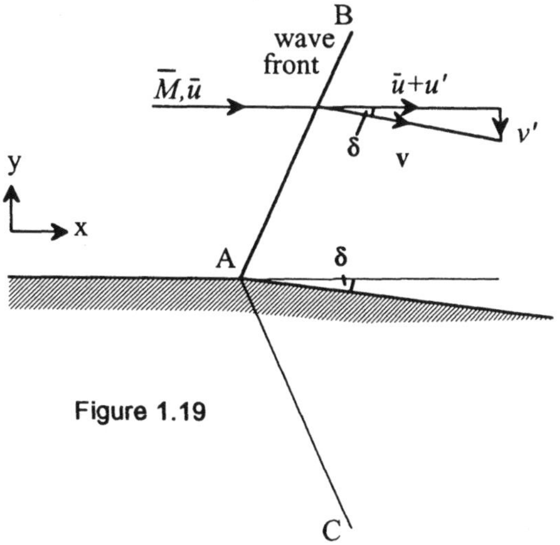

Figure 1.19

The pertinent equations, for two-dimensional flow, are:

continuity $\quad \frac{\partial}{\partial x}(\rho u) + \frac{\partial}{\partial y}(\rho v) = 0$

or $$\rho\left(\frac{\partial u}{\partial x}\right) + u\left(\frac{\partial \rho}{\partial x}\right) + \rho\left(\frac{\partial v}{\partial y}\right) + v\left(\frac{\partial \rho}{\partial y}\right) = 0$$

energy $$dp = -\rho v\, dv = -\tfrac{1}{2}\rho\, d(u^2 + v^2)$$

Now $d\rho = \dfrac{d\rho}{dp}dp = -\dfrac{\rho}{2a^2}d(u^2 + v^2)$ since $a^2 = \dfrac{dp}{d\rho}$

$$= -\frac{\rho}{2a^2}\left(\frac{\partial u^2}{\partial x}dx + \frac{\partial u^2}{\partial y}dy + \frac{\partial v^2}{\partial x}dx + \frac{\partial v^2}{\partial y}dy\right)$$

But $d\rho = \dfrac{\partial \rho}{\partial x}dx + \dfrac{\partial \rho}{\partial y}dy$

and equating the two expressions gives

$$\frac{\partial \rho}{\partial x} = -\frac{\rho}{2a^2}\left(\frac{\partial u^2}{\partial x} + \frac{\partial v^2}{\partial x}\right),$$

$$\frac{\partial \rho}{\partial y} = -\frac{\rho}{2a^2}\left(\frac{\partial u^2}{\partial y} + \frac{\partial v^2}{\partial y}\right)$$

Substituting in the continuity equation gives

$$(a^2 - u^2)\frac{\partial u}{\partial x} + (a^2 - v^2)\frac{\partial v}{\partial y} - uv\left(\frac{\partial v}{\partial x} + \frac{\partial u}{\partial y}\right) = 0$$

This equation can be solved by taking into account first order terms only, or as it can be termed, by linearisation. This means that the change in velocity across the wave front u', v' is small so that $(u')^2$ and $(v')^2$ can be neglected.

Also the velocity component in the x direction changes from $\bar{u}$ to $\bar{u} + u'$, therefore

$$\frac{\partial \bar{u}}{\partial x} = 0 \text{ (Putting } u = \bar{u} + u', v = v'\text{)}$$

into the equation and linearising gives

$$\left(1 - \frac{\bar{u}^2}{a^2}\right)\frac{\partial u'}{\partial x} + \left(1 - \frac{v'^2}{a^2}\right)\frac{\partial v'}{\partial x} = 2(\bar{u} + u')v'\left(\frac{\partial v'}{\partial x} + \frac{\partial u'}{\partial y}\right)$$

and neglecting second order terms,

$$(1 - \bar{M}^2)\frac{\partial u'}{\partial x} + \frac{\partial v'}{\partial y} = 0$$

The potential function ϕ is now introduced: it is defined by

$$u' = \frac{\partial \phi'}{\partial x}, \quad v' = \frac{\partial \phi'}{\partial y}$$

$$(1 - \bar{M}^2)\frac{\partial^2 \phi'}{\partial x^2} + \frac{\partial^2 \phi'}{\partial y^2} = 0$$

The general solution to this equation is of the form

$$\phi' = F_1(y - x\tan\bar{\mu}) + F_2(y + x\tan\bar{\mu}),$$

where F denotes 'a function of'. The angle μ is the Mach angle,

$$\bar{\mu} = \arcsin\left(\frac{1}{\bar{M}}\right)$$

and $y - x\tan\bar{\mu}$, $y + x\tan\bar{\mu}$ represent the pair of Mach lines (Fig. 1.13).

The convex corner (Fig. 1.19) can now be considered. Upstream of the wave front AB is the zone of forbidden signals, $F_1 = F_2 = 0$. Downstream of AB the right hand front AC plays no part and $F_2 = 0$. The remaining function can be expressed as a linear function, say

$$F_1 = k(y - x\tan\bar{\mu}) = \phi'$$

Hence $u' = -k\tan\bar{\mu}, v' = k$

Further $\tan\delta = -\dfrac{v'}{\bar{u} + u'}$ or $\delta = -\dfrac{v'}{u}$

for *small* deflections. Substituting $k = v' = -\bar{u}\delta$ and

$$u' = \bar{u}\delta \tan\bar{\mu}, \quad v' = -\bar{u}\delta$$

The energy equation (1.10) gives

$$dp + \bar{\rho}\bar{u}du = 0$$

or

$$dp = -\bar{\rho}\bar{u}u' = -\bar{\rho}\bar{u}^2\delta \tan\bar{\mu}$$

$$p = \bar{p} - \bar{\rho}\bar{u}^2\delta \tan\bar{\mu}$$

$$\frac{p}{\bar{p}} = 1 - \frac{\gamma\bar{M}^2u'}{\bar{u}} \quad \text{since } \frac{\bar{\rho}}{\bar{p}} = \frac{1}{R\bar{T}} = \frac{\gamma\bar{M}^2}{\bar{u}^2}$$

Finally $T + \dfrac{u^2}{2C_p} = \text{constant}$,

and $\quad C_p = \dfrac{\gamma R}{\gamma - 1}$

hence $\quad \bar{T} + \left(\dfrac{\gamma - 1}{2\gamma R}\right)\bar{u}^2 = T + \left(\dfrac{\gamma - 1}{2\gamma R}\right)\left(\bar{u} + u'\right)^2$

$$\frac{T}{\bar{T}} + 1 - \left(\frac{\gamma - 1}{\gamma R}\right)\frac{\bar{u}u'}{\bar{T}} = 1 - \frac{(\gamma - 1)\bar{M}^2u'}{\bar{u}}$$

Note. This analysis can also be used for compression (concave corners), and is reasonably accurate for small disturbances. The accuracy can be improved by consideration of second order terms.

A point of interest lies in the equation involving the potential function. In the case of incompressible flow it becomes

$$\frac{\partial^2\phi}{\partial x^2} + \frac{\partial^2\phi}{\partial y^2} = 0$$

(the Laplace equation). It can be seen that when compressible flow is considered the term $1 - \bar{M}^2$ appears, and, as indicated in Ex.1.7, this is to be expected.

1.13 Linearised flow

An air stream flows over a concave corner of angle 6°. The conditions upstream of the wave springing from the corner are Mach number = 2.0, and the static pressure and temperature are 0.7 bar, 300 K (Fig. 1.20).

Determine the Mach number, static pressure and temperature, and velocity downstream of the wave assuming

(a) Prandtl-Meyer flow,

(b) linearised flow.

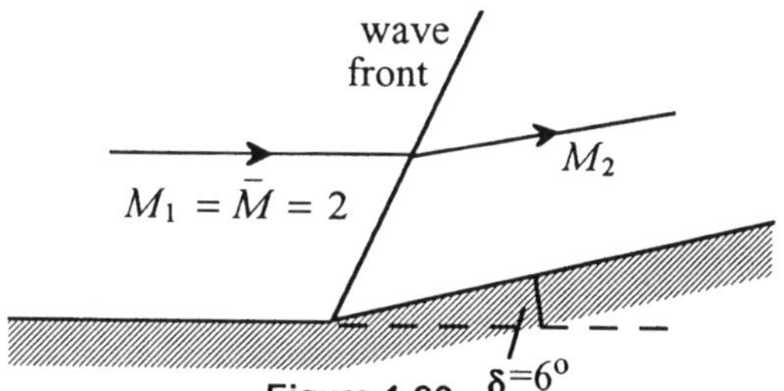

Figure 1.20

Solution.

(a) Using the flow tables, at $M_1 = 2.0$

T $\quad \nu_1 = 26.32$

T $\quad \dfrac{p_0}{p_1} = 7.830, \quad \dfrac{T_0}{T_1} = 1.806$

hence $p_0 = 7.830(0.7) = 5.48$ bar

$T_0 = 1.806(300) = 542$ K

In this problem the flow is *compressive* so that $\nu_2 = \nu_1 - 6 = 20.32$
Hence

T $\quad M_2 = \mathbf{1.79}, \quad \dfrac{p_0}{p_2} = 5.664, \quad \dfrac{T_0}{T_2} = 1.646$

giving $p_2 = \mathbf{0.97}$bar, $T_2 = \mathbf{329}$

Finally $a_2 = \sqrt{\gamma R T_2} = \sqrt{1.4(287)(329)} = 364$ m/s

and $\quad u_2 = M_2 a_2 = \mathbf{652}$ m/s

Note. The flow is isentropic, so that the stagnation pressure and temperature are constant. Also such flow is strictly applicable to expansive (accelerating) changes, but can be applied to compressive flow if the deflection is small.

(b) The results obtained in the previous example for linearised flow applied to a convex corner. In the case of a concave former the equations become

$$\frac{p}{\bar{p}} = 1 + \bar{\rho}\bar{u}^2\delta \tan\bar{\mu},$$

$$\frac{T}{\bar{T}} = 1 + \frac{(\gamma - 1)\bar{M}^2 u'}{\bar{u}}$$

and $\quad u' = -\bar{u}\delta \tan\bar{\mu}, \quad v' = +\bar{u}\delta.$

$\bar{M} = 2.0, \quad \bar{p} = 0.7$ bar, $\quad \bar{T} = 300$ K, $\quad \bar{\mu} = \arcsin\frac{1}{2} = 30°$

$\bar{a} = \sqrt{1.4(287)(300)} = 347$ m/s

$\bar{u} = \bar{M}\bar{a} = 2(347) = 694$ m/s

$u' = -(694)(0.1047)(\tan 30) = -42$ m/s

$v_2 = v' = 694(0.1047) = 72$ m/s

$u_2 = \bar{u} + u' = 652$ m/s

$\text{v} = \sqrt{u_2^2 + v_2^2} = \mathbf{656}$ m/s

$p_2 = \bar{p}(1 + \bar{\rho}\bar{u}^2\delta \tan\bar{\mu}) = \mathbf{0.86}$ bar

$$T_2 = \bar{T}\left(1 + \frac{(\gamma - 1)\bar{M}^2 u'}{\bar{u}}\right) = \mathbf{326}\text{ K}$$

$a_2 = \sqrt{\gamma R T_2} = 362$ m/s

$M_2 = \dfrac{\text{v}}{a_2} = \mathbf{1.81}$

The results are compared in the following table:

	Downstream		
	M	T (K)	velocity (m/s)
Prandtl-Meyer flow	1.79	329	652
linearised flow	1.81	326	656

Problems

Unless stated otherwise the following values are used in these problems:

R = 287J/kg K, γ = 1.40

1 A duct conveys air at a rate of 1.0 kg/s. The duct length = 20 m. The static conditions at the duct inlet are 0.9 bar, 300 K. Kinematic viscosity = 1.6×10^{-5} m²/s. The friction coefficient $f = 0.076/R_e^{0.25}$. Calculate the pressure drop due to friction when the duct is
(a) circular, diameter 200 mm
(b) square cross-section, side 200 mm.

Answer (a) 595 (b) 388 N/m²

2 A Venturi meter, throat diameter A/m, is inserted in a pipe of area A. The conditions in the pipe upstream of the throat are denoted by a subscript 1, and at the throat by the subscript 2. Show that for steady isentropic flow the mass flow rate $\dot{m}$ is given by the equation

$$\left(\frac{\dot{m}}{A}\right)^2 = \frac{\frac{2\gamma}{\gamma-1}(p_1\rho_1)k^{\frac{2}{\gamma}}(1-k^{\frac{\gamma-1}{\gamma}})}{m^2-k^{\frac{2}{\gamma}}}$$

where k = pressure ratio, $\frac{p_2}{p_1}$.

The meter conveys air at a rate of 0.9 kg/s. Pipe diameter = 125mm, throat diameter = 100 mm. The upstream static conditions are 3 bar, 60° C. Calculate the static pressure at the throat.

Answer 5 kN/m²

3 A Pitot tube is inserted into an air stream to measure the stagnation pressure. The static pressure is measured separately. Show how the measurement of the two pressures enables the Mach number of the flow to be determined.

In what circumstances can the Pitot tube be used to measure both pressures, and hence the fluid velocity, in one instrument?

In an air stream the velocity is 160 m/s, static pressure = 0.8 bar, static temperature = −12°C. Calculate the flow Mach number, and stagnation pressure and temperature.

Answer 0.49; 0.95 bar, 274 K

4 At a section in a duct conveying air the fluid velocity = 150 m/s, and the static conditions are 0.7 bar, 277 K. The mass flow rate is 13 kg/s. Assuming steady, isentropic flow calculate the critical

area, and the static pressure and temperature at the critical area. Also calculate the stagnation pressure and temperature at each area.

Answer $0.068\ m^2$;
0.425 bar, 240 K;
0.804 bar, 288K

5 The relationship between pressure and density for a fluid is

$$\frac{dp}{d\rho} = \frac{k}{\rho}$$

Show that, in isentropic flow,

$$\frac{p}{p_o} = 1 + \frac{k}{p_o}\ln(1 - \tfrac{1}{2}M^2)$$

and mass flow rate

$$\dot{m} = MA\sqrt{kp_o(1 - \tfrac{1}{2}M^2)}\ .$$

6 State the energy equation for one-dimensional, steady, isentropic flow and hence show that

$$a^* = \sqrt{\frac{2(\gamma - 1)}{\gamma + 1}.h_o}\ , \quad \text{and} \quad a_o = \sqrt{(\gamma - 1)h_o}\ .$$

The Crocco number Cr is defined as the ratio of the local fluid velocity to the maximum velocity, $\sqrt{2h_o}$. Show that

$$\frac{T_o}{T} = (1 + Cr)^2.$$

7 A convergent-divergent nozzle passes air from a *large* reservoir (in which the air temperature is 400 K), exhausting to atmosphere at a static pressure of 1.0 bar. The area of the divergent portion of the nozzle increases linearly with the axial distance from the throat. The exit area = 1.25 times the throat area.

Assuming isentropic flow plot the static pressure and velocity distribution along the nozzle when the reservoir pressure is
(a) 1.2, (b) 1.3, (c) 1.6 bar.

8 Air flow through a nozzle, inlet area $1.0\ m^2$ and exit area $2.0\ m^2$. The static conditions at the inlet are 2 bar, 300 K and the air velocity is 173 m/s. Assuming steady isentropic flow calculate the static pressure and temperature, and air velocity at the exit; and mass flow rate.

The air velocity at inlet is increased to 520 m/s, with the static conditions remaining the same. Determine the new exit conditions and mass flow rate.

Answer 2.29 bar, 312 K, 79 m/s; 402 kg/s
0.52 bar 204 K, 680 m/s; 1208 kg/s.

9 A vessel of volume 0.56 m^3 contains air at 205 bar, 200 °C. The air is discharged into the ambient atmosphere (static pressure 1.0 bar) through a valve and convergent nozzle, of exit area 130 mm^2.

Assuming isentropic flow estimate the time taken for the air pressure in the vessel to decrease to a value of 2 bar when the valve is opened.

Answer 52 sec.

10 A convergent-divergent nozzle discharges air from a large reservoir, in which the stagnation conditions are 10 bar, 80° C. The air expansion is isentropic down to a static pressure of 1 bar.

If the thrust exerted by the air jet leaving the nozzle is 11200 N, determine the nozzle throat and exit areas, and Mach number of the exit stream.

Answer 0.0089 m^2, 0.0172 m^2; 2.16.

11 A rocket motor nozzle is designed to give complete expansion of the combustion products. Assuming isentropic flow and an ideal gas show that the thrust is, per *unit* mass flow rate,

$$\sqrt{\frac{2\gamma}{\gamma - 1}(RT_o)(1 - k^{\frac{\gamma-1}{\gamma}})} \quad \text{where } k = \text{ ambient pressure } \frac{p_a}{p_o}.$$

At lift-off half of the total mass of the rocket is due to propellant, and the rocket designed to fire for 60 seconds at constant combustion chamber conditions of 20 bar, 3000 K. The propellant is totally consumed during this period. The rocket is fired to lift in a vertical direction.

Assuming that the ambient pressure is 1.0 bar, R = 250 J/kg K and γ = 1.20, and neglecting air resistance what height would be attained by the rocket during the firing period?

Answer 113 km.

12 A Venturi meter is used to measure the flow rate of steam, entering the meter at 14 bar, 250°C. The area at inlet = 0.074 m^2, and at the throat = 0.060 m^2. The static pressure at the throat = 10 bar. Assuming isentropic flow, and γ = 1.30 determine the flow rate.

Steam tables should be used.

Answer 133 kg/s.

13 Air discharges into the atmosphere (pressure 1.0 bar) through a convergent-divergent nozzle of throat diameter 25 mm. The air is drawn from a large reservoir, in which the pressure and temperature are 14 bar, 60°C. The axial length of the divergent portion is 200 mm.

Calculate the diameter, flow Mach number and the air velocity at the throat, exit and at sections 50, 100 and 150 mm axial distance from the throat. The pressure drop in the divergent portion is linear, and the flow isentropic.

Answer 334 m/s; 38.2 mm, 596 m/s
25.4 mm, 1.20, 387 m/s
26.3 mm, 1.44, 443 m/s
29.0 mm, 1.82, 524 m/s.

14 An ideal gas is discharged from a duct through a convergent nozzle at the end of the duct. The static pressure in the duct $= p_1$. Assuming isentropic flow show that when the mass flow rate is a maximum the throat pressure in the nozzle is

$$\left(\frac{2}{\gamma+1}\right)^{\frac{\gamma}{\gamma-1}}\left(1+\frac{1}{2}(\gamma-1)M_1^2\right)^{\frac{\gamma}{\gamma-1}}.$$

15 A gas flows along a variable area duct. Assuming steady, one-dimensional, isentropic flow show that

$$\frac{A}{A^*} = \frac{1}{M}\left(\frac{2+(\gamma-1)M^2}{\gamma+1}\right)^n$$

where $n = \dfrac{(\gamma+1)}{2(\gamma-1)}$

and A^* = area (critical) at which $M = 1$.
The equation

$$\frac{dA}{A} = (M^2-1)\frac{du}{u}$$

may be used without proof.

If the area ratio $A/A^* = 3$ calculate the Mach number. $\gamma = 4/3$.

Answer 0.2 or 2.55.

16 Show that for the steady, isentropic flow of air in a duct, area A, the flow Mach number, M, is given by the equation

$$\frac{MA}{(M^2+5)^3} = \text{constant}.$$

At a section in a square duct the area = 0.45 m^2 and $M = 0.35$. Calculate the Mach number at a section where the area = 0.3 m^2.

Answer 0.60.

17 A wind tunnel has a contraction (area) ratio of 7:1. The working section is rectangular, of dimensions 1.2 m by 0.9 m. In the working section the flow Mach number = 0.8, and the stagnation temperature 295 K. Assuming isentropic flow calculate the air velocity upstream of the contraction, and mass flow rate.

The static pressure at the upstream point is 1.02 bar. Calculate the static pressure difference between this point and the working section.

Answer 27 m/s; 246 kg/s; 0.35 bar.

18 A diffuser, of circular cross-section, has an area of 0.07 m^2 at inlet and 0.14 m^2 at exit. The static conditions at inlet are 4 bar, 450 K. The mass flow rate = 40 kg/s. Ambient pressure = 1 bar. Assuming isentropic flow calculate the flow Mach number, static pressure and air velocity at the exit; and the force on the diffuser walls.

Answer 0.20; 4.42 bar; 86 m/s; 30.8 kN.

19 An annular diffuser is shown in Fig. 1.21. The static conditions at the inlet are 4 bar, 450 K.
Mass flow rate = 40 kg/s.
Flow Mach number at exit = 0.20, velocity = 86.3 m/s.
Show that the flow is adiabatic, but not isentropic.

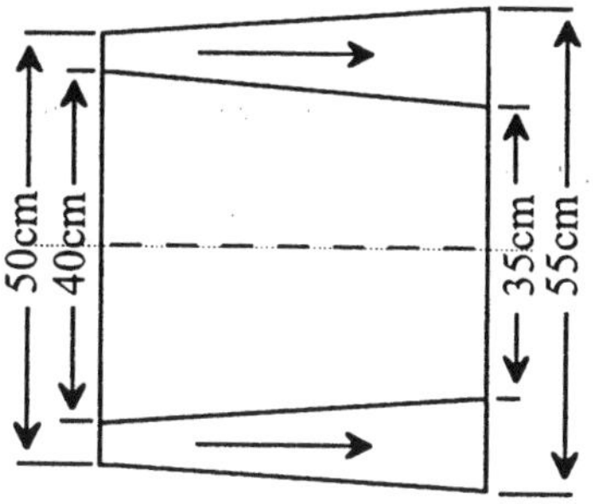

Figure 1.21

20 Air flowing along a duct meets a sudden enlargement, as shown in Fig. 1.22. Assuming steady, one-dimensional flow show by using the continuity and momentum equations that

$$p_1 - p_2 = \rho_2 u_2^2 - \frac{\rho_1 u_1^2}{k}$$

and $$\frac{p_2}{p_1} = \frac{7M_1^2 + 5k}{k(7M_2^2 + 5)}$$

where $k =$ area ratio, $\dfrac{A_2}{A_1}$

If $M_1 = 0.85$, $p_1 = 3$ bar, $u_1 = 250$ m/s and $k = 2$ calculate the static pressure, velocity and flow Mach number at section 2.
Is the flow isentropic? If not explain why.

Answer 3.72 bar, 131 m/s, 0.39; No.

21 A diffuser of circular cross-section is to be designed for the static pressure to increase linearly with the axial distance x.
At inlet the static conditions are 2 bar, 300 K and the gas velocity is 190 m/s. At the exit the gas velocity is 80 m/s. Mass

flow rate = 50 kg/s.

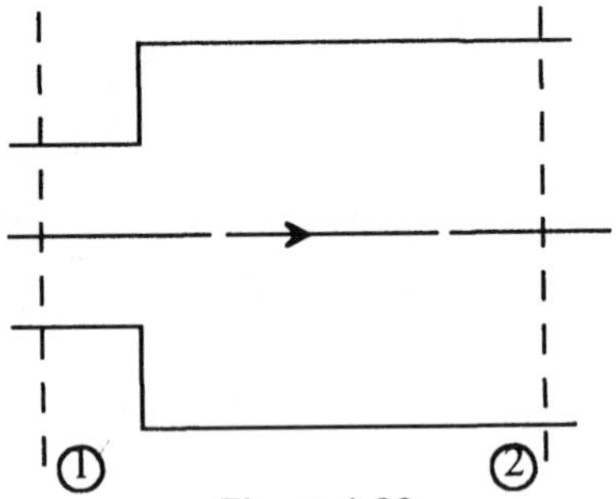

Figure 1.22

Calculate the static pressure and temperature at the exit; and the radius at inlet and exit. Also determine the Mach number, radius and axial distance (as a fraction of the diffuser length) at the section where the static pressure is

(a) 2.10,
(b) 2.20,
(c) 2.30 bar.

Assume steady, one-dimensional, isentropic flow.

$\gamma = \frac{4}{3}$, R = 300 J/kg K.

The following equations may be used without proof:

$$\frac{dp}{p} = \frac{\gamma M^2}{1 - M^2}\frac{dA}{A}$$

$$\frac{dM^2}{M^2} = \frac{2 + (\gamma - 1)M^2}{M^2 - 1}\frac{dA}{A}$$

$$\frac{A}{A^*} = \frac{1}{M}\left(\frac{M^2 + 6}{7}\right)^{3.5}$$

Answer 2.35 bar, 312 K; 388 mm, 563mm
(a) 0.473, 408 mm, 0.286
(b) 0.389, 441 mm, 0.571
(c) 0.289, 502 mm, 0.857.

22 A circular duct wall profile (Fig. 1.23) is given by the equation

$$\frac{r}{r_o} = 1 + k\left(\frac{x}{r_o}\right)^2.$$

The flow is isentropic. Using the relationship

$$\frac{dM^2}{M^2} = -\frac{2 + (\gamma - 1)M^2}{1 - M^2}\frac{dA}{A}$$

show that

$$\left(\frac{M}{M_o}\right)^2\left(\frac{M_o^2 + 5}{M^2 + 5}\right)^6 = \left(1 + \frac{kx^2}{r_o^2}\right)^4.$$

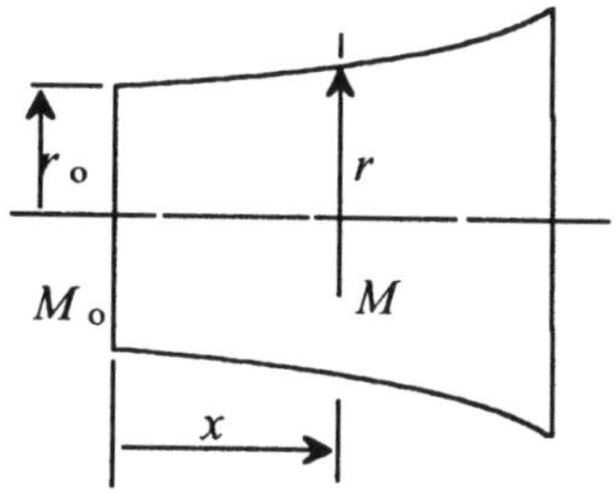

Figure 1.23

23 A supersonic air stream flows over a convex corner, and a Prandtl-Meyer fan originates from the corner (Fig. 1.24).

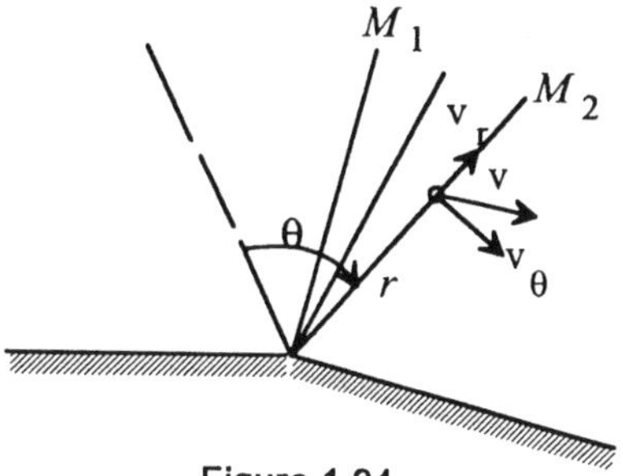

Figure 1.24

Show that, in terms of polar coordinates,

$$v_r = v_m \sin k(\theta - \theta_o)$$

$$v_\theta = k v_m \cos k(\theta - \theta_o)$$

$$r = r_o(\cos k(\theta - \theta_o))^{-\frac{1}{k^2}}$$

where

$$k^2 = \frac{(\gamma - 1)}{(\gamma + 1)}$$

$$v_m^2 = \frac{2\gamma R T_o}{\gamma - 1}$$

and θ_o is an integration constant. The following relationships may be used:

$$\frac{1}{2}v^2 + \int \frac{1}{\rho} dp = \text{constant} = \frac{1}{2}v_m^2 \text{ and}$$

$$\frac{1}{r}\frac{dr}{d\theta} = \frac{v_r}{v_\theta}.$$

Also show, by use of the energy equation, that the static pressure at a point is given by

$$\frac{p_o}{p} = \left[\frac{1}{2}(\gamma + 1)\sec^2 k\theta\right]^{\frac{\gamma}{\gamma - 1}}.$$

24 An air stream expands over a corner, as shown in Fig. 1.25. The stagnation conditions are 10 bar, 600 K. The wave fronts (Mach lines) OA, OD correspond to the initial and final Mach numbers.

Angle AOB = 19.25°, BOC = 5.92°. The flow Mach number upstream of OA is 1.70.

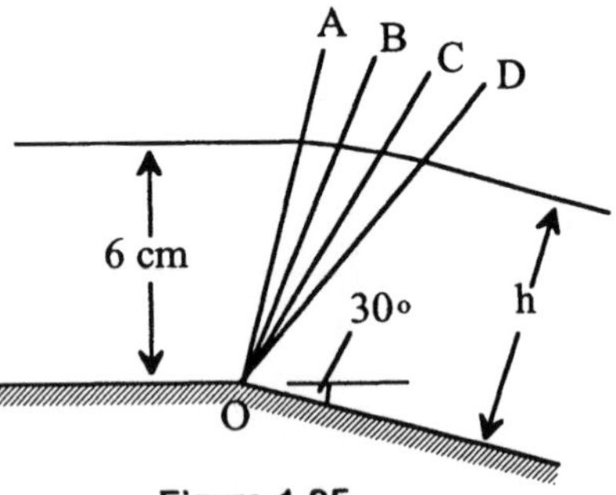

Figure 1.25

Determine the fan angle AOD, the height h of the streamline shown, and the Mach number and velocity at the intermediate fronts OB, OC.

Flow tables should be used.

Answer 45.93°; 17.4 cm;
2.11, 752 m/s; 2.26, 779 m/s

25 A two-dimensional channel is shown in Fig. 1.26. The fan originating at the corner A is reflected from the upper wall at B. The flow Mach number in region 1 is 2.15.

Determine the Mach number, and velocity ratio u/u_1, pressure ratio p/p_1 in regions 2 and 3.

Flow tables should be used.

Answer 2.35, 1.045, 0.732;
2.565, 1.087, 0.524

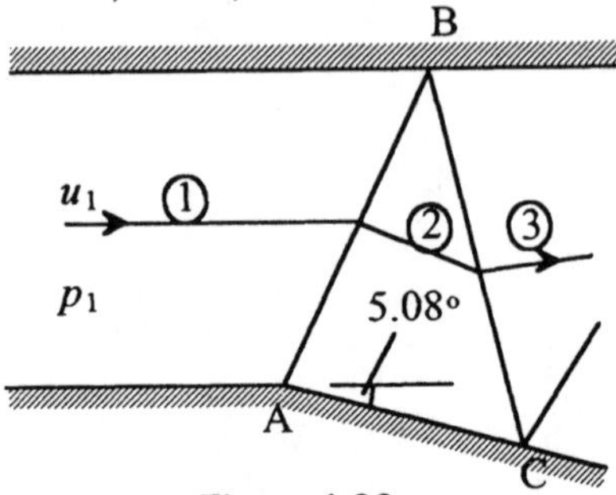

Figure 1.26

26 A supersonic air stream flows along a symmetrical duct, whose walls consist of linear sections (Fig. 1.27). The approach conditions in region 1 are Mach number = 1.5, static pressure and temperature = 2 bar, 300 K respectively.

Using flow tables determine the Mach number, static pressure and temperature, and velocity in regions 2, 3 and 4.

Answer 1.57, 1.81 bar, 291 K, 537 m/s;

1.635, 1.64 bar, 283 K, 551 m/s;
1.705, 1.48 bar, 275 K, 567 m/s

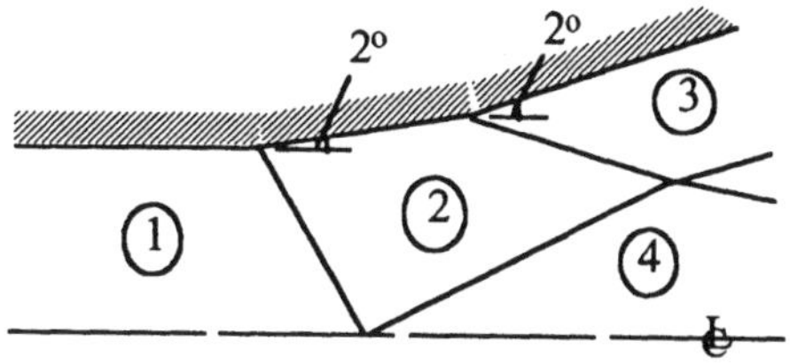

Figure 1.27

27 A flat plate aerofoil, chord c, span $2b$, is set at an angle of incidence α to a stream, Mach number $\overline{M}$. Using linearised theory show that the lift and drag coefficients and lift force L are given by

$$C_L = \frac{2\alpha}{\sqrt{(\overline{M}^2 - 1)}}$$

$$C_D = \alpha C_L$$

$$L = \frac{2bc\alpha}{\sqrt{\overline{M}^2 - 1}}(\gamma \overline{p} \overline{M}^2)$$

Neglect end effects.

$$C_L = \frac{L}{\frac{1}{2}\overline{\rho}\overline{u}^2 A}$$

$$C_D = \frac{D}{\frac{1}{2}\overline{\rho}\overline{u}^2 A}$$

where A = projected area = 2bc.

28 An air stream flows over a convex corner of angle 10.08°. The upstream conditions are flow Mach number = 2.0, static pressure 3 bar, static temperature 350 K.

Determine the conditions downstream of the disturbance springing from the corner

(a) using Prandtl-Meyer flow analysis,

(b) using linearised flow theory.

Express the differences between the results obtained by both methods as a percentage of the exact Prandtl-Meyer analysis.

Answer (a) M = 2.39,
pressure ratio = 0.543,
temperature ratio = 0.84,
velocity ratio = 1.095

(b) M = 2.43; ratios 0.433, 0.84, 1.115
Mach number 1.7%;
ratios -20.8%, 0, 1.8%.

2

Non-isentropic compressible flow

The flow of a fluid in pipes or ducts is often not isentropic, in that there are frictional effects at the walls, and there may be heat transfer through the wall. The effects of friction and heat transfer are different in some respects, depending on the nature of the flow, i.e. subsonic or supersonic.

Two points of importance are:

(a) in isentropic flow the stagnation pressure and temperature are constant. The presence of *friction* causes a *decrease* in the stagnation *pressure*;

(b) the presence of *heat transfer* causes a change in the stagnation *temperature* (or *enthalpy*).

These points can be deduced from the energy equation

$$dp + \rho u\,du + dp_f = 0 \tag{1.12}$$

or $$dp_o + dp_f = 0$$

and $$Q = \Delta(h + \tfrac{1}{2}u^2) = \Delta h_o \tag{1.7}$$

Fanno flow

This type of flow refers to the adiabatic flow of an ideal gas in a *constant area* duct, with *surface friction*.

The flow is adiabatic so that there is no heat transfer involved, but it is not isentropic due to the presence of wall friction. Considering steady, one-dimensional flow the relevant basic equations are:

continuity $\rho u A = \text{constant} = \dot{m}$

or $\rho u = \dfrac{\dot{m}}{A} = G \text{ say} = \text{constant}$

energy $h_o = h + \tfrac{1}{2}u^2 = \text{constant}$

momentum $A\,dp = G\,du - \tau_o P\,dx$

where τ_o = wall friction (shear) stress/unit area

P = perimeter of the cross-section.

The *Fanno* line (curve) is the curve relating the enthalpy to entropy. The relationship between entropy and other variables is

$$T\,ds = de + p\,dv = dh - \frac{dp}{\rho}.$$

$$h = h_o - \frac{1}{2}u^2 = h_o - \frac{G^2}{2\rho^2} \text{ (since } G = \rho u\text{)}$$

hence $$T\,ds = \frac{G^2\,d\rho}{\rho^3} - \frac{dp}{\rho}$$

A Fanno line is shown in Fig. 2.1, and there are two distinct branches corresponding to subsonic and supersonic flow. The entropy attains a maximum value at point A, where $ds = 0$

$$\frac{G^2\, d\rho}{\rho^3} = \frac{dp}{\rho}$$

and $$\frac{dp}{d\rho} = \frac{G^2}{\rho^2} = u^2$$

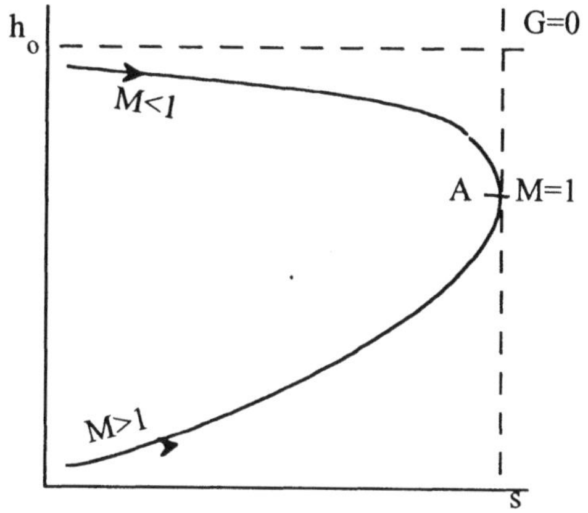

Figure 2.1

However the acoustic velocity

$$a = \sqrt{\frac{dp}{d\rho}},$$

so that at this point $u^2 = a^2$ or $M = 1$. This then represents a limiting or *choking* condition: a fixing of the maximum mass flow rate in the pipe or duct, similar to choking in a nozzle at the throat.

Important corollaries follow from the Fanno diagram, Fig. 2.1. The effect of wall friction is to *accelerate* subsonic flow (Mach number increasing), and *decelerate* supersonic flow (Mach number decreasing): in *both* types of flow the Mach number increases towards the limiting value $M = 1$.

In a pipe of length L, and given *inlet* conditions two situations may arise. Corresponding to the inlet conditions the maximum mass flow rate will give choking at the exit over a length L_{max} say. If the actual pipe length L is greater than L_{max}, then

(a) for subsonic flow, the mass flow rate decreases to give $L \leq L_{max}$ with a corresponding change of inlet conditions;
(b) for supersonic flow, a normal shock wave will stand in the pipe, reducing the flow to a subsonic regime.

The cross section of the duct may not be circular. In this case the friction coefficient f is based on the equivalent diameter D_e, as indicated in Chapter 1.

Note. In this volume the calculations involving Fanno (and Rayleigh) are, in most cases, executed with the aid of *flow tables*. The use of tables considerably simplifies calculations.

The basic assumptions of steady, one-dimensional flow, and constant friction coefficient are somewhat artificial. At any section in the duct the gas velocity is not uniform, as a boundary layer exists at the wall. Further the presence of bends etc in a pipe produces a non-uniform velocity. However in many situations the use of a mean velocity gives a reasonable accuracy. The friction coefficient depends upon the Reynolds number, and to a smaller extent upon the Mach number. The flow is often turbulent, so that the main factor is the surface roughness of the duct. The high velocity flow in a smooth duct can be considered with a constant friction coefficient with reasonable accuracy.

Rayleigh flow

This type of flow refers to the flow of an ideal gas in a *constant area* duct, with *heat transfer* but no friction effects.

For steady, one-dimensional flow the basic equations are:

continuity $\rho u = \frac{\dot{m}}{A} = G = \text{constant}$

energy $dh + u\,du + dQ = 0$

momentum $dp + G\,du = 0$

The Rayleigh line (curve) is the curve relating the enthalpy and entropy, and is shown in Fig. 2.2.

It should be noted that in real flows the specific heat ratio may not be constant, particularly if heat is added to the gas by combustion, and at high temperatures. In addition heat transfer through the duct wall would normally involve wall friction.

Again *choking* occurs at the limiting condition M = 1. The effects of heat addition and extraction are shown in Fig. 2.2: in both subsonic and supersonic flow the addition of heat to the gas causes the Mach number to approach the limiting value M = 1, and the extraction of heat causes a retreat from M = 1.

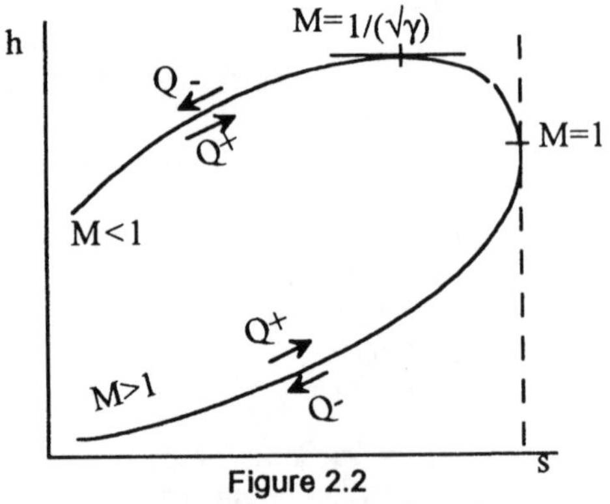

Figure 2.2

	Subsonic flow	Supersonic flow
Heat addition	*M* increases	*M* decreases
Heat extraction	*M* decreases	*M* increases

Critical conditions

In both types of flow the choking (critical) conditions occur at $M = 1$. In the same way that the critical conditions are a useful *datum* in isentropic flow, they can be used in Fanno and Rayleigh flow. It should be noted that in a pipe or duct the critical conditions may not be reached at any section, but still form a useful datum. This is found in flow tables, where, for example, the values are given in the following form: the asterisk * denoting critical values.

Fanno flow

M	p/p^*	p_o/p^*_o	T/T^*	Δs	$4f\|x-x^*\|/D$
1.00	1.00	1.00	1.00	0.00	0.00
1.05	0.944	1.002	0.983	–0.00014	0.0027
1.10	0.893	1.008	0.966	–0.00054	0.0099

Rayleigh flow

M	p/p^*	p_o/p^*_o	T/T^*	T_o/T^*_o	Δs
1.00	1.00	1.00	1.00	1.00	0.00
1.05	0.944	1.001	0.982	0.998	–0.00047
1.10	0.891	1.005	0.960	0.994	–0.0018

Generalised flow

The analysis of more realistic flows in which the duct area may be variable, friction and heat transfer are both present, and real gas properties of variable specific heat, molecular mass, etc is clearly more involved.

The generalised flow is examined in texts such as 'The Dynamics and Thermodynamics of Compressible Fluid Flow', S. H. Shapiro: and because of its complex nature a brief introduction only is considered in this book.

General flow equations for *shock-free* situations can be derived in terms of the influences which affect the flow. Thus, confining the text to variable area, heat transfer and friction, a variable V can be expressed in the form:

$$V = F_1 I_1 + F_2 I_2 + F_3 I_3$$

where I_1, I_2, I_3 are the influences

$$\frac{dA}{A}, \frac{dT_o}{T_o} \text{ and } \frac{4f\,dx}{D}$$

respectively; and F_1, F_2, F_3 are known as the *influence coefficients*. These are tabulated below.

Variable V	$\frac{dA}{A}$	$\frac{dT_o}{T_o}$	$\frac{4f\,dx}{D}$
$\frac{dM^2}{M^2}$	$\frac{-2(1+kM^2)}{1-M^2}$	$\frac{(1+\gamma M^2)(1+kM^2)}{1-M^2}$	$\frac{\gamma M^2(1+kM^2)}{1-M^2}$
$\frac{du}{u}$	$-\frac{1}{1-M^2}$	$\frac{1+kM^2}{1-M^2}$	$\frac{\frac{1}{2}\gamma M^2}{1-M^2}$
$\frac{dT}{T}$	$\frac{(\gamma-1)M^2}{1-M^2}$	$\frac{(1-\gamma M^2)(1+kM^2)}{1-M^2}$	$-\frac{\frac{1}{2}\gamma(\gamma-1)M^4}{1-M^2}$
$\frac{dp}{p}$	$\frac{\gamma M^2}{1-M^2}$	$-\frac{\gamma M^2(1+kM^2)}{1-M^2}$	$-\frac{\frac{1}{2}\gamma M^2(1+2kM}{1-M^2}$

$\frac{dp_o}{p_o}$	0	$-\frac{1}{2}\gamma M^2$	$-\frac{1}{2}\gamma M^2$

where $k = \frac{1}{2}(\gamma - 1)$

The use of this table is illustrated by the following example:

$$\frac{du}{u} = -\left(\frac{1}{1 - M^2}\right)\frac{dA}{A} + \left(\frac{1 + kM^2}{1 - M^2}\right)\frac{dT_o}{T_o} + \left(\frac{\frac{1}{2}\gamma M^2}{1 - M^2}\right)\cdot\frac{4f\,dx}{D}$$

The influence coefficients are all functions of the Mach number, and except for the variable dp_o/p_o involve the term $1 - M^2$ in the denominator. This emphasises the importance of the situation at $M = 1$, the critical conditions, where the coefficients become indeterminate: together with the change of sign between subsonic ($M < 1$) and supersonic ($M > 1$) flows. A final point that is considered in Ex. 2.5 is that the variable dT/T involves the influence coefficient

$$\frac{(1 - \gamma M^2)(1 + kM^2)}{1 - M^2}$$

with the influence dT_o/T_o. The numerator is zero when

$$M = \frac{1}{\sqrt{\gamma}}.$$

2.1 Choked Fanno flow

Air flows along a circular duct, diameter D. Show that for Fanno flow

$$\frac{p_o}{p_o^*} = \frac{1}{M}\left(\frac{2 + (\gamma - 1)M^2}{\gamma + 1}\right)^n$$

where $n = \dfrac{(\gamma + 1)}{2(\gamma - 1)}$.

The stagnation pressure at inlet is 5 bar, and the flow Mach number 0.5. If the flow is choked at the duct exit calculate the stagnation pressure drop, Mach number at exit, and the entropy increase /kg.

Solution. The stagnation pressure is defined as the static pressure that the fluid would attain if brought to rest isentropically, and therefore depends on the type of flow. Hence

$$\frac{p_o}{p} = (1 + kM^2)^{\frac{\gamma}{\gamma-1}}$$

where $k = \frac{1}{2}(\gamma - 1)$.

Also p_o^* is the stagnation pressure at the critical conditions, $M = 1$. Hence

$$\frac{p_o}{p_o^*} = \left(\frac{1 + kM^2}{1 + k}\right)^{\frac{\gamma}{\gamma-1}}\frac{p}{p^*} = \left(\frac{2 + (\gamma - 1)M^2}{\gamma + 1}\right)^{\frac{\gamma}{\gamma-1}}\cdot\frac{p}{p^*}$$

The continuity equation is $\rho u = \rho^* u^*$, and the state equation gives

$$\frac{p}{p^*} = \frac{\rho T}{\rho^* T^*}.$$

Also $T_o = (1 + kM^2)T =$ constant (adiabatic flow),

hence $\dfrac{T}{T^*} = \dfrac{1 + k}{1 + kM^2}$.

Further $u = M\sqrt{\gamma RT} = M\sqrt{\dfrac{\gamma RT_o}{1 + kM^2}}$

$$\therefore \quad \frac{u^*}{u} = \frac{1}{M}\sqrt{\frac{1 + kM^2}{1 + k}}$$

and $$\frac{p}{p^*} = \frac{u^*}{u}.\frac{T}{T^*} = \frac{1}{M}\sqrt{\frac{1 + kM^2}{1 + k}}.\frac{1 + k}{1 + kM^2}$$

Substituting

$$\frac{p_o}{p_o^*} = \left(\frac{1 + kM^2}{1 + k}\right)^{\gamma - 1}.\frac{1}{M}\left(\frac{1 + kM^2}{1 + k}\right)^2 = \frac{1}{M}\left(\frac{1 + kM^2}{1 + k}\right)^n$$

where $n = \frac{\gamma}{\gamma - 1} - \frac{1}{2} = \frac{\gamma + 1}{2(\gamma - 1)}$.

The conditions at the pipe exit are critical, corresponding to choking. Hence, at the exit,

$$p_o^* = p_o M\left(\frac{\gamma + 1}{2 + (\gamma - 1)M^2}\right)^n$$

Substituting $p_o = 5 \times 10^5$ N/m^2, $M = 0.5, \gamma = 1.4$ gives $p_o^* = 3.73$ bar. Hence the stagnation pressure drop is

$$\Delta p_o = p_o - p_o^* = \mathbf{1.27} \text{ bar}.$$

At the exit **M = 1**. The entropy increase can be determined by integration.

$$T ds = dh - \frac{dp}{\rho} = C_p dT - \frac{dp}{\rho}$$

$$ds = C_p\frac{dT}{T} - \frac{dp}{\rho T} = C_p\frac{dT}{T} - \frac{R\,dp}{p} \quad (\text{since } p = \rho RT)$$

Integrating gives

$$\Delta s = -s + s^* = -C_p \ln\left(\frac{T}{T^*}\right) + R\ln\left(\frac{p}{p^*}\right)$$

Now $C_p = \frac{\gamma R}{\gamma - 1} = \frac{1.4 \times 287}{0.4} = 1005$ J/Kg K

$$k = \tfrac{1}{2}(\gamma - 1) = 0.2$$

$$\frac{T}{T^*} = \frac{1 + k}{1 + kM^2} = \frac{1.2}{1 + 0.2(0.5)^2} = 1.143$$

$$\frac{p}{p^*} = \frac{1}{M}\left(\frac{1 + k}{1 + kM^2}\right)^{\frac{1}{2}} = 2.138$$

and $\Delta s = -1005 \ln 1.143 + 287 \ln 2.138 = \mathbf{+83.8}$ J/kg

2.2 Fanno flow

A circular pipe, diameter 5 cm, conveys air. The stagnation conditions at inlet are 6.5 bar, 340 K. The pipe length is 41.25 cm. Determine the static pressure and temperature at inlet and exit; the air velocity at inlet and exit; and mass flow rate. The friction coefficient can be taken as constant at 0.005.

Two cases should be considered: when the Mach number at inlet is
(a) 0.70;
(b) 1.60.
Flow tables should be used.

Solution. In the solution the Fanno flow and isentropic flow tables are used, the latter being employed to determine stagnation values.

(a) At inlet $M_1 = 0.70$

$$\frac{p_{o1}}{p_1} = 1.388 \text{ and } \frac{T_o}{T_1} = 1.099, \text{ giving}$$

$$p_1 = \mathbf{4.683} \text{ bar}, \; T_1 = \mathbf{309} \text{ K}$$

Note. The stagnation temperature is *constant*, but not the stagnation pressure.

$$\frac{4f}{D}|x_1 - x^*| = 0.2075 \quad \text{(from the tables)}$$

$$\text{Now } \frac{4f}{D}|x_1 - x_2| = \frac{4 \times 0.005 \times 0.4125}{0.05} = 0.165$$

$$\text{hence } \frac{4f}{D}|x_2 - x^*| = 0.2075 - 0.165 = 0.0425$$

and from the tables $M_2 = \mathbf{0.84}$ (at exit). The value 0.165 is *deducted* from the absolute value of

$$\frac{4f}{D}|x_1 - x^*|,$$

since the effect of friction is to make the Mach number approach unity, i.e. to *increase* in subsonic flow.

Also from the tables:

$$\text{at} \quad M_1 = 0.70 \quad \frac{p_{o1}}{p_o^*} = 1.094$$

$$\text{at} \quad M_2 = 0.84 \quad \frac{p_{o2}}{p_o^*} = 1.024$$

$$\text{hence } \frac{p_{o2}}{p_{o1}} = \frac{1.024}{1.094} = 0.936 \text{ and } p_{o2} = 6.084 \text{ bar.}$$

$$\text{Further } \frac{p_{o2}}{p_2} = 1.589, \; \frac{T_o}{T_2} = 1.142 \text{ and } p_2 = \mathbf{3.83} \text{ bar}, \; T_2 = \mathbf{298} \text{ K.}$$

The static pressure can alternatively be determined from the values of p/p^* in the tables:

$$\text{At} \quad M_1 = 0.70 \quad \frac{p_1}{p^*} = 1.494$$

$$M_2 = 0.84 \quad \frac{p_2}{p^*} = 1.221$$

$$\text{giving } \frac{p_2}{p_1} = \frac{1.221}{1.494} = 0.817$$

$$\text{and} \quad p_2 = \mathbf{3.83} \text{ bar.}$$

The air velocity $u = Ma = M\sqrt{\gamma RT}$,

$$u_1 = 0.70\sqrt{1.4 \times 287 \times 309} = \mathbf{247} \text{ m/s}$$

$$u_2 = 0.84\sqrt{1.4 \times 287 \times 298} = \mathbf{291} \text{ m/s.}$$

The mass flow rate

$$\dot{m} = \rho A u = \frac{pAu}{RT} = \frac{4.683 \times 10^5 \times \frac{\pi}{4}(0.05)^2 \times 247}{287 \times 309} = \mathbf{2.56} \text{ kg/s}$$

(b) At inlet $M_1 = 1.60$

$$\frac{p_{o1}}{p_1} = 4.255, \quad \frac{T_o}{T_1} = 1.516$$

$$\text{and} \quad p_1 = \mathbf{1.528} \text{ bar}$$

$$T_1 = \mathbf{224} \text{ K}$$

$$\frac{4f}{D}|x_1 - x^*| = 0.1716$$

$$\text{hence } \frac{4f}{D}|x_2 - x^*| = 0.0066$$

$$M_2 = \mathbf{1.08}.$$

Hence $\dfrac{p_{o2}}{p_{o1}} = \left(\dfrac{p_{o2}}{p_o^*}\right)\left(\dfrac{p_o^*}{p_{o1}}\right) = \dfrac{1.005}{1.2497}$

and $\quad p_{o2} = 5.227$

$$\frac{p_{o2}}{p_2} = 2.085, \quad \frac{T_o}{T_2} = 1.235$$

and hence $p_2 = \mathbf{2.507}$ bar

$$T_2 = \frac{340}{1.235} = \mathbf{275}\text{ K}$$

$$u_1 = 1.60\sqrt{1.4 \times 287 \times 224} = \mathbf{480}\text{ m/s}$$

$$u_2 = 1.08\sqrt{1.4 \times 287 \times 275} = \mathbf{359}\text{ m/s}$$

$$\dot{m} = \frac{1.528 \times 10^5 \times \frac{\pi}{4}(0.05)^2 \times 480}{287 \times 224} = \mathbf{2.24}\text{ kg/s}$$

2.3 Combined isentropic and Fanno flows

A convergent nozzle delivers air into a circular pipe, from a large reservoir, as shown in Fig. 2.3. The flow through the nozzle is isentropic and the stagnation conditions at the nozzle inlet are 7 bar, 400K.

The pipe is 3 cm diameter, 1.5 m long. The friction coefficient is 0.005.

Determine the maximum mass flow rate. Flow tables should be used.

Solution. Assume that the nozzle controls the flow, so that the conditions at section (1) are critical. The flow is isentropic in the nozzle, therefore

$$p_{o1} = 7\text{ bar}, \quad T_{01} = 400\text{ K}.$$

Also $\dfrac{4f}{D}|x_1 - x^*| = 0$

Now $\dfrac{4f}{D}|x_2 - x_1| = \dfrac{4 \times 0.005 \times 1.5}{0.03} = 1.00,$

and it can be seen that this situation cannot exist. In the first instance if the value 1.00 was added to give

$$\frac{4f}{D}|x_2 - x^*| = 1.00,$$

the corresponding value of M_2 would be approximately 0.51. At this Mach number

$$\frac{p_{o2}}{p_o^*} = 1.32$$

and $\quad p_{o2} = 9.24$ bar.

The stagnation pressure apparently *increases*, and this is impossible.

Secondly, the effect of friction is to cause an increase in entropy—the consequence of an irreversible process. A Mach number, increasing or decreasing along the pipe, would imply a decrease in entropy. This again is impossible.

Choking must therefore occur at the *pipe exit*. Then $M_2 = 1$ and

$$\frac{4f}{D}|x_1 - x^*| = 1.00,$$

giving $M_1 = \mathbf{0.508}$

and $\quad \dfrac{p_{o1}}{p_o^*} = 1.325, \qquad p_o^* = \dfrac{7.0}{1.325} = 5.28\text{ bar} = p_{o2}$

The stagnation pressure decreases along the pipe from 7.0 bar to 5.28 bar. The flow regime has now been determined and the mass flow rate can be calculated. At the exit

$$\frac{p_{o2}}{p_2} = 1.895, \quad p_2 = 2.79 \text{ bar}$$

$$\frac{T_{o2}}{T_2} = 1.201, \quad T_2 = \frac{400}{1.201} = 333 \text{ K}$$

$$\rho_2 = \frac{p_2}{RT_2} = 2.927 \text{ kg/m}^3$$

$$u_2 = M_2 a_2 = \sqrt{1.4 \times 287 \times 333} = 366 \text{ m/s}$$

$$\dot{m} = \rho_2 A_2 u_2 = 2.927 \times \tfrac{\pi}{4}(0.03)^2 \times 366 = \mathbf{0.757} \text{ kg/s}.$$

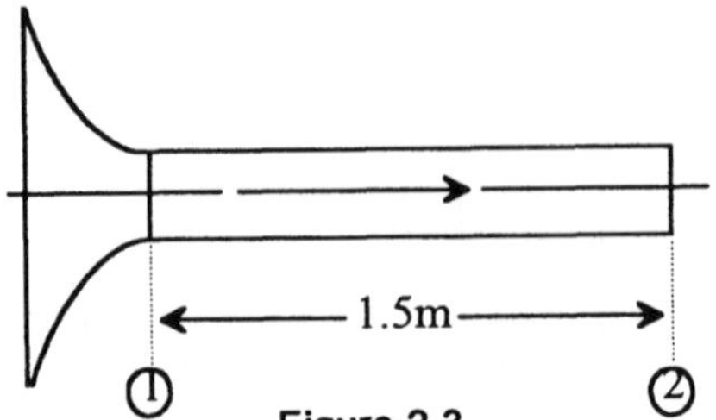

Figure 2.3

2.4 Non-circular duct

A duct, of rectangular cross-section, 50 cm by 25 cm, conveys air. $f = 0.004$. Duct length = 62 cm. At inlet the static pressure and temperature are 2 bar, 300 K and the flow Mach number is 0.30.

Determine the static conditions at the exit and mass flow rate.

Compare the static pressure drop with that assuming incompressible flow.

Solution. The duct cross-section is rectangular and the equivalent diameter is used.

$$D_e = \frac{4 \times \text{area}}{\text{perimeter}} = \frac{4 \times 0.5 \times 0.25}{1.50} = \frac{1}{3} \text{ m}$$

$$\frac{4f}{D}|x_2 - x_1| = \frac{4 \times 0.004 \times 62}{\frac{1}{3}} = 2.976$$

From the tables, at inlet $M_1 = 0.30$ and

$$\frac{p_1}{p^*} = 3.621, \quad \frac{T_1}{T^*} = 1.180$$

$$\frac{4f}{D_e}|x_1 - x^*| = 5.2865$$

The flow is subsonic so that the effect of friction is to make the Mach number *increase* towards the limiting (choking) value of unity. Hence

$$\frac{4f}{D_e}|x_2 - x^*| = 5.2865 - 2.976 = 2.3105$$

and from the tables $M_2 = 0.40$ (approximately)

$$\frac{p_2}{p^*} = 2.697, \quad \frac{T_2}{T^*} = 1.164$$

and $p_2 = \mathbf{1.49}$ bar, $T_2 = \mathbf{296}$ K

$$\dot{m} = \rho_2 A u_2 = \frac{p_2 A_2 u_2}{RT_2} = p_2 A_2 M_2 \sqrt{\frac{\gamma}{RT_2}} = \mathbf{30.24\ kg/s}$$

The static pressure drop = 2 – 1.49 = **0.51** bar. If the flow was considered incompressible, the pressure drop would be given by the Fanning equation 1.18,

$$\Delta p = \frac{4\rho f L u^2}{2D_e}$$

At inlet $p_1 = 2$ bar, $T_1 = 300$ K, and $a_1 = 347$ m/s hence

$$u_1 = M_1 a_1 = 104 \text{ m/s}$$

$$\rho 1 = \frac{p_1}{RT_1} = 2.323 \text{ kg/s}$$

and substituting

$$\Delta p = \frac{4 \times 2.323 \times 0.004 \times 62 \times (104)^2}{2 \times \frac{1}{3}} \text{ N/m}^2 = \mathbf{0.37\ bar}$$

2.5 Isothermal Fanno flow

An ideal gas flows along a circular pipe such that the flow is isothermal. The pipe diameter and friction coefficient are constant. The flow Mach number at inlet = M_1. Show that the length of the pipe L_{max} to reach choking conditions at the exit is given by the equation

$$\frac{4fL_{max}}{D} = \frac{(1-\gamma M_1^2)}{\gamma M_1^2} + \ln(\gamma M_1^2)$$

Neglecting the logarithmic term show that the equation can be written, between two sections, as

$$\frac{4fL}{D} = \frac{1-\left(\frac{p_2}{p_1}\right)^2}{\gamma M_1^2}$$

Natural gas is pumped along a pipe, 20 cm diameter, length 1.0 km. f = 0.004. The static conditions at the pipe *exit* are 2 bar, 300 K. If the flow rate is a maximum calculate the static pressure at the pipe inlet, and heat transfer per metre length (assumed uniform). $\gamma = 4/3$, R = 520 J/kg K.

Solution. The continuity and momentum equations for steady, one-dimensional, flow are:

$$\rho u = G = \text{constant}$$

or $$\frac{d\rho}{\rho} + \frac{du}{u} = 0$$

and $$dp + \rho u\, du + \frac{4f}{D}\left(\frac{1}{2}\rho u^2\right) dx = 0$$

or dividing by $\frac{1}{2}\rho u^2$

$$\frac{2}{\rho u^2} dp + \frac{1}{u} du + \frac{4f}{D} dx = 0$$

The first term cannot be integrated directly. since pressure, density and velocity are inter-related. The flow is isothermal and therefore

$$\frac{dp}{p} = \frac{d\rho}{\rho}$$

and from the continuity equation

$$\frac{d\rho}{\rho} = -\frac{du}{u}$$

Finally $\frac{1}{\rho u^2}dp = \frac{\rho}{\rho^2 u^2}dp = \frac{\rho}{G^2}dp = \frac{p}{G^2RT}dp$

Substituting

$$\frac{2p}{G^2RT}dp - \frac{2}{p}dp + \frac{4f}{D}dx = 0$$

and integrating between two sections x_1 and x_2

$$\frac{p_2^2 - p_1^2}{G^2RT} - 2\ln\left(\frac{p_2}{p_1}\right) + \frac{4fL}{D} = 0$$

where $x_1 - x_2 = L$

This equation can be expressed in more convenient terms as follows:

$$\frac{p^2}{G^2RT} = \frac{p^2}{\rho^2u^2RT} = \frac{RT}{u^2} = \frac{a^2}{\gamma u^2} = \frac{1}{\gamma M^2}$$

and substituting

$$\frac{1}{\gamma M_1^2}\left[\left(\frac{p_2}{p_1}\right)^2 - 1\right] - \ln\left(\frac{M_1}{M_2}\right)^2 + \frac{4fL}{D} = 0$$

The ln term is often small, and when neglected gives the equation stated.

The question of choking at the exit in this particular case is not solved by putting M = 1at the critical conditions. The flow is subject to friction at the wall and heat transfer through the wall. However choking at the exit implies that the static pressure at the exit cannot be reduced by increasing the pipe length. Hence at choking conditions

$$\frac{dx}{dp} = 0$$

Now $\frac{2}{\rho u^2}dp - \frac{2}{p}dp + \frac{4f}{D}dx = 0$

and $\frac{dx}{dp} = \frac{D}{4f}\left(\frac{2}{p} - \frac{2}{\rho u^2}\right)$

At choking conditions $\frac{2}{p^*} = \frac{2}{\rho^* u^{*2}}$ therefore $p^* = \rho^* u^{*2}$

or $u^* = \sqrt{\frac{p^*}{\rho^*}} = \sqrt{RT^*} = \frac{a^*}{\sqrt{\gamma}}$

giving $M^* = \frac{u^*}{a^*} = \frac{1}{\sqrt{\gamma}}$

Note. Referring to Fig. 2.2 it can be seen that this value of M corresponds to a maximum enthalpy.

Substituting this value of M gives the result

$$\left(\frac{p^*}{p_1}\right)^2 = \gamma M_1^2, \qquad \frac{1}{\gamma M_1^2}(\gamma M_1^2 - 1) - \ln(\gamma M_1^2) + \frac{4fL_{max}}{D} = 0$$

Natural gas (mainly methane in the UK) is transmitted through long pipelines, at substantial pressures. The effect of compressibility is significant and equations of the form derived must be used.

At the exit p_2 = 2 bar, T_2 = 300 K and the flow is a maximum, giving choking conditions. Hence

$$M_2 = \frac{1}{\sqrt{\gamma}} = 0.866, \qquad a_2 = \sqrt{\tfrac{4}{3}\times 520\times 300} = 456 \text{ m/s}$$

$$u_2 = 0.866\,a_2 = 395 \text{ m/s}, \qquad \rho_2 = \frac{2\times10^5}{520\times300} = 1.282 \text{ kg/m}^3$$

$$\dot{m} = \rho_2 A_2 u_2 = \mathbf{15.9} \text{ kg/s}$$

Substituting

$$\frac{4\times0.004\times1000}{0.2} = \frac{1-\gamma M_1^2}{\gamma M_1^2} + \ln(\gamma M_1^2)$$

$$80 = \frac{1}{\gamma M_1^2} + \ln(\gamma M_1^2)$$

Neglecting the ln term gives $M_1 = 0.097$

$$p_1 = \frac{p^*}{M_1\sqrt{\gamma}} = \frac{2}{0.097\sqrt{\frac{4}{3}}} = 17.86 \text{ bar}$$

and by trial-and-error, a more accurate value is obtained,

$M_1 = 0.094$, and $p_1 = \mathbf{18.43}$ bar

The heat transfer can be determined from the energy equation:

$$Q = \dot{m}(h_{o2} - h_{o1}) = \frac{\dot{m}C_p(u_2^2 - u_1^2)}{2C_p} \quad \text{since } T_o = T + \frac{u^2}{2C_p}$$

$$= \tfrac{1}{2}\dot{m}(u_2^2 - u_1^2)$$

$$= \tfrac{1}{2}(15.9)(395^2 - 42.9^2) \quad \text{since } u_1 = M_1\sqrt{\gamma R T_1}$$

$= 1226$ kW or **1.226** kW/m length.

2.6 Friction due to an obstruction

A fluid flows along a duct of constant area and at a section there is an obstruction in the duct. Neglecting the wall friction and assuming steady, one-dimensional flow show that the ratio of the downstream static pressure p_2 to the upstream static pressure p_1 is given by

$$\frac{p_2}{p_1} = \frac{1+\gamma M_1^2(1-\frac{1}{2}C_D)}{1+\gamma M_2^2}$$

$$C_D = \text{drag coefficient} = \frac{\text{drag force}}{\frac{1}{2}\rho_1 u_1^2 A}$$

Comment on the result.

Solution. A control volume can be drawn round the obstruction, and the momentum equation applied (Fig. 2.4).

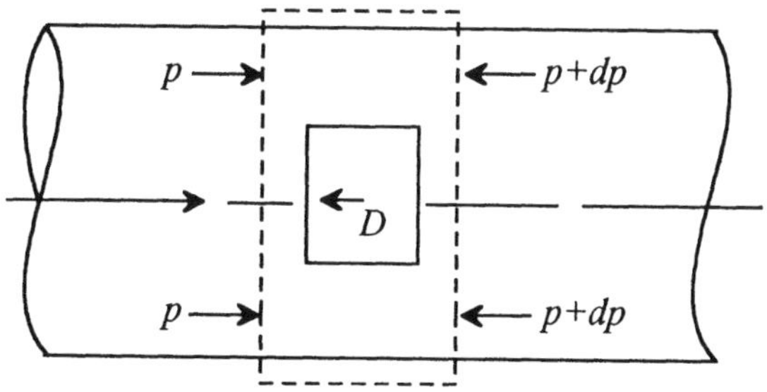

Figure 2.4

The net force is

$$pA - (p+dp)A - D = -A\,dp - D$$

and for steady flow the rate of change of momentum is $\dot{m}\,du$. Hence equating force and change of momentum

$$-A\,dp - D = \dot{m}\,du$$

Substituting $D = C_D A(\frac{1}{2}\rho_1 u_1^2)$ gives

$$-A\,dp - C_D A(\tfrac{1}{2}\rho_1 u_1^2) = \dot{m}\,du$$
$$= \rho A u\,du$$

$$\frac{1}{p}dp + C_D\frac{\rho_1 u_1^2}{2pA} + \frac{\dot{m}u}{pA} = 0$$

Now $\dfrac{\rho u^2}{2p} = \dfrac{u^2}{2RT} = \dfrac{\gamma u^2}{2a^2} = \dfrac{1}{2}\gamma M^2$

$$\frac{\dot{m}}{pA}du = \frac{\rho A u}{pA}du = \frac{\rho u}{p}du$$

and $u^2 = M^2\gamma RT$

$$2u\,du = \gamma R(M^2\,dT + T\,dM^2)$$
$$\dot{m} = \rho A u$$
$$= pAM\sqrt{\frac{\gamma}{RT}} = \text{constant}$$
$$\frac{p^2M^2}{T} = \text{constant}$$
$$\frac{2}{p}dp + \frac{1}{M^2}dM^2 - \frac{1}{T}dT = 0$$

or $\dfrac{1}{T}dT = \dfrac{2}{p}dp + \dfrac{1}{M^2}dM^2$

hence $\dfrac{\rho u}{p}du = \dfrac{\rho}{2p}(\gamma R)(\dfrac{2M^2T}{p}dp + 2T\,dM^2)$

$$= \frac{\rho\gamma RM^2T}{p}\left(\frac{1}{p}dp + \frac{1}{M^2}dM^2\right)$$
$$= \gamma M^2\left(\frac{1}{p}dp + \frac{1}{M^2}dM^2\right)$$

Substituting into the momentum equation gives

$$\frac{1}{p}dp + \frac{1}{2}C_D\frac{p_1}{p}\gamma M_1^2 + \gamma M^2\left(\frac{1}{p}dp + \frac{1}{M^2}dM^2\right) = 0$$

or $(1 + \gamma M^2)\dfrac{1}{p}dp + \gamma dM^2 + \dfrac{\frac{1}{2}C_D\gamma p_1 M_1^2}{p} = 0$

$$dp + \gamma d(pM^2) + \tfrac{1}{2}C_D\gamma p_1 M_1^2 = 0$$

and integrating

$$(p_2 - p_1) + \gamma(p_2M_2^2 - p_1M_1^2) + \tfrac{1}{2}C_D\gamma p_1 M_1^2 = 0$$

Hence $\boldsymbol{\dfrac{p_2}{p_1}(1 + \gamma M_2^2) = 1 + \gamma M_1^2(1 - \dfrac{1}{2}C_D)}$

Note. An obstruction of this nature can be regarded as equivalent to a valve or other restriction in the duct. Ideally a knowledge of the drag coefficient C_D enables the pressure drop to be estimated from the equation obtained, but in practice the drag coefficient is often difficult to predict with reasonable certainty. Its value depends upon the nature of the upstream flow (degree of turbulence), the uniformity of the flow across the duct area, and the geometry of the obstruction.

2.7 Rayleigh flow equations

Deduce the following equations for the flow of an ideal gas in a frictionless, constant area duct with heat exchange:

$$\frac{p_o}{p_o^*} = \frac{1+\gamma}{1+\gamma M^2}\left(\frac{2+(\gamma-1)M^2}{\gamma+1}\right)^{\frac{\gamma}{\gamma-1}}$$

$$\frac{T_o}{T_o^*} = \frac{(1+\gamma)M^2}{(1+\gamma M^2)^2}(2+(\gamma-1)M^2)$$

Hence show that at choking conditions $M = 1$.

Derive the result that the heat required (per kg) to raise the Mach number from $1/\sqrt{\gamma}$ to unity is

$$\frac{(\gamma-1)^2 C_p T_1}{2\gamma(\gamma+1)}$$

How does the static temperature change?

Solution. The derivation of the stated equations depends upon the manipulation of the basic equations of state, continuity and momentum.

state $\quad p = \rho RT \quad$ or $\quad \dfrac{T}{T^*} = \dfrac{p}{p^*}\dfrac{\rho^*}{\rho}$

continuity $\quad \rho u = \rho^* u^* \quad$ so that $\quad \dfrac{T}{T^*} = \dfrac{p}{p^*}\dfrac{u}{u^*}$

momentum $\quad p + \rho u^2 = \text{constant}$

Let the asterisk denote conditions at $M = 1$. Since $\rho u^2 = \gamma p M^2$,

$$p + \gamma p M^2 = \text{constant} = p^* + \gamma p^*$$

or $\quad p(1+\gamma M^2) = p^*(1+\gamma)$

Now $\quad \dfrac{p_o}{p} = (1 + \frac{1}{2}(\gamma-1)M^2)^{\frac{\gamma}{\gamma-1}}$

and $\quad \dfrac{p_o}{p_o^*} = \left(\dfrac{1+\frac{1}{2}(\gamma-1)M^2}{1+\frac{1}{2}(\gamma-1)}\right)^{\frac{\gamma}{\gamma-1}}\dfrac{p}{p^*}$

Substituting for p/p^* gives the required equation.

$$\frac{T_o}{T_o^*} = \frac{1+\frac{1}{2}(\gamma-1)M^2}{1+\frac{1}{2}(\gamma-1)}\frac{T}{T^*}$$

and $\quad \dfrac{T}{T^*} = \dfrac{p}{p^*}\dfrac{u}{u^*} = \dfrac{p}{p^*}\dfrac{M\sqrt{T}}{\sqrt{T^*}}$

$$\frac{T}{T^*} = M^2\left(\frac{p}{p^*}\right)^2$$

Substituting for T/T^* gives the required equation.

At choking conditions the heat exchange is a maximum and $T_o = T_o^*$. This is the case when $M = 1$.

Consider two stations in the duct where $M_1 = 1/\sqrt{\gamma}$ and $M_2 = 1$. Then using the previous results, the heat addition is /kg:

$$Q = C_p(T_{o2} - T_{o1}) = C_p(T_o^* - T_{o1}) = C_p T_{o1}\left(\frac{T_o^*}{T_{o1}} - 1\right)$$

Substituting the value of the Mach number $M_1 = 1/\sqrt{\gamma}$ and using the relationship

$$T_{o1} = T_1(1 + \tfrac{1}{2}(\gamma - 1)M_1^2)$$

gives the result stated. The change in the static temperature can be determined as follows

$$\frac{T_2}{T_1} = \frac{T^*}{T_1} = \frac{1}{M_1^2}\left(\frac{p^*}{p_1}\right)^2 = \frac{1}{M_1^2}\left(\frac{1 + \gamma M_1^2}{1 + \gamma}\right)^2 = \gamma\left(\frac{2}{1 + \gamma}\right)^2$$

$$= 1 - \left(\frac{\gamma - 1}{\gamma + 1}\right)^2$$

and since $\gamma > 1$, the ratio $T_2/T_1 < 1$ or the static temperature *decreases*.

2.8 Rayleigh flow calculation

> Air leaves a diffuser at a static pressure of 0.6 bar, and Mach number 0.2: and enters a combustion chamber in which 1400 kJ/kg of heat is added. The static temperature at the diffuser exit is 330 K.
>
> Assuming that the area of the chamber is constant and the air behaves as an ideal gas determine the static pressure and temperature, and velocity at the chamber exit.
>
> $$C_p = 1.15 \text{ kJ/kg K. } \frac{C_p}{C_v} = \gamma = 1.40.$$
>
> Determine the velocity at the exit and heat addition required to attain choking conditions at the exit. Flow tables should be used.

Solution. Denoting the conditions with the subscript 1, and using the tables, at $M_1 = 0.2$

$$\frac{p_1}{p^*} = 2.275, \quad \frac{T_1}{T^*} = 0.207, \quad \frac{T_{o1}}{T_o^*} = 0.174, \quad \frac{p_{o1}}{p_o^*} = 1.235$$

giving $p^* = 0.264$ bar, $T^* = 1594$ K,

$$\frac{p_{o1}}{p_1} = 1.028, \quad \frac{T_{o1}}{T_1} = 1.008,$$

$$p_{o1} = 0.617 \text{ bar}, \quad T_{o1} = 333 \text{ K},$$

$$p_o^* = 0.500 \text{ bar}, \quad T_o^* = 1914 \text{ K}.$$

At the chamber exit, denoted by subscript 2, the conditions can be determined from a knowledge of the heat transfer.

$$Q = 1400 \text{ kJ/kg} \quad = C_p(T_{o2} - T_{o1})$$

$$T_{o2} = 333 + \frac{1400}{1.15} = 1550 \text{ K}$$

$$\frac{T_{o2}}{T_o^*} = \frac{1550}{1914} = 0.810$$

and from the tables $M_2 = \mathbf{0.59}$

$$\frac{p_2}{p^*} = 1.615,$$

$$\frac{T_2}{T^*} = 0.907,$$

$$\frac{p_{o2}}{p_o^*} = 1.079$$

Hence $p_2 = \mathbf{0.426}$ bar,

$$T_2 = \mathbf{1446} \text{ K},$$

$$p_{o2} = \mathbf{0.666} \text{ bar}$$

$$a_2 = \sqrt{1.4 \times 329 \times 1446} = 816 \text{ m/s}$$

since $C_p = \dfrac{\nu R}{\nu - 1} = 3.5R$

$$R = \frac{1150}{3.5} = 329 \text{ J/m}$$

$$u_2 = M_2 a_2 = \mathbf{482} \text{ m/s}$$

For *choking* conditions at the exit

$$p_2 = p^* = \mathbf{0.264} \text{ bar},$$

$$T_2 = T^* = 1594 \text{ K}$$

$$u_2 = \mathbf{857} \text{ m/s}$$

The heat addition required is

$$C_p(T_o^* - T_{o1}) = 1.15(1914 - 333) = \mathbf{1818} \text{ kJ/kg}$$

Note. This is an application of Rayleigh flow theory which would give a first approximation. In reality the nature of the fluid changes in the combustion chamber: air enters the chamber and heat is 'added' to the fluid by injection of fuel. Combustion products are then formed, and the properties of the products differ from those of air.

In addition the area of the chamber would be unlikely to be constant; the variation of specific heat with temperature would be significant; and there would be frictional effects at the wall, and in some cases due to obstructions in the flow (e.g. flameholders).

2.9 Sudden enlargement in a duct

A gas flows *adiabatically* along a duct and there is a sudden enlargement at a particular section (Fig. 2.5). The flow Mach number upstream of the enlargement is 0.50.

If the area ratio is 2:1 determine the flow Mach number downstream of the enlargement, stating any assumptions made.

Briefly explain whether the same assumptions would apply to upstream supersonic flow.

$\gamma = 4/3$. Assume steady, one-dimensional flow and neglect wall friction.

Solution. The important part of the solution lies in the determination of the pressure p_3: taking the section 2 at a sufficient distance downstream of the sudden area change, the local effects (eddies at the corners) can be assumed as having evened out, and in the absence of wall friction p_3 can be taken equal to p_1.

The continuity, momentum and energy equations applied to the two sections are then

$$\rho_1 A_1 u_1 = \rho_2 A_2 u_2$$

or

$$\frac{p_1 A_1 M_1}{\sqrt{T_1}} = \frac{p_2 A_2 M_2}{\sqrt{T_2}}$$

$$p_1(A_2 - A_1) = A_2(p_2 + \rho_2 u_2^2) - A_1(p_1 + \rho_1 u_1^2)$$

$$h_1 + \tfrac{1}{2}u_1^2 = h_2 + \tfrac{1}{2}u_2^2$$

or

$$T_{o2} = T_{o1}$$

Rearranging the momentum equation

$$p_1(A_2 - A_1) + p_1 A_1(1 + \gamma M_1^2) = p_2 A_2(1 + \gamma M_2^2)$$

Combining the continuity and energy equations:

$$\frac{p_2}{p_1} = \frac{A_1M_1}{A_2M_2}\sqrt{\frac{T_2}{T_1}}$$

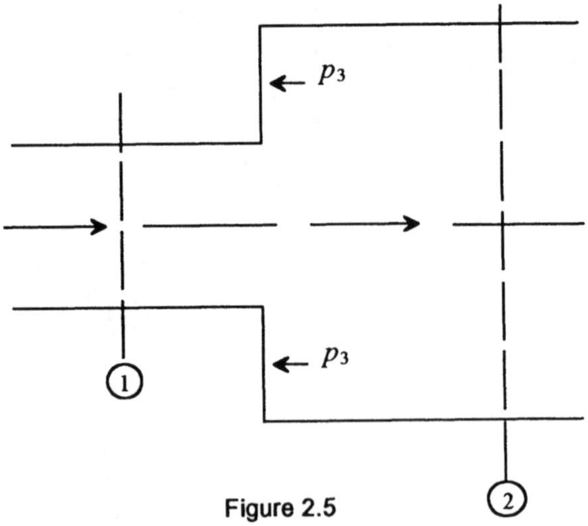

Figure 2.5

and $$\frac{T_2}{T_1} = \frac{T_{o2}}{T_{o1}}.\frac{1 + kM_1^2}{1 + kM_2^2} \quad \text{where } k = \frac{1}{2}(\gamma - 1)$$

$$= \frac{2 + (\gamma - 1)M_1^2}{2 + (\gamma - 1)M_2^2}$$

hence $$\frac{p_2}{p_1} = \frac{A_1M_1}{A_2M_2}\sqrt{\frac{2 + (\gamma - 1)M_1^2}{2 + (\gamma - 1)M_2^2}}$$

In this problem $\frac{A_2}{A_1} = 2$ and $M_1 = 0.5$. Hence

$$\frac{p_2}{p_1} = \frac{0.25}{M_2}\sqrt{\frac{6.25}{6 + M_2^2}}$$

Substituting into the momentum equation gives

$$\frac{A_2}{A_1} - 1 + (1 + \gamma M_1^2) = \frac{p_2A_2}{p_1A_1}(1 + \gamma M_2^2)$$

$$2 - 1 + 2\frac{1}{3} = 2(1 + \frac{4}{3}m_2^2).\frac{0.25}{M_2}\sqrt{\frac{6.25}{6 + M_2^2}}$$

$$2\frac{2}{3} = \frac{1 + \frac{4}{3}M_2^2}{M_2\sqrt{6 + M_2^2}}$$

and solving by trial and error gives

M_2 = approx. **0.16**

If the flow is supersonic upstream of the enlargement the pressure p_3 cannot be expressed in terms of the *upstream* conditions (by the nature of supersonic flow); the exit plane pressure is not necessarily equal to the back pressure p_3. The problem cannot therefore be solved.

2.10 Generalised flow equation

Derive the equation for steady one-dimensional flow of an ideal gas along a circular pipe:

$$(M^2 - 1)\frac{du}{u} = \frac{dA}{A} - \frac{Q}{C_pT} - \frac{2\gamma f M^2}{D}$$

where F = friction coefficient, Q = heat transfer rate.

Discuss this equation in the particular case of isentropic flow.

Solution. The equation stated can be derived by combining the basic equations of state, continuity and momentum.

(1) state: $p = \rho RT$ or $\frac{dp}{p} = \frac{d\rho}{\rho} + \frac{dT}{T}$

(2) continuity: $\rho Au = \text{constant}$ or $\frac{d\rho}{\rho} + \frac{dA}{A} + \frac{du}{u} = 0$

(3) energy: $Q = dT_o = dh + u\,du = C_p\,dT + u\,du$

(4) momentum: $dp + \rho u\,du + \frac{\tau_o P}{A} = 0$

where P = duct perimeter

τ_o = wall shear stress

$f = \tau_o.\frac{1}{2}\rho u^2$

Equation (2) gives $\frac{d\rho}{\rho} = -\frac{dA}{A} - \frac{du}{u}$, and substituting into equation (1)

(5) $\frac{dp}{p} = \frac{dT}{T} - \frac{dA}{A} - \frac{du}{u}$.

From equation (3)

$$\frac{Q}{C_pT} = \frac{dT}{T} + \frac{u\,du}{C_pT}$$

(6) $$= \frac{dT}{T} + (\gamma - 1)M^2.\frac{du}{u}$$

using the relationships $C_p = \frac{\gamma R}{\gamma - 1}$, $u^2 = \gamma RTM^2$.

From equation (4)

$$\frac{dp}{\rho u^2} + \frac{du}{u} + \frac{\tau_o P}{\rho u^2 A} = 0$$

since $\rho u^2 = \gamma pM^2$, $\tau_o = f.\frac{1}{2}\rho u^2$, and $\frac{A}{P} = \frac{\frac{1}{4}\pi D^2}{\pi D} = \frac{D}{4}$

this reduces to

$$\frac{dp}{\gamma pM^2} + \frac{du}{u} + \frac{2f}{D} = 0$$

Substituting for dp/p in equation (5) gives

$$-\gamma M^2.\frac{du}{u} - \gamma M^2.\frac{2f}{D} = \frac{dT}{T} - \frac{dA}{A} - \frac{du}{u}$$

Elimination of the temperature term dT/T by use of equation (6) gives

$$-\gamma M^2.\frac{du}{u} - \gamma M^2.\frac{2f}{D} = \frac{Q}{C_pT} - (\gamma - 1)M^2.\frac{du}{u} - \frac{dA}{A} - \frac{du}{u}$$

and this can be rearranged to give

$$(1 - M^2)\frac{du}{u} = -\frac{dA}{A} + \frac{Q}{C_pT} + \frac{2\gamma fM^2}{D}$$

In isentropic flow there are no frictional effects ($f = 0$) or heat transfer ($Q = 0$). This equation then reduces to

$$(M^2 - 1)\frac{du}{u} = \frac{dA}{A}.$$

This result, and discussion of its importance, have been obtained in worked example 1.7.

2.11 Generalised flow

> An ideal gas flows along a duct of constant area A and perimeter P. The flow Mach number is constant. Show that
>
> $$\frac{dT_o}{dx} = -\frac{\gamma M^2 T_o}{1 + \gamma M^2}.\frac{fP}{A}.$$
>
> The friction coefficient, f, may be taken as constant.
>
> The Mach number = 0.5, the stagnation temperature at inlet is 550 K, and f = 0.005. Determine the static temperature at inlet, and at a section 5m downstream when the duct is
>
> (a) circular cross-section, diameter 10cm;
>
> (b) rectangular cross-section, 8cm by 4cm.
>
> Also determine the heat exchange per kg in each case. Influence coefficient tables should be used.

Solution. Referring to the table given at the initial summary

$$\frac{dM^2}{M^2} = \frac{-2(1 + kM^2)}{1 - M^2}.\frac{dA}{A} + \frac{(1 + \gamma M^2)(1 + kM^2)}{1 - M^2}.\frac{dT_o}{T_o}$$
$$+ \frac{\gamma M^2(1 + kM^2)}{1 - M^2}.\frac{4f dx}{D_e}$$

In this problem the area is constant and $dA = 0$; the Mach number is also constant and $dM^2 = 0$. Hence

$$(1 + \gamma M^2).\frac{dT_o}{T_o} + \frac{4\gamma M^2 f dx}{D_e} = 0$$

The equivalent diameter $D_e = \dfrac{4 \times \text{area}}{\text{perimeter}} = \dfrac{4A}{P}$, therefore

$$(1 + \gamma M^2)\frac{dT_o}{T_o} = -\frac{\gamma f M^2 P}{A}dx$$

or

$$\frac{dT_o}{dx} = -\frac{\mu M^2 T_o}{1 + \gamma M^2}\frac{fP}{A}$$

Integrating gives

$$\int_1^2 \frac{dT_o}{T_o} = -\frac{\gamma M^2 fP}{(1 + \gamma M^2)A}\int_0^x dx, \quad \ln\frac{T_{o2}}{T_{o1}} = -\frac{\gamma M^2 F Px}{(1 + \gamma M^2)A}$$

In case (a) $M = 0.5$, $T_{o1} = 550$ K, $f = 0.005$

$$\ln\frac{T_{o2}}{T_{o1}} = \frac{-1.4(0.5)^2(0.005)\pi(0.1)(5)}{(1 + \frac{1.4}{4})\frac{\pi}{4}(0.1)^2} = -0.259$$

$$T_{o2} = 424 \text{ K}$$

The static temperature can be determined from the stagnation temperature:

$$\frac{T_o}{T} = 1 + \frac{1}{2}(\gamma - 1)M^2 = 1.05$$

$$T_1 = \frac{550}{1.05} = \mathbf{524}\text{ K},\quad T_2 = \frac{424}{1.05} = \mathbf{404}\text{ K}$$

The heat transfer along the section is

$$Q = C_p(T_{o2} - T_{o1})\text{ /kg} = 1.005(424 - 550)$$
$$= -\mathbf{126.6}\text{ kJ/kg (extracted)}$$

In case (b) for the rectangular section P = 24 cm, area A = 32 cm^2. Substituting

$$\ln\frac{T_{o2}}{550} = \frac{-1.4(0.5)^2(0.005)(0.24)(5)}{(1.35)(0.0032)} = -0.486$$

T_{o2} = **338** K, T_1 = **524** K, T_2 = **322** K

$Q = 1.005(338 - 550) = -\mathbf{213.1}$ kJ/kg

Problems

Unless stated otherwise the following values are used in these problems:

R = 287 J/kg K, γ = 1.40.

Many of the problems should be solved with the use of flow tables: where tables cannot be used an asterisk * is inserted after the problem number.

1 A circular duct, 15cm diameter, delivers 3.7 m^3/s of air at static conditions of 20 °C, 1.2 bar. The duct length is 30 m. The friction coefficient is constant and equal to 0.004.

Determine the static pressure and temperature at inlet, the flow Mach number at inlet and exit, and decrease in stagnation pressure.

The flow rate is reduced by 20%, with the inlet conditions unchanged. Determine the new static pressure and temperature at the exit, the flow Mach number at inlet and exit, and decrease in stagnation pressure.

Answer 2.17 bar, 307 K; 0.345, 0.609; 0.82 bar
1.63 bar, 304 K; 0.276, 0.365; 0.50 bar.

2* A horizontal pipe conveys air at a constant temperature. Neglecting changes in kinetic energy and assuming a constant friction coefficient show that

$$1 - \left(\frac{p_2}{p_1}\right)^2 = \frac{4\gamma f L M_1^2}{D},$$

where the subscript $_1$ and $_2$ refer to the pipe inlet and exit respectively.

If the pipe is 75 mm diameter, length L = 900 m, and the static pressure at each end is 13.2 bar and 4.7 bar calculate the mass flow rate, heat exchange rate, and stagnation pressure decrease. The static temperature = 18°C, f = 0.0045.

Answer 1.29 kg/s. 1.30 kW. 8.45 bar.

3 Air flows along a circular pipe, 50 mm diameter, length 1.5 m. The friction coefficient is constant and equal to 0.005. The static pressure at the pipe exit is 2 bar, and the stagnation temperature is 350 K. The flow rate is a maximum.

Determine the Mach number, static pressure and temperature at the pipe inlet; mass flow rate and air velocity at the exit.

Also determine the distance from the exit where the Mach number could equal 0.67.

Answer 0.575, 3.69 bar, 329 K
or 3.67, 0.31 bar, 94 K.
1.60 kg/s. 342 m/s. 68 cm from the exit.

4* Steam enters a pipe of diameter 50 mm, from a large reservoir in which the steam conditions are 7 bar, 205 °C. At a point downstream the steam conditions are 5.5 bar, 200 °C.

Plot the Fanno line.

Determine the mass flow rate, and the steam temperature at a section where the pressure is 2 bar.

Answer 0.39 kg/s. Approx. 180°C.

5 Air flows through a convergent-divergent nozzle from a large reservoir, in which the air conditions are 3 bar, 5000 K. A pipe is attached to the nozzle exit, of the same diameter.

Pipe area = 2 x nozzle throat area.
Pipe length = 98 x pipe diameter.
$f = 0.006$.

Assuming isentropic flow in the nozzle calculate the flow Mach number; static pressure and temperature, and air velocity at the pipe exit; and decrease (overall) in stagnation pressure and temperature.

Answer 0.38; 2.24 bar, 486 K, 168 m/s; 0.52 bar, zero.

6 A convergent-divergent nozzle of throat diameter 10 mm passes air from a reservoir. The stagnation conditions are 15 bar, 290 K and the flow can be taken as isentropic.

A circular pipe, of diameter equal to the nozzle exit diameter 30 mm, is attached to the nozzle. $f = 0.004$.

The pipe is choked at the exit. Determine the flow Mach number; static pressure and temperature, and air velocity at the pipe inlet; the static pressure and temperature at the pipe exit; decrease in stagnation pressure; and pipe length.

Determine the position of the section in the pipe where the flow Mach number = 3.09.

Answer 3.81, 0.128 bar, 74 K, 656 m/s.
0.883 bar, 241 K,

13.33 bar. 1.15 m.
1.0 m from the pipe exit.

7* The mass flow rate of a gas along a circular pipe, diameter D, length L can be determined from the formula

$$\dot{m} = \frac{\pi}{8}\sqrt{\frac{(p_1^2 - p_2^2)D^5}{fRTL}}$$

where p_1 and p_2 are the static pressure at the pipe inlet and exit respectively. Outline how the formula is derived, including the assumption made.

Calculate the mass flow rate and heat transfer rate when D = 1.0 m, L = 100 km, f = 0.006, p_1 = 50 bar, p_2 = 34 bar. The static temperature is 300 K. R = 520 J/kg K. γ = 1.30.

Answer

Assumptions: isothermal flow
constant friction coefficient
negligible change in kinetic energy
149 kg/s.

8* Show that for Fanno flow in a circular pipe

$$\frac{u}{u^*} = M\left(\frac{\gamma + 1}{2 + (\gamma - 1)M^2}\right)^{\frac{1}{2}}$$

$$\frac{p_o}{p_o^*} = \frac{1}{M}\left(\frac{2 + (\gamma - 1)M^2}{\gamma + 1}\right)^{\frac{\gamma+1}{2(\gamma-1)}}$$

and the entropy change is given by the equation

$$\Delta s = C_p \ln\left[M^2\left(\frac{\gamma + 1}{2 + (\gamma - 1)M^2}\cdot\frac{1}{M^2}\right)^{\frac{\gamma+1}{2\gamma}}\right].$$

9* The gas flow along a constant area duct is isothermal. The friction coefficient, f, is constant. Show that at any section in the duct

$$\frac{4fL}{D} = \frac{p_1}{\rho_1}\left(\frac{1}{u_1^2} - \frac{1}{u^2}\right) + 2\ln\left(\frac{u_1}{u}\right)$$

where the subscript $_1$ refers to the inlet conditions and L = distance from the inlet of the section.

Hence show that at the section where choking occurs (M = 1)

$$\frac{4fL^*}{D} = \frac{1}{\gamma}\left(\frac{1}{M_1^2} - 1\right) + 2\ln M_1.$$

If the heat transfer rate /kg is Q, show that

$$dQ = \gamma RTM\,dM$$

and hence

$$\frac{dQ}{dx} = \frac{2\gamma fRT}{D}\left(\frac{\gamma M^4}{1 - \gamma M^2}\right).$$

10 Air enters a circular pipe, diameter 10 cm, at a velocity of 150 m/s. The static conditions at inlet are 5 bar, 350 K. Pipe length = 10 m. $f = 0.004$.

Determine the static pressure and temperature at the exit; mass flow rate; and decrease in stagnation pressure.

The pipe becomes choked at the exit. If the static pressure and temperature at exit remain the same calculate the new mass flow rate, and static conditions at the inlet.

Briefly explain why the effect of friction is to reduce the flow Mach number in supersonic flow, and increase it in subsonic flow.

Answer 3.55 bar, 340 K; 5.86 kg/s; 120 bar.
9.88 kg/s; 8.58 bar, 393 K.

11* A duct is 30 cm diameter, 10 m length. The stagnation conditions at inlet are 1.5 bar, 300 K and the static pressure is 1.23 bar.

Calculate the flow Mach number at inlet, and the mass flow rate.

The friction coefficient = 0.005. Calculate the flow Mach number; static pressure and temperature; and velocity at the exit. The following equation may be used without proof

$$\frac{4f}{D}(x - x^*) = \frac{1 - M^2}{\gamma M^2} + \frac{\gamma + 1}{2\gamma}\ln\left(\frac{(\gamma + 1)M^2}{2 + (\gamma - 1)M^2}\right)$$

Also calculate the decrease in the stagnation pressure.

Answer 0.54, 19.49 kg/s.
0.755, 0.86 bar, 269 K; 248 m/s.
0.25 bar.

12 Air flows along a constant area duct at a velocity of 85 m/s. Fuel is injected into the air stream and is completely burnt. The static temperature upstream of the injection point = 300 K. The combination products leave the duct at a static pressure = 1.5 bar.

Duct area = 75 cm^2
Heat of reaction (of the fuel) = 12 MJ/kg
Fuel : air ratio = 1/16 kg/kg.

Determine the stagnation pressure upstream of the injection point; gas velocity at exit; and mass flow rate of air.

The change in mass flow rate due to fuel injection should be neglected, and the properties of the gas (combustion products) taken to be the same as those of air; and the air considered as an ideal gas.

Determine the injection rate if choking conditions are attained at the exit. Comment on the validity of the assumptions made.

Answer 2.27 bar; 400m/s; 1.62 kg/s. 0.077 kg/kg.

13 Air flows along a circular duct, 30 cm diameter, 6 m length. At the inlet the static pressure is 0.3 bar, and the stagnation conditions are 1.2 bar, 300 K. The stagnation temperature at exit is 240 K.

Determine the static and stagnation pressure, static temperature, and flow Mach number at the exit; and heat transfer rate /kg.

Calculate the exit values if heat is *added* to the air at half the previous rate.

Answer 0.14 bar, 2.23 bar, 108 K, 2.46.
16.21 kJ rejected.
0.46 bar, 1.06 bar, 260 K, 1.16.

14* An ideal gas flows along a constant area, smooth (frictionless) duct and heat exchange takes place through the duct walls. Show that

$$\frac{T}{T^*} = M^2\left(\frac{\gamma + 1}{1 + \gamma M^2}\right)^2$$

$$\frac{T_o}{T_o^*} = \frac{(\gamma + 1)M^2}{(1 + \gamma M^2)^2}(2 + (\gamma - 1)M^2)$$

The stagnation temperature at exit = 3.5 × stagnation temperature at inlet. The flow Mach number at inlet = 0.25. γ = 1.30. Determine the flow Mach number at the exit, and the ratio of the static pressure at exit to that at inlet.

Answer 0.66, 0.69.

15* Show that in Rayleigh flow if the flow Mach number increases from

$$M_1 = \frac{1}{\sqrt{\gamma}} \quad \text{to} \quad M_2 = 1$$

the decrease in static temperature is given by

$$T_1 - T_2 = T_1\left(\frac{1 - \gamma}{1 + \gamma}\right)^2, \text{ and}$$

$$\frac{p_1 - p_2}{p_1} = \frac{\gamma - 1}{\gamma + 1}.$$

Also show that the heat transfer rate per kg is

$$Q = \frac{(\gamma - 1)^2 h_1}{2\gamma(\gamma + 1)}.$$

Derive the results

$$\frac{p}{p^*} = \frac{1 + \gamma}{1 + \gamma M^2}, \quad \frac{T}{T^*} = M^2\left(\frac{1 + \gamma}{1 + \gamma M^2}\right)^2$$

and hence show that the entropy increase between two sections at which the flow Mach numbers are M and 1.0 is given by

$$\frac{\Delta s}{C_p} = \frac{\gamma + 1}{\gamma}\ln\left(\frac{1 + \gamma}{1 + \gamma M^2}\right) + \ln M^2.$$

16* Steam enters a short pipe, diameter 150 mm, at a velocity of 170 m/s and static conditions 35 bar, 325 °C. Estimate the velocity and static conditions of the steam at the pipe exit; and the heat transfer rate (kW).

Answer 34 bar, 375 °C (approx.); 5160 kW.

17 By reference to an enthalpy-entropy diagram outline the effect of heat transfer to, and from, a gas flowing along a smooth, constant area duct.

A gas is injected into an ait stream flowing along a duct, and due to the combustion of the gas the stagnation temperature increases from 560 to 1400 K.

The heat of reaction of the gas = 35 MJ/kg.

If the flow Mach number is constant at 0.5 determine the ratio of the area, and static pressure, before combustion to those after combustion; and the gas : air ratio (by mass).

It may be assumed that the properties of the combustion products are the same as those of air.

Answer 0.85, 0.52; 0.025 kg/kg.

18* Air flowing along a duct of area A encounters a sudden enlargement of area nA. Heat is added to the subsonic flow at a rate Q kJ/kg. Neglecting frictional effects show that

$$\sqrt{\frac{T_2}{T_1}} = \frac{n + \gamma M_1^2}{1 + \gamma M_2^2} \cdot \frac{M_2}{M_1}$$

and $$\frac{2 + (\gamma - 1)M_1^2}{2 + (\gamma - 1)M_2^2}\left(1 + \frac{(\gamma - 1)Q}{a_{o1}^2}\right) = \frac{T_2}{T_1}$$

where subscripts $_1$ and $_2$ refer to sections upstream and downstream of the enlargement respectively, and $a_{o1}^2 = \gamma R T_{o1}$.

19 Air flows along a chamber at a velocity of 60 m/s and static conditions 0.7 bar, 10 °C. Heat is added at a rate of 1400 kJ/kg.

Determine the static conditions and air velocity after the heat addition; the stagnation pressure drop; and the maximum amount of heat that can be added without any change of the inlet conditions.

The heat added is to be increased to 2800 kJ/kg, and a change of the inlet conditions is avoided by insertion of a sudden enlargement in the chamber. Determine the area ratio for choking conditions downstream of the enlargement, using the results of Ex.18.

Answer 0.36 bar, 1490 K, 620 m/s.
0.16 bar; 1690 kJ/kg.
2.87.

20 Air flows through a duct at a rate of 1.3 kg/s. At section 1 the area is 0.0015 m^2, and the static conditions are 2.3 bar, 350 K. At another section 2 the corresponding values are 0.0025 m^2, 2.6 bar, 450 K.

Determine the magnitude and direction of the hear transfer, and direction of flow of the air.

Answer 87.5 kW supplied;
From section 2 to section 1.

21 A diffuser, of circular cross-section, has an area of 700 cm^2 at inlet, and 1400 cm^2 at exit. Mass flow rate = 40 kg/s. Ambient pressure = 1.0 bar. The static conditions at inlet are 4 bar, 450K.

Assuming isentropic flow calculate the static pressure, flow Mach number and air velocity at the exit; and the force on the diffuser walls.

Due to friction the stagnation pressure decreases by 0.4 bar. Show that the flow Mach number at exit is approximately 0.22. Calculate the static pressure at the exit.

Answer 4.42 bar, 0.20, 86 m/s; 37 kN.
4.0 bar.

Note. The following problems involve the use of the Influence Coefficients table.

22 An ideal gas flows along a pipe of variable area. Show that, for isentropic flow

$$\frac{A_2}{A_1} = \frac{M_1}{M_2}\left(\frac{1 + kM_2^2}{1 + kM_1^2}\right)^m$$

$$\frac{p_2}{p_1} = \left(\frac{1 + kM_1^2}{1 + kM_2^2}\right)^{\frac{\gamma}{\gamma-1}}$$

where $k = \frac{1}{2}(\gamma - 1)$, $m = \dfrac{\gamma + 1}{2(\gamma - 1)}$.

Hence derive the result

$$\frac{p_o^*}{p^*} = \left(\frac{\gamma + 1}{2}\right)^{\frac{\gamma}{\gamma-1}}.$$

23 Air flows along a duct of constant area, and is frictionless. Heat is transferred to the air at a uniform rate. Derive the relationship

$$\frac{T_{o2}}{T_{o1}} = \left(\frac{M_2}{M_1}\right)^2\left(\frac{1 + kM_2^2}{1 + kM_1^2}\right)\left(\frac{1 + \gamma M_1^2}{1 + \gamma M_2^2}\right)$$

$$\frac{p_2}{p_1} = \frac{1 + \gamma M_1^2}{1 + \gamma M_2^2} \qquad \text{where } k = \tfrac{1}{2}(\gamma - 1).$$

24 An ideal gas flows along a duct of constant area A and perimeter P. The flow Mach number is constant along the axial length (×

direction).

Show that $\dfrac{dT_o}{dx} = -\dfrac{\gamma M^2 T_o}{1+\gamma M^2}\cdot\dfrac{fP}{A}$.

At the duct inlet the stagnation temperature is 550 K. The duct cross-section is rectangular, 15 cm by 10 cm. Friction coefficient = 0.006. Flow Mach number = 0.5. $\gamma = 4/3$.

Determine the static temperature at a section 5m downstream from the inlet; and the ratio of the static pressure at this section to that at the inlet.

Answer 411 K; 0.88.

25 Air flows through a diffuser: the velocity and static conditions at inlet are 200 m/s, 1.0 bar, 280 K. Mass flow rate = 50 kg/s. The static pressure at exit = 1.1 bar. Axial length of the diffuser = 1.0m. The static pressure increases linearly with the axial length. Assuming isentropic flow plot a graph of area and flow Mach number against the axial distance.

Answer

x(m)	0	0.4	0.8	1.0
A(m^2)	0.200	0.211	0.227	0.237
M	0.60	0.55	0.49	0.47

26 Air flows through a *smooth* pipe such that the static pressure is constant. Show that area A and stagnation temperature T_o are related by the equation

$$\frac{A}{A^*} = \frac{\gamma+1}{2}\left(\frac{T_o}{T_o^*}\right) - \left(\frac{\gamma-1}{2}\right)$$

The diameter at inlet is 10 cm, and the stagnation conditions are 1.0 bar, 20 °C. The mass flow rate = 0.3 kg/s. The heat addition is 250 kW. Determine the diameter and flow Mach number at the exit.

Answer 32.2 cm, 1.056.

27 A circular duct conveys air, and at the inlet the flow Mach number = 0.2, and the static conditions are 7 bar, 440 K. The friction coefficient is constant and equal to 0.003. The duct radius varies with the axial distance from the inlet according to the equation

$$\frac{\tau}{\tau_1} = 1 + k\left(\frac{x}{\tau_1}\right)^2$$

Assuming adiabatic flow estimate the duct length required to achieve critical conditions and the static pressure and temperature at these conditions. $k = 10^{-4}$.

Answer $10.5\tau_1$; 1.256 bar, 370 K.

28 Air flows through a horizontal pipe of constant diameter 150 mm, length 300 m, at a steady rate of 4.5 kg/s. The static pressure is 5.4 bar at inlet, and 1.4 bar at exit.

Assuming shock free, isothermal flow at a static temperature of 60 °C determine the friction coefficient (assumed constant); the heat transfer rate; and flow Mach number at inlet and exit.

Answer 0.0055; 81.4 kW; 0.12, 0.53.

29 Air flows along a circular pipe of length 3.5 m at a flow rate of 20 kg/s. The diameter is 30 cm and constant. The static conditions at inlet are 0.4 bar, 220 K. Calculate the flow Mach number and stagnation conditions at the inlet.

The pipe is heated uniformly along its length so that

$T_o = T_{o1} + 8x$ (K),

where x= axial distance (m). The friction coefficient is constant and equal to 0.0005. Derive a differential equation relating the Mach number and distance x in the form

$$\frac{dM^2}{dx} = f_1(M^2) + f_2(M^2, x)$$

The equation cannot be integrated directly. Hence using finite steps of $\Delta x = 0.5$ m show that choking occurs near to the pipe exit.

Answer 1.50, 1.47 bar, 319 K.

3

Shock waves

Waves

The relative motion between a fluid and a body, at supersonic velocities, generates disturbance waves. The disturbance may be small so that a Mach wave is propagated, travelling at the acoustic velocity $a = (\gamma RT)^{1/2}$: and is characterised by a continuous variation of the variables across the wave. This type has been considered in Chap.1, and can be referred to as weak linear waves (Prandtl-Meyer flow).

The disturbance may be much stronger, generating a non-linear *shock* wave. In this situation, a *compression* occurs, and there is a sudden discontinuity in the flow. This can only occur in supersonic flow, and the process of change across the shock wave is adiabatic but not isentropic. The wave has a finite thickness, though very small, and the conditions on each side of the wave can be determined without a consideration of the properties within the wave front.

The shock wave may be *weak* or *strong*: in the former the supersonic flow upstream remains supersonic in the downstream region, but in the latter the effect is much greater and the supersonic flow is reduced to subsonic flow. Shock waves can be made visible by flow visualisation techniques (eg. Schlieren), and have been witnessed by jet aircraft pilots and observers of atomic explosions. Examples are sonic booms (weak waves), and detonation or blast waves (strong waves).

Waves can also be described as stationary or moving; normal or oblique; attached or detached (to or from the body).

Shock waves in a gas are analogous to hydraulic jumps (standing waves) that occur in the flow of water in an open channel: for example the Severn Bore (moving normal shock front).

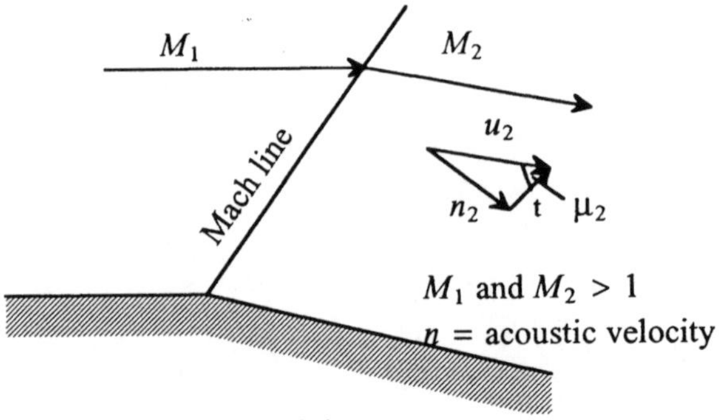

Figure 3.1

A Mach wave is shown in Fig. 3.1, and an oblique shock wave in Fig. 3.2. The wave may be weak or strong (M_2 greater or less than unity) depending upon the downstream pressure. However, for a fixed value of the upstream Mach number M_1, as the deflection δ increases a point is reached at which the shock wave becomes detached (Fig. 3.3). A bow wave stands clear of the body.

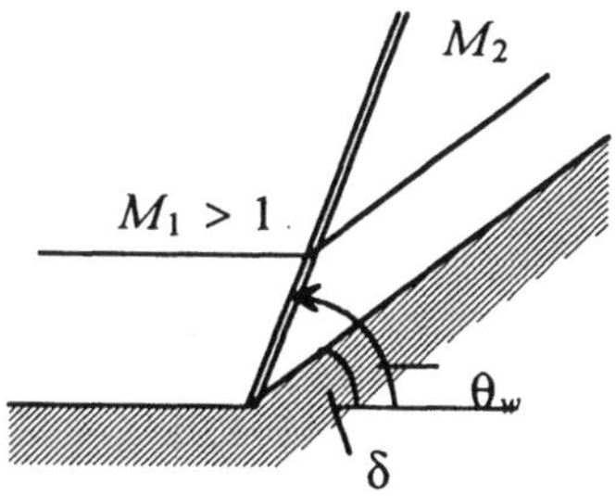

Figure 3.2

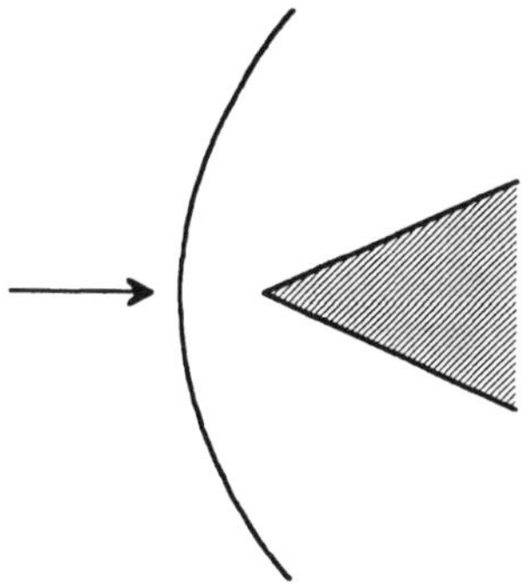

Figure 3.3

Normal shock wave

A particular, but important, case is the situation when the wave angle θ_w=90°. The plane wave front, normal to the flow direction, is a *strong* shock: the downstream flow is subsonic, associated with a high pressure rise and entropy increase across the shock. Again a normal shock may be stationary or moving (as in a nuclear bomb explosion, or a shock tube). In addition such waves, combined with heat transfer, give rise to condensation shocks and detonation waves.

Wave reflections

Shock waves generated at a point may be reflected from a surface (such as a wall, or a jet boundary). The reflection may be a *simple* or a *Mach* (Y) type, as shown in Fig. 3.4. Reflections also occur when oblique shock waves intersect (Fig. 3.5). Wave reflections are analysed in Ex. 3.

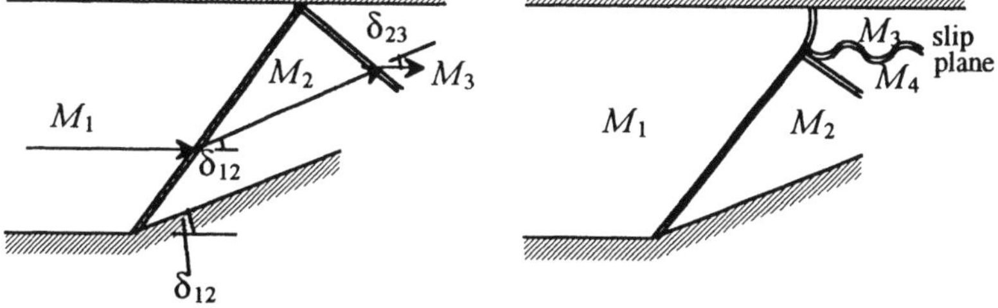

simple reflection

Mach reflection $M_3 \neq M_4$
due to slip plane

Figure 3.4

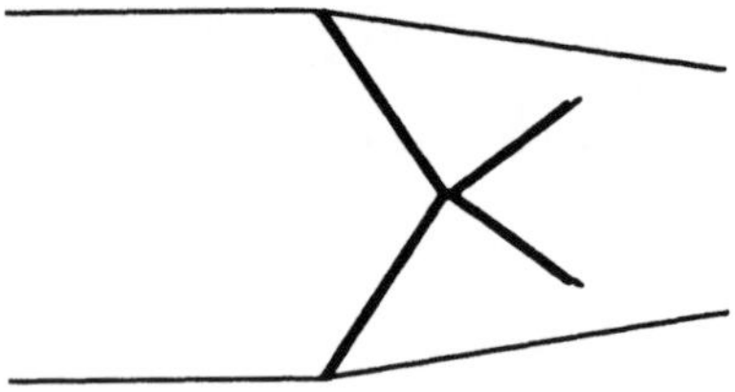

Figure 3.5

3.1 Plane normal shock wave

Derive the following equations for a plane, normal shock wave

$$\frac{p_2}{p_1} = \frac{(\gamma+1)\rho_2 - (\gamma-1)\rho_1}{(\gamma+1)\rho_1 - (\gamma-1)\rho_2} = \frac{2\gamma M_1^2 - (\gamma-1)}{\gamma+1}$$

where the subscripts 1, 2 refer to the upstream and downstream conditions respectively.

A gas flows along a circular pipe (Fig. 3.6) of diameter 10 cm, and a plane, normal shock wave stands at a section such that the upstream static conditions are 2 bar, 350 K. The gas velocity upstream of the shock is 600 m/s. Calculate the mass flow rate of gas, temperature and Mach number just downstream of the shock.

$\gamma = \frac{4}{3}$. $R = 520$ J/kg K.

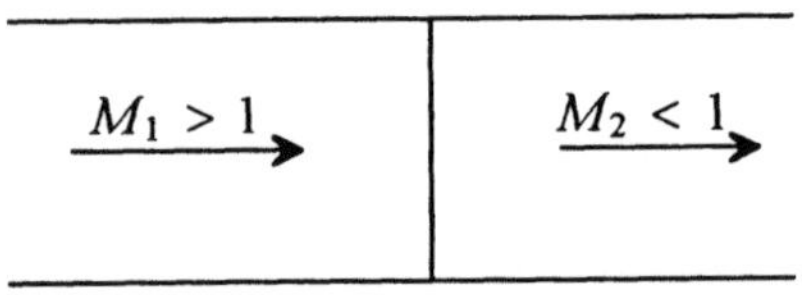

Figure 3.6

Solution. For steady, one-dimensional flow the basic equations are:

continuity $\quad \rho_1 u_1 = \rho_2 u_2 = G$ say

momentum $\quad p_2 - p_1 = G(u_1 - u_2)$

energy $\quad T_1 + \dfrac{u_1^2}{2C_p} = T_2 + \dfrac{u_2^2}{2C_p} = T_o$

For an ideal gas

$$C_p = \frac{\gamma R}{\gamma - 1}$$

and hence

$$T_1 - T_2 = \frac{u_2^2 - u_1^2}{2C_p} = \frac{\gamma-1}{2\gamma R}(u_2^2 - u_1^2)$$

$$\frac{\gamma R}{\gamma-1}(T_1 - T_2) = u_2^2 - u_1^2 = \tfrac{1}{2}(u_2 - u_1)(u_2 + u_1)$$

Using the state equation $p = \rho RT$, and the continuity and momentum equations gives

$$\frac{\gamma R}{\gamma-1}\left(\frac{p_1}{\rho_1 R} - \frac{p_2}{\rho_2 R}\right) = \frac{1}{2}\left(\frac{p_1 - p_2}{G}\right)\left(\frac{G}{\rho_2} + \frac{G}{\rho_1}\right)$$

$$\frac{2\gamma p_1}{\gamma-1}\left(\frac{1}{\rho_1} - \frac{p_2}{p_1\rho_2}\right) = \left(\frac{1}{\rho_2} + \frac{1}{\rho_1}\right)p_1\left(1 - \frac{p_2}{p_1}\right)$$

$$\frac{2\gamma}{\gamma-1}\cdot\frac{1}{\rho_1} - \frac{1}{\rho_2} - \frac{1}{\rho_1} = \left(\frac{2\gamma}{\gamma-1}\cdot\frac{1}{\rho_2} - \frac{1}{\rho_2} - \frac{1}{\rho_1}\right)\left(\frac{p_2}{p_1}\right)$$

and $(\gamma+1)\rho_2 - (\gamma-1)\rho_1 = ((\gamma+1)\rho_1 - (\gamma-1)\rho_2)\left(\frac{p_2}{p_1}\right)$

hence $\boldsymbol{\frac{p_2}{p_1} = \frac{(\gamma+1)\rho_2 - (\gamma-1)\rho_1}{(\gamma+1)\rho_1 - (\gamma-1)\rho_2}}$

Note. This equation is known as the Rankine-Hugoniot relationship.

The Mach number is now introduced into the momentum and continuity equations

$$\frac{p_2 - p_1}{p_1} = \frac{G}{p_1}(u_1 - u_2) = \frac{\rho_1 u_1^2 - \rho_2 u_2^2}{p_1} = \gamma M_1^2\left(1 - \frac{u_2}{u_1}\right)$$

since $\frac{\rho_2}{\rho_1} = \frac{u_1}{u_2}$, $\frac{\rho_1 u_1^2}{p_1} = \frac{\rho_1 M_1^2 \gamma R T_1}{p_1} = \gamma M_1^2$

From the equation derived previously for the pressure ratio, the density ratio is

$$\frac{\rho_2}{\rho_1} = \frac{(\gamma+1)p_2 + (\gamma-1)p_1}{(\gamma+1)p_1 + (\gamma-1)p_2}$$

Hence substituting for $\frac{p_2}{p_1}$ gives

$$\frac{p_2}{p_1} - 1 = \gamma M_1^2\left(1 - \frac{(\gamma+1)p_1 + (\gamma-1)p_2}{(\gamma+1)p_2 + (\gamma-1)p_1}\right)$$

which reduces to

$$\boldsymbol{\frac{p_2}{p_1} = \frac{2\gamma M_1^2 - (\gamma-1)}{\gamma+1}}$$

The mass flow rate can be calculated directly:

$$\dot{m} = \rho_1 A u_1 = \frac{p_1 A u_1}{RT_1}$$

$$= \frac{2\times10^5\times0.00785\times600}{520\times350} = \mathbf{5.176}\ \text{kg/s}$$

The downstream conditions can be determined from the equation involving the Mach number or from the basic equations.

$$a_1 = \sqrt{\gamma R T_1} = \sqrt{\tfrac{4}{3}\times520\times350} = 493\ \text{m/s}$$

$$M_1 = \frac{u_1}{a_1} = \frac{600}{493} = 1.218$$

Hence $\frac{p_2}{p_1} = \frac{2\gamma M_1^2 - (\gamma-1)}{\gamma+1} = 1.55$

and $p_2 = \mathbf{3.11}$ bar

$$p_2 - p_1 = G(u_1 - u_2)$$

hence $u_1 - u_2 = \frac{(3.11 - 2.0)10^5}{\frac{5.176}{0.00785}} = 168$

$$u_2 = 600 - 168 = \mathbf{432}\ \text{m/s}$$

$$T_o = T_1 + \frac{u_1^2}{2C_p} = 350 + \frac{(600)^2}{2(2080)} \quad \text{since } C_p = \frac{\gamma R}{\gamma - 1}$$

$$= 436\ \text{K}$$

hence $T_2 = T_o - \frac{u_2^2}{2C_p} = \mathbf{392}$ K

$$a_2 = 452\ \text{m/s}$$

$$M_2 = \frac{432}{452} = \mathbf{0.96}$$

Note. The flow downstream of the shock wave is subsonic, indicating a strong shock. Further there is an entropy increase (indicating irreversibility),

$$\Delta s = C_p \ln\frac{T_2}{T_1} + R\ln\frac{p_1}{p_2} = 2080\ln\frac{392}{350} + 520\ln\frac{2}{3.11}$$

$$= 235.7 - 229.6 \quad \text{or } \mathbf{6.1}\ \text{J/kg}$$

3.2 Convergent-divergent nozzle

A convergent-divergent nozzle passes air from a large reservoir in which the air conditions are 5 bar, 400 K. The throat area is 0.5 times the exit area.

The ambient pressure is 1.0 bar.

The nozzle is designed for use with a static pressure of 3 bar at the exit plane. Assuming isentropic flow where appropriate, show that design conditions are satisfied if a normal shock wave stands in the divergent portion of the nozzle where the area is approximately 1.77 times the throat area.

Flow tables should be used.

Solution. The flow through the nozzle can take several values, depending upon the back-pressure or pressure at the exit plane. The possible regimes are illustrated in Fig. 3.7, where the flow is taken as isentropic except across the shock wave.

The conditions given in the reservoir can be taken as the stagnation conditions, since the reservoir is large and therefore the velocity at the nozzle inlet is small.

At the throat the critical conditions are attained, so that

$$\frac{p_{o1}}{p_t} = 1.895, \quad \frac{T_{o1}}{T_t} = 1.201$$

and $p_t = 2.64$ bar, $T_t = 330$ K.

In this solution the critical conditions at the throat are denoted by the subscript t, not the usual superscript *. This has been done to avoid confusion when a normal shock wave stands in the divergent portion of the nozzle: the shock is a discontinuity in the flow so that the critical conditions in the upstream flow are not the same as those in the downstream flow. For example A^* in the region 3-d is not equal to the critical area in region a-2, namely A_t.

The area ratio A_e/A_t is given as 2.0, and from the tables (for *isentropic* flow)

$$M_e = 0.305, \quad \frac{p_o}{p_e} = 1.067, \quad \frac{T_o}{T_e} = 1.018$$

or $$M_e = 2.20, \quad \frac{p_o}{p_e} = 10.695, \quad \frac{T_o}{T_e} = 1.975$$

Hence $M_e = 0.305$, $p_e = 4.69$ bar, $T_e = 393$ K

or $M_e = 2.20$, $p_e = 0.47$ bar, $T_e = 203$ K

The first possible flow corresponds to curve a-c; with subsonic flow along the whole length of the nozzle (and $M = 1$ at the throat, point a).

The second possible flow corresponds to complete expansion of the air to a low exit pressure, curve a-b. Here the flow in the divergent portion is supersonic.

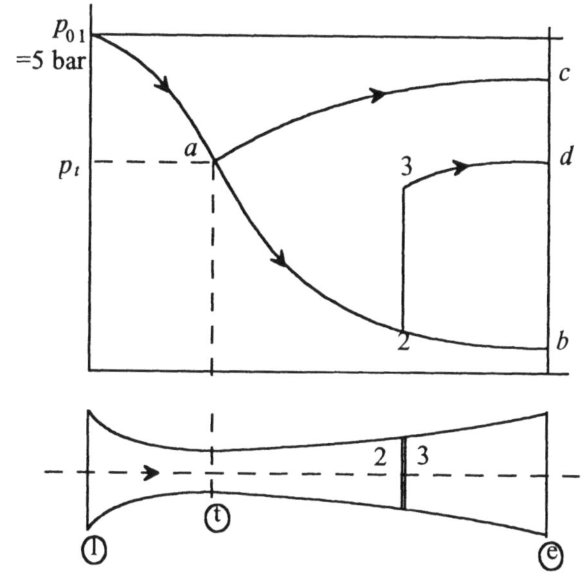

Figure 3.7

If the exit plane pressure is greater than 0.47 bar (to point *d* say) the situation now becomes one of a normal shock standing at some section in the nozzle. This is the way in which, physically, the static pressure in the supersonic flow can be increased: across the shock the flow is rapidly decelerated from supersonic to subsonic, with a consequent substantial rise in pressure. Thus the flow from the throat to point 2 is supersonic, and from point 3 to the exit is subsonic.

The *position* of the shock is determined by the design *exit pressure* only, and as that pressure increases the shock moves nearer to the throat. Eventually the chock reaches the throat, t, and is *swallowed*. Clearly the shock cannot proceed beyond the throat.

In this problem the exit pressure is given as 3.0 bar, and the position of the shock is to be verified. This is done by evaluating the pressure at points 2, 3, e for the shock standing in the position stated and showing that $p_e = 3.0$ bar.

The flow is isentropic from the throat to point 2, and from point 3 to the exit; but not across the shock from point 2 to point 3. Hence the isentropic flow and normal shock tables are used.

t-2: $\dfrac{A_2}{A_t} = 1.77$

and hence, from tables,

$$M_2 = 2.06, \quad \frac{p_{o2}}{p_2} = 8.596$$

$$p_2 = \frac{5}{8.596} = 0.58 \text{ bar}$$

2-3: from normal shock tables, at

$$M_2 = 2.06, \quad M_3 = 0.57, \quad \frac{p_3}{p_2} = 4.788, \quad \frac{p_{o3}}{p_2} = 5.961$$

hence $p_3 = 2.78$ bar, $p_{o3} = 3.46$ bar

3-e: at $M_3 = 0.57$, $\dfrac{A_3}{A^*} = 1.226$

(where A^* = critical area of the flow between the shock and the exit plane, and is *not* equal to A_t).

$$\text{Now } \frac{A_e}{A^*} = \frac{A_e}{A_3}\cdot\frac{A_3}{A^t} = \frac{2}{1.77}(1.226) = 1.385$$

$$M_e = 0.48, \quad \frac{p_{oe}}{p_e} = 1.171$$

and since $p_{oe} = p_{o3} = 3.46$ bar, $p_e = 2.95$ bar.

Hence the position of the shock is approximately at the stated value, where $A_2 = A_3 = 1.77A_t$.

Note. In practice the position of the shock would have to be determined by trial-and-error: a position would be assumed and the calculation performed to check that the exit plane pressure met the design requirement. The reader can obtain some experience by repeating the calculation for an exit pressure of say 3.5 bar. The shock would then be found to stand at a section where the area is approx. 1.5 times the throat area.

The decrease in stagnation pressure is, in the first case, 5.0 – 3.46 = 1.54 bar; and in the additional problem, 5.0 – 3.92 = 1.08 bar.

3.3 Pitot tube

A Pitot tube is inserted into a supersonic air stream, and records a pressure of 0.7 bar. The static pressure upstream of the tube is 0.15 bar, and the static temperature is 350 K.

Calculate the flow Mach number upstream of the tube; and the static pressure and temperature downstream of the shock.

The following equations, relating to the shock wave, may be used without proof:

$$\frac{p_2}{p_1} = \frac{2\gamma M_1^2 - (\gamma - 1)}{\gamma + 1}, \quad M_2^2 = \frac{(\gamma - 1)M_1^2 + 2}{2\gamma M_1^2 - (\gamma - 1)}$$

Solution. A Pitot tube is a small tube open at the end, facing the upstream direction. The tube then measures the *stagnation* pressure as the fluid comes to rest inside the tube. When the approaching stream is supersonic a shock wave is formed ahead of the tube (Fig. 3.8), usually *detached* from the tube nose. Although the wave is curved it is normally accurate, to a reasonable degree, to take it as a normal plane shock in front of the nose. The equations given relate to a normal plane shock.

$$\frac{p_{o2}}{p_1} = \frac{p_{o2}}{p_2}\cdot\frac{p_2}{p_1} = \left(1 + \frac{1}{2}(\gamma - 1)M_2^2\right)^{\frac{\gamma}{\gamma-1}}\cdot\frac{p_2}{p_1}$$

$$= \left(1 + \frac{1}{5}M_2^2\right)^{3.5}\cdot\frac{p_2}{p_1}$$

Substituting the values given

$$\frac{0.7}{0.15} = \left(1 + \frac{1}{5}M_2^2\right)^{3.5}\left(\frac{2.8\,M_1^2 - 0.4}{2.4}\right)$$

$$M_2^2 = \frac{0.4\,M_1^2 + 2}{2.8\,M_1^2 - 0.4} = \frac{M_1^2 + 5}{7M_1^2 - 1}$$

$$\text{hence} \quad \frac{0.7}{0.15} = \left(1 + \frac{1}{5}\left(\frac{M_1^2 + 5}{7M_1^2 - 1}\right)\right)^{3.5} \left(\frac{7M_1^2 - 1}{6}\right)$$

$$= \left(\frac{36M_1^2}{7M_1^2 - 1}\right)^{3.5} \left(\frac{1}{5}\right)^{3.5} \left(\frac{7M_1^2 - 1}{6}\right)$$

$$\text{or} \quad 0.028 = \frac{M_1^7}{(7M_1^2 - 1)^{2.5}}$$

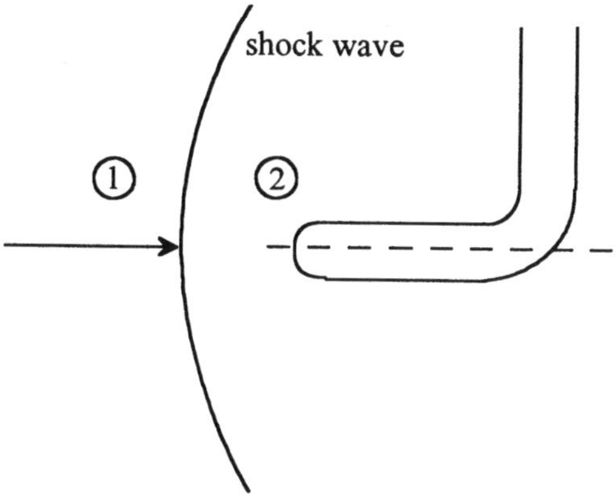

Figure 3.8

Solving, by trial-and-error, gives $M_1 = \mathbf{1.80}$ and $M_2 = 0.616$

$$\frac{p_2}{p_1} = \frac{7M_1^2 - 1}{6}, \quad p_2 = \mathbf{0.54} \text{ bar}$$

The stagnation temperature is constant (since no heat transfer is involved),

$$T_{o2} = T_{o1}, T_{o1} = T_1(1 + \tfrac{1}{2}(\gamma - 1)M_1^2) = 350(1.648) = 577 \text{ K}.$$

$$\text{hence} \quad T_{o2} = 577 = T_2(1 + \tfrac{1}{2}(\gamma - 1)M_2^2) = 1.076T_2$$

$$T_2 = \mathbf{536} \text{ K}$$

Note. If the flow is incompressible (negligible changes in density) the static pressure can be measured by use of another tube, concentric with the open tube, as shown in Fig. 3.9. In this case the difference between the measured static and stagnation pressures is

$$p_{o1} - p_1 = \tfrac{1}{2}\rho u_1^2$$

$$\text{giving} \quad u_1 = \sqrt{\frac{2(p_{o1} - p_1)}{\rho}}$$

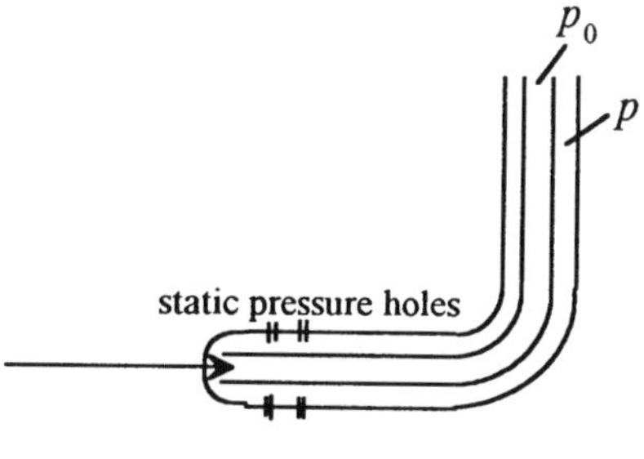

Figure 3.9

3.4 Rayleigh flow with a normal shock

Air flows through a convergent-divergent nozzle into a smooth circular pipe (Fig. 3.10). The flow through the nozzle is isentropic, with stagnation conditions of 3 bar, 300 K. The pipe diameter is twice the nozzle throat diameter.

The pipe is heated so that a normal shock wave stands at the exit plane, and the stagnation temperature just before the shock is 400 K.

Calculate the flow Mach number at the pipe inlet; the static pressure on each side of the shock; the mass flow rate /unit are of the pipe; and the heat transfer /kg.

Flow tables should be used.

Solution. The tables used in the solution are the isentropic and Rayleigh flow, and normal shock tables.

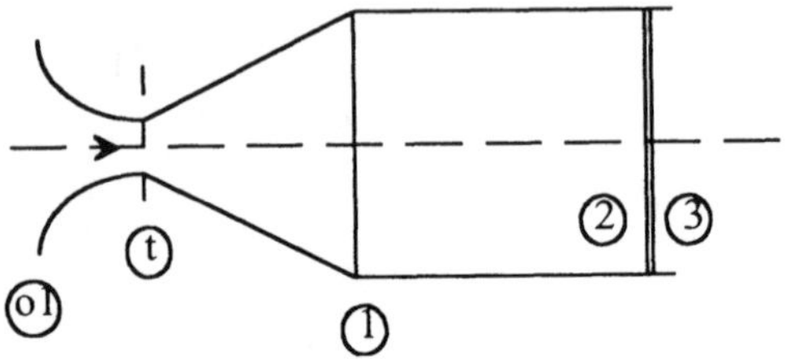

Figure 3.10

Nozzle The flow is isentropic, and again the critical conditions in the pipe are not the same as those at the throat.

$$\frac{A_1}{A_t} = (2)^2 = 4$$

and from the tables $M_1 = 0.145$ or 2.945.

In this situation the flow in the pipe must be supersonic (since a shock wave stands at the exit). Also in the pipe heat addition causes the Mach number to approach unity, or $M_2 < M_1$, but must still be supersonic at section 2. Hence $M_1 = \mathbf{2.945}$.

$$\frac{p_{o1}}{p_1} = 33.744, \quad \frac{T_{o1}}{T_1} = 2.748$$

giving $p_1 = 0.089$ bar, $T_1 = 109$ K

$$\frac{\dot{m}}{A_1} = p_1 M_1 \sqrt{\frac{\gamma}{RT_1}} = \mathbf{175}\ \text{kg/m}^2\text{s}.$$

Pipe From the tables, at $M_1 = 2.945$

$$\frac{p_1}{p^*} = 0.1825, \quad \frac{T_1}{T^*} = 0.289, \quad \frac{T_o}{T^*} = 0.6605, \quad \frac{p_{o1}}{p_o^*} = 3.250$$

giving $p^* = 0.488$ bar, $T^* = 377$ K

$p_{o1}^* = 0.923$ bar, $T_o^* = 454$ K

Now at section 2, $T_{o2} = 400$ K

$$\frac{T_{o2}}{T_o^*} = \frac{400}{454} = 0.881$$

and from the tables $M_2 = \mathbf{1.61}$

$$\frac{p_2}{p^*} = 0.518, \quad \frac{T_2}{T^*} = 0.696, \quad \frac{p_{o2}}{p_o^*} = 1.181 \text{ bar}$$

giving p_2 = **0.253** bar , T_2 = **262** K, p_{o2} = **1.090** ba

Normal shock From the tables, at $M_2 = 1.61$

$$\frac{p_3}{p_2} = 2.859, \quad \frac{T_3}{T_2} = 1.398, \quad M_3 = \mathbf{0.666}, \quad \frac{p_{o3}}{p_2} = 3.851$$

giving p_3 = **0.723** bar , T_3 = 366 K, p_{o3} = 0.974 bar.

The heat transfer rate is, per kg

$$C_p(T_{o2} - T_{o1}) = 1.005(400 - 300) = \mathbf{100.5}\text{ kJ (addition).}$$

3.5 Moving normal shock

> A normal plane shock moves at a steady velocity of 400 m/s, in air, towards a stationary plane surface. The air is at rest in front of the shock wave, at a static pressure p_a. The air velocity behind the shock wave is 300 m/s, in the same direction as the wave velocity. The wave is reflected from the surface leaving the air in its wake at a static pressure p_2. Determine the ratio p_2/p_a.
>
> The following relationships for a *stationary* normal shock may be of assistance:
>
> $$u_1u_2 = (a^*)^2, \quad \frac{p_2}{p_1} = \frac{2\gamma M_1^2 - (\gamma - 1)}{\gamma + 1}$$

Solution. The situation can be analysed by consideration of the *relative* velocities. Thus, if the velocity of the reflected wave = u_r, the relative velocity of the advancing wave is 400 – 300 = 100 m/s, and of the reflected wave 300 + u_r (Fig. 3.11).

The energy equation for steady, one-dimensional flow is

$$\frac{1}{2}u^2 + h = h_o = C_pT_o = \frac{\gamma RT_o}{\gamma - 1}$$

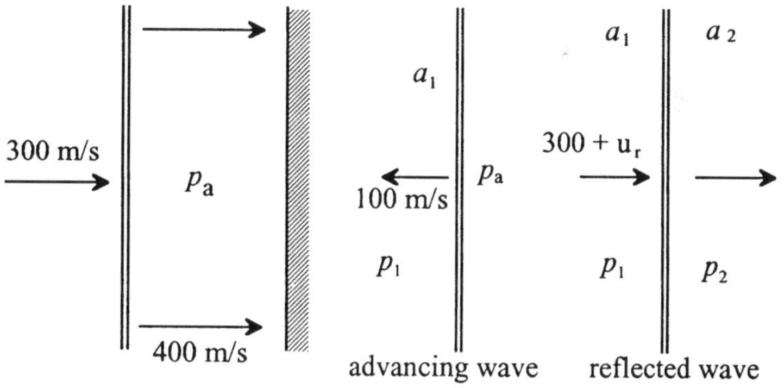

Figure 3.11

or $$\frac{1}{2}u^2 + \frac{a^2}{\gamma - 1} = \frac{\gamma RT_o}{\gamma - 1}$$

Applying the equation to this problem, using the relative velocities gives

$$\frac{1}{2}(400)^2 + \frac{a^2}{\gamma - 1} = \frac{1}{2}(100)^2 + \frac{a_1^2}{\gamma - 1} = \frac{\gamma RT_o}{\gamma - 1}$$

and $$\frac{1}{2}u_r^2 + \frac{a_2^2}{\gamma - 1} = \frac{1}{2}(300 + u_r)^2 + \frac{a_1^2}{\gamma - 1} = \frac{\gamma RT_o}{\gamma - 1}$$

The first relationship given can now be introduced,

$$u_1u_2 = (a^*)^2$$

Here $a^* = \sqrt{\gamma R T^*}$ or, since

$$T^* = \frac{2T_o}{\gamma + 1},$$

$$(a^*)^2 = \frac{\gamma R 2T_o}{\gamma + 1}$$

hence $$\frac{\gamma R T_o}{\gamma - 1} = \frac{\frac{1}{2}(\gamma + 1)(a^*)^2}{\gamma - 1} = \frac{1}{2}k(a^*)^2 \text{ say.}$$

Again using the *relative* velocities it becomes

$$400(400 - 300) = (a^*)^2$$

and $$u_r(u_r + 300) = (a^*)^2$$

giving $a^* = 200$ m/s, $u_r = 100$ m/s.

The pressure ratio p_2/p_1 can now be determined from the Mach numbers (again relative), namely

$$M_1 = \frac{400 - 300}{a_1} = \frac{100}{a_1} \text{ and } M_2 = \frac{u_r + 300}{a_1} = \frac{400}{a_1}.$$

The pressure ratio across the shock wave is given as

$$\frac{2\gamma M^2 - (\gamma - 1)}{\gamma + 1},$$

and applying it to the advancing and reflected wave

$$\frac{p_a}{p_1} = \frac{2\gamma M_1^2 - (\gamma - 1)}{\gamma + 1}$$

and $$\frac{p_2}{p_1} = \frac{2\gamma M_2^2 - (\gamma - 1)}{\gamma + 1}$$

The acoustic velocity, a, is determined from the energy equation:

$$\frac{a_1^2}{\gamma - 1} = \frac{1}{2}k(a^*)^2 - \frac{1}{2}(100)^2$$

and taking $\gamma = 1.4$ this gives $k = 6$, $a_1 = 214.5$ m/s. Substituting for a_1

$$M_1 = 0.466, \quad M_2 = 2.144$$

and $$\frac{p_a}{p_1} = 0.087, \quad \frac{p_2}{p_1} = 5.196$$

Hence $\frac{p_2}{p_a} = \mathbf{59.73}$

Note. The study of moving shock waves, and their reflection from surfaces, is important in many practical applications. Examples include the behaviour of detonation fronts in an engine cylinder, shock tubes, nuclear bombs, and entry of high speed vehicles into tunnels. The analogous area in hydraulics is water hammer (pressure surges), where, for example, the travel of the wave fronts is catered for in hydroelectric generation by the use of surge tanks. (See S.P. in 'Fluid Mechanics', Pt.2, J. F. Douglas.)

3.6 Hydraulic analogy

Discuss the hydraulic jump in a channel conveying water as an analogy to a normal shock wave in gas flow. Derive an equation for the ratio of the downstream depth to upstream depth in terms of the upstream Froude number.

Solution. The flow of water in an open channel can be classified in a similar manner to that in gas flow, as high or low speed flow. The dividing critical condition is, in the flow of water, the *Froude* number. This is defined as

$$Fr = \frac{u}{\sqrt{gy}} \text{ (or sometimes } \frac{u^2}{\sqrt{gy}}\text{)}$$

where y is the depth of the stream. In high speed flow $Fr > 1$, and it is referred to as rapid or supercritical flow: in low speed flow $Fr < 1$ and it is referred to as tranquil or subcritical flow.

The static pressure in a stream of water is $\rho g y$ at a depth y, i.e. a vertical distance y below the free surface. Hence the pressure force over a depth of stream y_1 is

$$\int_0^{y_1} \rho g y \, dy = \frac{1}{2}\rho g y_1^2$$

Consider the situation in a channel where a rapid flow discharges into a much deeper tranquil flow: analogous to a supersonic gas flow into subsonic flow conditions. In the gas flow this can only be achieved by the mechanism of a normal shock wave, and in the water flow by a hydraulic jump (standing wave). The substantial pressure rise across a normal shock in a gas flow corresponds to the rise in level of the water (increasing depth) in the water flow.

In both cases the change is irreversible, and in the hydraulic jump some of the upstream energy of the water is converted into eddies and turbulence in the jump. However the changes across a hydraulic jump are not as rapid as those across a shock wave in gas flow. Finally the analogy is not exact because of the existence of a free surface (open to atmosphere) in the water flow.

The analogy is useful in qualitative terms, from the aspect of flow visualisation. The presence, and behaviour, of hydraulic jumps can be clearly seen in water flow. For example the flow of a river round a bridge pier, or obstacle in the flow, is clearly visible to the naked eye.

In gas flow various techniques have to be used to enable the shock waves to become visible, such as Schlieren or inferometer equipment. The clear visibility is particularly useful in the study of oblique shock waves and wave interference and reflection.

A jump is formed when the downstream water level is increased above the critical depth (which is analogous to the critical pressure) by an obstruction, or in the case of a sloping channel where the bed slope is too low to overcome the friction force for rapid flow. The illustration used in this solution is the rapid discharge from a sluice into a tranquil stream.

The channel is of a rectangular cross-section and horizontal (or very small slope) (Fig. 3.12).

The continuity and momentum equations applied to sections 1 and 2 are, for incompressible flow,

$$\dot{m} = \rho b y_1 u_1 = \rho b y_2 u_2$$

and $\frac{1}{2}\rho g(y_1^2 - y_2^2) = \dot{m}(u_2 - u_1)$

where b = channel width (constant)

Introducing, for convenience, the flow rate /unit width q

$$y_1^2 - y_2^2 = \frac{2q}{g}(u_2 - u_1)$$

and $u_1 = \frac{q}{y_1}, \quad u_2 = \frac{q}{y_2}$

Hence $y_1^2 - y_2^2 = \frac{2q^2}{g}\left(\frac{1}{y_2} - \frac{1}{y_1}\right)$

$$y_2^2 y_1 + y_1^2 y_2 - \frac{2q^2}{g} = 0$$

giving $y_2 = -\frac{1}{2}y_1 \pm \sqrt{\frac{y_1^2}{4} + \frac{2q^2}{gy_1}}$

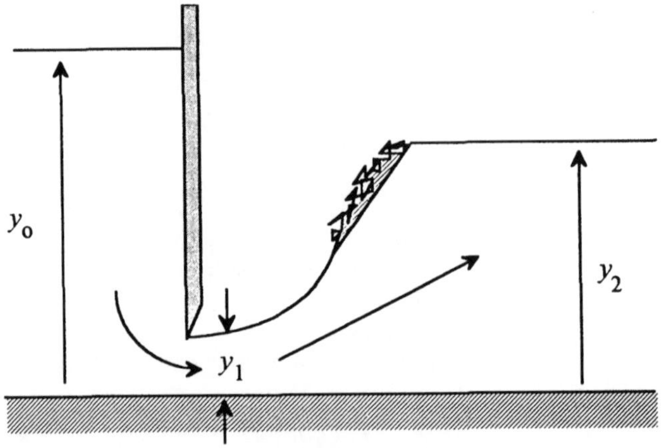

Figure 3.12

This result can be expressed in terms of the Froude number

$$Fr = \frac{u}{\sqrt{gy}} = \frac{q}{\sqrt{gy^3}}.$$

At the critical conditions $Fr = 1, y = y_c$ (say) and $q = \sqrt{gy_c^3}$ or

$$y_c = \left(\frac{q^2}{g}\right)^{\frac{1}{3}}$$

Thus $\frac{y_2}{y_1} = -\frac{1}{2} \pm \sqrt{\frac{1}{4} + 2Fr_1^2} = \frac{1}{2}\left(\sqrt{1 + 8Fr_1^2} - 1\right)$

since the negative value has no physical significance.

The energy 'less' is

$$y_1 + \frac{u_1^2}{2g} - y_2 - \frac{u_2^2}{2g} = y_1 - y_2 + \frac{q^2}{2g}\left(\frac{1}{y_1^2} - \frac{1}{y_2^2}\right)$$

$$= \frac{(y_2 - y_1)^3}{4y_1y_2} \qquad \text{since } \frac{q^2}{g} = \frac{1}{2}y_1y_2(y_1 + y_2)$$

This less can be expressed in terms of a jump efficiency, defined as

$$\left(y_2 + \frac{u_2^2}{2g}\right)\Big/\left(y_1 + \frac{u_1^2}{2g}\right)$$

The two fluid flows can now be summarised in the following table.

Water flow	Gas flow
Free surface: effect of gravitational forces.	Enclosed flow: no gravitational effect.
Critical depth $y_c = \left(\frac{q^2}{g}\right)^{\frac{1}{3}}$	Critical pressure $p^* = \left(\frac{2}{\gamma+1}\right)^{\frac{\gamma}{\gamma-1}} p_o$
$Fr_c = 1$	$M = 1$
Ratio of depths $\frac{y_2}{y_1} = \frac{1}{2}\left(\sqrt{1 + 8Fr_1^2} - 1\right)$	Pressure ratio $\frac{p_2}{p_1} = \frac{2\gamma M_1^2 - (\gamma - 1)}{\gamma + 1}$
Energy loss $\frac{(y_2 - y_1)^3}{4y_1y_2}$	Energy loss $p_{o1} - p_{o2}$

3.7 Plane oblique shock wave

A symmetrical wedge, of semi-angle δ, is inserted into an air stream. The static conditions upstream of the wedge are 2 bar. 350 K and the flow Mach number = 2.

The air is contained in a tunnel and the shock waves emanating at the wedge apex are reflected from the tunnel walls.

Determine the static pressure and temperature downstream of the reflected wave when the semi-angle δ is

(i) 10° (ii) 15°

Flow tables should be used.

Solution

(i) An obstruction in a supersonic air stream generates oblique shock waves at every point on the surface of the obstruction where there is a change in direction. Air passing through a plane oblique shock is deflected through an angle to maintain a streamline parallel to the surface: near to the surface boundary layer effects may modify the situation.

Considering a wedge, as shown in Fig. 3.13, for a given upstream Mach number M_1 it can be shown that there is a limiting angle of deflection δ_m, and if $\delta < \delta_m$ there are two possible physical situations. One shock wave, corresponding to a smaller wave angle β, gives supersonic flow downstream of the wave and is termed a *weak* wave. The other possibility produces subsonic flow downstream of the wave and a larger wave angle, and is termed a *strong* wave.

Note. A third value of the wave angle is possible mathematically but is of no physical significance, because this situation would correspond to an entropy decrease!

When $\delta = \delta_m$ the two physically possible waves become identical, and only a single strong shock can arise. When $\delta > \delta_m$ a plane shock cannot be formed, attached to the corner. Instead a curved detached shock is formed, along which the shock changes from a strong to a weak shock.

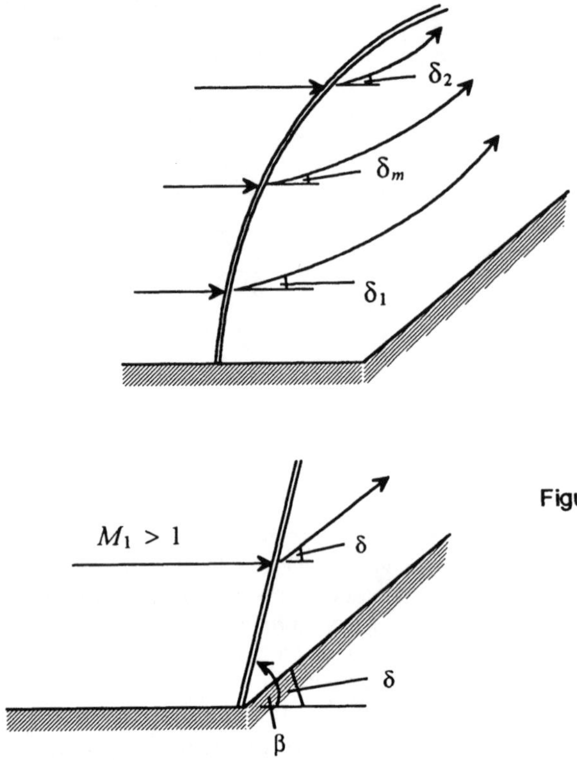

Figure 3.13

From the flow tables, at $M_1 = 2$, $\delta_{12} = 10°$

$$\frac{p_2}{p_1} = 1.708, \quad \frac{T_2}{T_1} = 1.172, \quad M_2 = 1.64 \text{ and } \beta = 39.33°$$

or $$\frac{p_2}{p_1} = 4.447, \quad \frac{T_2}{T_1} = 1.682, \quad M_2 = 0.60 \text{ and } \beta = 83.68°$$

In this particular problem the shock wave must be a *weak* wave, as otherwise there would be no reflection from the tunnel wall. Hence

$$p_2 = \mathbf{3.416} \text{ bar}, \quad T_2 = \mathbf{410} \text{ K}, \quad M_2 = 1.64$$

Referring to Fig. 3.14: As the streamline crosses the reflected wave it is deflected to become parallel to the tunnel wall, so that $\delta_{23} = \delta_{12} = 10°$. From the tables, at

$$M_2 = 1.64, \quad \delta_{23} = 10°$$

$$\frac{p_3}{p_2} = 1.645, \quad \frac{T_3}{T_2} = 1.158, \quad M_3 = 1.28, \quad \beta_3 = 49.45°$$

or $$\frac{p_3}{p_2} = 2.876, \quad \frac{T_3}{T_2} = 1.400, \quad M_3 = 0.71, \quad \beta_3 = 79.87°$$

Again for a further reflection at the wedge the shock must be a weak wave, and

$$p_3 = \mathbf{5.619} \text{ bar}, \quad T_3 = \mathbf{574} \text{ K}, \quad M_3 = 1.28.$$

(ii) At $M_1 = 2.0$ the limiting deflection (from tables) δ_m is 22.93°. The shock is therefore still attached to the corner when δ is increased.

At $M_1 = 2.0$, $\delta_{12} = 15°$

$$\frac{p_2}{p_1} = 2.201, \quad \frac{T_2}{T_1} = 1.272, \quad M_2 = 1.44$$

giving p_2 = **4.402** bar, T_2 = **445** K.

However consideration of the reflected wave shows that a *simple* reflection (as in part (i)) is not possible. At $M_2 = 1.44$ the limiting deflection is 10.5°, so that the required deflection of 15° cannot be achieved by an attached shock.

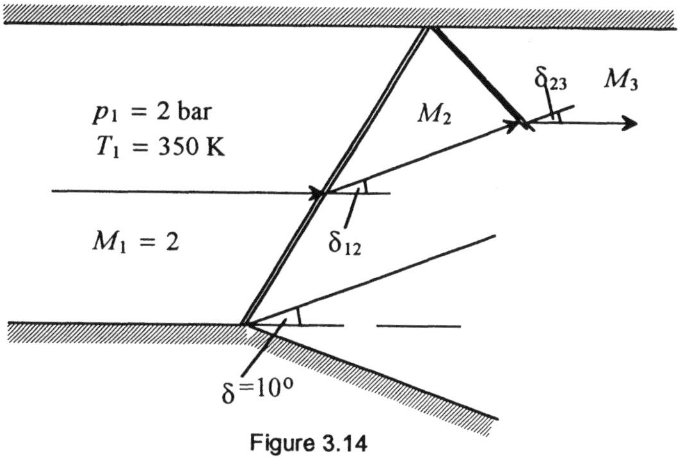

Figure 3.14

The situation thus becomes one in which a *Mach* (or Y) reflection occurs, as shown in Fig. 3.15. The simple reflection springs, not from the tunnel wall, but at some point P standing away from the wall. The reflected wave from point P is still a plane wave, but between the wall and this point a curved wave is formed. This wave must be normal to the wall at the wall approach.

The region downstream of this combined reflection is divided into two regions, 3 and 4, separated by a *slip plane*.

The conditions in regions 3 and 4 will be different *except* for the static pressure. This follows from the fact that if a pressure difference existed flow would take place *across* the streamlines, which is not possible.

Also the angles of deflection must satisfy the requirement that the streamlines in the regions 3 and 4 must be parallel to each other.

Hence $\delta_{14} = \delta_{12} - \delta_{23} = 15 - \delta_{23}$

These two requirements determine the downstream flow conditions.

A trial-and-error procedure, using the tables, can be used. A value of δ_{23} is assumed giving p_3; the corresponding value of $\delta_{14} = 15 - \delta_{23}$ gives p_4. The angles are correct if $p_3 = p_4$. The conditions in region 2 are

$$M_2 = 1.44, \quad \frac{p_2}{p_1} = 2.201, \quad \frac{T_2}{T_1} = 1.272$$

It can be seen from the following table of values that *no* solution will be obtained. However an examination of the flow pattern reveals why this solution arises. Close to the wall the shock wave is normal to the wall, and across such a normal plane shock the downstream flow must be *subsonic*, $M_4 < 1$. The conditions in region 3 are therefore also subsonic, and the reflected wave is not a *weak* wave as assumed but a *strong* wave.

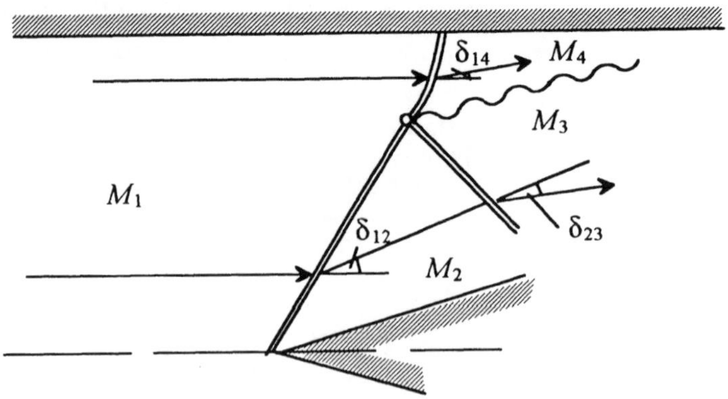

Figure 3.15

δ_{23}	p_3/p_2	p_3 (bar)	T_3/T_2	T_3 K	δ_{14}	p_4/p_1	p_4 (bar)	T_4/T_1	T_4 K
6°	1.35	5.94	1.01	486	9°	1.63	3.25	1.15	404
8°	1.51	6.63	1.13	502	7°	1.47	2.93	1.12	391
4°	1.22	5.36	1.06	471	11°	1.8	3.6	1.2	421
2°	1.1	4.86	1.03	458	13°	1.99	3.98	1.23	431
1°	1.05	4.63	1.01	451	14°	2.09	4.18	1.25	438

The solution is now obtained with these circumstances in mind.

δ_{23}	p_3/p_2	p_3 (bar)	T_3/T_2	T_3 K	δ_{14}	p_4/p_1	p_4 (bar)	T_4/T_1	T_1 K	M_3	M_4
6°	2.2	9.69	1.27	566	9°	4.46	8.91	1.68	589		
8°	2.14	9.44	1.26	561	7°	4.48	8.95	1.69	590		
9°	2.09	9.2	1.24	552	6°	4.48	8.97	1.69	591	0.81	0.59
10°	1.72	7.57	1.17		5°	4.49	8.97	1.69	591		

The conditions are approximately

$$M_3 = 0.81, p_3 = \mathbf{9.0}\text{ bar}, T_3 = \mathbf{550}$$

$$M_4 = 0.59, p_4 = \mathbf{9.0}\text{ bar}, T_4 = \mathbf{591}$$

Note. The velocities in regions 3 and 4 are different.

Thus $u_3 = M_3 a_3 = M_3\sqrt{\gamma R T_3} = 381$ m/s

$u_4 = 288$ m/s

The difference in velocities is absorbed by the slip plane, which is a vortex sheet. The effect of the sheet of vertices can be pictured as an endless belt, carrying the fluid velocity, in an anti-clockwise direction. Thus the 'top' belt reduces and the 'bottom' belt increases a mean fluid velocity of 385 m/s.

3.8 Supersonic aerofoil

A supersonic aerofoil is shown in Fig. 3.16 and has a symmetrical double wedge section. The angle of incidence is +10°, and the free (undisturbed) flow Mach number = 2.5.

Sketch the flow pattern over the aerofoil, indicating any shock waves and/or Prandtl-Meyer fans. Determine the static pressure variation over the aerofoil surfaces, and hence the lift and drag coefficients.

Flow tables should be used.

Solution. The principles involved in establishing the nature of the disturbances created in the air flow over an aerofoil can be summarised as follows:

(a) At every change in direction of the air flow a disturbance of some kind arises.

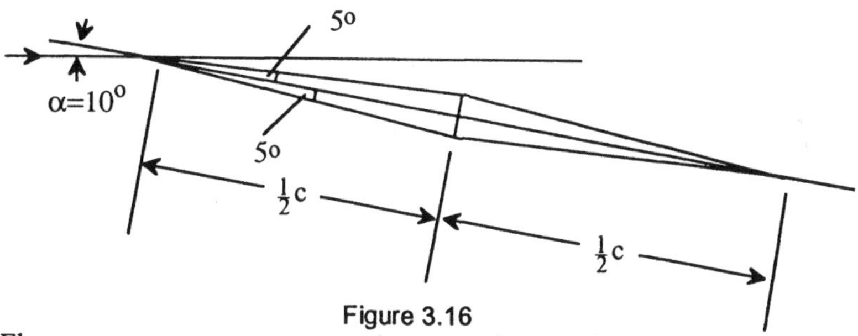

Figure 3.16

(b) Flow over a convex corner is expansive, and a Prandtl-Meyer fan originates at the corner.

(c) Flow over a concave corner is compressive, and a shock wave is generated. The strength of the shock depends upon the downstream conditions.

The physical situation is shown in Fig. 3.17. Over the upper surface of the aerofoil the air expands from region 1 to region 2 through an angle of 5°, and a Prandtl-Meyer fan springs from the wedge apex.

From region 2 to region 3 a further expansion takes place through an angle of 10°, and a Prandtl-Meyer fan springs from the mid-chord vertex.

At the aerofoil trailing edge the flow is turned through an angle of 15°, and the compression generates a shock wave.

Over the lower surface a compression from region 1 to region 4 takes place via a shock wave; from region 4 to region 5 expansion through a Prandtl-Meyer fan; and at the trailing edge a compression through 15° via a shock wave.

The static pressure ratio can now be obtained in each region

1-2 $M_1 = 2.5 \quad \nu_1 = 39.01° \quad \dfrac{p_{o1}}{p_1} = 17.075$

$\nu_2 = \nu_1 + 5 = 44.01°$

hence $M_2 = 2.725, \quad \dfrac{p_{o2}}{p_2} = 24.162$

and since $p_{o2} = p_{o1}$,

$$\frac{p_2}{p_1} = \mathbf{0.707}$$

2-3 $\nu_3 = \nu_2 + 10 = 54.01°$

hence $M_3 = 3.24, \quad \frac{p_{o3}}{p_3} = 52.246$

and since $p_{o3} = p_{o2}$,

$$\frac{p_3}{p_1} = \mathbf{0.327}$$

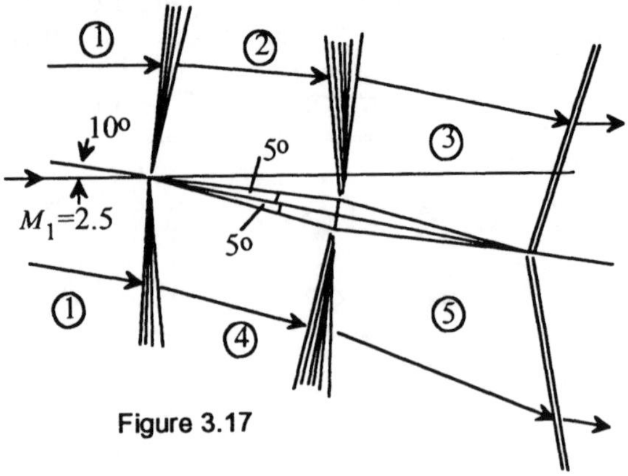

Figure 3.17

1-4 $\quad M_1 = 2.5$, deflection $\delta_{14} = 15°$

hence $M_4 = 1.87, \quad \frac{p_4}{p_1} = \mathbf{2.474}$

$$p_{o4} = 6.403 p_4 = 15.841 p_1$$

4-5 $\quad M_4 = 1.87, \quad \nu_4 = 22.68°, \quad \frac{p_{o4}}{p_4} = 6.403$

hence $\nu_5 = 32.68°$

$$M_5 = 2.24, \quad \frac{p_{o5}}{p_5} = 11.385$$

$$p_5 = \frac{15.841 p_1}{11.385} = \mathbf{1.391} p_1$$

The lift and drag forces can be computed from the pressure forces: they are the components of the resultant pressure force on the aerofoil normal to, and in the direction of, the free stream. The pressure force on the parts of the aerofoil, relative to the free stream pressure p_1, are shown in Fig. 3.18. The pressure force is, of course, normal to the surface, and is based on a unit width (span) of the aerofoil.

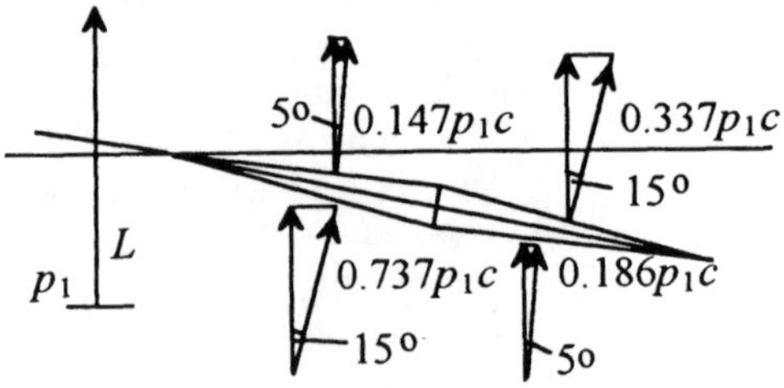

Figure 3.18

In region 2, pressure force is

$$(p_2 - p_1)(\tfrac{1}{2}c) = -0.147 p_1 c$$

and is therefore a 'suction' force.

region 3 force = $\frac{1}{2}c(p_3 - p_1) = -0.337p_1c$
region 4 force = $\frac{1}{2}c(p_4 - p_1) = +0.737p_1c$
region 5 force = $\frac{1}{2}c(p_5 - p_1) = +0.186p_1c$

The forces can now be resolved into the two components:

$$\text{lift } L = 0.147p_1c\cos 5 + 0.337p_1c\cos 15 + 0.737p_1c\cos 15 + 0.186p_1c\cos 5$$
$$= 1.369p_1c$$
$$\text{drag } D = 0.147p_1c\sin 5 + 0.337p_1c\sin 15 + 0.737p_1c\sin 15 + 0.186p_1c\sin 5$$
$$= 0.307p_1c$$

The lift and drag coefficients C_L, C_D are defined as

$$C_L = \frac{L}{\frac{1}{2}\rho_1 u_1^2 c}, \quad C_D = \frac{D}{\frac{1}{2}\rho_1 u_1^2 c}$$

Since $\rho u^2 = \dfrac{pu^2}{RT} = \gamma p M^2$

these can be put in the form

$$C_L = \frac{L}{\frac{1}{2}\gamma p_1 M_1^2 c}, \quad C_D = \frac{D}{\frac{1}{2}\gamma p_1 M_1^2 c}$$

Hence substituting $\frac{1}{2}\gamma = 0.7$,

and $$C_L = \frac{1.369p_1c}{0.7(2.5)^2p_1c} = \mathbf{0.313}$$
$$C_D = \frac{0.307}{0/7(2.5)^2} = \mathbf{0.070}$$

Note. The lift and drag coefficients could be calculated without the use of flow tables, by linearised flow theory (q.v. Ex.1.12). The flow over aerofoils is discussed in Chap.10, where the result is derived, from linearised theory, that

$$C_L = \frac{4\alpha}{\sqrt{M_1^2 - 1}}$$
$$C_D = \alpha C_L$$

In this problem the values are $\alpha = 10° = 0.1745$ radian, $M_1 = 2.5$ giving

$$C_L = 0.305, \; C_D = 0.053$$

3.9 Closed supersonic wind tunnel

Briefly outline the layout of a continuous, closed circuit, supersonic wind tunnel; and compare this type with the open tunnel.

Discuss the sequence of flow states in the process of starting the closed circuit tunnel, and explain what is meant by swallowing of a shock.

Solution. A schematic of a closed circuit tunnel is shown in Fig. 3.19. The compressor delivers high pressure air to the reservoir, from where the air flows through a nozzle into the test (working) section. The air then flows through a diffuser into a receiver, and via a cooler to the compressor. The subsonic flow into the nozzle requires a convergent entry to attain choking at the throat, and the supersonic flow from the test section decelerates in the convergent entry to the diffuser.

The air is cooled before entry to the compressor in order to reduce the work input to it, W_s. The compressor makes up pressure drops in the nozzle, diffuser and bends, valves etc. Hence the power required is less than would be required in an open tunnel, where the high velocity air is discharged from the test section into ambient surroundings.

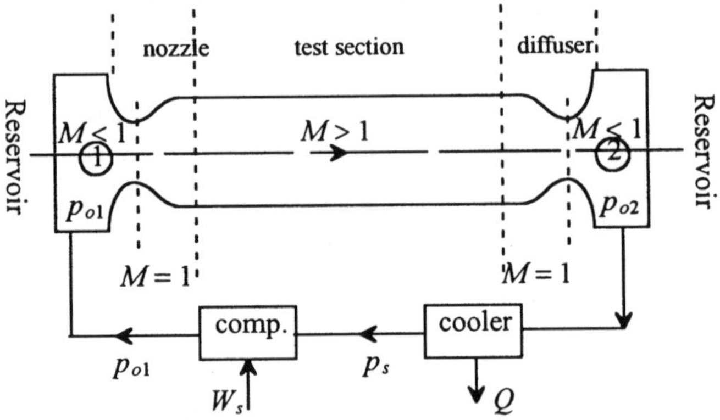

Figure 3.19

The starting up of a supersonic tunnel is somewhat different to that of a subsonic tunnel due to the formation of shock waves in the former. If the tunnel geometry is fixed and the flow started from rest, p_{o1} (reservoir) increases and p_{o2} (receiver) reduces. Eventually the conditions will become critical at the throats.

Any further reduction in the compressor suction pressure p_s will not produce any changes upstream from the diffuser throat (which is choked); supersonic flow is therefore established in the divergent part of the diffuser, and a normal shock appears.

Now to start the tunnel, choking at the diffuser throat should occur after choking at the nozzle throat. Hence the diffuser throat area A^*_d must be greater than the nozzle throat area, A^*_n. When the normal shock occurs (involving a stagnation pressure drop) the choking area increases, and choking may then occur at the diffuser throat before the start-up shock wave passes through the test section. Thus a minimum value of the area ratio A^*_d/A^*_n is required to start the flow in the first section. The area A^*_d must be large enough to accommodate the maximum stagnation pressure drop (due to the shock) at the test section flow Mach number.

The effect of friction at the tunnel wall modifies the flow: friction causes the starting shock to move up the test section into the diffuser, where it becomes stabilised in the divergent portion. This would occur at a section where the diffuser and test section areas were equal. This process is known as *swallowing* of the shock.

After the shock has been swallowed supersonic flow can be established in the test section. The conditions at the diffuser throat would now not be critical. Also the shock can be then moved further upstream by increasing the compressor suction pressure, in order to reduce the stagnation pressure drop and hence reduce the compressor drive power.

The effect of the area ratio is shown in Fig. 3.20.

Note. The starting up and swallowing of a shock is of importance in other situations, as, for example, a supersonic aircraft engine intake.

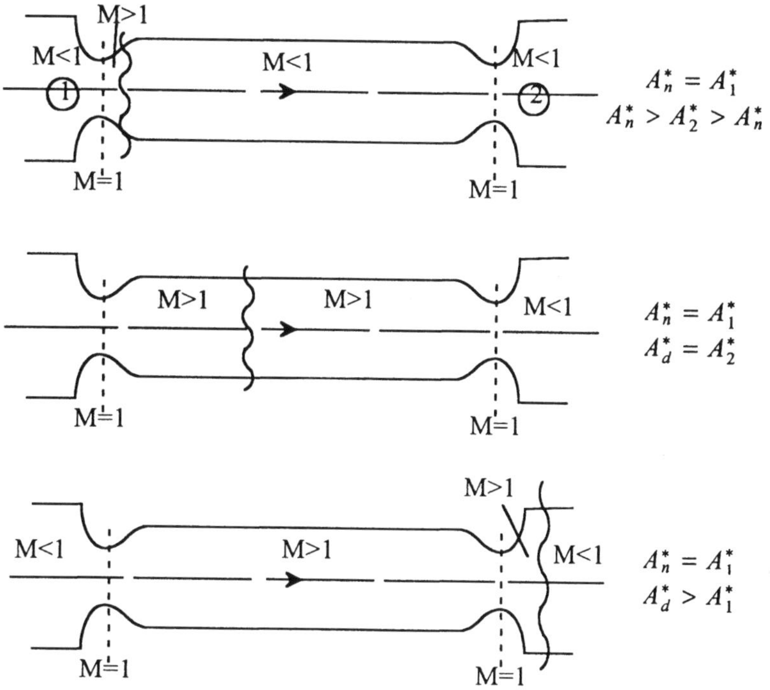

Figure 3.20

3.10 Open wind tunnel

An open wind tunnel has a working section of area 950cm^2. Static pressure in the working section is 0.7 bar, and the flow Mach number is 2.5. The ambient air conditions are 1 bar, 20 °C. Calculate the compressor power required (taking the compressor efficiency = 0.75).

The power required is to be reduced by discharging the air through a diffuser. Determine the diffuser throat and power now required.

Flow tables should be used.

Solution. In a continuous, open tunnel the air is discharged into the ambient atmosphere, as shown in Fig. 3.21. The compressor draws in ambient air at conditions p_a, T_a; and a dryer would normally be included in the line.

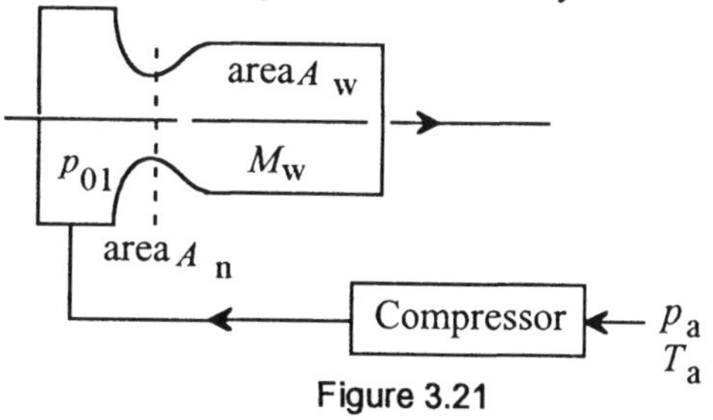

Figure 3.21

From the tables, at $M_w = 2.5$

$$\frac{p_{o1}}{p_w} = 17.075, \quad \frac{T_{o1}}{T_w} = 2.259, \quad \frac{A_w}{A^*} = 2.629$$

The compressor pressure ratio is

$$\frac{p_{o1}}{p_a} = \frac{p_{o1}}{p_w}\cdot\frac{p_w}{p_a} = 17.075\times0.7 = 11.953,$$

and hence

$$\frac{T_{o1}}{T_a} = (11.953)^{\frac{0.4}{1.4}} = 2.032$$

giving $T_w = T_a.\frac{T_w}{T_{o1}}.\frac{T_{o1}}{T_a} = 293\left(\frac{1}{2.259}\right)(2.032) = 264\text{ K}$

and $\quad T_{o1} = 2.259\,T_w = 596\text{ K}$

The nozzle throat area,

$$A_n = \frac{A_w}{2.629} = 361\text{ cm}^2$$

The mass flow rate must be determined:

$$\dot{m} = p_n A_n\sqrt{\frac{\gamma}{RT_n}} \qquad (M_n = 1)$$

where $p_n = \dfrac{p_{o1}}{(1+\frac{1}{2}(\gamma-1))^{\frac{\gamma}{\gamma-1}}}$

$$T_n = \frac{T_{o1}}{1+\frac{1}{2}(\gamma-1)}$$

Substituting

$$p_n = \frac{17.075(0.7)}{1.2^{3.5}} = 6.314\text{ bar}$$

$$T_n = \frac{596}{1.2} = 497\text{ K}$$

$$\dot{m} = 6.314\times10^5\times361\times10^{-4}\sqrt{\frac{1.4}{287\times497}} = 71.41\text{ kg/s}$$

The compressor power (drive) is thus

$$W_s = \dot{m}C_p(T_{o1} - T_a)$$

$$= \frac{71.41(1.005)(596-293)}{0.75} = \mathbf{28993}\text{ kW}$$

Note. The power required, 29.0 MW, is rather high, and produces a flow Mach number of 2.5 in a working section say 38 cm × 25 cm. The power requirement can be reduced by using a closed circuit tunnel (as in the previous example), or installation of a diffuser.

When a diffuser is fitted, a normal shock is formed. At $M_w = 2.5$, from shock tables

$$\frac{p_{o2}}{p_{o1}} = \frac{p_{o2}}{p_1}\cdot\frac{p_1}{p_{o1}} = \frac{8.539}{17.075} = 0.50$$

where $p_{o2}=$ the stagnation pressure in the receiver (q.v. Ex.3.9). Hence

$$A_d^* = \frac{A_n}{0.50} = \mathbf{722}\text{ cm}^2.$$

The pressure ratio to *start* the tunnel is 1.0/0.5 = 2, and the compressor suction temperature is

$$T_s = T_{o1}(\tfrac{1}{2})^{\frac{0.4}{1.4}}$$

$$= 489\text{ K}$$

The starting power is then

$$\frac{71.41(1.005)(596-489)}{0.75} = \mathbf{10240}\text{ kW}$$

The operating power is somewhat lower: after the starting shock is swallowed the Mach number at the diffuser throat is the value corresponding to

$$\frac{A}{A^*} = 2.0, \text{ i.e. } M_d = 2.20$$

A shock occurs at this value, with a stagnation pressure ratio

$$\frac{p_{o2}}{p_{o1}} = \frac{6.726}{10.695} = 0.629$$

and the compressor suction temperature is now

$$596(0.629)^{\frac{0.4}{1.4}} = 522 \text{ K}$$

Hence the power required is

$$\frac{71.41(1.005)(596 - 522)}{0.75} = \mathbf{7080} \text{ kW}$$

Problems

*In many of these problems flow tables should be used. Where tables are not required the problem number is followed by an asterisk *.*

1* State the continuity, momentum and energy equations for steady, one-dimensional flow across a plane, normal shock wave. Hence derive the following relationships, where the subscripts 1 and 2 refer to the upstream and downstream conditions respectively:

$$\frac{p_2}{p_1} = \frac{2\gamma M_1^2 - (\gamma - 1)}{\gamma + 1}$$

$$M_2^2 = \frac{(\gamma - 1)M_1^2 + 2}{2\gamma M_1^2 - (\gamma - 1)}$$

Derive an expression for the entropy change across the shock in terms of M_1 and M_2; and hence show that $M_2 < 1$.

Hint: The entropy must increase across the shock as a consequence of the second law of thermodynamics.

2* A plane normal shock stands in an air stream, and the static pressure ratio is 6:1. Determine the static pressure ratio; the flow Mach number on each side of the shock; and the ratio of the downstream stagnation pressure to the upstream static pressure.

Answer 1.95; 2.30, 0.53; 7.30

3 Explain why a combined Pitot-static tube cannot be used directly in a supersonic air stream to measure the upstream air velocity. Illustrate the explanation by consideration of a Pitot tube which records a stagnation pressure of 8 times the free stream static pressure, and determine the upstream flow Mach number.

Answer 2.42

4 A convergent-divergent nozzle passes air from a large reservoir in which the stagnation conditions are 10 bar, 300 °C. A plane normal shock wave stands in the divergent part of the nozzle such that the *static* temperature, just upstream of the shock, is 263 K.

Determine the static pressure and temperature just downstream of the shock, and the area at the plane of the shock (in terms of the throat area).

If the exit area is 3 times the throat area determine the static pressure at the exit plane. Also calculate the air velocity at the throat, on each side of the shock, and at the exit.

Answer 4.41 bar, 546 K; 2.46
4.75 bar
438, 789, 243, 189 m/s

5* A jet engine air intake is designed to take the maximum air flow at an aircraft velocity corresponding to a flow Mach number of 1.5, at an altitude where the static conditions are 0.20 bar, 230 K. At these design conditions a normal shock wave stands at the inlet.

Calculate the change in stagnation pressure, static temperature and air velocity across the shock. The following equations may be used:

$$\frac{p_2}{p_1} = \frac{7M_1^2 - 1}{6}$$

$$M_2^2 = \frac{M_1^2 + 5}{7M_1^2 - 1}$$

Briefly explain why it is necessary to allow for a normal shock wave to form in the intake.

Determine the ratio of the mass flow rate at these conditions to the mass flow rate at a flow Mach number of 0.3 at an altitude where the static conditions are 1.0 bar, 280 K.

Answer 0.06 bar, 74 K, 211 m/s
1.10

6 Air flows from a large reservoir, in which the stagnation conditions are 2 bar, 300 K, through a convergent-divergent nozzle. The nozzle throat diameter = 50 mm, and the exit diameter = 90 mm. A normal shock stands at a section where the diameter = 70 mm.

Calculate the static pressure and temperature, and air velocity at the throat; the mass flow rate; and the static pressure and temperature, and air velocity on each side of the shock wave, and at the exit plane.

The static pressure at the exit plane decreases to 1.0 bar. Show that the shock wave moves to a section where the diameter is approximately 80 mm.

Answer 1.055 bar, 250 K, 317 m/s.
0.915 kg/s.
0.19 bar, 153 K, 540 m/s; 1.04 bar, 282 K, 185 m/s.
1.20 bar, 295 K, 102 m/s.

7 A convergent-divergent nozzle passes air from a large reservoir, in which the stagnation conditions are 10 bar, 350 K. If the mass flow rate is 10 kg/s calculate the throat area.

The exit area is twice the throat area. Assuming supersonic, isentropic flow calculate the static pressure and air velocity at the exit plane.

The static pressure at the exit plane increases to 5.13 bar. Show that a normal shock wave is formed, at the exit plane.

The static pressure at the exit plane is increased to 6.2 bar. Determine the position of the normal shock.

Answer 0.0046 m^2.
0.935 bar, 587 m/s.
Where the area is 1.7 times the throat area.

8* A convergent-divergent nozzle passes a gas from a reservoir, in which the stagnation pressure is p_o, into ambient air at a static pressure p_a. Show that for supersonic flow to be maintained up to the nozzle exit plane the minimum pressure ratio is given by the equation

$$\frac{p_o}{p_a} = (1 + kM_e^2)^{\frac{\gamma}{2k}} \Big/ \left(\frac{2\gamma M_e^2 - 2k}{\gamma + 1}\right)$$

where $k = \frac{1}{2}(\gamma - 1)$.

The pressure ratio across a normal shock is given by the equation

$$\frac{p_2}{p_1} = \frac{2\gamma M_1^2 - 2k}{\gamma + 1}$$

Discuss the flow situation through the nozzle when the pressure ratio is
(a) less than
(b) greater than
this minimum value.

9* A rocket motor expands the combustion chamber products (for which R = 320 J/kg K, and

$$\frac{C_p}{C_v} = \gamma = 1.25)$$

through a convergent-divergent nozzle of throat area 500 cm^2. The stagnation conditions are 32 bar, 3300 K. Ambient pressure = 0.2 bar.

Calculate the area, static temperature and flow Mach number at the exit plane; mass flow rate; thrust; specific impulse and thrust coefficient. Assume that the flow is isentropic and full expansion (i.e. the static pressure at the exit plane = ambient pressure).

A normal shock wave is formed in the divergent portion of the nozzle at a position where the area is 5460 cm^2. Determine the static pressure at the exit plane.

The following relationships for a normal shock wave can be used:

$$\frac{p_2}{p_1} = \frac{2\gamma M_1^2 - (\gamma - 1)}{\gamma + 1}$$

$$M_2^2 = \frac{(\gamma - 1)M_1^2 + 2}{2\gamma M_1^2 - (\gamma - 1)}$$

Answer 0.8m^2, 1197 K, 3.75; 108 kg/s;
281.5 kN; 692 Ns/kg; 1.76.
0.45 bar.

10* A normal shock wave stands in a gas stream. Show, by use of the continuity, momentum and energy equations, that for a perfect gas

$$u_1 u_2 = (a^*)^2 = \gamma R T^*$$

$$\frac{p_2}{p_1} = \frac{(\gamma + 1)\rho_2 - (\gamma - 1)\rho_1}{(\gamma + 1)\rho_1 - (\gamma - 1)\rho_2}$$

where the subscripts 1, 2 refer to upstream and downstream conditions respectively.

Heat is added to the gas, Q, across the shock wave. Show that the first equation now becomes

$$\frac{(a_1^*)^2}{u_1 u_2} = 1 + \frac{\gamma + 1}{2(\gamma - 1)} \cdot \frac{Q}{u_2(u_2 - u_1)}$$

Briefly indicate the field of application of this result.

Answer Detonation waves in combustion.

11 A vehicle is travelling at a velocity of 1850 m/s in air at an altitude of 15 km, where the static air conditions are 0.12 bar, 217 K. A normal shock wave stands in front of the vehicle. Determine the static pressure and temperature, and air velocity downstream of the wave.

The specific heat ratio may be taken as constant at a value of 1.40, but the variation of specific heat with temperature should be taken into account.

Answer 5.73 bar, 1547 K, 276 m/s approx.

12* A normal plane shock stands in an air stream. The specific heat varies with the static temperature according to a linear law

$$C_p = a + bT$$

although the specific heat ratio can be taken as constant. Show that

$$\left(\frac{T_2}{T_1}\right)^2 + \alpha\left(\frac{T_2}{T_1}\right) + \beta = 0$$

where

$$\alpha b T_1\left(\frac{p_2}{p_1}\right) = 2a\left(\frac{p_2}{p_1}\right) - R\left(\frac{p_2}{p_1} - 1\right)$$

$$\beta b T_1 = R\left(1 - \frac{p_2}{p_1}\right) - 2a - bT_1$$

If a = 900, b = 0.18 J/kg K, R = 287 J/kg K, calculate the downstream temperature T_2 when the upstream temperature T_1 = 370 K and the pressure ratio = 10.

Compare the value with that obtained by assuming a mean value of the specific heat, 1.005 kJ/kg K.

Answer 960 K. 973 K.

13 Air flows along a circular pipe of diameter 50 mm. The stagnation conditions at inlet are 7 bar, 350 K. The pipe length = 50 cm, and the friction coefficient is constant and equal to 0.005.

The pipe is choked at the exit plane. Calculate the static pressure and temperature at the inlet; flow Mach number at the inlet; mass flow rate; and stagnation pressure decrease between the inlet and exit.

The static pressure at the exit plane changes to a value of 3.7 bar. Show that a normal shock wave stands in the pipe, and determine its approximate location.

Answer 5.04 bar, 318 K, 0.70, 2.71 kg/s, 0.61 bar
or 1.46 bar, 223 K, 1.68, 2.25 kg/s, 1.69 bar
10cm from the inlet.

14* Water flows along a rectangular channel of width 50 cm at a velocity of 3 m/s. The flow rate = 0.20 m^3/s. Calculate the depth of flow, and determine the nature of the flow.

Due to an obstruction a hydraulic jump occurs. Calculate the depth of flow just downstream of the jump, the energy loss and jump efficiency.

Answer 133 mm;

Fr = 2.63 (corresponding to supercritical flow)

432 mm, 0.116 m head (1140 N/m^2), 0.80.

15 A wedge is inserted into a uniform stream (Fig. 3.22), such that an attached shock wave is formed at the apex. The shock is reflected from the tunnel wall as shown.

Determine the flow Mach number and pressure ratio p/p_1 in regions 2 and 3; and the angles between the incident and reflected waves and the wall.

The half-angle of the wedge is increased to 20°. Show that a Mach reflection occurs, and determine the Mach number and pressure ratio in each region.

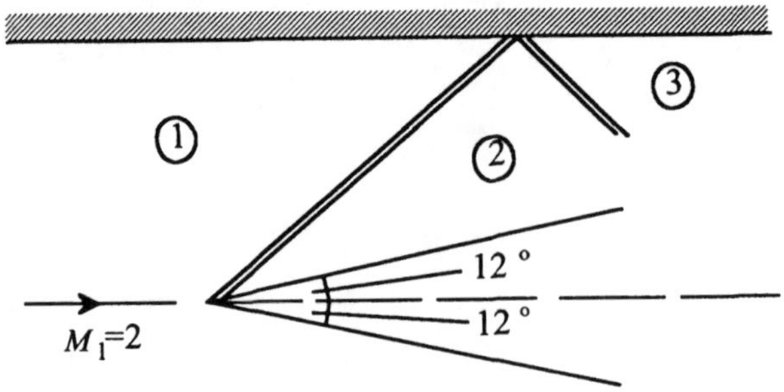

Figure 3.22

Answer 1.56, 1.89 and 1.09, 3.51; 41.6°, 57.6°.
1.21, 2.85; 0.85, 4.20; 0.70, 4.20 with the slip plane at approx. 18.5° to the free stream direction.

16 A supersonic diffuser is shown in Fig. 3.23. The approach flow Mach number = 3. Determine the section height *h*, and convergent portion length *L*.

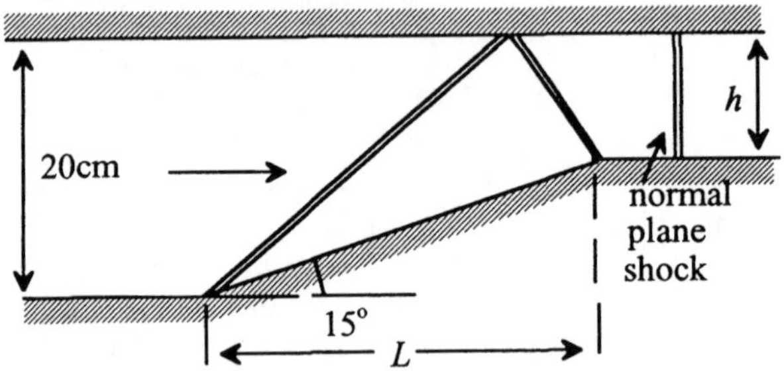

Figure 3.23

Determine the overall stagnation pressure ratio, and compare its value with that obtained by a single normal plane shock.

Answer 7.37 cm , 47.13 cm
0.73, 0.33.

17 A supersonic air intake is shown in Fig. 3.24. The static conditions in region 1 are 0.5 bar, 230 K and the air velocity = 912 m/s.

Determine the static pressure, flow Mach number and air velocity in regions 2, 3, 4, 5.

Discuss the nature of the reflected wave from region 5.

Show, on a sketch, the angles (to the surfaces) of the incident and reflected waves.

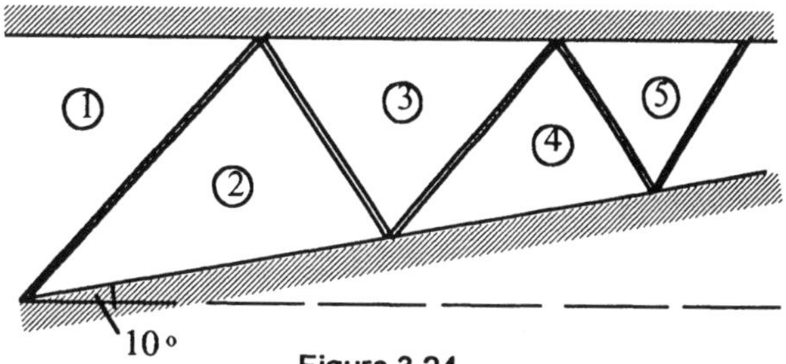

Figure 3.24

Answer 1.03 bar, 2.50, 848 m/s
1.92 bar, 2.08, 775 m/s
3.32 bar, 1.71, 690 m/s
5.48 bar, 1.36, 590 m/s

18 A wedge, of half-angle 11°, is situated in a uniform flow as shown in Fig. 3.25. A Mach reflection occurs at the wall.

Calculate the static pressure and temperature, air velocity, and flow Mach number in the labelled regions. Also determine the angle of the slip plane, and briefly discuss its nature.

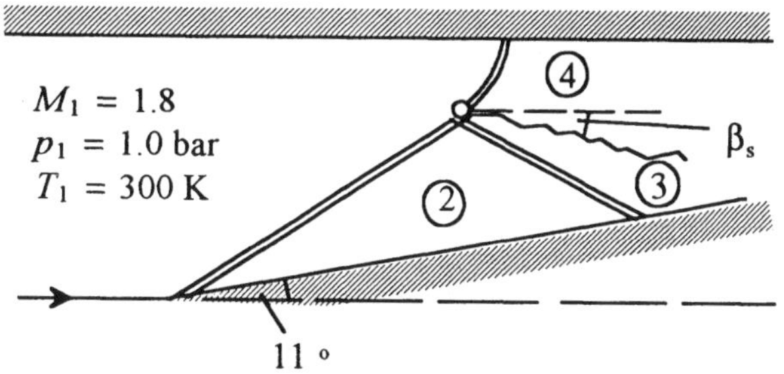

Figure 3.25

Answer 1.75 bar, 354 K, 532 m/s, 1.41
3.60 bar, 440 K, 310 m/s, 0.74
3.60 bar, 460 K, 270 m/s, 0.62
δ_s = 3° (approx.)

19 A supersonic air intake is shown in Fig. 3.26. The air stream approaches the intake at static conditions of 0.7 bar, 270 K and a flow Mach number of 2.5. Throat area = 0.1 m^2. A normal plane shock stands at a section where the area = 0.013 m^2.

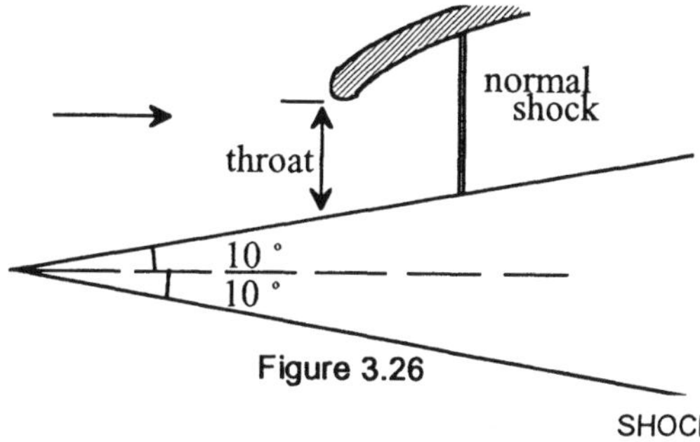

Figure 3.26

Determine the mass flow rate into the intake; the static pressure and temperature just downstream of the shock; and overall reduction in stagnation pressure.

Answer 9.84 kg/s
3.94 bar, 562 K
6.79 bar.

20 Two types of intake duct are shown in Fig. 3.27. In both cases the approach air stream static conditions are 0.7 bar, 7°C and the flow Mach number 1.90. The minimum area = 1.5 m^2 in each intake.

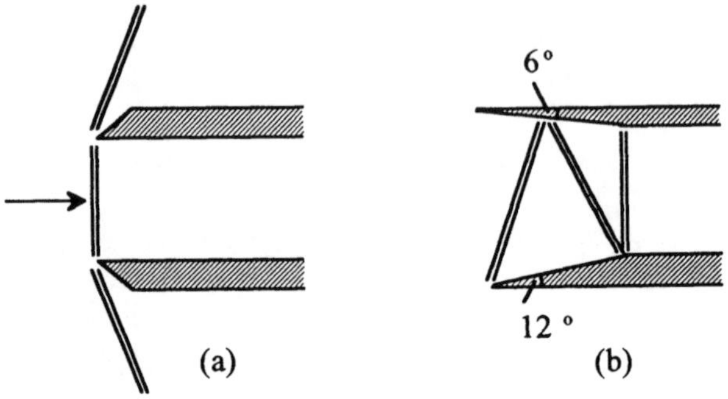

Figure 3.27

Calculate the mass flow rate and recovery factor in each intake.

[The recovery factor is the ratio of the final to approach stream stagnation pressure.]

Answer (a) 833 kg/s, 0.77
(b) 1167 kg/s, 0.92.

21 A supersonic inlet diffuser operates (in an aircraft travelling at 500 m/s) with atmospheric conditions of 0.30 bar, 228 K. The starting shock is to be swallowed.

Discuss the meaning of this statement, and calculate the area ratio of the diffuser.

Answer 5:1.

22 A continuous flow supersonic wind tunnel operates with air. The working section has an area of 1860 cm^2, and the static pressure = 0.3 bar, and flow Mach number = 2.5 in the section. The stagnation temperature = 260°C.

The fixed geometry diffuser is required to just pass the starting shock. Calculate the nozzle and diffuser throat areas; the starting and operating pressure ratios; and starting and operating power requirements.

Briefly indicate why a supersonic tunnel would normally contain a drier in the circuit. Under what circumstances would a fluid other than air be used?

Answer 707, 1414 cm^2; 2:1, 0.629; 6117, 4205 kW.

23 A wedge aerofoil is shown in Fig. 3.28. The free stream Mach number = 2.0.

Calculate the lift and drag coefficients at an incidence of
(a) zero,
(b) +7°.

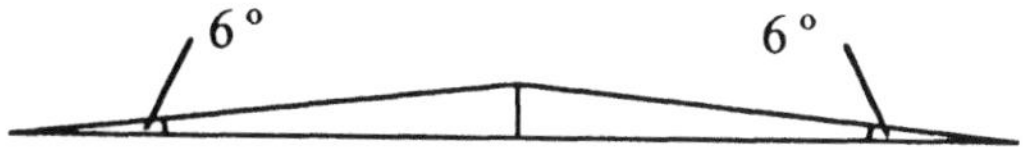

Figure 3.28

Answer (a) 0.017, 0.018
(b) 0.263, 0.042.

24 A double wedge aerofoil is shown in Fig. 3.29. Calculate the lift and drag coefficients. Compare the values with those obtained by linearised flow theory.

Would the coefficients be zero at zero incidence? If not determine their values.

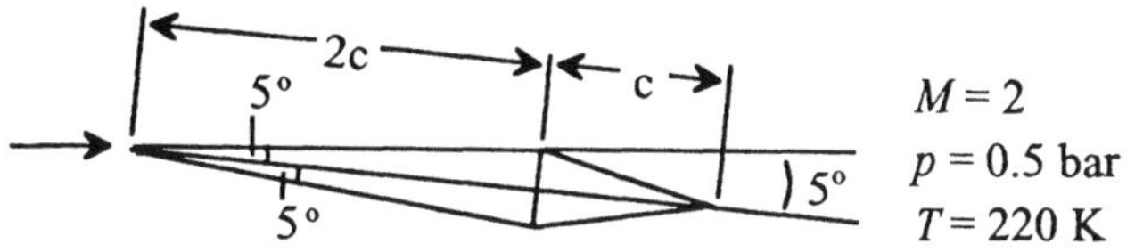

Figure 3.29

Answer 0.140, 0.053. 0.202, 0.018.

4

Hydrodynamics: two-dimensional, incompressible inviscid fluid flow

Hydrodynamics is the name given to the study of the behaviour of an ideal fluid, that is incompressible and inviscid (zero viscosity). The flow analysis determines flow patterns which are a good approximation to real fluid flow outside the boundary layer.

A summary of the terms used is given in the following text:

Basic terms

A pathline is the locus of the position of *a* particle, at successive intervals of time. A streakline (or filament line) is a line which gives an instantaneous picture of the positions of all particles passing through *a* particular point. Both of these can be observed, by the naked eye, using flow visualisation methods. A streamline is an imaginary curve in the fluid flow such that the velocity of every particle along the streamline is tangential to the streamline at a particular instant in time. It follows that there cannot be fluid flow across a streamline: only between streamlines. Also it follows that a solid boundary can be taken as a streamline. An important point (especially in visualisation techniques) is that if the flow is steady (no variation with time) the pathlines and streamlines are identical.

Stream and potential functions

Considering a flow pattern (Fig.4.1), the flow between two streamlines C_1 and C_2, say is $Q = \mathbf{v}\ ds$. The *stream function* ψ is defined in the following manner: if the equations of the streamlines C_1 and C_2 are $\psi = a$, $\psi = b$ then the flow between them is $\psi(b) - \psi(a) = d\psi$.

The fluid velocity $\mathbf{v}$ can be expressed in terms of velocity component u, v in the x, y directions respectively. Hence

$$\text{flow } d\psi = u\,dy - v\,dx$$

The total differential can be expressed in terms of the partial derivatives:

$$d\psi = \frac{\partial\psi}{\partial x}dx + \frac{\partial\psi}{\partial y}dy$$

Equating the two equations expressions' gives the important relationship between the stream function and velocity component:

$$u = \frac{\partial\psi}{\partial y}, \quad v = -\frac{\partial\psi}{\partial x}$$

It is sometimes convenient to employ polar coordinates rather than Cartesian coordinates. In this case, as shown in Fig. 4.2:

$$d\psi = v_r.r\,d\theta - v_\theta.dr$$

and $$d\psi = \frac{\partial\psi}{dr}dr + \frac{\partial\psi}{\partial\theta}d\theta$$

giving $v_r = \frac{1}{r}\frac{\partial \psi}{\partial x}, \quad v_\theta = -\frac{\partial \psi}{\partial r}$

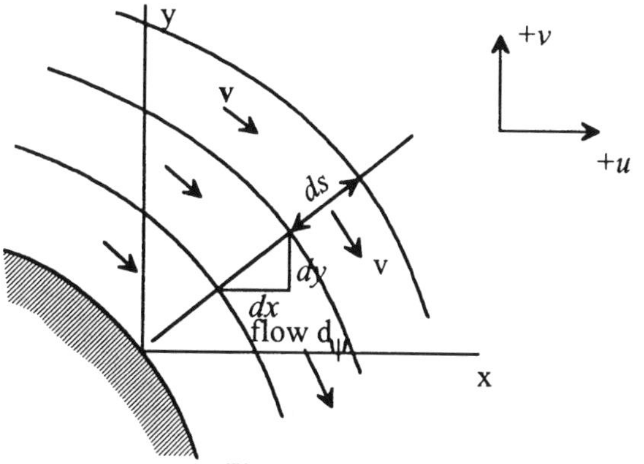

Figure 4.1

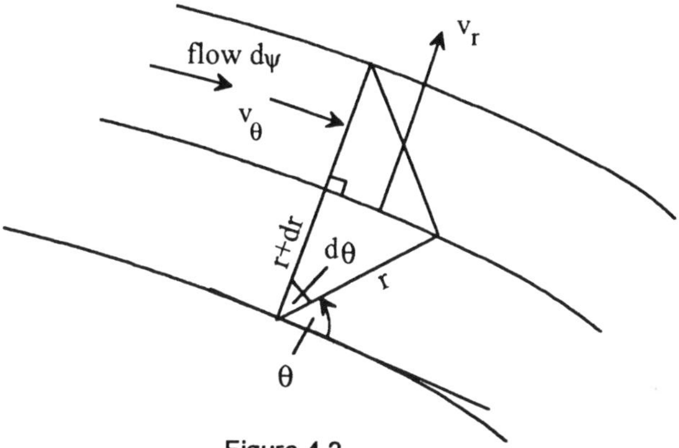

Figure 4.2

Irrotational flow: circulation and vorticity

The velocity potential function ϕ is defined in terms of the velocity component along the streamline, v_s, and the line integral (i.e. along the streamline) as shown in Fig. 4.3.

$$\phi = \int_A^B v_s \, ds$$

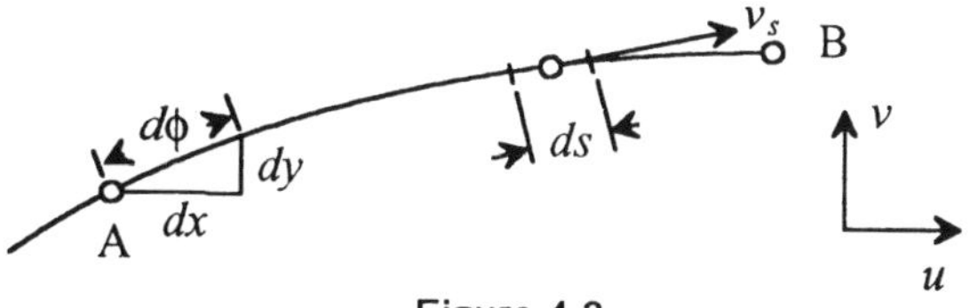

Figure 4.3

If the potential function ϕ is independent of the path AB the flow is termed *irrotational*. The velocity components u, v and potential function are related by the equation:

$$u = \frac{\partial \phi}{\partial x}, \quad v = \frac{\partial \phi}{\partial y}$$

or

$$v_r = \frac{\partial \phi}{\partial r}, \quad v_\theta = \frac{1}{r}\frac{\partial \phi}{\partial \theta}$$

The continuity equation (1.6) is

$$\frac{\partial u}{\partial x} + \frac{\partial v}{\partial y} = 0$$

or $$\frac{\partial v_r}{\partial r} + \frac{v_r}{r} + \frac{1}{r}\frac{\partial v_\theta}{\partial \theta} = 0$$

and substituting for u, v in terms of ϕ gives

$$\frac{\partial^2 \phi}{\partial x^2} + \frac{\partial^2 \phi}{\partial y^2} = 0$$

This is known as the *Laplace* equation.

The flow of a fluid may be *rotational*, where rotation of a fluid element is superimposed on the linear motion of the element. The flow paths in each case are illustrated in Fig.4.4.

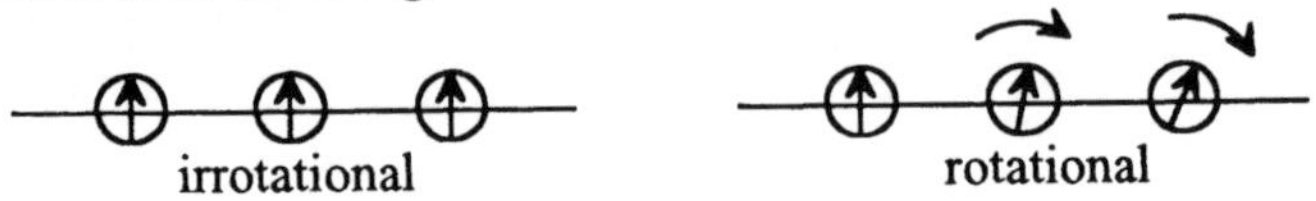

Figure 4.4

Rotational flow is characterised by the use of the term *verticity* ζ given by the equations

$$\zeta = \frac{\partial v}{\partial x} - \frac{\partial u}{\partial y}$$

$$\zeta = \frac{\partial v_\theta}{\partial r} + \frac{v_\theta}{r} - \frac{1}{r}\frac{\partial v_r}{\partial \theta}$$

The *circulation* Γ is defined in terms of the velocity tangential to the streamline,

$$\Gamma = \oint v_s ds$$

and relates to the flow along a line forming a *closed* circuit. The anti-clockwise direction is taken as positive.

The circulation and vorticity are related. Thus considering a small circuit which encloses an area δA, around which the circulation is $\delta\Gamma$, the value of

$$\frac{\delta \Gamma}{\delta A} \text{ as } \delta A \to 0 \text{ is the vorticity } \zeta$$

It is a measure of the spin, or rotation; which varies with position (unlike a solid body).

Also $\nabla^2\psi = -\zeta$, where ∇^2 (Laplacian operator) $= \frac{\partial^2}{\partial x^2} + \frac{\partial^2}{\partial y^2}$.

The vorticity is further related to the stagnation pressure p_o. Thus *across* streamlines

$$\frac{\partial p_0}{\partial n} = \rho\zeta v$$

where n is the direction *normal* to the local streamline. In irrotational flow the vorticity ζ is zero, the stagnation pressure is constant, and

$$\nabla^2\psi = \nabla^2\phi = 0.$$

The analysis of fluid flow is considerably enhanced by the use of complex functions; or functions of the complex variable

$$z = x + iy = r\exp(i\theta)$$

It should be noted that $i = \sqrt{-1}$ is used in this text rather than j (as in electrical field theory).

$$x = r\cos\theta, \qquad y = r\sin\theta,$$

$$r = \sqrt{x^2 + y^2} = \text{modulus of } z \text{ denoted by } |z|$$

$$\theta = \text{argument of } z \text{ denoted by } \arg z = \arctan\frac{y}{x}$$

The complex potential function w is defined as

$$w = \phi \text{ , where } \phi, \psi \text{ are functions of the variable } z.$$

Hence w is a function of z, or $w = f(z)$. The stream and potential functions are related to the velocity components u, v. Thus

$$\frac{dw}{dz}\left(\text{or } f'(z)\right) = u - iv$$

$$\left|\frac{dw}{dz}\right| = \sqrt{u^2 + v^2} = \mathbf{v}$$

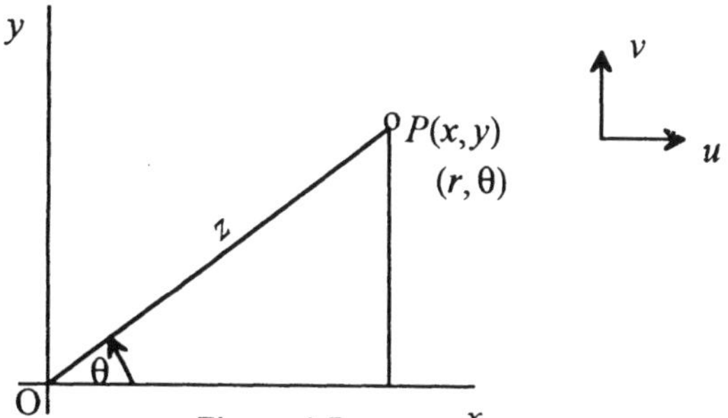

Figure 4.5

Elementary functions

The functions for the elementary flows are shown in the following table, and the corresponding flow nets in Fig. 4.6.

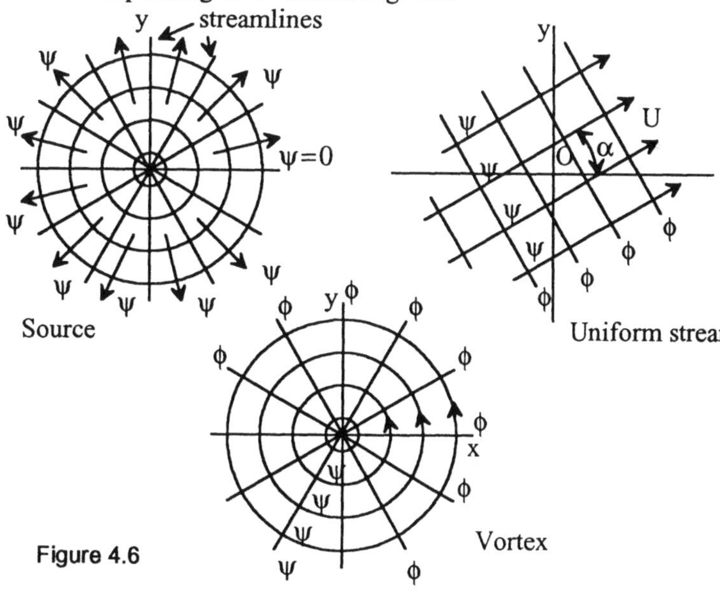

Figure 4.6

flow	stream function	potential function	complex potential function
uniform stream velocity U	$\psi = U(y\cos\alpha - x\sin\alpha)$	$\phi = U(x\cos\alpha + y\sin\alpha)$	$w = Uz\exp(i\alpha)$

Source, strength m $\quad \psi = \dfrac{m\theta}{2\pi} \qquad \phi = \dfrac{m}{2\pi}\ln r \qquad w = \dfrac{m}{2\pi}\ln z$

Vortex, strength Γ, $\quad \psi = -\dfrac{\Gamma}{2\pi}\ln\dfrac{r}{a}, \quad \phi = -\dfrac{\Gamma\theta}{2\pi}, \quad w = -\dfrac{i\Gamma}{2\pi}\ln\dfrac{z}{a}$

Principle of superposition

An important principle in the building up of flow patterns is that of superposition, namely that the stream and potential functions of the vector sum of several flows is equal to the sum of the separate functions.

The use of this principle and the fact that flow cannot take place across a streamline enables the flow patterns to be determined in a wide variety of situations, such as the flow over an aerofoil, over a bluff body, etc.

Conformal transforms

An area, or region, in the z-plane can be mapped into an area in another plane (the ζ-plane say) by a transform. If $\zeta = \xi + i\eta$ the transform is determined by relationships between ξ, η and x,y: thus

functions $\xi = \xi(x,y), \; \eta = \eta(x,y)$

set up a correspondence between points in the two planes. A transform in which the angles between corresponding lines are the same is termed conformal, although the linear scale is different.

The use of conformal transforms is a useful tool in the study of flow patterns. Some widely used transforms include:

(a) Bilinear (Möbius) $\quad \zeta = \dfrac{az + b}{cz + d} \quad (ad \neq bc)$

(b) Joukowsky $\quad \zeta = z + \dfrac{a^2}{z}$

4.1 Stream and potential functions

(a) The velocity components in a fluid flow are given by

$$u = x - 4y, \quad v = -4x - y$$

Show that the continuity equation is satisfied and determine the stream function. Is the flow irrotational? If it is determine the potential function.

(b) The complex potential function for a certain flow is given by

$$w = 5z \exp\left(\frac{i\pi}{3}\right)$$

Sketch the streamlines and equipotential lines

Solution. (a) The continuity equation is

$$\frac{\partial u}{\partial x} + \frac{\partial v}{\partial y} = 0.$$

In this problem $\dfrac{\partial u}{\partial x} = 1, \quad \dfrac{\partial v}{\partial y} = -1$

and the continuity equation is therefore satisfied. This condition is, of course, essential for the flow to be possible without fluid addition or extraction.

The stream function can be determined from the relationships

$$u = \frac{\partial \psi}{\partial y}, \quad v = -\frac{\partial \psi}{\partial x}$$

Thus $\dfrac{\partial \psi}{\partial y} = x - 4y$

and integrating $\psi = xy - 2y^2 + f(x)$

and $\dfrac{\partial\psi}{\partial x} = 4x + y, \quad \psi = 2x^2 + xy + f(y)$

Note. The integration requires functions of x, and y, respectively since the differentials are *partial* with respect to y, x respectively.

Thus $\dfrac{\partial f(x)}{\partial y} = 0, \quad \dfrac{\partial f(y)}{\partial x} = 0$ for *any* function f.

Combining the two integrated equations gives

$$\boldsymbol{\psi = xy - 2y^2 + 2x^2}$$

The flow is irrotational if the vorticity ζ is zero, or consequently the stream function satisfies the Laplace equation $\nabla^2\psi = 0$.

Now $\nabla^2\psi = \dfrac{\partial^2\psi}{\partial x^2} + \dfrac{\partial^2\psi}{\partial y^2} = \dfrac{\partial}{\partial x}(y + 4x) + \dfrac{\partial}{\partial y}(x - 4y) = 4 - 4 = 0$

and hence the flow is irrotational.

Alternatively the vorticity is

$$\zeta = \frac{\partial v}{\partial x} - \frac{\partial u}{\partial y} = (-4) - (-4) = 0$$

Since the flow is irrotational the potential function ϕ has a *single* value, or depends on the position of the final point *only*.

Now $u = \dfrac{\partial\phi}{\partial x}, \quad v = \dfrac{\partial\phi}{\partial y}$

and integrating as before,

$$\frac{\partial\phi}{\partial x} = x - 4y \qquad \phi = \frac{1}{2}x^2 - 4xy + f(y)$$

$$\frac{\partial\phi}{\partial y} = -4x - y \qquad \phi = -4xy - \frac{1}{2}y^2 + f(x)$$

giving $\boldsymbol{\phi = \frac{1}{2}x^2 - \frac{1}{2}y^2 - 4xy}$

The streamlines and equipotential lines are shown in Fig. 4.7.

(b) The complex potential function $w = \phi + i\psi$ so that the potential and stream functions can be determined by equating the real and imaginary parts of w, respectively.

$$w = 5z\exp\left(\frac{i\pi}{3}\right)$$

The function $\exp(i\alpha)$ can be expressed in the form

$$\exp(i\alpha) = \cos\alpha + i\sin\alpha$$

hence $w = 5(x + iy)\exp(i\alpha) = 5(x + iy)(\cos\alpha + i\sin\alpha)$

$= 5(x\cos\alpha + y\sin\alpha) + 5i(y\cos\alpha + x\sin\alpha)$

giving $\boldsymbol{\phi = 5(x\cos\alpha + y\sin\alpha)}, \qquad \psi = 5(y\cos\alpha - x\sin\alpha)$

Note. $i^2 = -1$

The streamlines and equipotential lines are shown in Fig. 4.7.

4.2 Combination of sources

Explain what is meant by a source, and derive expressions for the stream and potential functions.

Two sources, each of strength $2\pi m$, are situated at the points (a, 0), (-a, 0). Sketch the streamlines for the combined flow, showing the position of any stagnation points (if any).

Determine the velocity at the points (0, a).

Solution. A *source* is a concept in fluid flow, where the fluid is considered to appear at a point and spread uniformly in all directions over the two-dimensional plane. The converse is a *sink*, where the fluid disappears.

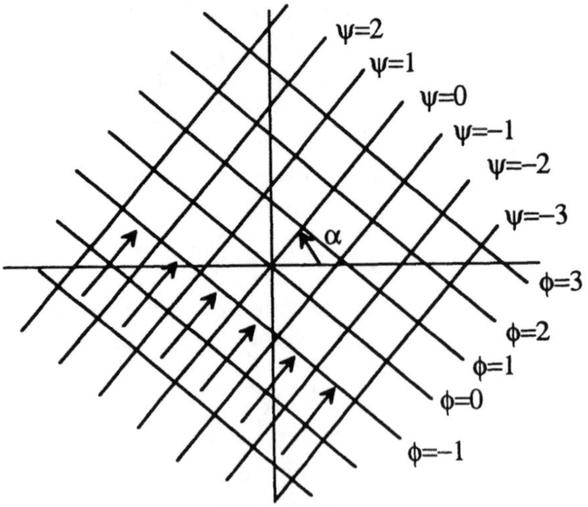

Figure 4.7

Let the quantity of flow from the source be m (m^3/s per m width normal to the x-y plane). Then as the flow is uniformly distributed the flow between streamlines OA and OB (see Fig.4.8) is

$$\frac{\theta}{2\pi}(m)$$

and taking the positive x-axis as the zero streamline $\psi = 0$, the streamline OB is

$$\psi = \frac{m\theta}{2\pi}$$

The equation of any streamline is therefore

$$\Psi = \frac{m\theta}{2\pi}$$

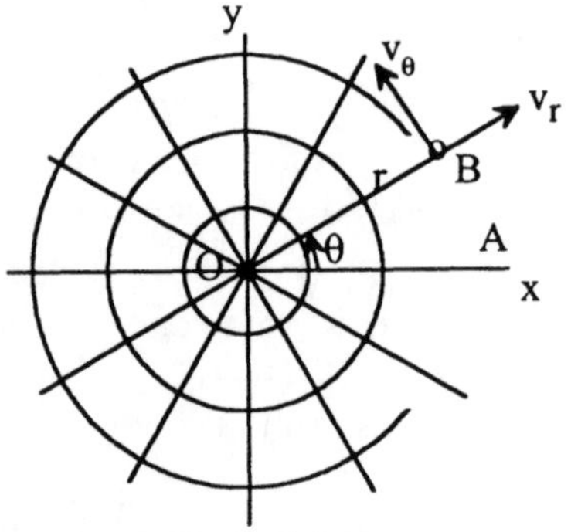

Figure 4.8

The velocity components at point B are

$$v_r = \frac{1}{r}\frac{\partial\psi}{\partial\theta} = \frac{1}{r}\left(\frac{m}{2\pi}\right) = \frac{m}{2\pi r}$$

$$v_\theta = -\frac{\partial\psi}{\partial r} = 0$$

Hence, as expected, the flow is in a radial direction only with no transverse component.

Also $v_r = \frac{\partial\phi}{\partial r}$, $\quad v_\theta = \frac{1}{r}\frac{\partial\phi}{\partial\theta}$

hence $\frac{m}{2\pi r} = \frac{\partial\phi}{\partial\theta}$ and $\phi = \frac{m}{2\pi}\ln r + f(\theta)$, $O = \frac{1}{r}\frac{\partial\phi}{\partial\theta}$ and $\phi = f(r)$

giving $\boldsymbol{\phi = \frac{m}{2\pi}\ln r}$

The complex potential function is

$$w = \phi + i\psi = \frac{m}{2\pi}\ln r + \frac{im\theta}{2\pi r} = \frac{\mathbf{m}}{\mathbf{2\pi}}\ln \mathbf{z}$$

Since $z = x + iy = r\exp(i\theta) = r(\cos\theta + i\sin\theta)$, $\quad \ln z = \ln r + i\theta$

Note. In the case of a sink m is replaced by $-m$. The value of m is termed the *strength* of the source (or sink).

The combined flow can be determined by use of the principle of superposition. This can be done graphically (Fig.4.9), by plotting the individual streamlines for each source and then adding them (for two sources).

The flow pattern is symmetrical about the x-axis, and about the y-axis. The stagnation point is clearly at the origin O ($x = 0, y = 0$).

A point of interest is that, since no flow can cross a streamline, the y-axis could be replaced by a surface. The flow pattern on either side of the axis would then correspond to the flow from a source at a distance a from the wall.

The complex potential function of the combined flow is equal to the sum of the combined functions of the sources. They are situated at the points $z = a$, $x = -a$ so that

$$w = \frac{2\pi m}{2\pi}\ln(z - a) + \frac{2\pi m}{2\pi}\ln(z + a) = m\ln(z^2 - a^2)$$

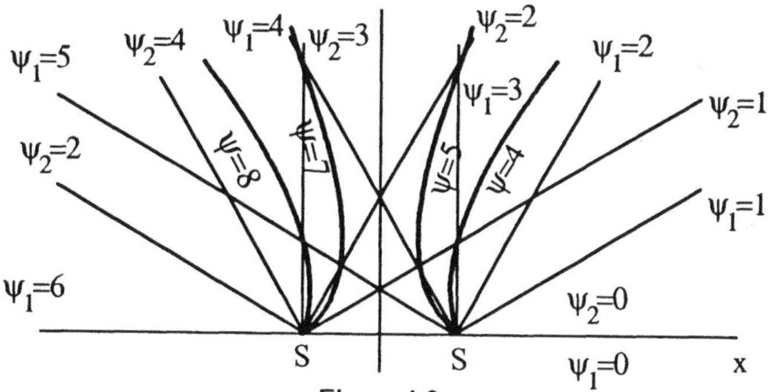

Figure 4.9

At the point (0, a) (Fig. 4.10):

$$r_1 = \sqrt{2a^2} = r_2$$

$$v_{r_1} = \frac{2\pi m}{2\pi a\sqrt{2}} = \frac{m}{a\sqrt{2}}, \qquad v_{r_2} = \frac{m}{a\sqrt{2}}$$

and $\quad v_r = \sqrt{v_{r_1}^2 + v_{r_2}^2} = \frac{m}{a}, \qquad v_\theta = 0$

Alternatively the complex potential function can be used as follows:

$$w = m\ln(z^2 - a^2)$$

$$\frac{dw}{dz} = m\frac{2z}{z^2 - a^2} = u - iv$$

and at $z = ia$, $\quad u - iv = \dfrac{2mia}{-a^2 - a^2} = -\dfrac{mi}{a}$

giving $u = 0, v = \dfrac{m}{a}$

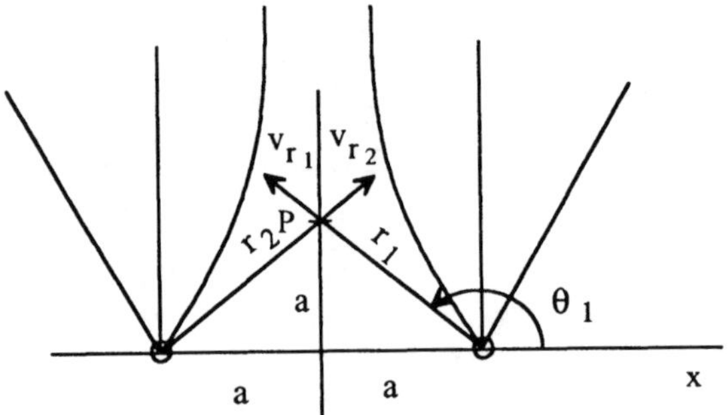

Figure 4.10

4.3 Half body

A uniform stream flows at a velocity U in the direction of the negative x-axis. Show how the combination of the stream width and source can give the flow pattern around a half body. Determine the position of the stagnation points, and the pressure distribution on the body.

Solution. The position x-axis is taken as the zero streamline $\psi = 0$. The streamlines of the uniform stream are lines parallel to the x-axis, and are numbered $\psi_1 = 0, 1, 2, 3, \ldots\ldots$ in Fig.4.11.

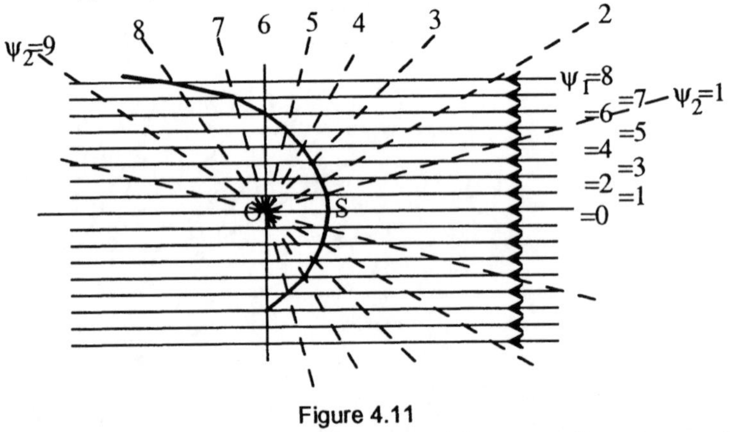

Figure 4.11

A source is added at the origin (0, 0), and the streamlines are numbered, as shown, $\psi_2 = 0, 1, 2, 3, \ldots$. The uniform flow is in the direction of the negative x-axis, so that the streamlines of the combined flow are the curves passing through points of equal value $\psi_1 - \psi_2$.

The zero streamline $\psi = 0$ can be replaced by a surface: the streamlines to the right then give the flow pattern around a solid body of the shape shown. It is known as a half body, extending continuously along the negative x-axis.

The stream functions are:

uniform stream $\psi_1 = U(y\cos\pi - x\sin\pi) = -Uy = -Ur\sin\theta$

source at (0, 0) $\qquad \psi_2 = \dfrac{m\theta}{2\pi}$

combined flow $\qquad \psi = \dfrac{m\theta}{2\pi} - Ur\sin\theta$

The zero streamline is therefore

$$\frac{m\theta}{2\pi} = Ur\sin\theta \qquad \text{or} \qquad r = \frac{m\theta}{2\pi U\sin\theta}$$

The width of the body is

$$2\lim_{\theta\to\pi} y = 2\lim_{\theta\to\pi}\left(\frac{m\theta}{2\pi U}\right) = \frac{m}{U}$$

The velocity components can be determined from the stream function

$$v_r = \frac{1}{r}\frac{\partial\psi}{\partial\theta} = \frac{1}{r}\left(\frac{m}{2\pi} - Ur\cos\theta\right)$$

$$v_\theta = -\frac{\partial\psi}{\partial r} = -(-U\sin\theta)$$

Now the stagnation point S is situated on the x-axis, since the flow is symmetrical about the axis. Further $v_r = v_\theta = 0$. hence $\theta = 0$ and

$$r = \frac{m}{2\pi U} \qquad \text{giving point S.}$$

The pressure distribution is determined from the Bernoulli equation. For two-dimensional, incompressible, inviscid flow

$$p_o\,(\text{stagnation pressure}) = p + \tfrac{1}{2}\rho \mathbf{v}^2 = \text{constant}$$

Considering the *half-body surface* ($\psi = 0$), given by the equation

$$r = \frac{m\theta}{2\pi U\sin\theta}$$

the velocity components at any point are

$$v_r = \frac{m}{2\pi r} - U\cos\theta, \qquad v_\theta = U\sin\theta$$

and substituting for the radius vector, r, gives

$$v_r = \frac{m}{2\pi}\cdot\frac{2\pi U\sin\theta}{m\theta} - U\cos\theta = U\left(\frac{\sin\theta}{\theta}\right) - u\cos\theta$$

Hence $\mathbf{v}^2 = v_r^2 + v_\theta^2 = U^2\left(\dfrac{\sin^2\theta}{\theta^2} - \dfrac{2\sin\theta\cos\theta}{\theta} + \cos^2\theta\right)$

$$= U^2\left(1 - \frac{\sin 2\theta}{\theta} + \left(\frac{\sin\theta}{\theta}\right)^2\right)$$

Applying the Bernoulli equation to the point and a point well upstream of the body (free or undisturbed stream), where the pressure is p_∞,

$$p_o = p_\infty + \tfrac{1}{2}\rho U^2 = p + \tfrac{1}{2}\rho\mathbf{v}^2$$

giving $p - p_\infty = \dfrac{1}{2}\rho U^2\left(\dfrac{\sin 2\theta}{\theta} - \left(\dfrac{\sin\theta}{\theta}\right)^2\right)$

At the stagnation point $\theta = 0$, $p_s = p_\infty + \tfrac{1}{2}\rho U^2$

On the body surface $p = p_\infty$

when $\dfrac{\sin 2\theta}{\theta} = \left(\dfrac{\sin\theta}{\theta}\right)^2$,

$$2\sin\theta\cos\theta = \frac{\sin^2\theta}{\theta}$$

or $\qquad \tan\theta = 2\theta$ (at which $\theta = 66.8°$ approx.)

This is marked as point A in Fig. 4.12. Between A and S, $p > p_\infty$ and from A onwards, $p < p_\infty$.

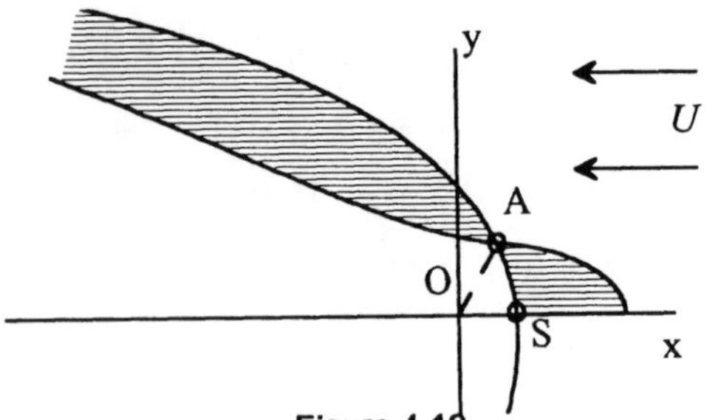

Figure 4.12

4.4 Doublet (Dipole)

> Define a doublet, and derive an expression for the complex potential function. Sketch the streamlines for a doublet.
>
> A doublet, strength $2\pi\mu$, is combined with a uniform stream of velocity U. Show how the combined flow pattern can be used to determine the pressure distribution on a cylinder in a uniform stream.

Solution. Consider the combination of a source, strength m, at a point (a, 0) with a sink of strength m at a point (-a, 0).

The complex potential functions are

source, at $z = a$ $w = \frac{m}{2\pi} \ln(z - a)$

sink, at $z = -a$ $w = -\frac{m}{2\pi} \ln(z + a)$

Combination $w = \frac{m}{2\pi} \ln(z - a) - \frac{m}{2\pi} \ln(z + a) = -\frac{m}{2\pi} \ln \frac{z + a}{z - a}$

The flow pattern is shown in Fig.4.13, and bears some resemblance to the magnetic field lines of force between the N and S poles.

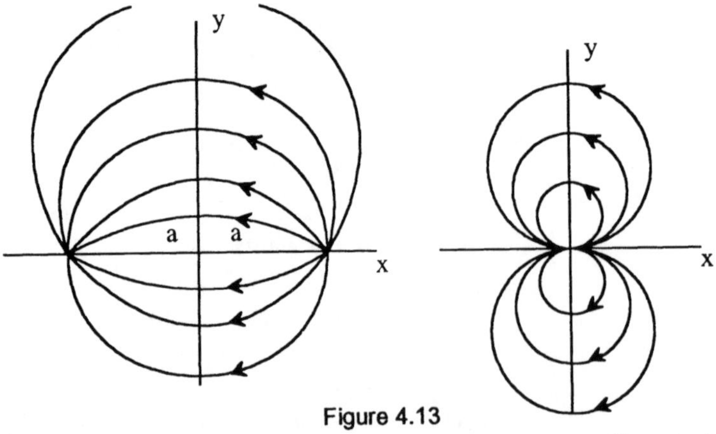

Figure 4.13

Suppose the source and sink approach each other, eventually coinciding at the origin. Clearly without any conditions the result would be a total zero. However, if the condition that $2ma$ = constant is imposed a rather different situation arises. In this case

$$w = \lim_{a \to 0} \left(-\frac{m}{2\pi} \ln \frac{z + a}{z - a} \right) \qquad \text{provided } 2ma = \mu, \text{ say}$$

$$= \lim \left(-\frac{m}{2\pi} \ln \left(1 + \frac{2a}{z - a} \right) \right)$$

$$= \lim\left(-\frac{m}{2\pi}\left(\frac{2a}{z-a} - \frac{1}{2}\left(\frac{2a}{z-a}\right)^2 + \frac{1}{3}\left(\frac{2a}{z-a}\right)^2 - \ldots\ldots\right)\right)$$

$$= -\frac{1}{2\pi}.\lim\left(\frac{\mu}{z-a} - \frac{\mu a}{(z-a)^2} + \frac{4\mu a^2}{3(z-a)^3} - \ldots\ldots\right)$$

$$w = -\frac{1}{2\pi}.\frac{\mu}{z}$$

This limiting case is known as a *doublet* or dipole.

Note. The mathematical result for the expansion of a logarithmic term as an infinite series is used:

$$\ln(1+x) = x - \frac{1}{2}x^2 + \frac{1}{3}x^3 - \ldots$$

The stream function can be obtained as follows:

$$w = \phi + i\psi = -\frac{\mu}{2\pi z} = -\frac{\mu}{2\pi}.\frac{1}{x+iy} = -\frac{\mu}{2\pi}.\frac{x-iy}{x+iy}$$

hence $\psi = -\frac{\mu}{2\pi}.\frac{y}{x^2+y^2}$

The streamlines $\psi = K$ are the curves

$$x^2 + y^2 = \left(\frac{\mu}{2\pi K}\right)y.$$

These are circles, centred at the point $\left(0, \frac{\mu}{4\pi K}\right)$ and radius $\frac{\mu}{4\pi K}$ and are shown in Fig.4.13. In polar coordinates $x = r\cos\theta$, $y r\sin\theta$ the stream function is

$$\psi = \frac{\mu}{2\pi r}\sin\theta.$$

The doublet is taken with its axis along the x-axis, and the uniform stream parallel to the x-axis (Fig. 4.14.). For convenience polar coordinates (r,θ) will be used. The stream functions are

doublet, at $z = 0$	$\psi = \frac{2\pi\mu}{2\pi r}.\sin\theta$
stream	$\psi = -Uy = -Ur\sin\theta$
Combination	$\psi = \left(\frac{\mu}{r} - Ur\right)\sin\theta$

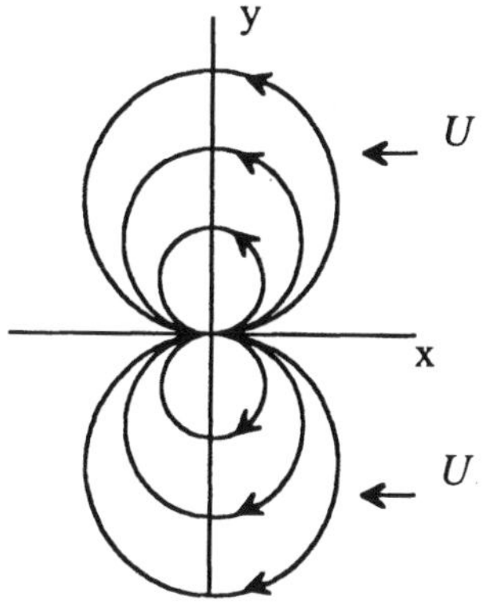

Figure 4.14

The zero streamline is therefore

$$\frac{\mu}{r} = Ur, \qquad \sin\theta = 0$$

The first value, $r^2 = Ur$

corresponds to a *circle* (in the x-y plane) or circular cylinder, of radius

$$a = \sqrt{\frac{\mu}{U}}$$

The second value $\theta = 0$ or π corresponds to the x-axis. The combined flow pattern therefore gives the flow around a circular cylinder.

Introducing the cylinder radius a

$$\psi = \left(\frac{Ua^2}{r} - Ur\right)\sin\theta = \left(\frac{a^2}{r} - r\right)U\sin\theta$$

The velocity distribution, and hence the pressure distribution, on the surface of the cylinder can now be obtained.

The velocity components at any point are

$$v_r = \frac{1}{r}\frac{\partial \psi}{\partial \theta} = \frac{1}{r}\left(\frac{a^2}{r} - r\right)U\cos\theta$$

$$v_\theta = -\frac{\partial \psi}{\partial r} = -\left(-\frac{a^2}{r^2} - 1\right)U\sin\theta$$

On the cylinder surface, $r = a$, these become

$$v_r = 0, \qquad v_\theta = 2U\sin\theta$$

Note. It is to be expected that the radial component of the velocity is zero!

The Bernoulli equation gives

$$p_\infty + \tfrac{1}{2}\rho U^2 = p + \tfrac{1}{2}\rho v^2, \qquad p_\infty - p = \tfrac{1}{2}\rho(v_r^2 + v_\theta^2 - U^2)$$

or $\quad p - p_\infty = \tfrac{1}{2}\rho U^2(1 - 4\sin^2\theta)$

The stagnation points are at $v_\theta = 0$, and therefore at $\theta = 0$, or π: the stagnation pressure is $p_\infty + \tfrac{1}{2}\rho U^2$. The local pressure $= p_\infty$ (free stream pressure) at $\sin\theta = \pm\tfrac{1}{2}$, or $\theta = 30°, 150°$. The minimum local pressure occurs at $\theta = 90°$ and is $p = p_\infty - \tfrac{3}{2}\rho U^2$ (Fig. 4.15).

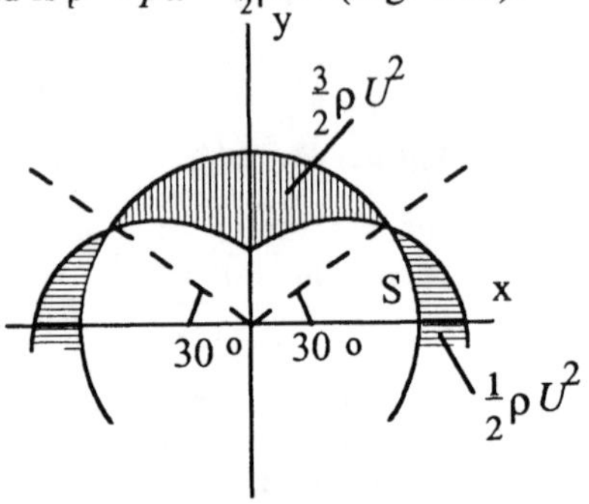

Figure 4.15

4.5 Vortex

> Explain what is meant by a free vortex, and show that the flow is irrotational with a constant circulation. Describe the radial pressure gradient.
>
> Outline the difference between a free and a forced vortex, and discuss the practical applications.
>
> Discuss a free vortex and source combination.

Solution

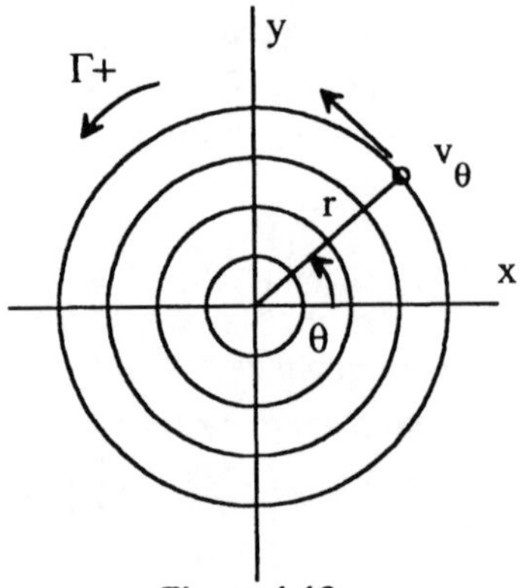

Figure 4.16

A free vortex is a flow in which the fluid particles rotate, in circular paths, about a central point. The 'particles' do not rotate about the particle centre however. The streamlines are concentric circles so that the radial velocity component is zero. The transverse (and tangential) velocity component is constant, and varies inversely with the radius.

Let $v_\theta = \dfrac{k}{2\pi r}$ where k is a constant.

Then the circulation Γ round a streamline, radius r (Fig. 4.16), is

$$\Gamma = \int v_\theta \, ds = \int_0^{2\pi} \frac{k}{2\pi r} r \, d\theta = \frac{k}{2\pi}(2\pi) = k$$

The circulation is therefore constant. The stream function follows from the equation

$$v_\theta = -\frac{\partial \psi}{\partial r}$$

Thus $\psi = -\dfrac{\Gamma}{2\pi}\displaystyle\int \frac{dr}{r} = -\dfrac{\Gamma}{2\pi}\ln r$

The vorticity is given by

$$\zeta = \frac{\partial v_\theta}{\partial r} + \frac{v_\theta}{r} - \frac{1}{r}\frac{\partial v_r}{\partial \theta} = -\frac{\Gamma}{2\pi r^2} + \frac{\Gamma}{2\pi r^2} - 0 = 0$$

and the flow is therefore irrotational.

A free vortex is similar to the natural phenomena of cyclones, tornados, whirlpools, and the discharge of water through a plug hole. In the last situation the direction of rotation depends mainly upon the nature of any initial disturbances rather than whether it is in the northern or southern hemispheres. However cyclones, etc. are affected by Coriolis forces and do tend to rotate in opposite directions in the two hemispheres.

In all these natural vortices a core is usually observed, and is to be expected from an analysis of the velocity and pressure distribution.

$$v_\theta = \frac{\Gamma}{2\pi r} \quad \text{or} \quad r v_\theta = \frac{\Gamma}{2\pi} = \text{constant}$$

Thus the tangential (or swirl) velocity increases as the radius decreases, and approaches an infinite value as the radius approaches zero. Theoretically $v_\infty = \infty$ at $r = 0$, and this point (the centre of the vortex) is then termed a *singularity* in the flow.

In practice a *core* is formed around the centre. As the velocity increases the pressure decreases, and is a minimum in this central core. It is this suction in the core of a tornado that is the primary cause of damage to buildings. Similarly in a whirlpool an air core is formed in the water.

The Bernoulli equation is

$$p_o = p + \tfrac{1}{2}\rho v^2 = p + \tfrac{1}{2}\rho v_\theta^2 = \text{constant}$$

and $$\frac{dp}{dr} = -\rho v_\theta \frac{dv_\theta}{dr} = -\rho v_\theta\left(-\frac{\Gamma}{2\pi r^2}\right) = \rho v_\theta\left(\frac{2\pi r v_\theta}{2\pi r^2}\right)$$

$$\frac{dp}{dr} = \frac{\rho v_\theta^2}{r}$$

A *forced* vortex is one in which the fluid rotates like a solid body, that is

$v_\theta = r\Omega$ where Ω = angular velocity.

It is generated by external forces, as, for example, a centrifugal pump rotor. In this case

$$v_\theta = -\frac{\partial v_\theta}{\partial r}$$

and $\psi = -r^2\Omega$

The flow is rotational since the vorticity is

$$\zeta = \frac{\partial v_\theta}{\partial r} + \frac{v_\theta}{r} = \Omega + \Omega = 2\Omega$$

The pressure gradient is

$$\frac{dp}{dr} = -\rho v_\theta \frac{dv_\theta}{dr} = -\rho v_\theta(\Omega) = -\rho r\Omega^2$$

The tangential velocity increases with the radius, and consequently the pressure decreases in the radial direction. The velocity is zero at the centre of rotation.

A combined (Rankine) vortex can arise in some situations. For example in a centrifugal pump rotor discharging into a fixed volute (or diffuser) casing, the flow in the rotor is akin to a forced vortex and in the volute to a free vortex.

The combination of a source and free vortex gives a *spiral* vortex, and is similar to the flow in a centrifugal machine with the entry flow at the centre (the eye of the machine).

Consider a source, strength m, and a free vortex, strength Γ, centred at the same point (0, 0). Since the origin is a singularity (ie. the stream function is not defined at $r = 0$), assume that the zero streamline is at a radius a. Then for the vortex

$$\psi = -\frac{\Gamma}{2\pi} \ln\frac{r}{a}$$

The stream function of the combined flow is

$$\psi = \frac{m\theta}{2\pi} - \frac{\Gamma}{2\pi} \ln\frac{r}{a}$$

The streamlines ψ = constant, C are then

$$\ln\frac{r}{a} = \frac{2\pi}{\Gamma}\left(\frac{m\theta}{2\pi} - C\right) = \frac{m\theta}{\Gamma} - \frac{2\pi C}{\Gamma}$$

These curves are spirals, as illustrated in Fig. 4.17.

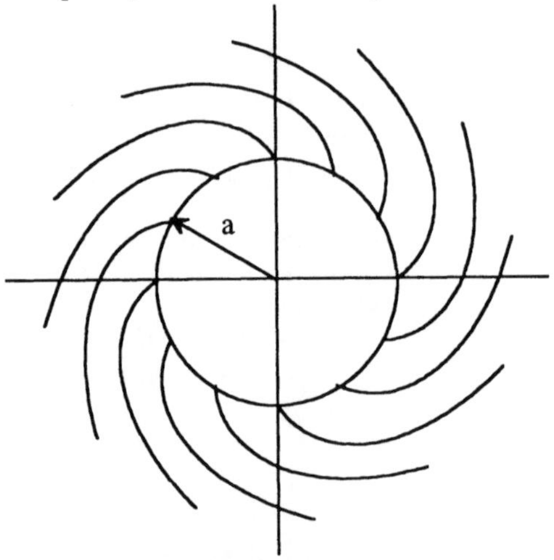

Figure 4.17

4.6 Kutta-Joukowsky law

Show how the combination of a doublet and uniform stream, with a free vortex, can give the pressure distribution on a circular cylinder. Derive a relationship between the lift force on the cylinder and the strength of the vortex.

Solution. The combination of a doublet and a uniform stream has been discussed in Ex.4.4, and the results are used directly.

The addition of a vortex at the origin gives a stream function for the combined flow as

$$\psi = \left(\frac{a^2}{r} - r\right)U\sin\theta + \frac{\Gamma}{2\pi}\ln\frac{r}{a}$$

The circle $r = a$ still corresponds to the zero streamline $\psi = 0$.

The velocity components at any point are

$$v_r = \frac{1}{r}\frac{\partial\psi}{\partial\theta} = \frac{1}{r}\left(\frac{a^2}{r} - r\right)U\cos\theta$$

$$v_\theta = -\frac{\partial\psi}{\partial r} = -\left(-\frac{a^2}{r^2} - 1\right)U\sin\theta + \frac{\Gamma}{2\pi r}$$

and on the surface of the cylinder $r = a$,

$$v_r = 0, \qquad v_\theta = \frac{\Gamma}{2\pi a} + 2U\sin\theta$$

The pressure distribution is given by

$$p - p_\infty = \tfrac{1}{2}\rho(U^2 - v_\theta^2) = \frac{1}{2}\rho U^2\left(1 - \left(\frac{\Gamma}{2\pi aU} + 2\sin\theta\right)^2\right)$$

The stagnation points are at $v_\theta = 0$

$$\sin\theta = -\frac{\Gamma}{4\pi aU}$$

Thus there are two points, S_1, S_2, symmetrically placed about the y-axis (Fig. 4.18): except when $\Gamma = 4\pi aU$, in which case there is one stagnation point at $\theta = 270°$. The lift force, L, is the component of the pressure force on the cylinder, in a direction normal to the free stream. Considering an element ds, the pressure force on the element (relative to the free stream) is $(p - p_\infty)a\,d\theta$.

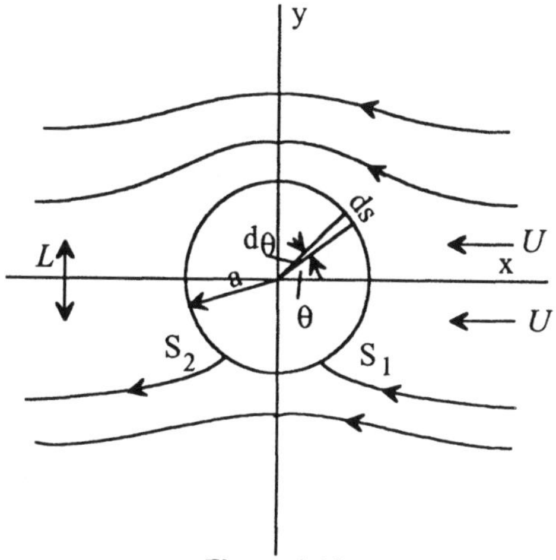

Figure 4.18

The lift force is

$$L = \int_0^{2\pi}(p - p_\infty)a\,d\theta\,\sin\theta = \frac{1}{2}\rho U^2 a\int_0^{2\pi}\left(1 - \left(\frac{\Gamma}{2\pi aU} + 2\sin\theta\right)^2\right)\sin\theta\,d\theta$$

$$= \frac{1}{2}\rho U^2\int_0^{2\pi}\left(\left(1 - \frac{\Gamma}{4\pi^2a^2U^2}\right)\sin\theta - \frac{2\Gamma}{\pi aU}\sin^2\theta - 4\sin^3\theta\right)d\theta$$

$$= \frac{1}{2}\rho a U^2 \left(- \left(1 - \frac{\Gamma}{4\pi^2 a^2 U^2}\right)\cos\theta - \frac{2\Gamma}{2\pi a U}(\theta - \sin\theta\cos\theta) - 4\left(- \cos\theta + \tfrac{1}{3}\cos^3\theta\right)\right)$$

and inserting the limits, 0, 2π

$$L = \frac{1}{2}\rho a U^2\left(0 - \frac{\Gamma}{\pi a U}2\pi\right) = -\rho\Gamma U$$

The lift force is therefore given by the simple expression

$$L = \rho\Gamma U$$

and this result is known as the Kutta-Joukowsky law.

The circulation around the cylinder can be considered as equal to $a\Omega 2\pi a$ (tangential velocity × circumference) when the cylinder is rotating, about its centre, with an angular velocity Ω. The lift force generated, normal to the direction of the free stream, is then

$$L = \rho U 2\pi a^2 = 2\pi\rho a^2 U\Omega$$

This is termed the Magnus effect, and to some extent, explains why a rotating sail ship can be propelled in no wind conditions, or why a spinning ball tends to swerve from a straight line path.

4.7 Use of complex functions

The complex potential function for the flow between two planes inclined at an angle α to each other is $w = az^{\pi/\alpha}$.

Determine the stream and potential functions, and velocity components when

(a) $\alpha = \frac{\pi}{4}$, (b) $\alpha = \frac{\pi}{2}$

Briefly explain the meaning of the terms streamline, equipotential line, flow net.

Solution

(a) $w = az^4$ for $\alpha = \frac{\pi}{4}$, and substituting $z = x + iy$,

$$w = \phi + i\psi = a(x + iy)^4 = a(x^4 + 4ix^3y - 6x^2y^2 - 4ixy^3 + y^4)$$

since $i^2 = -1$, $i^3 = -i$, $i^4 = 1$

Equating the real and imaginary parts on each side,

$$\phi = a(x^4 - 6x^2y^2 + y^4)$$
$$\psi = a(4x^3y - 4xy^3)$$

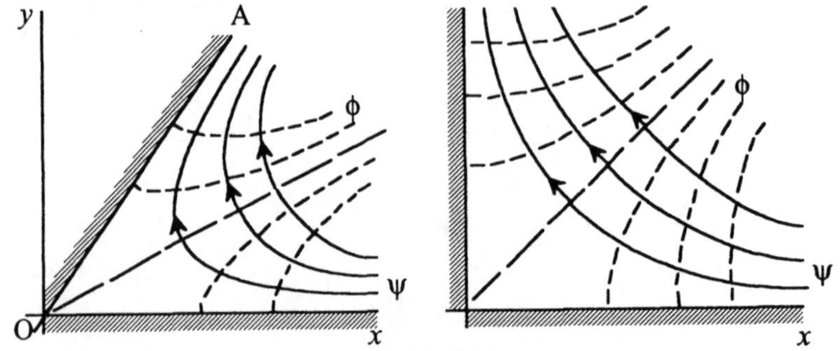

Figure 4.19

The streamlines ψ = constant C, are the curves

$$4axy(x^2 - y^2) = C$$

In particular the zero streamline is $x = 0$, or $y = 0$, or

$$x^2 - y^2 = 0 \text{ (i.e. } y = \pm x).$$

Clearly this corresponds to the planes $y = 0$ and OA (Fig.4.19). The velocity components are

$$u = \frac{\partial \psi}{\partial y} = a(4x^3 - 12xy^2) = 4ax(x^2 - 3y^2)$$

$$v = -\frac{\partial \psi}{\partial x} = -a(12x^2y - 4y^3) = 4ay(y^2 - 3x^2)$$

The stagnation point is at $u = v = 0$, that is $x = 0, y = 0$.

(b) At $\alpha = \frac{\pi}{2}$, $w = az^2$

$$\phi + i\psi = a(x^2 + 2ixy - y^2), \ \phi = a(x^2 - y^2), \ \psi = 2axy$$

The velocity components can be determined from the stream function, or more directly from the complex potential function.

$$\frac{dw}{dz} = u - iv = 2az = 2a(x + iy)$$

and hence $u = 2ax$, $v = -2ay$

A *streamline* is a curve such that the fluid velocity at a point is tangential to the streamline; and the stream function is constant at all the points on the streamline. Thus there cannot be any flow across a streamline, and the flow between any two streamlines is constant and proportional to the distance between them. Hence converging streamlines indicate an increasing velocity.

An *equipotential* line is a line joining points which are at the same value of the potential function. The potential function is a measure of the velocity gradient: a decreasing distance between equipotential lines indicates an increasing velocity.

The equipotential lines are *normal* to the streamlines in an inviscid fluid.

Graphical flow nets

A *flow net* is a plot of the streamlines and equipotential lines. Converging streamlines show an increasing velocity and therefore a decreasing pressure, so that a flow net gives a visual picture of the velocity and pressure variation.

Streamlines can be obtained directly by flow visualisation methods (e.g. the Hele-Shaw table); flow nets can be plotted by electric analogues (e.g. Teledeltos paper) or trial and error graphical methods. At any point the velocity is

$$\frac{\delta \psi}{\delta n} = \frac{\delta \phi}{\delta s}$$

where δn, δs are the spacings along the streamlines and equipotential lines. If the spacings (intervals) are made equal the flow net then consists of approximate squares.

The net is constructed by trial-and-error sketching of the squares between the given boundaries. The equipotential lines (including the boundaries) intersect the streamlines at right angles, and this is an important aid in the method. An example is shown in Fig. 4.20.

A numerical method can be used to obtain more accurate patterns, and is suitable for use in computer graphics. The basis of the method is to assume a network of values of ψ or ϕ, and then adjust them to match the Laplace equation $\nabla^2\psi = \nabla^2\phi = 0$ and the boundary conditions. Thus, considering a square mesh of side a, for values of the stream function at the intersection points 1, 2, 3, 4 the stream function at the centre O

$$\psi_o = \tfrac{1}{4}(\psi_1 + \psi_2 + \psi_3 + \psi_4)$$

The *electrical analogy* uses the analogy between the potential ϕ and the electrical potential V; and the velocity and electric field E. A sheet of conducting material (Teledeltos paper) or a shallow bath of electrolyte is shaped so that its boundary is similar to the desired boundary. A voltage drop is established between the flow entry and exit boundaries: and using a potentiometer probe the potential pattern can be determined which is geometrically similar to the flow pattern. Similarly a voltage drop established between the boundaries enables the streamline pattern to be determined.

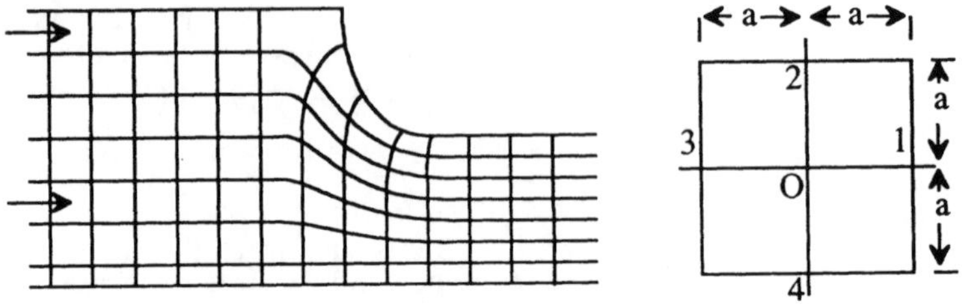

Figure 4.20

4.8 Circulation and vorticity

> Outline the concepts of circulation and vorticity in a fluid. Derive the Cauchy-Riemann conditions for irrotational flow
>
> $$\frac{\partial\psi}{\partial x} = -\frac{\partial\phi}{\partial y},$$
> $$\frac{\partial\psi}{\partial y} = \frac{\partial\phi}{\partial x}$$
>
> The velocity components in a flow field are
>
> $$u = x + y, \qquad v = x^2 - y$$
>
> Calculate the circulation around the square given by the lines
>
> $$x = \pm 1, \qquad y = \pm 1$$

Solution. Consider a fluid element ABCD of side dx, dy (Fig. 4.21). The circulation Γ around the element is the contour (or line) integral

$$\oint v_s\, ds$$

Hence $\Gamma = u\,dx + \left(v + \frac{\partial v}{\partial x}dx\right)dy - \left(u + \frac{\partial u}{\partial v}dy\right)dx - v\,dy$

$$= \left(\frac{\partial v}{\partial x} - \frac{\partial u}{\partial y}\right)dx\,dy$$

taking the anti-clockwise direction as positive.

$$\Gamma = \left(\frac{\partial v}{\partial x} - \frac{\partial u}{\partial y}\right)dA$$

where dA = area of element.

Now the vorticity ζ = circulation/unit area,

hence $\zeta = \frac{\partial v}{\partial x} - \frac{\partial u}{\partial y}$

In irrotational flow the vorticity is zero and hence

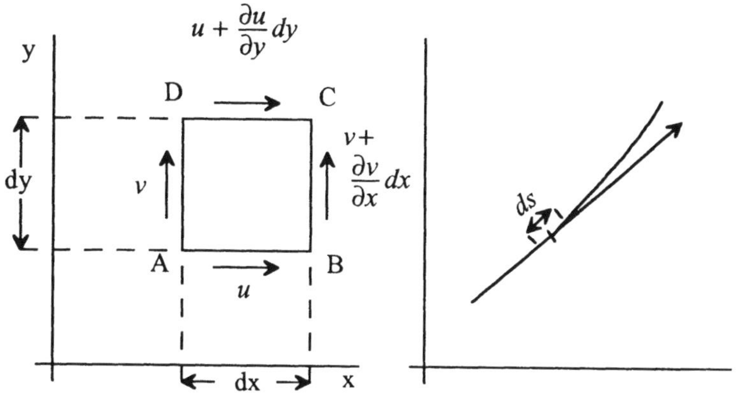

Figure 4.21

$$\frac{\partial v}{\partial x} = \frac{\partial u}{\partial y}$$

Expressing the velocity components in terms of the stream or potential functions leads to the Laplace equation.

The Cauchy-Riemann conditions are a test of irrotational flow; and connect the stream and potential functions. They can be derived from the complex potential function.

$$w = \phi + i\psi$$

$$\frac{dw}{dz} = \frac{d\phi}{dz} + i\frac{d\psi}{dz} = \frac{\partial \phi}{\partial x}\frac{dx}{dz} + \frac{\partial \psi}{\partial x}\frac{dx}{dz}$$

$$= \frac{\partial \phi}{\partial x} + i\frac{\partial \psi}{\partial x} \qquad \left(\text{since } \frac{dz}{dx} = 1\right)$$

or

$$\frac{dw}{dz} = \frac{\partial \phi}{\partial y}\frac{dy}{dz} + i\frac{\partial \psi}{\partial y}\frac{dy}{dz}$$

$$= \frac{1}{i}\frac{\partial \phi}{\partial y} + \frac{\partial \psi}{\partial y} \qquad \left(\text{since } \frac{dz}{dy} = i\right)$$

$$= -i\frac{\partial \phi}{\partial y} + \frac{\partial \psi}{\partial y}$$

Equating the real and imaginary parts gives the stated conditions. Alternatively,

$$u = \frac{\partial \psi}{\partial y}, \qquad v = -\frac{\partial \psi}{\partial x}$$

and for irrotational flow the potential function is defined:

$$u = \frac{\partial \phi}{\partial x}, \qquad v = \frac{\partial \phi}{\partial y}$$

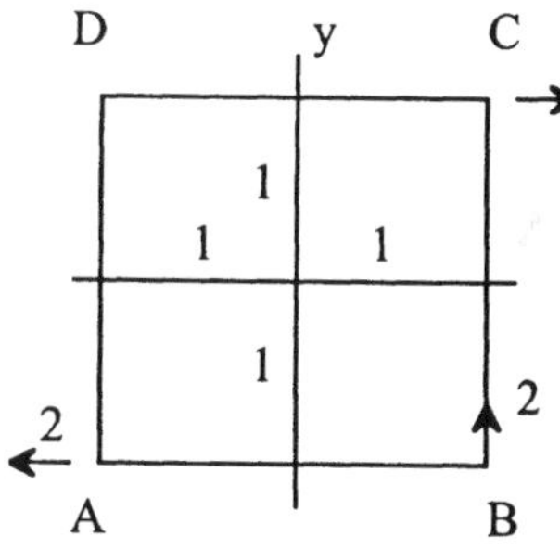

Figure 4.22

Hence the stated conditions are valid.

The circulation around the square ABCD (Fig. 4.22) is calculated by the line integrals. The velocity components at any point are given as

$$u = x + y, \qquad v = x^2 - y$$

Hence the velocity along each side of the square is

AB: $y = -1, \quad u = x - 1, \quad v = x^2 + 1$

BC: $x = 1, \quad u = 1 + y, \quad v = 1 - y$

CD: $y = 1, \quad u = x + 1, \quad v = x^2 - 1$

DA: $x = -1, \quad u = y - 1, \quad v = 1 - y$

The circulation is

$$\Gamma = \int_A^B u\,dx + \int_B^C v\,dy - \int_C^D u\,dx - \int_D^A v\,dy$$

$$= \int_{-1}^{1}(x-1)\,dx + \int_{-1}^{1}(1-y)\,dy - \int_{1}^{-1}(x+1)\,dx - \int_{1}^{-1}(1-y)\,dy = \mathbf{4}$$

Note. The vorticity $\zeta = \Gamma/\text{area} = 1$, and the flow is irrotational. This also follows from the general relationship

$$\zeta = \frac{\partial v}{\partial x} - \frac{\partial u}{\partial y} = 2x - 1$$

which is not equal to zero (except at the value $x = \frac{1}{2}$). The stream function can be determined from the velocity components:

$$u = \frac{\partial \psi}{\partial y} = x + y \qquad \text{and} \quad \psi = xy + \frac{1}{2}y^2 + f(x)$$

$$v = -\frac{\partial \psi}{\partial x} = x^2 - y \quad \text{and} \quad \psi = -\frac{1}{3}x^3 + xy + f(y)$$

giving $\psi = xy + \frac{1}{2}y^2 - \frac{1}{3}x^3$

4.9 Vortex systems

Two vortices, of equal but opposite strengths, Γ, are initially at the points $z = \pm c$. Each vortex is free to move under the influence of the other. Show that the vortex pair move in the direction of the y-axis with a velocity

$$\frac{\Gamma}{4\pi c}$$

A single row of vortices, each of strength Γ, are placed at the points $z = 0, \pm a, \pm 2a, \ldots$ Determine the equation of the streamlines, and expressions for the velocity components.

Solution. **Vortex pair** (Fig. 4.23)

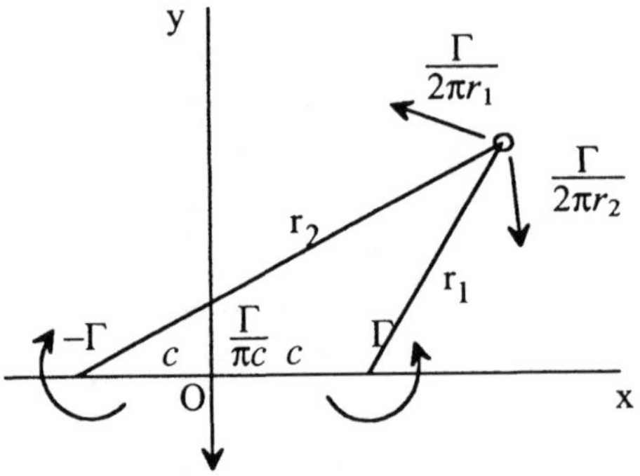

Figure 4.23

The complex potential function for a vortex at the point z = c is

$$w = \frac{i\Gamma}{2\pi}\ln\left(\frac{z-c}{a}\right)$$

so that initially the function for the vortex pair is

$$w = \frac{i\Gamma}{2\pi}\ln\left(\frac{z-c}{a}\right) + \frac{i\Gamma}{2\pi}\ln\left(\frac{z+c}{a}\right)$$

$$\frac{dw}{dz} = u - iv = \frac{i\Gamma}{2\pi}\frac{1}{z+c} - \frac{i\Gamma}{2\pi}\frac{1}{z-c} = \frac{i\Gamma}{2\pi}\frac{-2c}{z^2+c^2}$$

At the origin (0, 0)

$$u - iv = \frac{i\Gamma}{2\pi}\frac{-2c}{-c^2} \quad \text{and} \quad u = 0,\ v = -\frac{\Gamma}{\pi c}$$

This is the *fluid* velocity at this point. However, if the vortices are free to move under the influence of each other, the velocity at (0, 0) of each vortex is

$$\frac{\Gamma}{2\pi(2c)} = \frac{\Gamma}{4\pi c}$$

in the same direction. Hence the *vortex pair* moves in the direction of the y-axis with a velocity of

$$\frac{\Gamma}{4\pi c}$$

Vortex row (Fig. 4.24)

The complex potential function for the row of vortices is

$$w = -\frac{i\Gamma}{2\pi}(\ln z + \ln(z-a) + \ln(z-2a) + \ldots$$
$$+ \ln(z+a) + \ln(z+2a) + \ldots)$$
$$= -\frac{i\Gamma}{2\pi}\ln z(z^2-a^2)(z^2-4a^2)\ldots \qquad = -\frac{i\Gamma}{2\pi}\ln\,\sin\left(\frac{\pi z}{a}\right)$$

$$\frac{dw}{dz} = -\frac{i\Gamma}{2\pi}\left(\frac{\pi}{a}\cos\left(\frac{\pi z}{a}\right)/\sin\left(\frac{\pi z}{a}\right)\right) = -\frac{i\Gamma}{2a}\cot\left(\frac{\pi z}{a}\right)$$

The stream function can be obtained by the use of complex conjugates: the conjugate of w $(= \phi + i\psi)$ is $\bar{w} = \phi - i\psi$, and of z $(= x + iy)$ is $\bar{z} = x - iy$..

$$\text{Thus } w - \bar{w} = 2i\psi = -\frac{i\Gamma}{2\pi}\ln\,\sin\left(\frac{\pi z}{a}\right) - \frac{i\Gamma}{2\pi}\ln\,\sin\left(\frac{\pi\bar{z}}{a}\right)$$
$$= -\frac{i\Gamma}{2\pi}\ln\,\sin\left(\frac{\pi z}{a}\right)\sin\left(\frac{\pi\bar{z}}{a}\right)$$

Using the trigonometric relationship

$$\sin A \sin B = \tfrac{1}{2}(\cos(A-B) - \cos(A+B))$$

$$2i\psi = -\frac{i\Gamma}{2\pi}\ln\frac{1}{2}\left(\cos\frac{2\pi iy}{a} - \cos\frac{2\pi x}{a}\right) = -\frac{i\Gamma}{2\pi}\ln\frac{1}{2}\left(\cosh\frac{2\pi y}{a} - \cos\frac{2\pi x}{a}\right)$$

giving the streamlines as

$$\mathbf{\cosh\frac{2\pi y}{a} - \cos\frac{2\pi x}{a} = constant}$$

The velocity components can be determined from the complex potential or stream functions.

$$\psi = -\frac{\Gamma}{4\pi}\ln\frac{1}{2}\left(\cosh\frac{2\pi y}{a} - \cos\frac{2\pi x}{a}\right)$$

$$u = \frac{\partial\psi}{\partial y} = -\frac{\Gamma}{2a}\frac{\sinh\frac{2\pi y}{a}}{\cosh\frac{2\pi y}{a} - \cos\frac{2\pi x}{a}}$$

$$v = -\frac{\partial\psi}{\partial x} + \frac{\Gamma}{2a}\frac{\sin\frac{2\pi x}{a}}{\cosh\frac{2\pi y}{a} - \cos\frac{2\pi x}{a}}$$

Note. If y/a is large the velocity component u approaches the value

$$-\frac{\Gamma}{2a}\tanh\left(\frac{2\pi y}{a}\right),\ \text{since } \cos\left(\frac{2\pi x}{a}\right) \text{ is small,}$$

and this value becomes $\pm\Gamma/2a$

$$\tanh\left(\frac{2\pi y}{a}\right) = \frac{\exp\left(\frac{2\pi y}{a}\right) - \exp\left(-\frac{2\pi y}{a}\right)}{\exp\left(\frac{2\pi y}{a}\right) + \exp\left(-\frac{2\pi y}{a}\right)} \rightarrow \mp 1$$

for large values of $2\pi y/a$.

If this ratio a/Γ is kept constant, as both a and Γ approach zero, in the limit a *plane vortex sheet* is obtained.

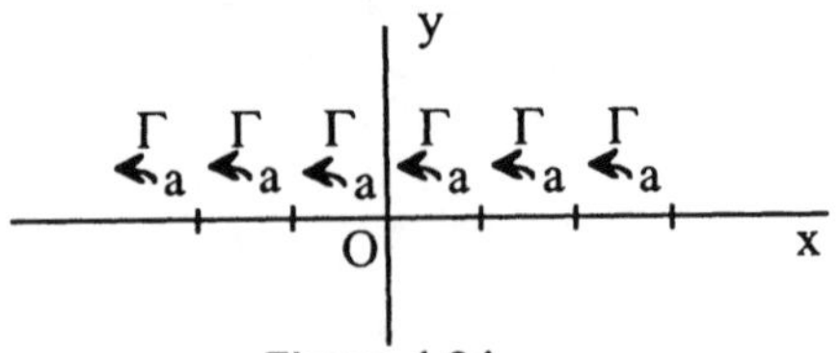

Figure 4.24

4.10 Conformal transforms

> Outline the meaning of the term *conformal transform*, and explain how it can be applied to potential flow problems.
>
> The quadrant $x \geq 0, y \geq 0$ in the z-plane is mapped onto the ζ-plane by the transform
>
> $\zeta = z^2$
>
> Discuss the results of the transform.

Solution. A transform is a mathematical process by which an area in the z-plane, A, is mapped into another area A', in the ζ-plane.

A correspondence is set up between two points in the two areas by some relationship between the x, y coordinates and the ζ, η coordinates (Fig. 4.25):

$$\zeta = \zeta(x, y), \quad \eta = \eta(x, y)$$

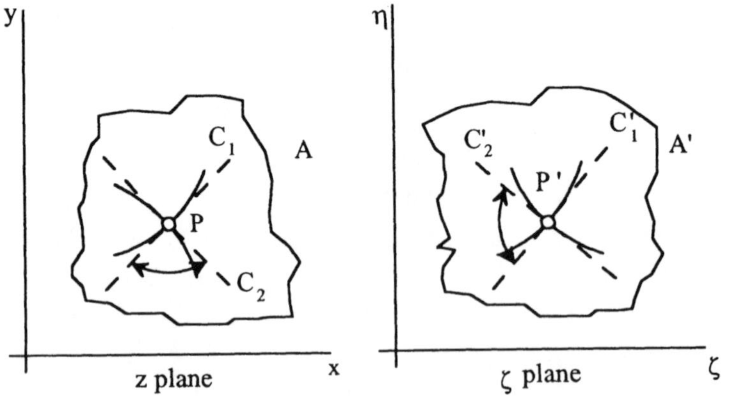

Figure 4.25

The correspondence can only exist if the functions of x, y are continuous, and the partial derivatives $\partial/\partial x$, $\partial/\partial y$ are also continuous at every point (which can be summarised by stating that the functions are analytic).

Consider a point P in the z-plane (Fig. 4.26), inside the area A, and suppose two curves C_1 and C_2 intersect at the point, at an angle β. The corresponding curves in the ζ-plane are C'_1 and C'_2 say, intersecting at the corresponding point P'. Then if the angles between the curves are equal, i.e. $\beta = \beta'$, the transform is said to be *conformal.*

It should be noted that the scale is usually different, and, in fact the *linear* magnification (and hence local velocity) at any point is given by

$$\left|\frac{d\zeta}{dz}\right|$$

at that point.

Conformal transforms can be a useful tool in the study of potential flow. The flow pattern (and hence velocity and pressure distribution) can be determined around or over a simple body; a conformal transform can then change the shape of the body into a more complicated geometry, and the transform also determines the flow pattern over the new body. A prime example is the determination of the potential flow over an aerofoil: the flow over a cylinder is first determined and then a suitable transform used to change the cylinder into an aerofoil and determine the new flow pattern (Ex.4.12). Other applications are in the determination of flow patterns around a cascade of blades (in a turbo machine), and map making (as in the Mercator projection).

Transform $\zeta = z^2$

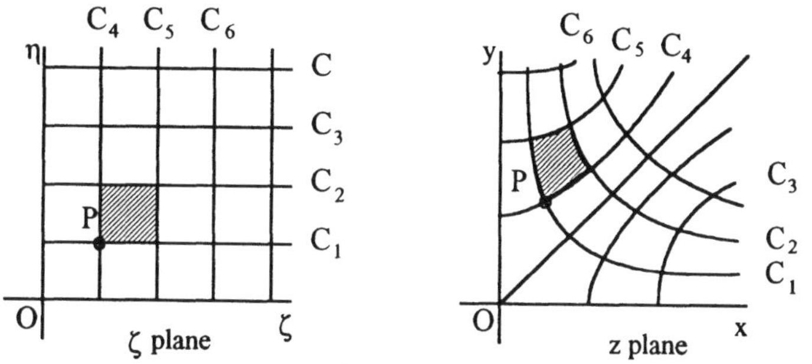

Figure 4.26

The correspondence between points in the two planes can be established by equating the real and imaginary parts of ζ and z. Thus

$$\zeta = \xi + ih = z^2 = (x + iy)^2 = x^2 - y^2 + 2ixy$$

hence $\xi = x^2 - y^2$, $\quad \eta = 2xy$.

The real axis $\quad 0 \le \xi \le \infty,\ \eta = 0$

transforms into $xy = 0,\ x^2 - y^2 = \xi$

or the real axis $y = 0$ and $x = \sqrt{\xi}$.

Similarly the η-axis, $\xi = 0,\ 0 \le \eta \le I$, transforms into the y-axis and $y = \sqrt{\xi}$.

A line ξ = constant (lines C_4, C_5, C_6) transforms into the curves; and $x^2 - y^2$ = constant; and a line η = constant (lines C_1, C_2, C_3) into the curves xy = constant. The corresponding curves are shown in Fig. 4.26, and two corresponding areas are also indicated.

The curves in the z-plane intersect at a right angle, since the slope of the curves at a point P are

$$\frac{dy}{dx} = \frac{x}{y} \quad \text{and} \quad -\frac{y}{x}$$

The product of the slopes is clearly −1, showing the orthogonality (intersection at a right angle). Hence the corresponding angles are the same and the transform is conformal.

Further the linear magnification is, at any point,

$$\left|\frac{d\zeta}{dz}\right| = |2z| = 2\sqrt{x^2 + y^2}$$

4.11 Conformal transform

> Obtain the result of applying the transform
>
> $$\zeta = \frac{1 + iz}{1 + z}$$
>
> to the upper half of the z-plane,
>
> $$-\infty \le x \le +\infty, \qquad 0 \le y \le \infty$$

Solution. The transform stated can be considered as the sum of successive transforms

$$\zeta_2 = z + i, \quad \zeta_1 = \frac{1}{\zeta_2}, \quad \zeta = 1 + 2\zeta_1$$

since $\dfrac{2}{z + i} + i = \dfrac{2 + iz + i^2}{z + i} = \dfrac{1 + iz}{i + z}$

The transform $\zeta_2 = z + i$ corresponds to a *translation* in which any point z is moved a distance of unity parallel to the y-axis. The transform

$$\zeta_1 = \frac{1}{\zeta_2}$$

corresponds to an *inversion*: thus, using polar coordinates,

if $\quad \zeta_2 = r_2 \exp(i\theta_2), \qquad$ then $\quad \zeta_1 = \dfrac{1}{r_2}\exp(-i\theta_2)$

Finally the transform $\zeta = 1 + 2\zeta_1$ corresponds to a translation through a distance of unity, together with a *magnification* of ζ_1. These elementary transforms are illustrated in Fig. 4.27.

The only elementary transform which affects the *shape* is the inversion, which transforms circles into straight lines.

Proceeding as before

$$\zeta = \xi + i\eta = \frac{1 + i(x + iy)}{i + (x + iy)} = \frac{(1 - y) + ix}{x + i(1 + y)}$$

$$= \frac{(1 - y) + ix}{x + i(1 + y)} \cdot \frac{x - i(1 + y)}{x - i(1 + y)} = \frac{2x + i(x^2 + y^2 - 1)}{x^2 + (1 + y)^2}$$

giving $\xi = \dfrac{2x}{x^2 + (1 + y)^2}, \qquad \eta = \dfrac{x^2 + y^2 - 1}{x^2 + (1 + y)^2}$

Consider the real axis, $y = 0$. At any point on this axis

$$\xi = \frac{2x}{x^2 + 1}, \qquad \eta = \frac{x^2 - 1}{x^2 + 1}$$

Hence eliminating x gives

$$\xi^2 + \eta^2 = 1$$

The real axis therefore transforms into a circle, centred at the origin, of radius 1.

As $x \to \infty, \xi \to 0, \eta \to 1$ and as $x \to +\infty, \xi \to 0, \eta \to 1$. The point (0, 0) in the z-plane transforms into the point $\xi = 0, \eta = -1$.

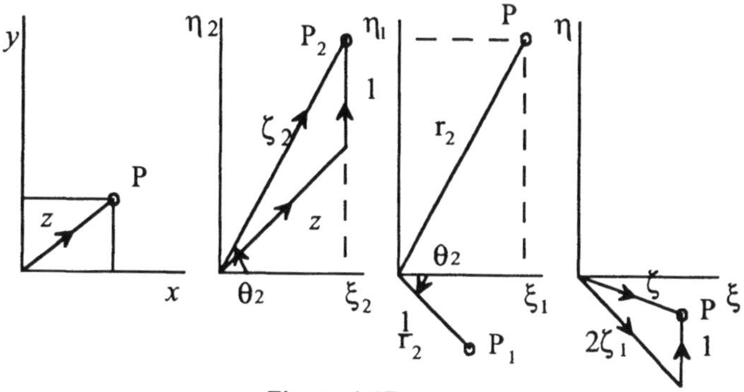

Figure 4.27

Thus the upper half of the z-plane is transformed into the *interior* of a unit circle in the ζ-plane.

As a check consider point A(0, 1) (Fig. 4.28) where $z = i$. Then $\xi = 0$, $\eta = 0$. Another point B(0, 2) transforms into the point

$$\xi = 0, \eta = \frac{4 - 1}{(3)^2} = \frac{1}{3}$$

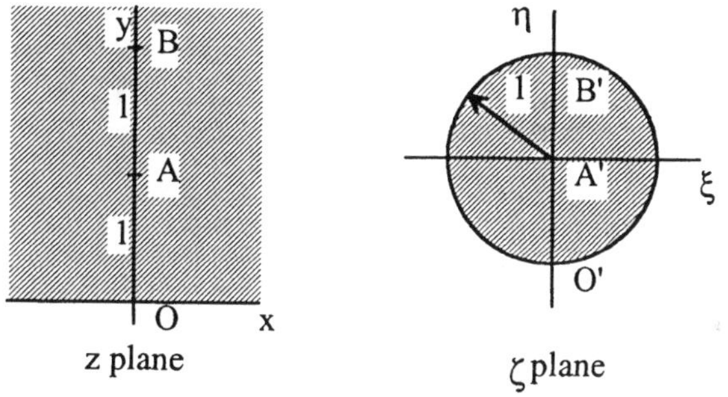

Figure 4.28

4.12 Joukowsky transform

Show how the Joukowsky transform

$$\zeta = z + \frac{a^2}{z}$$

can map a circle in the z-plane into an ellipse or an aerofoil in the ζ-plane.

Outline how the pressure distribution over the aerofoil surface can be determined. Show that the lift coefficient is given by

$$C_L = 2\pi \sin(\alpha - \alpha_o)$$

where α = angle of attack (incidence), α_o = the value of α at a zero lift coefficient.

Solution. Consider the circle in the z-plane, of radius c, centred at the point $z = z_o$ (Fig. 4.29). The transform is

$$\zeta = z + \frac{a^2}{z}$$

or $$\xi + i\eta = x + iy + \frac{a^2}{x + iy} = x + iy + a^2 \frac{x - iy}{x^2 + y^2}$$

and hence $\xi = x\left(1 + \frac{a^2}{x^2 + y^2}\right), \quad \eta = y\left(1 - \frac{a^2}{x^2 + y^2}\right)$

(a) If the circle is centred at the origin (0, 0) the profile of the circle is given by the equation $x^2 + y^2 = c^2$.

The corresponding profile in the ζ-plane is therefore given by the equation

$$\left(\frac{\xi}{1 + \frac{a^2}{c^2}}\right)^2 + \left(\frac{\eta}{1 - \frac{a^2}{c^2}}\right)^2 = c^2$$

This profile is an *ellipse*, centred at the origin $\xi = 0, \eta = 0$.

(b) If the circle is centred at the point $x_o = 0, y = y_o$ the circle profile is given by the equation $x^2 + (y - y_o)^2 = c^2$.

The corresponding profile in the ζ-plane is given by the equation

$$\left(\frac{\xi}{1 + \frac{a^2}{x^2 + y^2}}\right)^2 + \left(\frac{\eta}{1 - \frac{a^2}{x^2 + y^2}} - y_o\right)^2 = c^2$$

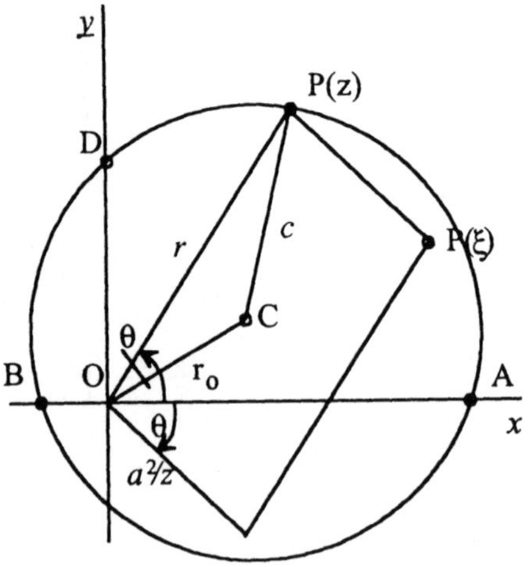

Figure 4.29

This profile is a *circular arc*, as shown in Fig. 4.30.

Point A $x = 0, y = 0$ $\rightarrow \xi = 2a, \eta = 0$

B $x = -a, y = 0$ $\rightarrow \xi = -2a, \eta = 0$

D $x = 0, y = y_o + c$ $\rightarrow \xi = 0, \eta = y_o + c - \frac{a^2}{y_o + c} = 2y_o$

C $x = 0, y = y_o$ $\rightarrow \xi = 0, \eta = y_o - \frac{a^2}{y_o}$

(c) In the general case shown in Fig. 4.29 the circle centred at $z = z_o$ is transformed into a Joukowsky *aerofoil*. This can be shown by constructing the profile by geometry: the transform consists of vector addition of z and a^2/z. The latter term is the inverse of z with respect to a circle of radius a: using $z = r\exp(i\theta)$ then

$$\frac{a^2}{z} = \frac{a^2}{r}\exp(-i\theta)$$

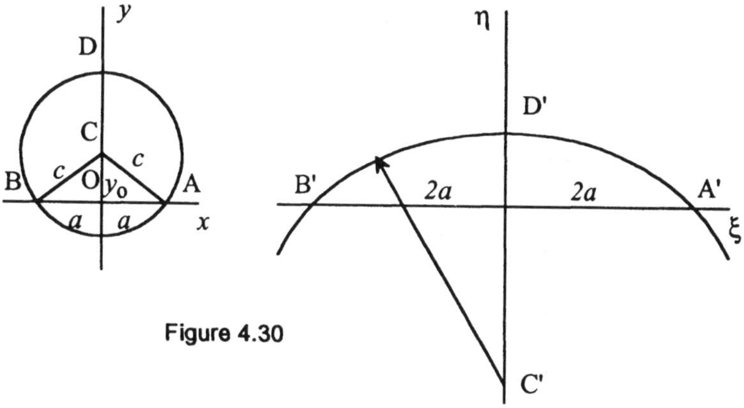

Figure 4.30

The construction of the position of the corresponding point P' is shown: vector OP" is the inverse, a^2/z, and is added vectorially to z (line P'P").

A complete construction is shown in Fig. 4.31.

The aerofoil has a cusp at the trailing edge where $\xi = -2a, \eta = 0$. This is a general result:

$$B(x = 0, y = 0) \rightarrow \xi = -2a, \eta = 0$$

The flow around a circular cylinder is known (Ex.4.6) and the transform can be used to determine the corresponding flow pattern over the aerofoil.

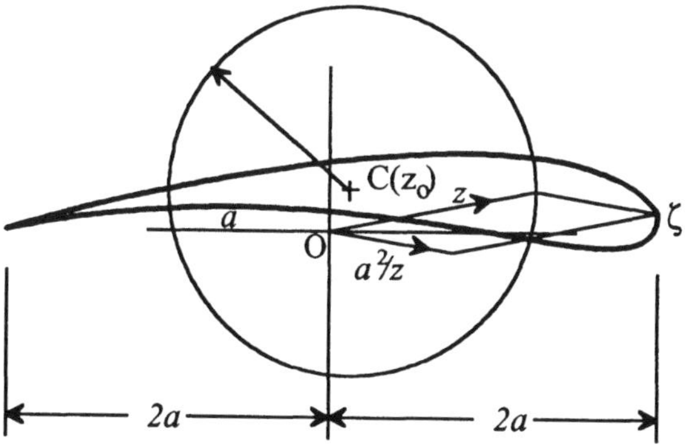

Figure 4.31

The angle of attack (or incidence) is the angle between the free stream direction and the chord line (which is the line joining the leading and trailing edges of the aerofoil).

Returning to the flow around a circular cylinder the complex potential function (discussed in Ex.4.6) at zero incidence is a combination of a uniform stream, doublet and free vortex

$$w = -Uz - \frac{\mu}{2\pi z} + \frac{i\Gamma}{2\pi}\ln\frac{z}{c}$$

and the circle $x^2 + y^2 = c^2$ is the zero streamline if $\mu = 2\pi c^2 U$

Hence $w = -U\left(z_1 + \frac{c^2}{z_1}\right) + \frac{i\Gamma}{2\pi}\ln\frac{z_1}{c}$

where z_1 refers to the coordinates in the z_1-plane (Fig.4.32).

To move towards the general case of the aerofoil at an incidence α the free stream is turned through the angle α, the centre of the circle displaced, and then the Joukowsky transform applied. These steps are shown in Fig. 4.32, and the relevant mathematical operations are:

$$z_2 = z_1 \exp(-i\alpha), \quad z_3 = z_2 + m\exp(i\delta), \quad \zeta = z_3 + \frac{c^2}{z_3}$$

The stagnation points are denoted by S_1 and S_2. Now the velocity at any point in the ζ-plane is

$$\frac{dw}{d\zeta} = \frac{dw}{dz_1}\frac{dz_1}{dz_2}\frac{dz_2}{dz_3}\frac{dz_3}{d\zeta}$$

$$= \left[\left(-U\left(1 - \frac{c^2}{z_1^2}\right) + \frac{i\Gamma}{2\pi z_1}\right)\exp(i\alpha)(1)\right] / \left[1 - \frac{c^2}{z_3^2}\right]$$

and if the trailing edge, S_2, is to be a stagnation point then

$$\frac{dw}{d\zeta} = 0 \text{ at this point.}$$

Hence $-U\left(1 - \dfrac{c^2}{z_1^2}\right) + \dfrac{i\Gamma}{2\pi z_1} = 0$

and $\quad \Gamma = \dfrac{2\pi U z_1}{i}\left(1 - \dfrac{c^2}{z_1^2}\right) = -2\pi i U z_1\left(1 - \dfrac{c^2}{z_1^2}\right)$

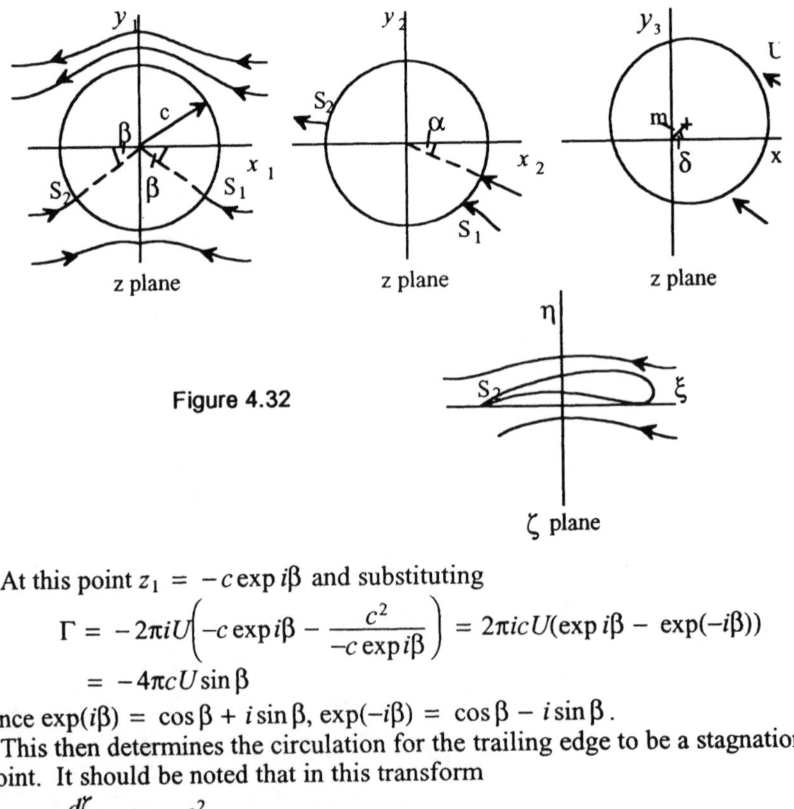

Figure 4.32

At this point $z_1 = -c\exp i\beta$ and substituting

$$\Gamma = -2\pi i U\left(-c\exp i\beta - \frac{c^2}{-c\exp i\beta}\right) = 2\pi i c U(\exp i\beta - \exp(-i\beta))$$

$$= -4\pi c U \sin\beta$$

since $\exp(i\beta) = \cos\beta + i\sin\beta$, $\exp(-i\beta) = \cos\beta - i\sin\beta$.

This then determines the circulation for the trailing edge to be a stagnation point. It should be noted that in this transform

$$\frac{d\zeta}{dz_3} = 1 - \frac{c^2}{z_3^2} = 0$$

when $z_3 = \pm c$. The physical impossibility of an infinite velocity at these points is overcome by the *Joukowsky hypothesis*, that the circulation adjusts itself to the value $4\pi cU\sin\beta$ so that these critical points in the ζ-plane correspond to the stagnation points in the z-plane.

Finally $\beta = \alpha - \alpha_o$, where α_o is the incidence at zero lift.

Hence $\Gamma = 4\pi cU\sin(\alpha - \alpha_o)$
and the lift force

$$L = \rho U\Gamma = 4\pi c\rho U^2 \sin(\alpha - \alpha_o)$$

The lift coefficient

$$C_L = \frac{L}{\frac{1}{2}\rho U^2 4c} = 2\pi\sin(\alpha - \alpha_o)$$

Problems

1 The velocity components in a fluid flow are given by

$$u = 2xy,\ v = a^2 + x^2 - y^2$$

Show that the continuity equation is satisfied, and that the flow is irrotational. Determine the stream and potential functions, and sketch the flow pattern.

Answer $\psi = xy^2 - a^2x - \frac{1}{3}x^3$;
$\phi = a^2y + x^2y - \frac{1}{3}y^3$.

2 The potential function of a fluid flow is

$$\phi = \tfrac{1}{3}x^3 - x^2 - xy^2 + y^2$$

Determine the stream function and sketch the zero streamline. Deduce the complex potential function. (*Hint.* Use the complex conjugate $\bar{z} = x - iy$.)

Answer $\psi = x^2y - 2xy - \frac{1}{3}y^3$
$w = \frac{1}{3}z^3 - z^2$

3 The complex potential function for a fluid flow is
(a) $w = z^2 - 1$, (b) $w = \sqrt{z}$
Determine the stream and potential function in each case.
Show that in case (a) the velocity at the points (1,1) and (2,½) are tangential to the streamline $\psi = 2$.

Answer (a) $\psi = 2xy$, $\phi = x^2 - y^2 - 1$
(b) $\psi^2 = \frac{1}{2}(x \pm \sqrt{x^2 + y^2})$, $\phi^2 = \frac{1}{2}(-x \pm \sqrt{x^2 + y^2})$

4 A strut, of maximum thickness

$$\frac{2m\pi}{U}$$

is represented by the zero streamline in the flow due to a source, strength $2\pi m$ at the origin (0,0) in a uniform stream, velocity U, parallel to the x-axis.

Show that the pressure at any point on the strut, relative to the free stream pressure p_∞, is given by the equation

$$p - p_\infty = \frac{1}{2}\rho U^2\left(\frac{\sin 2\theta}{\theta} - \left(\frac{\sin\theta}{\theta}\right)^2\right)$$

Estimate the drag per unit width on that part of the strut between $\theta = 0$ and $\theta = 67°$.

Answer $\frac{1}{3}\rho m U$

5 A source, and sink, each of strength $2\pi kU$, are situated at the points $(a,0)$ and $(-a,0)$ respectively, in a uniform stream of velocity U parallel to the x-axis.

Show that the stream function is given by

$$\psi = Uk \arctan\left(\frac{2ay}{x^2 + y^2 - a^2}\right) - Uy$$

Determine the position of the stagnation point, and the locus of the points at which the velocity is equal to the free stream velocity, U.

Answer $x = \pm\sqrt{a^2 + 2ak}\,, y = 0$

$x^2 - y^2 = a(a + k)$

6 A source, strength 50π, at the point (1,1), and a source of strength 50π, at the point (1,-1) are combined with a uniform stream of velocity 5 m/s parallel to the x-axis.

State the stream function of the combined flow and determine the equation of the zero streamline.

State the complex potential function of the combined flow, and hence determine the position of the stagnation points.

Answer $\dfrac{2y(x-1)}{(x-1)^2 - (y^2 - 1)} = \tan\dfrac{y}{5}$

$x = 10.90$ or 1.10, $y = 0$

7 Two sources, each of strength $2\pi m$, are situated at the points $(a,0)$, $(-a,0)$ together with a sink, strength $4\pi m$, at the origin (0,0).

Determine the stream function, and the velocity at the point $(0,a)$.

Answer $(x^2 + y^2)^2 = a^2\left(x^2 - y^2 + 2xy\cot\dfrac{\psi}{m}\right)$

$u = \dfrac{m}{2a}, v = \dfrac{m}{a}$

8 Sources of strength 2π are situated at the points (1,0) and (4,0); and sinks of strength 2π at the points (−1,0), (−4,0).

Sketch the streamlines, and determine the streamline $\psi = 0$.

Answer $x^2 + y^2 = 4$, and $y = 0$

9 A source, strength $2\pi m$, at the point $(a,0)$ is combined with another source of the same strength at the point $(-a,0)$. Show that the y-axis is a zero streamline and hence the flow pattern corresponds to a source at a distance a from a wall.

Determine the pressure at any point on the wall, and hence calculate the pressure force on the wall between the points $y = \pm 2a$ (relative to the free stream pressure).

Answer $\quad \dfrac{-2\rho m^2 y^2}{(a^2 + y^2)^2}; \quad \dfrac{-0.426\rho m^2}{a}$

10 The velocity components of a fluid flow are given by

$$u = 3x + y,\ v = 2x - 3y$$

Show that the continuity equation is satisfied.
Is the flow irrotational?

Determine the stream function, and calculate the circulation around the circle $x^2 + y^2 = 4$, and the square of side 4 centred at the origin.

Answer No: $\zeta = 1$

$\psi = 3xy + \frac{1}{2}y^2 - x^2$

0; 16

11 Show that for a free vortex the circulation taken round any rectangle which includes the vortex centre is constant, and if the rectangle does not include the vortex centre the circulation is zero.

Derive the pressure variation in a direction *normal* to a streamline in the form

$$\frac{d}{dr}\left(p + \frac{1}{2}\rho v^2\right) = \rho v \zeta$$

where ζ = vorticity = $\dfrac{v_\theta}{r} + \dfrac{\partial v_\theta}{\partial r}$

A vortex contains a core, of radius a, in which the vorticity is *uniform*, and outside of which the flow is irrotational. The circulation round the core = Γ. If the free stream pressure is p_∞ show that the pressure at the core centre is

$$p = p_\infty - \frac{\rho\Gamma}{4\pi^2 a^2}$$

12 Show that the complex potential function for a free vortex, strength Γ, is given by

$$w = \frac{i\Gamma}{2\pi}\ln z$$

A vortex and source, strength $2\pi m$, are combined at the origin. The vortex strength is $2\pi\Gamma$. Show that at any point the pressure, relative to the free stream pressure, is

$$-\frac{\rho(m^2 + \Gamma^2)}{2r^2}$$

13 Two stations S_1 and S_2 are 16 Km apart, and S_1 is due west of S_2. A tornado is known to be in the area, due north-east of station S_1. The wind speeds were measured at 1200 hours as 32 m/s at station S_1 and 18 m/s at station S_2.

Estimate the position of the tornado centre from station S_1, and the pressure difference between the two stations. Take the air density = 1.2 Kg/m^3.

It is suspected that the tornado centre is moving in the due north direction. At 1230 hours the pressure difference between the two stations had decreased to 37 N/m^2. Estimate the velocity of the tornado centre.

A graphical solution is acceptable.

Answer 8 Km; 420 N/m^2. 20 Km/h

14 Two doublets, each of strength $2\pi\mu$, are placed at the points $(0,a)$ and $(0,-a)$ with their axes in the direction of the x-axis. A uniform stream, of velocity U parallel to the x-axis, is superimposed on the flow. Show that for the combined flow the complex potential function is given by

$$w = Uz - \frac{2\mu z}{z^2 + a^2}$$

Show that the x-axis could be replaced by a plane surface. Also deduce the result that there are no stagnation points on the x-axis if $0 < \mu < 4a^2U$.

15 The flow around an oval cylinder can be represented by the combination of a source, strength $2\pi m$, at the point $(-a,0)$ with a sink, strength $2\pi m$, at the point $(a,0)$ in a uniform stream, velocity U, parallel to the x-axis.

Determine the length of the major chord. If the length of the minor chord = $2b$ show that

$$Ub + m \arctan \frac{2ab}{b^2 - a^2} =$$

Calculate the fluid velocity at the point $(0,b)$.

Answer $2\sqrt{a^2 + \frac{2ma}{U}}$

$$u = U - \frac{2ma}{a^2 - b^2},\ v = 0$$

16 A system of vortices consists of the following:

vortex, strength Γ, at the point $(4a,0)$

vortex, strength $-\Gamma$, at the point $(\frac{1}{4}a,0)$

vortex, strength $(n+1)\Gamma$, at the point $(0,0)$

Show that if the vortex at the point $(4a,0)$ is stationary, n = 1/15.

Determine the stagnation points.

Answer $r = a, \theta = \pm 68.5°$

17 The complex potential function of a flow is given by

$$z = \frac{w}{U} + \exp\left(\frac{w}{U}\right)$$

Show that the flow pattern is that between two plane surfaces

$$y = 0, y = \frac{\pi}{U}$$

Determine the equation of the streamline $\psi = \frac{1}{2}\pi U$, and the velocity along the streamline.

Answer
$$y = \frac{\pi}{2} + \exp x$$
$$u = \frac{U}{1 + \exp x}$$

18 The complex potential function for a doublet, strength μ, at the origin with its axis along the x-axis is

$$w = -\frac{\mu}{2\pi z}$$

Using this information investigate the flow corresponding to the function

$$w = \mu\left(\frac{1}{z - 2a} + \frac{1}{4z - 2a}\right)$$

Show that the zero streamline is a circle, and determine the position of the stagnation points.

Answer Zero streamline is $x^2 + y^2 - \frac{5}{2}ax + \frac{17}{8}a^2 = 0$

$$z = \left(\frac{8 \pm 6i}{10}\right)a$$

19 Show that the transform

$$\zeta = \frac{1 + iz}{1 + z}$$

maps the section of the real axis (AB, Fig. 4.33) onto a semicircle in the ζ-plane, and determine the radius of the semicircle. What point in the ζ-plane corresponds to the origin O in the z-plane.

Which area in the z-plane corresponds to the upper half of the z-plane?

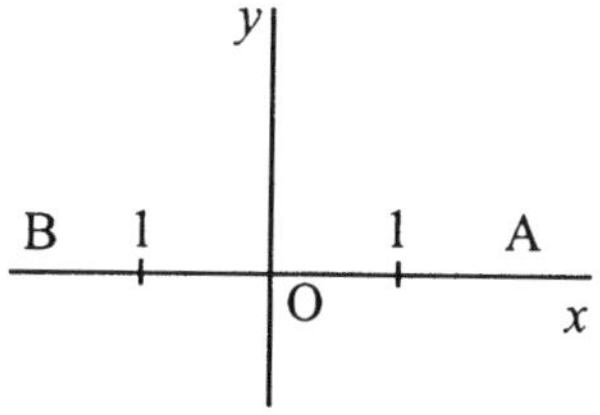

Figure 4.33

Answer Radius = 1.
Semicircle, radius 1, in the upper half plane.

20 (a) Show that under the transform

$$\zeta = \frac{z - i}{z + i}$$

the circle, radius 1, centred at the origin (0,0) in the z-plane becomes a line of length z along the imaginary axis in the ζ-plane.

(b) Under the same transform show that the circle, centred at the point (0,–1), radius 1, becomes a circle, centred at the point (1,0) of radius 2.

21 Show how a circle in the z-plane, centred at the origin (0,0), radius c, can be conformally transformed into an ellipse, and determine the lengths of the semi-axes.

An ellipse in a uniform stream, velocity U, has a stagnation point at the downstream end of the major axis. The major axis length = 8 times the minor axis length.

Calculate the fluid velocity at the upstream end of the minor axis.

Answer $\frac{9}{8}U$

22 A circle of radius c is centred at the point $z = ae$ in the z-plane. Sketch the result of applying a Joukowsky transform

$$\zeta = z + \frac{a^2}{z}$$

to the circle.

Take $a(1 + e) = c$ where $\frac{a}{e}$ is small.

Determine the maximum thickness: chord ratio.

If a uniform stream, velocity U, in a direction at an angle α to the x-axis flows over the circle, around which the circulation is Γ, show that $\Gamma = 4\pi c U \sin\alpha$ and the lift coefficient

$$C_L = 2\pi(1 + e)\sin\alpha$$

Answer $0.65e$

23 A turbo machine has four straight radial blades: the inner and outer radii in the z-plane are R_1 and R_2 respectively. Show that the circular cascade can be transformed in to a circle of unit radius in the ζ-plane by the successive transforms:

$$z' = z^n$$

$$z' = d + c\left(\zeta + \frac{1}{\zeta}\right)$$

Determine the constants c, d in terms of R_1 and R_2.

Answer $n = 4$

$c = \frac{1}{4}(R_2^4 - R_1^4)$

$d = \frac{1}{2}(R_2^4 + R_1^4)$

5

Viscous flow: Newtonian fluids

Fluid flow can be described as viscous (laminar) or turbulent flow. As the name implies viscous flow is dominated by viscous (shear) forces, and considering Newtonian fluids, in this chapter the important relationship between shear stress and *viscosity* is given by Newton's law (Fig. 5.1):

$$\tau = \mu\left(\frac{du}{dy}\right)$$

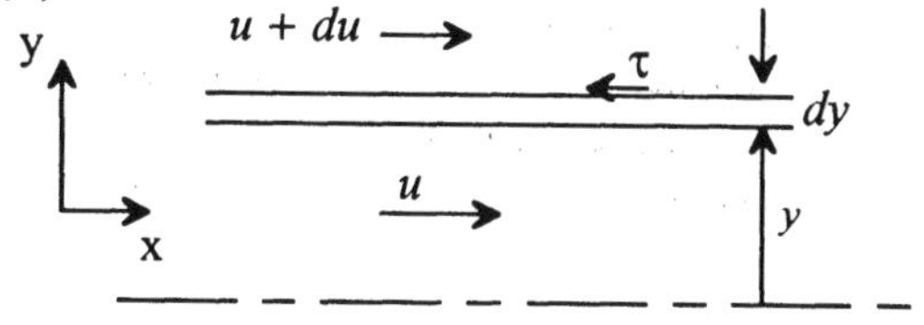

Figure 5.1

The coefficient μ is termed the coefficient of *absolute* (or *dynamic*) viscosity.

The absolute viscosity divided by the density ρ is termed the kinematic viscosity ν.

The flow regime (viscous or turbulent) depends upon the Reynolds number,

$$R_e = \frac{uL}{\nu} = \frac{\rho uL}{\mu}$$

where L is a characteristic dimension. Thus for a circular pipe it would be taken as the diameter; for a plane surface the length; for an aerofoil the chord. The transition from viscous to turbulent flow is not, in general, a sudden one; and the value of Reynolds number at which transition begins to occur is very dependent upon the cross-section of the flow, and the degree of initial disturbance in the fluid. In the case of a circular pipe, the value of Reynolds number often quoted at which transition begins is about 2 000: however it has been shown experimentally that with extremely smooth inlet conditions this value can be as high as 60 000.

The units of viscosity are as follows:

absolute viscosity $\quad Ns/m^2$ or Kg/m s

kinematic viscosity $\quad m^2/s$

However older metric units are still used in the commercial and industrial fields, namely

absolute viscosity $\quad$ 1 poise = 1 g/cm s

kinematic viscosity   1 stroke = 1 cm^2/s

Basic equations

The basic equations for steady, incompressible fluid flow are quoted for Cartesian and cylindrical polar coordinates:

continuity

$$\frac{\partial u}{\partial x} + \frac{\partial v}{\partial y} = 0$$

$$\frac{1}{r}\cdot\frac{\partial}{\partial r}(rv_r) + \frac{1}{r}\cdot\frac{\partial v_\theta}{\partial \theta} + \frac{\partial v_z}{\partial z} = 0$$

Navier-Stokes (momentum)

$$u\frac{\partial u}{\partial x} + v\frac{\partial u}{\partial y} = \frac{F_x}{\rho} - \frac{1}{\rho}\frac{\partial p}{\partial x} + \nu\left(\frac{\partial^2 u}{\partial x^2} + \frac{\partial^2 u}{\partial y^2}\right)$$

$$u\frac{\partial v}{\partial x} + v\frac{\partial v}{\partial y} = \frac{F_y}{\rho} - \frac{1}{\rho}\frac{\partial p}{\partial y} + \nu\left(\frac{\partial^2 v}{\partial x^2} + \frac{\partial^2 v}{\partial y^2}\right)$$

or

$$v_r\frac{\partial v_r}{\partial r} + \frac{v_\theta}{r}\frac{\partial v_r}{\partial \theta} + v_z\frac{\partial v_r}{\partial z} - \frac{v_\theta^2}{r}$$

$$= \frac{F_r}{\rho} - \frac{1}{\rho}\frac{\partial p}{\partial r} + \nu\left(\frac{\partial^2 v_r}{\partial r^2} + \frac{1}{r}\frac{\partial v_r}{\partial r} + \frac{1}{r^2}\frac{\partial^2 v_r}{\partial \theta^2} + \frac{\partial^2 v_r}{\partial z^2} - \frac{v_r}{r^2} - \frac{2}{r^2}\frac{\partial v_\theta}{\partial \theta}\right)$$

$$v_r\frac{\partial v_\theta}{\partial r} + \frac{v_\theta}{r}\frac{\partial v_\theta}{\partial \theta} + v_z\frac{\partial v_\theta}{\partial z} + \frac{v_r v_\theta}{r}$$

$$= \frac{F_\theta}{\rho} - \frac{1}{\rho r}\frac{\partial p}{\partial \theta} + \nu\left(\frac{\partial^2 v_\theta}{\partial r^2} + \frac{1}{r}\frac{\partial v_\theta}{\partial r} + \frac{1}{r^2}\frac{\partial^2 v_\theta}{\partial \theta^2} + \frac{\partial^2 v_\theta}{\partial z^2} - \frac{v_\theta}{r^2} + \frac{2}{r^2}\frac{\partial v_r}{\partial \theta}\right)$$

$$v_r\frac{\partial v_z}{\partial r} + \frac{v_\theta}{r}\frac{\partial v_z}{\partial \theta} + v_z\frac{\partial v_z}{\partial z}$$

$$= \frac{F_z}{\rho} - \frac{1}{\rho}\frac{\partial p}{\partial z} + \nu\left(\frac{\partial^2 v_z}{\partial r^2} + \frac{1}{r}\frac{\partial v_z}{\partial r} + \frac{1}{r^2}\frac{\partial^2 v_z}{\partial \theta^2} + \frac{\partial^2 v_z}{\partial z^2}\right)$$

where F = *external* force.

In many applications of viscous flow theory reasonable assumptions lead to substantial simplifications of the Navier-Stokes equations and solutions can be obtained directly. In this chapter the fluid is considered as *incompressible* and the flow as two-dimensional or axi-symmetrical.

5.1 Flow in a circular pipe

A viscous fluid flows along a circular pipe, diameter D, length L. Assuming one-dimensional flow show that the pressure drop is given by the equation

$$\Delta p = \frac{32\mu L\bar{u}}{D^2}$$

where $\bar{u}$ = mean velocity of flow.

State the Fanning equation, and show that this result is the same as taking the friction coefficient

$$f = \frac{16}{R_e}$$

in this equation.

Comment on the result.

Solution. The pipe is of a circular cross-section (Fig. 5.2), and therefore cylindrical polar coordinates are used. The flow is taken as one-dimensional, so that there are no radial or transverse velocity components, v_r, v_θ. The continuity equation reduces to

$$\frac{\partial v_z}{\partial z} = 0$$

There are no external forces (the fluid flows along the pipe under the influence of internal pressure and viscous forces) and the momentum equations reduce to

$$0 = -\frac{1}{\rho}\frac{\partial p}{\partial r}, \qquad 0 = -\frac{1}{\rho r}\frac{\partial p}{\partial \theta}$$

$$v_z\frac{\partial v_z}{\partial z} = -\frac{1}{\rho}\frac{\partial p}{\partial z} + \nu\left(\frac{\partial^2 v_z}{\partial r^2} + \frac{1}{r}\frac{\partial v_z}{\partial r}\right)$$

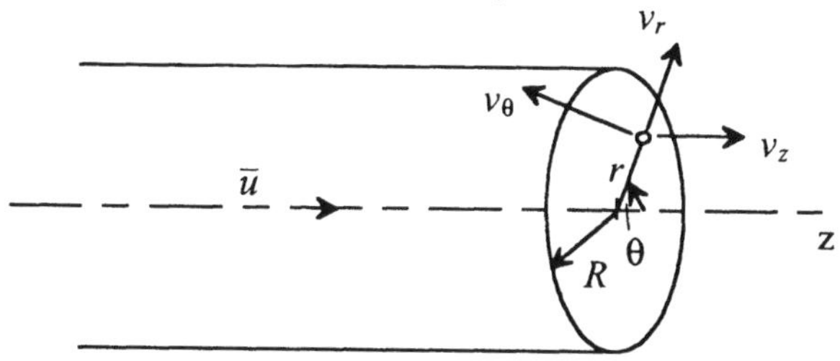

Figure 5.2

Now v_z is constant (from the continuity equation), and the pressure gradient can therefore be replaced by ordinary derivatives in the z-direction (i.e. flow direction) only. The partial derivatives giving

$$v_z\frac{dv_z}{dz} = 0 = -\frac{1}{\rho}\frac{dp}{dz} + \nu\left(\frac{d^2 v_z}{dr^2} + \frac{1}{r}\frac{dv_z}{dr}\right)$$

$$\frac{dp}{dz} = \rho\nu\left(\frac{d^2 v_z}{dr^2} + \frac{1}{r}\frac{dv_z}{dr}\right)$$

$$-P = \frac{\mu}{r}\frac{d}{dr}\left(r\frac{dv_z}{dr}\right) \qquad \text{where } P = -\frac{dp}{dz}$$

$$\int -\frac{Pr}{\mu}dr = r\frac{dv_z}{dr} = -\frac{Pr^2}{2\mu} + \text{constant } C\text{, say.}$$

Hence $\dfrac{dv_z}{dr} = \dfrac{C}{r} - \dfrac{Pr}{2\mu}$

and integrating again,

$$v_z = C\ln r - \frac{Pr^2}{4\mu} + \text{constant } B.$$

The integration constants can be determined from the boundary conditions: the fluid cannot slip over the surface at the pipe wall.

Thus $v_z = 0$ at the radius $r = R$ for all values of θ: and hence

$$C = 0,\ B = \frac{PR^2}{4\mu}$$

Substituting these values gives $v_z = \dfrac{P}{4\mu}\left(R^2 - r^2\right)$

The variation of the velocity with the radius has been determined, and is parabolic with a maximum value at the centre.

The flow rate Q can be determined by integration over the cross-section:

$$Q = \int_0^R v_z 2\pi r\, dr = \frac{2\pi P}{4\mu} \int_0^R r(R^2 - r^2)\, dr = \frac{\pi P R^4}{8\mu}$$

The mean velocity $\bar{u} = \dfrac{Q}{\pi R^2} = \dfrac{PR^2}{8\mu}$

and finally this can be rearranged to give

$$P = -\frac{dp}{dz} = \frac{8\mu\bar{u}}{R^2} = \frac{32\mu\bar{u}}{D^2}$$

and over a length L, the pressure drop is then $\Delta p = \dfrac{32\mu L\bar{u}}{D^2}$

This equation is known as the *Poseuille* equation. It is equivalent to the more general Fanning equation (1.18)

$$\Delta p = \frac{4\rho f L\bar{u}^2}{2D}$$

if $\quad f = \dfrac{32\mu L\bar{u}}{D^2}\dfrac{2D}{4\rho L\bar{u}^2} = \dfrac{16\mu}{\rho D\bar{u}} = \dfrac{16}{R_e}$

The Fanning equation applies to smooth pipes in which the surface roughness of the wall is negligible. In pipes where the roughness is significant, an additional factor known as the roughness coefficient appears. A plot of friction coefficient against Reynolds number, with a set of curves corresponding to different roughness coefficients (the Moody diagram), is illustrated in Fig. 5.3. It is a convenient graph for the determination of the friction coefficient and is widely used.

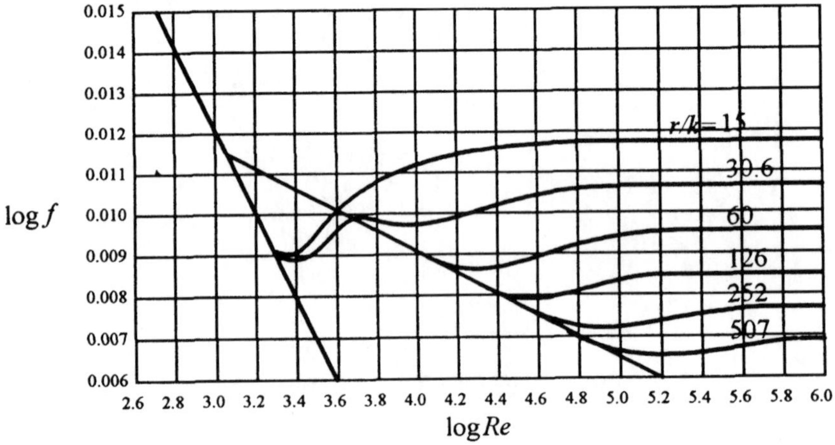

Figure 5.3

5.2 Flow in plane passages

A viscous, incompressible fluid flows along a passage between two parallel plane walls, distance apart t. Assuming steady flow show that the flow rate/unit width is given by

$$Q = \frac{t^3}{12\mu}\frac{dp}{dx}$$

End effects should be ignored.

If one wall moves with a velocity u_0 in the direction of flow determine the velocity distribution across the flow passage, and discuss the results.

Solution. The flow is one-dimensional in the x-direction say (Fig.5.4). The continuity equation

$$\frac{\partial u}{\partial x} + \frac{\partial v}{\partial y} = 0 \qquad \text{becomes} \qquad \frac{\partial u}{\partial x} = 0$$

Again there are no external forces, and the momentum equations reduce to

$$0 = -\frac{1}{\rho}\frac{\partial p}{\partial x} + \nu\left(\frac{\partial^2 u}{\partial y^2}\right) \quad \text{since } \frac{\partial u}{\partial y} = 0, \frac{\partial u}{\partial x} = 0$$

$$0 = -\frac{1}{\rho}\frac{\partial p}{\partial y}$$

Thus the pressure gradient is in the x-direction (that is in the direction of flow), and again putting

$$P = -\frac{dp}{dx}$$

gives $\frac{P}{\rho} + \nu\frac{d^2u}{dy^2} = 0$ or $\qquad \frac{d^2u}{dy^2} = -\frac{P}{\mu}$

Integrating twice

$$\frac{du}{dy} = -\frac{Py}{\mu} + A$$

$$u = -\frac{Py^2}{2\mu} + Ay + B$$

The boundary conditions of no-slip of fluid at the walls give

$$u = 0, \text{ at } y = \tfrac{1}{2}t, y = -\tfrac{1}{2}t.$$

Substituting gives

$$A = 0, B = \frac{Pt^2}{8\mu}$$

and $\quad u = \frac{P}{2\mu}\left(\frac{t^2}{4} - y^2\right)$

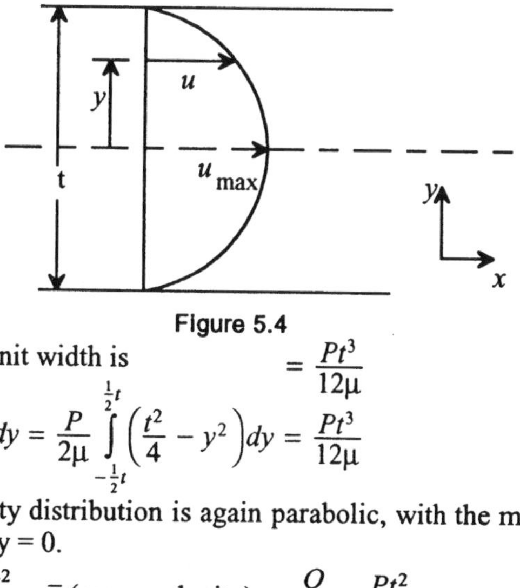

Figure 5.4

The flow rate/unit width is $\qquad = \frac{Pt^3}{12\mu}$

$$Q = \int_{-\frac{1}{2}t}^{\frac{1}{2}t} u\,dy = \frac{P}{2\mu}\int_{-\frac{1}{2}t}^{\frac{1}{2}t}\left(\frac{t^2}{4} - y^2\right)dy = \frac{Pt^3}{12\mu}$$

Note. The velocity distribution is again parabolic, with the maximum value at the centre line y = 0.

$$u_{max} = \frac{Pt^2}{8\mu}, \quad \bar{u} \text{ (mean velocity)} = \frac{Q}{t} = \frac{Pt^2}{12\mu}$$

and $\quad \bar{u} = \frac{2}{3}u_{max}$

This result is similar to that obtained in a circular pipe flow, where

$$u_{max} = \frac{PR^2}{4\mu} \quad \text{and} \quad \bar{u} = \frac{PR^2}{8\mu} = \frac{1}{2}u_{max}$$

Moving wall. The solution is the same as before, but the boundary conditions now differ. For convenience the lower wall is taken as the stationary surface and the x-axis (Fig. 5.5).

Thus the no-slip boundary conditions are

$$u = 0 \text{ at } y = 0, \qquad u = u_o \text{ at } y = t$$

and substituting

$$0 = B, \quad u_o = B + At - \frac{Pt^2}{2\mu} \quad \text{and} \quad A = \frac{u_o}{t} + \frac{Pt}{2\mu}$$

Hence $u = \left(\frac{u_o}{t} + \frac{Pt}{2\mu}\right)y - \frac{Py^2}{2\mu} = \frac{u_o y}{t}\left(1 + \beta\left(1 - \frac{y}{t}\right)\right)$, where $\beta = \frac{Pt^2}{2\mu u_o}$

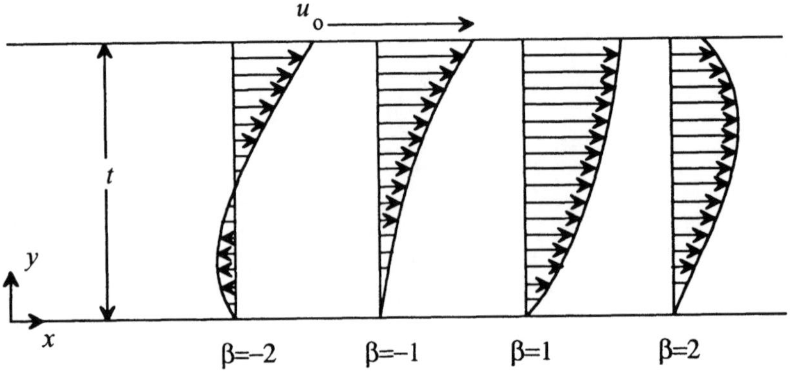

Figure 5.5

The velocity distribution is no longer parabolic or symmetrical: the profile clearly depends upon the value of β, which is inversely proportional to the wall velocity u_o. A point of interest is that if β is negative, i.e. the wall velocity is in the opposite direction to the flow, a *reverse* flow can occur near to the stationary wall.

The flow rate $Q = \int_0^t u\,dy = \frac{u_o}{t}\int_0^t \left(y + \beta y\left(1 - \frac{y}{t}\right)\right)dy$

$$= \frac{u_o}{t}\left(\frac{1}{2}t^2 + \frac{1}{6}\beta t^2\right) = \frac{u_o t}{6}(3 + \beta)$$

The mean velocity $\bar{u} = \frac{Q}{t} = \frac{u_o}{6}(3 + \beta)$

Note. This situation corresponds to oil flow in plane bearings, and can be extended to circular surfaces (journal bearings).

5.3 Concentric rotating cylinders

Two concentric cylinders, radii R_1 and R_2, rotate at an angular velocity Ω_1 and Ω_2 respectively. The space between them is filled with a viscous, incompressible fluid. Assuming that there is no flow along the axis of the cylinders, show that the tangential velocity of the fluid at any radius r is given by the equation

$$v_\theta = \left(\frac{R_2^2\Omega_2 - R_1^2\Omega_1}{R_2^2 - R_1^2}\right)r - \frac{R_1^2R_2^2(\Omega_2 - \Omega_1)}{R_2^2 - R_1^2}\left(\frac{1}{r}\right)$$

Solution. In this problem it is more convenient to use cylindrical polar rather than Cartesian coordinates. There is no flow along the axis so that $v_z = 0$; and also there is no radial flow (pure rotation) so that $v_r = 0$.

The continuity and momentum equations then become

$$\frac{1}{r}\frac{\partial v_\theta}{\partial \theta} = 0$$

and

$$-\frac{v_\theta^2}{r} = -\frac{1}{\rho}\frac{\partial p}{\partial r}$$

$$0 = \nu\left(\frac{\partial^2 v_\theta}{\partial r^2} + \frac{1}{r}\frac{\partial v_\theta}{\partial r} - \frac{v_\theta}{r^2}\right)$$

$$0 = -\frac{1}{\rho}\frac{\partial p}{\partial z}$$

The third equation can be written as

$$\frac{d^2 v_\theta}{dr^2} + \frac{d}{dr}\left(\frac{v_\theta}{r}\right) = 0$$

and integrating gives

$$\frac{dv_\theta}{dr} + \frac{v_\theta}{r} = \text{constant, } A \text{ say.}$$

This can be further integrated as follows:

$$r\frac{dv_\theta}{dr} + v_\theta = Ar = \frac{d}{dr}(rv_\theta)$$

$$rv_\theta = \tfrac{1}{2}Ar^2 + B$$

The boundary conditions of no-slip at the solid surfaces are:

$v_\theta = R_1\Omega_1$ at $r = R_1$ (inner cylinder)

$v_\theta = R_2\Omega_2$ at $r = R_2$ (outer cylinder)

Substituting

$$R_1^2\Omega_1 = \tfrac{1}{2}AR_1^2 + B, \qquad R_2^2\Omega_2 = \tfrac{1}{2}AR_2^2 + B$$

and therefore

$$A = \frac{2(R_2^2\Omega_2 - R_1^2\Omega_1)}{R_2^2 - R_1^2}, \; B = \frac{R_1^2R_2^2(\Omega_1 - \Omega_2)}{R_2^2 - R_1^2}$$

Hence $$\boldsymbol{v_\theta} = \left(\frac{\boldsymbol{R_2^2\Omega_2 - R_1^2\Omega_1}}{\boldsymbol{R_2^2 - R_1^2}}\right)\boldsymbol{r} + \frac{\boldsymbol{R_1^2R_2^2(\Omega_1 - \Omega_2)}}{\boldsymbol{R_2^2 - R_1^2}}\left(\frac{\boldsymbol{1}}{\boldsymbol{r}}\right)$$

Note. The maximum velocity is at some radius R_m where

$$\frac{dv_\theta}{dr} = 0,$$

$$\frac{R_2^2\Omega_2 - R_1^2\Omega_1}{R_2^2 - R_1^2} - \frac{R_1^2R_2^2(\Omega_1 - \Omega_2)}{R_2^2 - R_1^2}\left(\frac{1}{r^2}\right) = 0$$

giving $$R_m = \sqrt{\frac{R_1^2R_2^2(\Omega_1 - \Omega_2)}{R_2^2\Omega_2 - R_1^2\Omega_1}}$$

Several possible situations can arise, depending on the values of the angular velocities Ω_1 and Ω_2.

(a) If $\Omega_2 > \Omega_1$ there is no real value of R_m. This mean that the fluid velocity changes continuously from

$v_\theta = R_1\Omega_1$ at the inner surface

to $v_\theta = R_2\Omega_2$ at the outer surface.

(b) The expression obtained for R_m can be written as

$$R_m = R_1 \sqrt{\frac{\Omega_1 - \Omega_2}{\Omega_2 - \left(\frac{R_1}{R_2}\right)^2 \Omega_1}}$$

If $\Omega_2 < \Omega_1$ the numerator $\Omega_2 - \Omega_1$ is positive. However there are three possibilities:

$$\Omega_2 > \left(\frac{R_1}{R_2}\right)^2 \Omega_1$$

the denominator is positive and there is a value of R_m.

$$\Omega_2 < \left(\frac{R_1}{R_2}\right)^2 \Omega_1$$

the denominator is negative and there is no real value of R_m.

$$\Omega_2 = \left(\frac{R_1}{R_2}\right)^2 \Omega_1$$

the value of R_m is indeterminate.

To summarise, the tangential velocity attains a maximum value at some radius $R_1 < R_m < R_2$ only if

$$\Omega_1 > \Omega_2 > \left(\frac{R_1}{R_2}\right)^2 \Omega_1$$

The use of concentric rotating cylinders in practical terms lies in certain types of *viscometer*, one common type employing one fixed and one rotating cylinder. The viscous drag on the rotating cylinder, or viscous torque, is measured and used to determine the viscosity. If the outer cylinder is fixed, then at the inner cylinder surface the shear stress is

$$\tau = \mu\left(\frac{dv_\theta}{dr}\right)_{r=R_1} = \mu\left(\frac{-R_1^2\Omega_1}{R_2^2 - R_1^2} - \frac{R_1^2R_2^2\Omega_1}{R_2^2 - R_1^2}\frac{1}{r^2}\right)_{r=R_1}$$

$$= \mu\left(\frac{R_1^2 + R_2^2}{R_1^2 - R_2^2}\right)$$

and the viscous torque is $\tau 2\pi R_1 R_1$/unit length of cylinder, i.e.

$$2\pi R_1^2\left(\frac{R_1^2 + R_2^2}{R_1^2 - R_2^2}\right)\mu$$

The method can also be used to measure the viscosity of some non-Newtonian fluids.

5.4 Variation of viscosity with temperature

Discuss the effect of temperature on the viscosity of a fluid.

A circular pipe, 20mm diameter, 10m long, conveys a viscous fluid at a steady velocity of 50cm/s. The absolute viscosity of the fluid varies with the distance from the pipe inlet x(m) according to the equation

$$\mu = 0.01 - 5\times10^{-5}x^2 \ \ \text{Ns/m}^2$$

Calculate the pressure drop along the pipe, and the pumping power required.

Solution. The absolute viscosity of a fluid varies with pressure and temperature, although the effect of pressure is usually small. The effect of temperature is significant, and is shown in Fig.5.6. For example the lubricating oil viscosity varies as follows:

ν (stokes)	1.0	0.1	10
T (°C)	80	145	45

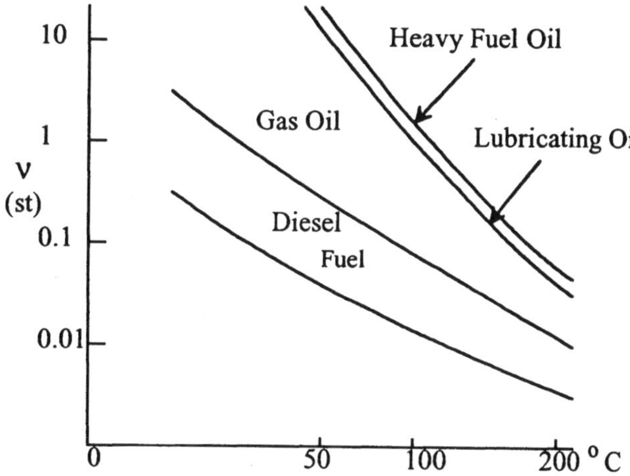

Figure 5.6

Another method of plotting, which gives linear graphs, is the ASTM system. This uses log(ν + 0.8) plotted against log$T$, where T is the absolute temperature (K).

The pressure drop is a linear function of the viscosity (Poiseuille equation), and therefore as the fluid temperature increases the rapid decrease in viscosity produces a decrease in the pressure drop. Alternatively for the same pressure drop a substantial increase in the flow rate would occur. The variation of viscosity with temperature is of importance in many applications, such as engine cylinder lubrication, power hydraulic equipment, oil coolers (Prob.1).

Consider an element, length dx, at a distance x from the pipe inlet. Then

$$\frac{dp}{dx} = \frac{32\bar{u}\mu}{D^2} = \frac{32\bar{u}}{D^2}(0.01 - 5\times10^{-5}x^2)$$

and integrating

$$\Delta p = \frac{32\bar{u}}{D^2}\int_0^{10}(0.01 - 5\times10^{-5}x^2)\,dx$$

$$= \frac{32\bar{u}}{D^2}\left(0.01x - \frac{5}{3}\times10^{-5}x^3\right)_0^{10} = \frac{32\bar{u}}{D^2}(0.0833)$$

and substituting $\bar{u}$ = 0.5 m/s, D = 0.02 m gives **Δp = 66.6 N/m²**

The pumping power required = $Q\Delta p = \frac{\pi}{4}(0.02)^2(0.5)(66.6)$ = **0.01 W**.

5.5 Cylindrical dashpot

A piston, 75 mm diameter, 100 mm long, slides vertically in a dashpot which contains a viscous fluid. The radial clearance between the piston and dashpot is 0.15 mm.

The piston descends, under its own weight, at a constant speed of 0.5 mm/s. When a load of 1.3 N is added to the piston the constant speed of descent increases to 0.6 mm/s.

Estimate the viscosity of the fluid, stating any assumptions made.

Solution

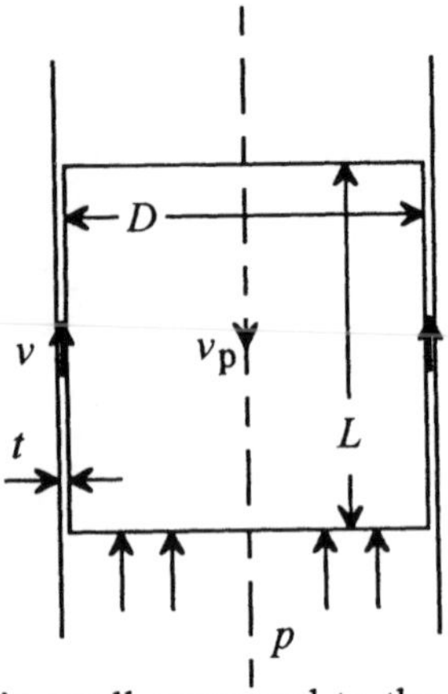

Figure 5.7

The clearance is small compared to the radius of the piston (in the ratio 1:250), and the fluid flow in the annulus between the piston and dashpot can therefore be considered as the flow between two parallel, plane surfaces (Fig. 5.7). The pressure drop over the annulus length is then given by

$$\Delta p = \frac{12\mu LQ}{t^3} = \frac{12\mu L\bar{u}}{t^2}$$

It is also assumed that the flow is viscous, or laminar, which is highly probable at such low piston velocities: and that as the piston descends the piston and dashpot remain concentric, i.e. the radial clearance remains constant over the whole piston circumference.

Let W = piston weight (N).

The volume of fluid displaced from below the dashpot = the volume swept out by the descending piston, or

$$\pi Dtv = \frac{\pi D^2}{4}v_p \quad \text{and} \quad v = \frac{Dv_p}{4t}$$

For steady movement of the piston, the pressure on the underside of the piston is

$$p = \frac{12\mu Lv}{t^2} \quad \text{but} \quad p = \frac{W}{\frac{1}{4}\pi D^2}$$

and equating

$$W = \frac{1}{4}\pi D^2\left(\frac{12\mu L}{t^2}\right)\left(\frac{Dv_p}{4t}\right) = \frac{3\pi\mu LD^3 v_p}{4t^3}$$

The fluid velocity v is taken as the mean velocity. Substituting the values given

$$W = 29.45\times10^6\mu v_p = 29.45\times10^6\mu\times0.5\times10^{-3}$$
$$W + 1.3 = 29.45\times10^6\mu\times0.6\times10^{-3}$$

giving $\mu = 4.41\times10^{-4}$ Ns/m^2 or 0.44 cP

since 1 Ns/m^2 = 1 kg/m s = 10 poise = 1000 centipoise (cP).

Note. The Reynolds number of the fluid flow is

$$R_e = \frac{\rho vt}{\mu} = \frac{\rho(0.6\times10^{-3})(0.15\times10^{-3})}{4.41\times10^{-4}} = 2\times10^{-4}\rho$$

Thus for a typical dashpot fluid of density 1200 kg/m^3, R_e = 0.24. As anticipated this is well below the transition Reynolds number.

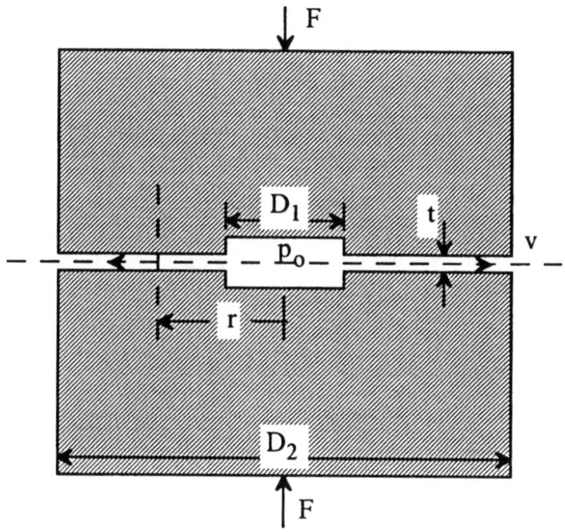

Figure 5.8

5.6 Radial bearing

Two circular cylinders are separated by an oil film of thickness t, as shown in Fig. 5.8. A load F compresses the cylinders together. The oil is supplied, under pressure p_o, to the central chamber and flows radially outwards from the chamber.

Show that

$$F = \frac{3\mu Q}{4t^3}(D_2^2 - D_1^2), \quad \text{where } Q = \text{flow rate of oil}$$

Comment on the result.

Solution. The flow can be taken as that between two parallel, plane surfaces provided that the gap, t, is very small compared to the diameters.

Thus $\dfrac{dp}{dr} = -\dfrac{12\mu v}{t^2}$ or $v = -\dfrac{t^2}{12\mu}\dfrac{dp}{dr}$

Now, at any radius r, the flow rate is

$$Q = 2\pi r t v$$

so that substituting

$$Q = -2\pi r \frac{t^3}{12\mu}\frac{dp}{dr}$$

Integrating gives

$$dp = -\frac{6\mu Q}{\pi t^3}\frac{dr}{r} \quad \text{and} \quad p = C - \frac{6\mu Q}{\pi t^3}\ln r$$

The integration constant can be determined from the condition that at the outer radius $r = R_2$ the pressure can be taken as zero. Hence

$$C = \frac{6\mu Q}{\pi t^3}\ln R_2, \qquad p = \frac{6\mu Q}{\pi t^3}\ln\frac{R_2}{r}$$

The pressure force at a ring, radius r, width dr, is

$$dF_1 = p\,2\pi r\,dr$$

and integrating,

$$F_1 = \frac{12\mu Q}{t^3}\int_{R_1}^{R_2} r \ln\frac{R_2}{r}\,dr = \frac{12\mu Q}{t^3}\left(\frac{r^2}{4} + \frac{r^2}{2}\ln\frac{R_2}{r}\right)_{R_1}^{R_2}$$

$$= \frac{12\mu Q}{t^3}\left(\frac{R_2^2 - R_1^2}{4} - \frac{R_1^2}{2}\ln\frac{R_2}{R_1}\right)$$

The pressure force on the central area is

$$F_2 = p_o \pi R_1^2 \quad \text{but} \quad p = \frac{6\mu Q}{\pi t^3}\ln\frac{R_2}{r}$$

and therefore

$$p_o = \frac{6\mu Q}{\pi t^3}\ln\frac{R_2}{R_1}$$

Hence $F_2 = \dfrac{6\mu Q R_1^2}{t^3}\ln\dfrac{R_2}{R_1}$

and the total pressure force, balancing the load, is

$$F = F_1 + F_2 = \frac{12\mu Q}{t^3}\left(\frac{R_2^2 - R_1^2}{4} - \frac{R_1^2}{2}\ln\frac{R_2}{R_1} + \frac{R_1^2}{2}\ln\frac{R_2}{R_1}\right)$$

$$= \frac{12\mu Q}{t^3}\left(\frac{R_2^2 - R_1^2}{4}\right)$$

or $$F = \frac{3\mu Q}{4t^3}(D_2^2 - D_1^2)$$

A bearing of this type can sustain high loads at moderate supply pressures and flow rates. For example, $D_1 = 30$ mm, $D_2 = 100$ mm, $t = 1$ mm, and $\mu = 2$ poise $= 0.2$ Ns/m^2.

$$F = 1.365\times 10^6 Q \quad \text{(N)}$$
$$p_o = 0.46\times 10^9 Q \quad \text{(N/m}^2\text{)}$$
or $$= 4600Q \quad \text{(bar)}$$

A load of 100 kg (981 N) would require a flow rate of 7.2×10^{-4} m^3/s (0.72 l/s) and a supply pressure of 3.3 bar.

5.7 Rotating pad

A plate rotates coaxially with a stationary lower plate, as shown in Fig.5.9, at an angular velocity of 60 rev/min. The space between them is filled with oil, of absolute viscosity 0.1 Ns/m^2.

Determine the viscous torque on the upper plate.

Solution. Consider an elementary ring at radius R. The shear stress is

$$\tau = \mu\frac{dv}{dr} = \frac{\mu R\Omega}{2h}$$

and the tangential force is

$$\tau 2\pi R\,dr = \frac{\mu\pi R^2\Omega}{h}dr = \mu\pi\Omega R\cot\alpha\,dR$$

The viscous torque over the tapered portion $R_1 \le R \le R_2$ is therefore

$$T_1 = \int_{R_1}^{R_2} \mu\pi\Omega\cot\alpha\,R^2\,dR = \tfrac{1}{3}\mu\pi\Omega\cot\alpha\,(R_2^3 - R_1^3)$$

The viscous torque over the central portion $0 \le R \le R_1$ is

$$T_2 = \int_0^{R_1} \frac{\mu R\Omega}{2h_1} 2\pi R^2\, dR = \tfrac{1}{4}\pi\mu\Omega R_1^3 \cot\alpha$$

giving the total viscous torque

$$= T_1 + T_2 = \tfrac{1}{12}\pi\mu\Omega \cot\alpha\,(4R_2^3 - R_1^3)$$

Substituting the data given

$T_1 = 2.14\,\text{Nm},\ T_2 = 0.06\,\text{Nm}$

$T =$ **2.20 Nm**

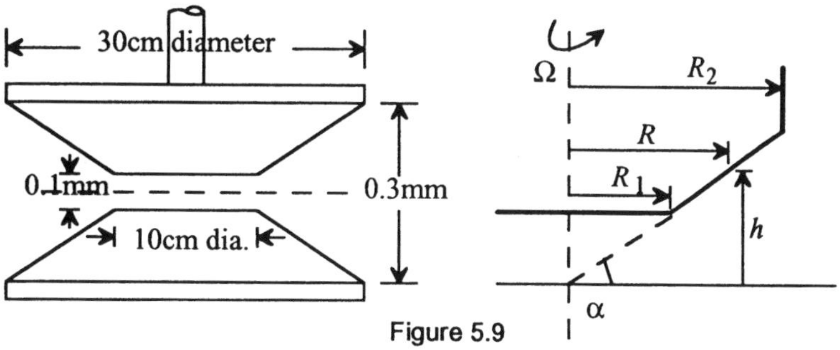

Figure 5.9

Note. Without the tapered surface the viscous torque would be much less. Thus, for a parallel slot of width 0.5 mm, the

$$\text{torque} = \frac{\tfrac{1}{4}\pi\mu\Omega R_2^4}{h} = 0.50\ \text{Nm}$$

and for a slot of width 0.3 mm, the viscous torque is 0.83 Nm.

5.8 Reynolds theory of lubrication

A viscous, incompressible fluid flows between two inclined plane surfaces, as shown in Fig. 5.10. The upper surface is stationary and the lower surface moves with a velocity u_o.

Assuming that the pressure gradient in the x-direction is constant, obtain equation for

(a) the pressure in the fluid film;
(b) the maximum pressure in the film;
(c) the total thrust per unit width.

Solution

(a) The flow is one-dimensional, and the momentum equation (Ex.5.2) is

$$\mu\frac{d^2u}{dy^2} = -P, \qquad \text{where } P = -\frac{dp}{dx}$$

Integrating twice gives

$$\mu\frac{du}{dy} = -Py + A, \qquad \mu u = -\tfrac{1}{2}Py^2 + Ay + B$$

The no-slip boundary conditions are

$$y = 0,\ u = u_o \qquad \text{and} \qquad y = h,\ u = 0$$

Also at $x = 0$ and $x = L$ the pressure $p = p_o$. Substituting

$$\mu u_o = B$$

$$0 = -\tfrac{1}{2}Ph^2 + Ah + B$$

and $$A = \frac{1}{2}Ph - \frac{\mu u_o}{h}$$

Hence the velocity distribution is given by

$$\mu u = \frac{1}{2}P(hy - y^2) + \mu u_o\left(1 - \frac{y}{h}\right)$$

The flow rate

$$Q = \int_0^h u\,dy = \frac{Ph^3}{12\mu} + \frac{u_o h}{2}$$

so that the pressure gradient is

$$P = \frac{12\mu}{h^3}\left(Q - \frac{1}{2}u_o h\right)$$

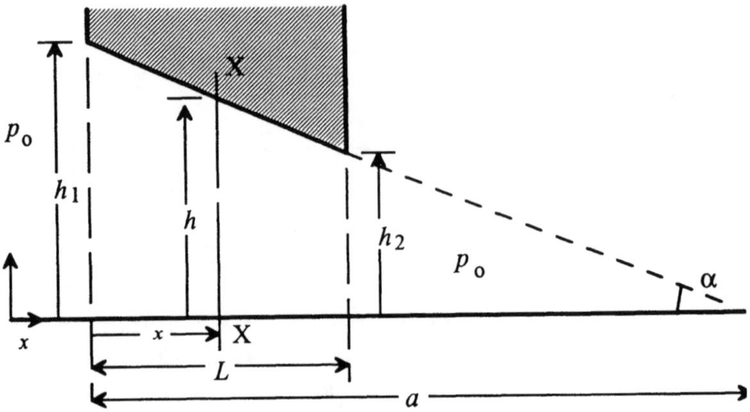

Figure 5.10

Now $\quad \dfrac{h}{h_1} = \dfrac{a-x}{a}, \qquad$ where $\dfrac{h_1}{a} = \dfrac{h_2}{a-L}$ or $a = \dfrac{h_1 L}{h_1 - h_2}$

and $\quad \dfrac{dp}{dx} = \dfrac{dp}{dh}\dfrac{dh}{dx} = -\dfrac{h_1}{a}\dfrac{dp}{dh}$

Substituting for $\dfrac{dp}{dx} = -P$

$$\frac{12\mu}{h^3}\left(\frac{1}{2}u_o h - Q\right) = -\frac{h_1}{a}\frac{dp}{dh}$$

$$\frac{dp}{dh} = -\frac{12\mu a}{h_1}\left(\frac{u_o}{2h^2} - \frac{Q}{h^3}\right)$$

and integrating

$$p = -\frac{12\mu a}{h_1}\left(-\frac{u_o}{2h} + \frac{Q}{2h^2}\right) + \text{constant, } C$$

The integration constant is determined from the condition that the pressure outside the pad is p_o (Fig. 5.11). Hence

$$p = p_o \text{ at } x = 0\ (h = h_1)$$

and $\qquad x = L\ (h = h_2)$

Using these conditions

$$p_o = -\frac{12\mu a}{h_1}\left(\frac{Q}{2h_1^2} - \frac{u_o}{2h_1}\right) + C$$

$$p_o = -\frac{12\mu a}{h_1}\left(\frac{Q}{2h_2^2} - \frac{u_o}{2h_2}\right) + C$$

and therefore

$$Q = \frac{h_1 h_2 u_o}{h_1 + h_2}$$

$$C = p_o - \frac{6\mu a u_o}{h_1(h_1 + h_2)}$$

Substituting gives

$$p = p_o - \frac{6\mu u_o a(h - h_1)(h - h_2)}{h^2(h_1 + h_2)h_1}$$

or

$$p = p_o - \frac{6\mu u_o L(h - h_1)(h - h_2)}{h^2(h_1^2 - h_2^2)}$$

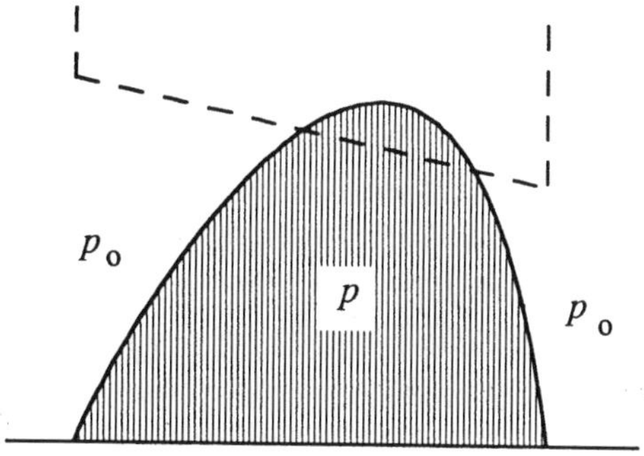

Figure 5.11

(b) The pressure is a maximum when

$$\frac{dp}{dx} = 0 \text{ (or } \frac{dp}{dh} = 0)$$

At this station

$$Q = \tfrac{1}{2} u_o h$$

or

$$h = \frac{2h_1 h_2}{h_1 + h_2}$$

and

$$p_{\max} = p_o - \frac{6\mu L u_o}{h_1^2 - h_2^2} \frac{(h - h_1)(h - h_2)}{h^2} = p_o + \frac{6\mu L u_o}{4h_1 h_2}$$

(c) The total thrust per unit width is

$$\int p\, dx$$

$$F = -\frac{a}{h_1} \int \left(p_o - \frac{6\mu L u_o(h - h_1)(h - h_2)}{(h_1^2 - h_2^2)h^2} \right) dh$$

$$= -\frac{a}{h_1} \int_{h_1}^{h_2} p_o\, dh + \frac{6\mu L u_o a}{h_1(h_1^2 - h_2^2)} \int_{h_1}^{h_2} \frac{(h - h_1)(h - h_2)}{h^2} dh$$

$$= -\frac{p_o a(h_2 - h_1)}{h_1} + \frac{6\mu L a u_o}{h_1(h_1^2 - h_2^2)} \left(2h_2 - 2h_1 - (h_1 + h_2) \ln \frac{h_2}{h_1} \right)$$

which reduces to

$$p_o a \left(1 - \frac{h_2}{h_1} \right) - \frac{12\mu L a u_o}{h_1(h_1 + h_2)} - \frac{6\mu L a u_o}{h_1(h_1 - h_2)} \ln \frac{h_2}{h_1}$$

or

$$p_o L - \frac{12\mu L^2 u_o}{h_1^2 - h_2^2} - \frac{6\mu L^2 u_o}{(h_1 - h_2)^2} \ln \frac{h_2}{h_1}$$

Note. O. Reynolds formulated a theory of lubrication which showed how a converging oil film can sustain high pressures; the theory being similar to the solution of this problem. This property is key to the high load carrying capabilities of thrust bearings. The Reynolds theory was extended at a later date by Sommerfeld and Michell.

5.9 Plane thrust pad

A loaded stationary pad is in contact with a plane surface, which is free to move with a velocity u_o. Briefly outline the lubrication mechanism as the surface velocity increases from zero.

A plane pad is 10 cm long (in the direction of the velocity), 20 cm wide. The pad velocity is 10 m/s. Minimum film thickness = 0.02 mm. Absolute viscosity of oil = 0.025 Ns/m^2. Film thickness ratio = 2.

Neglecting side leakage, and using the Reynolds equation in the form

$$\frac{dp}{dx} = -\frac{6\mu u_o(h - h_m)}{h^3}$$

estimate the power required to drive the pad, and the flow rate.

h_m = film thickness at the position of maximum pressure.

Solution. At very low pad velocities boundary lubrication occurs, where a protective film is produced preventing metallic contact. The film may be produced by chemical reaction between the metal surface and the lubricant oil. This type of lubrication tends to occur between the high spots on both surfaces.

As the pad velocity increases the lubricant completely fills the gap between the surfaces, this being termed hydrodynamic lubrication (Fig. 5.12). In this case there is no contact at all between the surfaces.

In this solution the distance x is measured from point A (as shown in Fig. 5.13). Also the analysis commences from the given Reynolds equation

$$\frac{dp}{dx} = -\frac{6\mu u_o(h - h_m)}{h^3}$$

$$\int_{x_1}^{x_2} dp = -6\mu u_o\left(\int_x^{x_2}\frac{dx}{h^2} - h_m\int_x^{x_2}\frac{dx}{h^3}\right)$$

$$p_o - p = -6\mu u_o\left(\frac{1}{\alpha^2}\int_x^{x_2}\frac{dx}{x^2} - \frac{h_m}{\alpha^3}\int_x^{x_2}\frac{dx}{x^3}\right)$$

where $h = x\tan\alpha = \alpha x$ for small angles.

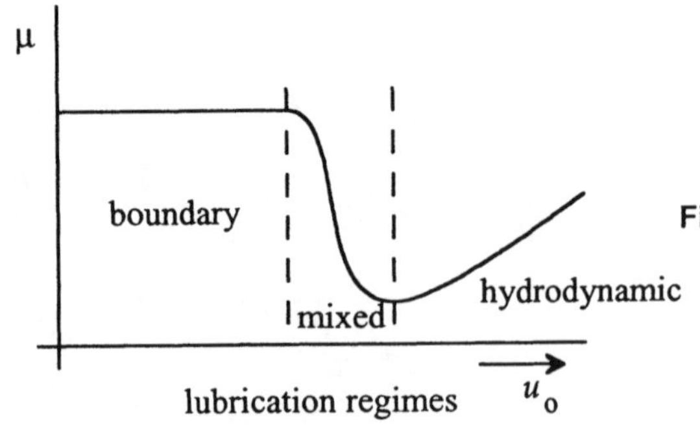

Figure 5.12

Now, at $x = x_1, p = p_o$, hence

$$0 = -6\mu u_o\left(\frac{1}{\alpha^2}\int_{x_1}^{x_2}\frac{dx}{x^2} - \frac{h_m}{\alpha^3}\int_{x_1}^{x_2}\frac{dx}{x^3}\right)$$

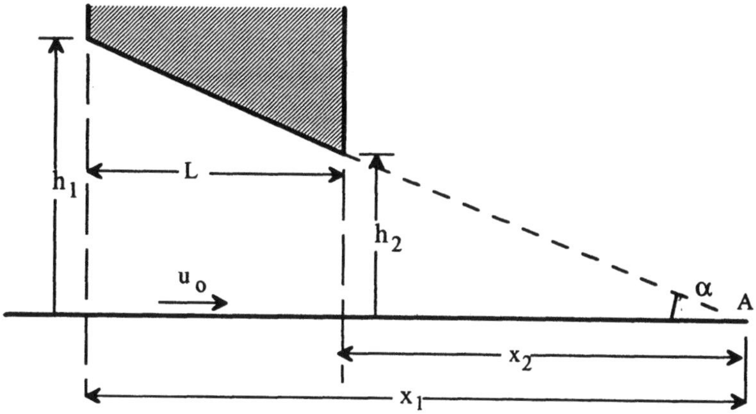

Figure 5.13

$$\int_{x_1}^{x_2} \frac{dx}{x^2} = \frac{h_m}{\alpha}\int_{x_1}^{x_2} \frac{dx}{x^3}$$

$$-\left(\frac{1}{x_2} - \frac{1}{x_1}\right) = -\frac{h_m}{2\alpha}\left(\frac{1}{x_2^2} - \frac{1}{x_1^2}\right)$$

giving
$$h_m = \frac{2\alpha x_1 x_2}{x_1 + x_2} = \frac{2h_1 h_2}{h_1 + h_2}$$

or, in terms of the film thickness ratio,

$$a = \frac{h_1}{h_2},$$

$$h_m = \frac{2ah_2}{a+1}$$

Returning to the pressure variation, taking $p_o = 0$ for convenience, and substituting h for x,

$$p = 6\mu u_o\left(\frac{1}{\alpha}\int_h^{h_2} \frac{dh}{h^2} - \frac{h_m}{\alpha}\int_h^{h_2} \frac{dh}{h^3}\right) = \frac{6\mu u_o}{\alpha}\left(\frac{h_2 - h}{hh_2} + \frac{h_m}{2}\frac{h^2 - h_2^2}{h^2 h_2^2}\right)$$

$$= \frac{6\mu u_o(h_2 - h)(h - ah_2)}{\alpha h_2 h^2(a+1)}$$

The total force per unit width is

$$F = \int_{x_1}^{x_2} p\,dx = \frac{1}{\alpha}\int_{h_1}^{h_2} p\,dh$$

$$= \frac{6\mu u_o}{\alpha^2 h_2(a+1)}\left(\frac{(h_1 - h_2)(h_1 + ah_2)}{h_1} + (a+1)h_2 \ln\frac{h_2}{h_1}\right)$$

$$= \frac{\mu u_o L}{h_2(a-1)}\left(4\ln a - \frac{6(a-1)}{a+1}\right)$$

Substituting the given data: $a = 2$

$$F = \frac{0.025(10)(-0.1)}{0.02\times 10^{-3}\times 1}\left(4\ln 2 - \frac{6}{3}\right) = 966 \text{ N/m width}$$

$= 966(0.2)$ or **193 N**

The power required is

$Fu_o = 193\times 10 =$ **1930 W**

The flow rate

$$Q = \int_0^h u\,dy = \frac{h_1 h_2 u_o}{h_1 + h_2}$$

(as derived in the previous example), or

$$Q = \tfrac{1}{2} u_o h_m \text{ /unit width.}$$

In this problem

$$h_m = \frac{2ah_2}{a+1} = \tfrac{4}{3}h_2$$

giving $Q = \tfrac{1}{2}(10)(\tfrac{4}{3})(2 \times 10^{-5})$ m^3/s per m width

$= \mathbf{2.67 \times 10^{-5}}$ m^3/s

or **0.0267** l/s.

5.10 Journal bearing

> A shaft rotates concentrically in a journal bearing (Fig. 5.14). Derive an equation for the viscous torque in terms of the angular velocity of the shaft Ω, shaft diameter D, and radial clearance t.
> Explain how the Petroff equation is determined. Discuss the pressure distribution in a journal bearing, including the Sommerfeld number.

Solution. Assuming incompressible fluid, purely rotational flow and neglecting end effects, the shear stress at the shaft surface is

$$\tau = \mu \frac{\tfrac{1}{2}D\Omega}{t}$$

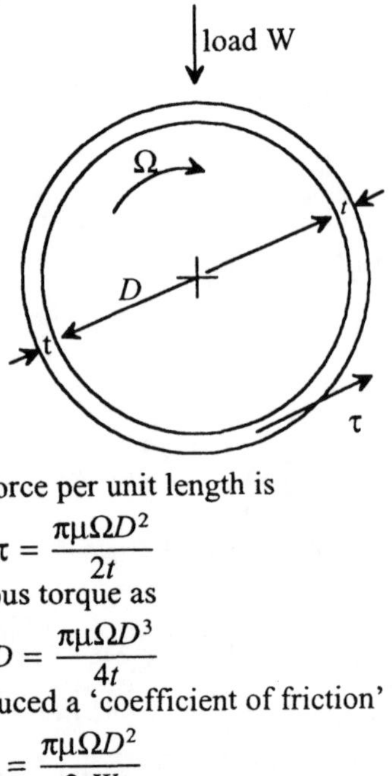

Figure 5.14

The viscous force per unit length is

$$F = \pi D \tau = \frac{\pi\mu\Omega D^2}{2t}$$

giving the viscous torque as

$$T = \tfrac{1}{2}FD = \frac{\pi\mu\Omega D^3}{4t}$$

Petroff introduced a 'coefficient of friction'

$$\mu_f = \frac{F}{W} = \frac{\pi\mu\Omega D^2}{2tW}$$

or since $W = \text{pressure} \times \text{projected area} = pD$,

$$\mu_f = \frac{\pi\mu\Omega D}{2tp}$$

This is known as the Petroff equation.

Under substantial loads; if the bearing is not supplied with pressurised oil, the load can only be supported if the oil film forms a convergent wedge. This has been shown by the Reynolds theory of lubrication. It follows that to support the load, the shaft must rotate eccentrically.

Consider such a situation, as shown in Fig. 5.15. The eccentricity e is taken as small in comparison with the shaft diameter, so that

$$h = t + e\cos\theta$$

Assuming that the viscosity is constant, and there is no side leakage, the equations derived in Ex.5.8 , 5.9 can be used.

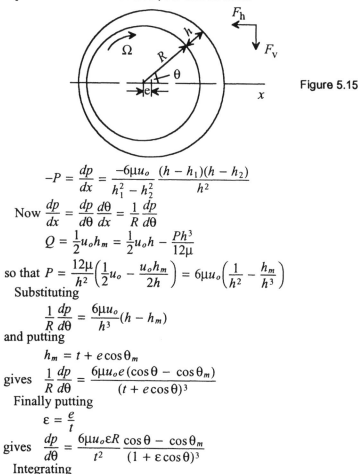

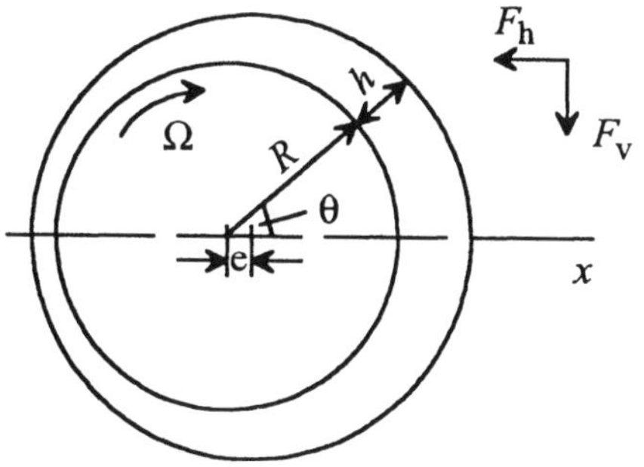

Figure 5.15

$$-P = \frac{dp}{dx} = \frac{-6\mu u_o}{h_1^2 - h_2^2}\,\frac{(h - h_1)(h - h_2)}{h^2}$$

Now $\dfrac{dp}{dx} = \dfrac{dp}{d\theta}\dfrac{d\theta}{dx} = \dfrac{1}{R}\dfrac{dp}{d\theta}$

$$Q = \frac{1}{2}u_o h_m = \frac{1}{2}u_o h - \frac{Ph^3}{12\mu}$$

so that $P = \dfrac{12\mu}{h^2}\left(\dfrac{1}{2}u_o - \dfrac{u_o h_m}{2h}\right) = 6\mu u_o\left(\dfrac{1}{h^2} - \dfrac{h_m}{h^3}\right)$

Substituting

$$\frac{1}{R}\frac{dp}{d\theta} = \frac{6\mu u_o}{h^3}(h - h_m)$$

and putting

$$h_m = t + e\cos\theta_m$$

gives $\dfrac{1}{R}\dfrac{dp}{d\theta} = \dfrac{6\mu u_o e(\cos\theta - \cos\theta_m)}{(t + e\cos\theta)^3}$

Finally putting

$$\varepsilon = \frac{e}{t}$$

gives $\dfrac{dp}{d\theta} = \dfrac{6\mu u_o \varepsilon R}{t^2}\,\dfrac{\cos\theta - \cos\theta_m}{(1 + \varepsilon\cos\theta)^3}$

Integrating

$$p - p_o = \frac{6\mu u_o \varepsilon R}{t^2}\int_0^{2\pi}\frac{\cos\theta - \cos\theta_m}{(1 + \varepsilon\cos\theta)^3}\,d\theta$$

$$= \frac{6\mu R u_o}{t^2}\,\frac{\varepsilon\sin\theta(2 + \varepsilon\cos\theta)}{(2 + \varepsilon)^2(1 + \varepsilon\cos\theta)^2}$$

The pressure is a maximum when $dp/d\theta = 0$

or $$\frac{d}{d\theta}\left(\frac{\sin\theta(2+\varepsilon\cos\theta)}{(1+\varepsilon\cos\theta)^2}\right) = 0$$

$$(1+\varepsilon\cos\theta)^2\left(2\cos\theta + \varepsilon(\cos^2\theta - \sin^2\theta)\right)$$
$$= 2\sin\theta\,(2+\varepsilon\cos\theta)(1+\varepsilon\cos\theta)(-\varepsilon\sin\theta)$$

giving $\cos\theta = -\dfrac{3\varepsilon}{2+\varepsilon^2}$

or, since by definition $\theta = \theta_m$ at the point of the maximum pressure

$$\cos\theta_m = -\frac{3\varepsilon}{2+\varepsilon^2}$$

The position of this point is clearly dependent on

$$\varepsilon = \frac{e}{t}$$

and this is illustrated by the following table:

ε_o	0.05	0.10	0.15	0.20	0.25	0.30	0.35	0.40
θ_m	94.3	98.6	102.9	107.1	111.3	115.5	119.6	123.7

Consider the positive pressure between $\pi \le \theta \le 2\pi$. The components of the load on the bearing, per unit width, are

$$F_h = R\int_{\pi}^{2\pi}(p - p_o)\cos\theta\,d\theta = \frac{12\mu u_o R^2\varepsilon^2}{t^2(2+\varepsilon^2)(1-\varepsilon^2)}$$

and $$F_v = R\int_{\pi}^{2\pi}(p - p_o)\sin\theta\,d\theta = \frac{6\pi\mu u_o R^2\varepsilon}{t^2(2+\varepsilon^2)\sqrt{(1-\varepsilon^2)}}$$

or $$\frac{\mu N}{F}\left(\frac{R}{\varepsilon}\right)^2 = S = \frac{(2+\varepsilon^2)\sqrt{(1-\varepsilon^2)}}{6\pi^2\varepsilon}$$

where $N = R\Omega$, $F = \dfrac{F_v}{2RB}$, B = bearing width

The dimensionless group S is known as the *Sommerfeld* number.

Note. The half of the pressure distribution between $0 \le \theta < \pi$ is negative: this leads to any entrained air separating out from the lubricant, the film becomes discontinuous and there is no contribution to the load support.

Problems

1 Oil, density 850 kg/m^3, is pumped along a pipe of diameter 15 cm, length 1200 m, at a rate of 0.02 m^3/s. The pump efficiency = 0.65. If the pump drive power = 7.5 kW calculate the absolute and kinematic viscosity of the oil.

The viscosity changes along the pipe due to cooling of the oil, such that the viscosity at the exit is twice that at inlet (as determined in the previous calculation). The density can be taken as constant. Calculate the pump power required if the viscosity changes linearly with the distance along the pipe.

Answer 0.126 Ns/m^2, 1.48x10^{-4} m/s^2;
11.25 kW.

2 A cylindrical tank, cross-sectional area 10 m^2, is connected at the base to the base of another tank, cross-sectional area 2 m^2, by a smooth, horizontal pipe of diameter 25 cm, length 10 cm. Both tanks are open to the atmosphere, and contain oil of kinematic viscosity 0.15 m/s^2.

Initially the depth of oil in the larger tank is 6 m, and in the smaller tank is 3 m.

Estimate the time taken for the difference in level to decrease to 1 m

(a) neglecting inlet and exit losses in the pipe;
(b) taking the inlet and exit losses into account.

Answer (a) 4 340 s (b) 7 000 s.

3 A cylinder, diameter 100 mm, discharges oil through a vertical pipe, 1 mm diameter, at the centre of the cylinder. The pipe length is 500 mm. The density of the oil = 850 kg/m^3. Initially the depth of oil in the cylinder is 50 mm.

A measurement of the flow gave a collection of 50 ml in 3000 seconds: from this result estimate the absolute viscosity of the oil.

Assume that the viscosity is constant, and neglect entry and exit effects.

Describe an application of this method of viscosity measurement to practical instruments, commenting on the validity of the assumptions made in the calculation.

Answer 0.013 Ns/m^2 .

4 A conical funnel contains oil, which discharges through the base (Fig. 5.16): the base is considered as an orifice, of discharge coefficient C_d . The oil surface is open to atmosphere.

Assuming that C_d is constant, and the oil free surface remains horizontal, show that the time taken to empty the funnel is given by the expression

$$t = \frac{1}{\sqrt{2g}} \int \sqrt{\frac{az^4 - 1}{z - z_o}}\, dz$$

between limits $z_o + h$, and z,

$$a = \left(C_d^2 z_o^4\right)^{-1}$$

If r_o = 10 mm, h = 50 mm, z_o = 30 mm and C_d = 0.60 estimate the time taken. It is suggested that numerical integration is used, with steps Δz = 10 mm.

Briefly comment on the validity of assuming a constant coefficient C_d.

What is the significance of the assumption that the free surface of the oil remains horizontal?

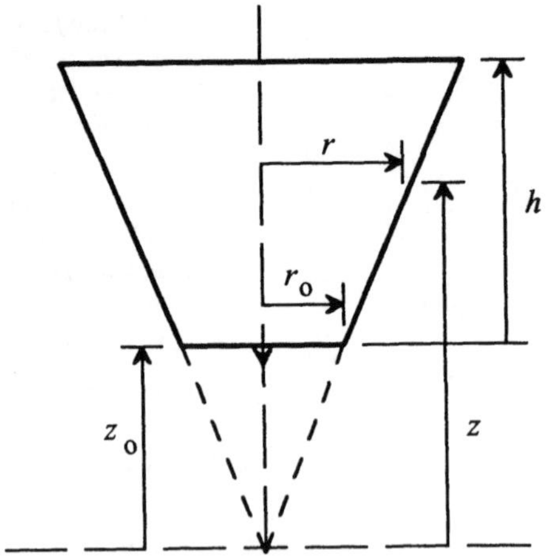

Figure 5.16

Answer 18.2 s.
C_d is a function of Reynolds number.
No vortex formation.

5 A U-tube contains a viscous fluid: the tube diameter D is constant. The fluid levels are disturbed, moving with an initial velocity v_o, so that an oscillation is set up.

Derive the equation

$$\frac{d^2z}{dt^2} + \frac{32\nu}{D^2}\frac{dz}{dt} + \frac{2gz}{L} = 0$$

where $2z$ = difference of level, and the datum is midway between the two levels.

Hence show that, at time t after the initial disturbance,

$$z = \left(\frac{v_o}{b}\right)\exp(-at)\sinh(bt)$$

where $a = \dfrac{16\nu}{D^2}$, $\quad b^2 = a^2 - \dfrac{2g}{L}$

L = length of fluid column.

Determine the maximum displacement.

Answer $\dfrac{v_o \exp(-at)}{\sqrt{a^2 - b^2}}$, $\quad z = \dfrac{v_o}{b}\exp(-at)\sinh(bt)$

Note $\exp(bt) - \exp(-bt) = 2\sinh(bt)$

$$\sinh^2\alpha = \frac{1}{\tanh^2\alpha} - 1$$

6 A viscous incompressible fluid flows axially along a concentric annulus, of radii 5 cm and 10 cm. Assuming the relationship

$$\frac{dp}{dx} = \mu\left(\frac{d^2u}{dr^2} + \frac{1}{r}\frac{du}{dr}\right) = \frac{\mu}{r}\frac{d}{dr}\left(r\frac{du}{dr}\right)$$

show that the velocity distribution is given by the equation

$$u = \left(\frac{r^2}{4\mu} - 0.0027 \ln r - 0.00873\right)\frac{P}{\mu}$$

where P = pressure gradient.

Determine the radius at which the velocity is a maximum; the flow rate in terms of μ and P; and the ratio of the mean to maximum velocity.

Answer 7.36 cm; 0.0053 l/s; 0.65.

7 A piston, 50 mm long, 25 mm diameter, descends at a steady velocity of 3 m/s in a cylinder containing oil. The pressure difference across the piston is 150 N/m^2, and the radial clearance is 3 mm. Calculate the viscosity of the oil, stating any assumptions made.

A mass of 0.01 kg is added to the piston. Calculate the new velocity of descent.

Answer 3.6×10^{-4} Ns/m^2. 7.0 m/s.

8 A compression testing machine is shown in Fig. 5.17. The fluid viscosity = 1.5 poise.

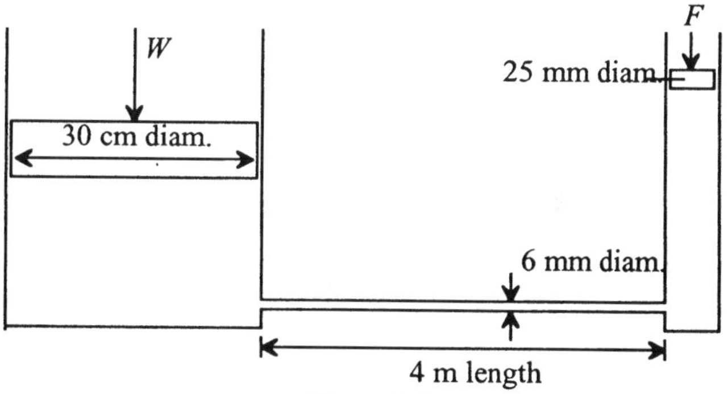

Figure 5.17

A force F = 760 N is applied to the plunger, producing a downward velocity of 15 mm/s. Calculate the load on the ram W, and the ram velocity.

Answer 1190 kN; 0.1 mm/s.

9 Two viscous, incompressible fluids flow between two parallel, plane surfaces. The pressure gradient in the direction of flow, P, is constant. The gap thickness between the surfaces is $2t$. The upper half of the gap is filled with fluid of viscosity μ, and the lower half with fluid of viscosity $k\mu$.

Derive expressions for the velocity profile across the gap assuming that the fluids do not mix, taking $k = 3$.

Obtain an expression for the flow rate; and hence determine the equivalent viscosity of a single fluid filling the gap to give the same flow rate.

Answer
$$u_1 = \frac{P}{6\mu}(3y^2 - ty - 2t^2)$$
$$u_2 = \frac{P}{6\mu}(y^2 - ty - 2t^2)$$
$$Q = \frac{11Pt^3}{18\mu}, \quad \mu\ (\text{equivalent}) = \frac{3\mu}{22}$$

10 The load on a vertical shaft is supported by an externally pressurised bearing (Fig. 5.18).

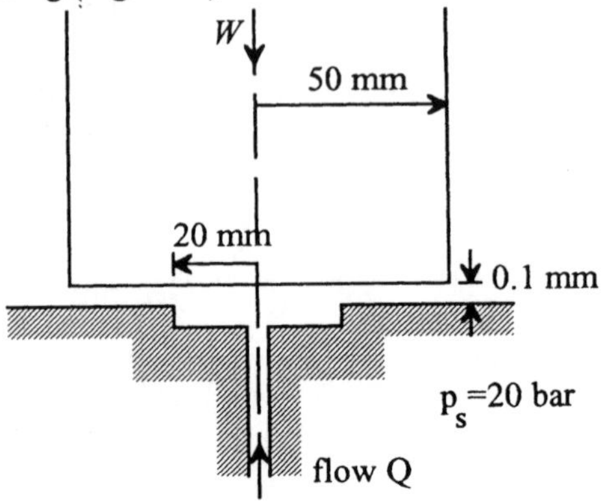

Figure 5.18

The properties of the oil are:
kinematic viscosity = 53×10^{-6} m^2/s
density = 880 kg/m^3
specific heat = 1.9 kJ/kg K

Assuming a uniform film thickness determine the flow rate Q, and the power required to maintain the flow rate.

The rotational speed of the shaft is 900 rev/min at these conditions. Calculate the power required to drive the shaft, and the temperature rise of the oil.

Answer 2.45×10^{-5} m^3/s; 49 W
39.6 W; 1 K.

11 A piston, diameter D, length L, slides at a steady velocity u_o in a horizontal cylinder. The annular gap, of constant width t, between the piston and cylinder is filled with oil. The pressure behind, and in front of, the piston is p_1 and p_2 respectively. Assuming laminar flow and neglecting end effects show that the flow through the gap is given by the equation

$$Q = \frac{\pi D t^3}{24\mu L}(p_1 - p_2) + \frac{\pi D t u_o}{4}$$

Calculate the shear force on the piston when t = 1 mm, D = 10 cm, L = 20 cm, u_o = 4 m/s, μ = 0.1 Ns/m^2, p_1 = 1 bar, p_2 = 3 bar.

Answer 56.6 N

12 An oil film of thickness (initially) h is compressed by a load W (Fig. 5.19).

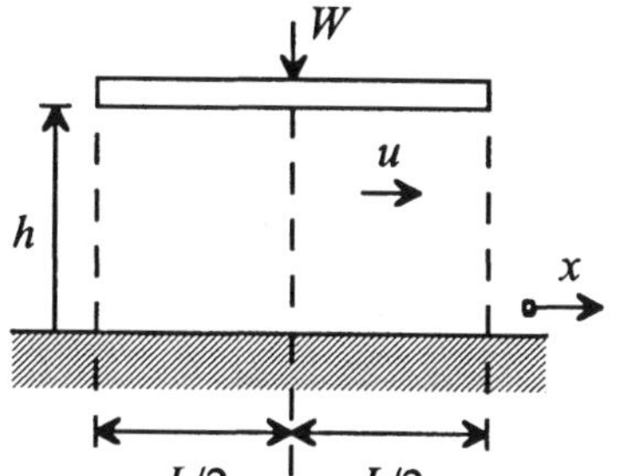

Figure 5.19

Show that, per unit width, and neglecting end effects, as the thickness decreases with time t,

mean velocity $\bar{u} = \dfrac{x}{h}\dfrac{dh}{dt}$

flow rate $Q = 2x\dfrac{dh}{dt}$

pressure $p = \dfrac{6\mu}{h^3}\left(\dfrac{L^2}{4} - x^2\right)\dfrac{dh}{dt}$

load $W = \dfrac{\mu L^3}{h^3}\dfrac{dh}{dt}$

At what value of dh/dt does the flow at the outlet plane become non-laminar? Assume that it occurs at a Reynolds number (based on the mean velocity and gap thickness) = 2000.

Answer $\dfrac{4000\nu}{L}$

13 Outline how the viscosity of a fluid can be measured using rotating cylinders, or a cylinder which oscillates in the fluid.

A cone and plate viscometer is illustrated in Fig. 5.20.

The space between the flat stationary plate and the rotating cone is filled with a viscous fluid. Assuming pure rotation and a linear velocity profile, show that the torque on the shaft T is given by the equation

$$T = \frac{2\pi\mu\Omega R_o^3}{3\sin\alpha}.$$

14 A footstep bearing is shown in Fig. 5.21. Oil is supplied to the central chamber at a pressure p_o, uniformly over the chamber area. The oil flows radially outwards through the gap of thickness t (which may be assumed to be constant), leaving at atmospheric pressure.

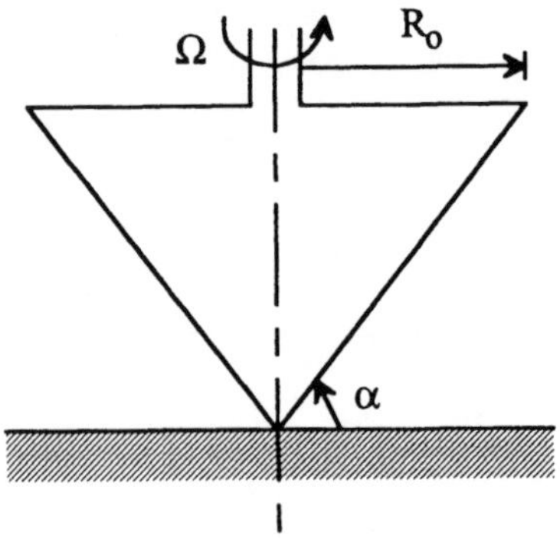

Figure 5.20

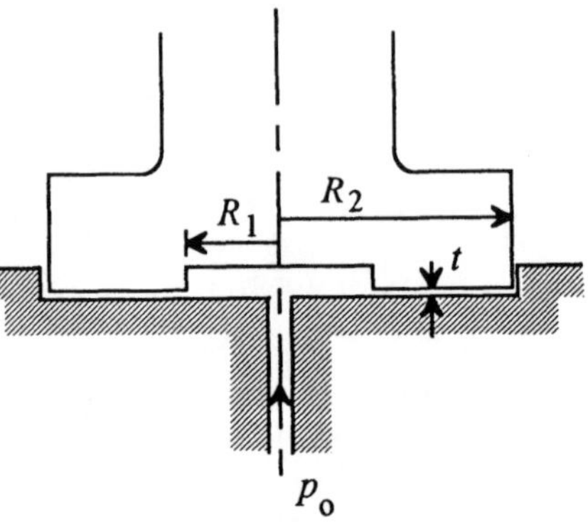

Figure 5.21

Show that the force on the shaft F is given by

$$F = \frac{\frac{1}{2}\pi p_o (R_2^2 - R_1^2)}{\ln\left(R_2/R_1\right)}$$

Calculate the oil flow rate when $R_1 = 50$ mm, $R_2 = 150$ mm, $t =$ 0.10 mm, $p_o = 2$ bar, and $\mu = 0.25$ Ns/m^2.

Answer 3.8×10^{-7} m^3/s.

15 A rectangular bearing pad is shown in Fig. 5.22. Oil is supplied, via a restrictor of diameter D, length L, from a reservoir where the pressure is p_s. Assuming that the pressure in the chamber p_c is uniform show that the flow rate Q is given by the equation

$$Q = \frac{h^3}{12\mu}(p_c - p_o)w$$

where w = effective flow path width

$$= \frac{2}{b}(E - e) + \frac{2}{e}(B - b)$$

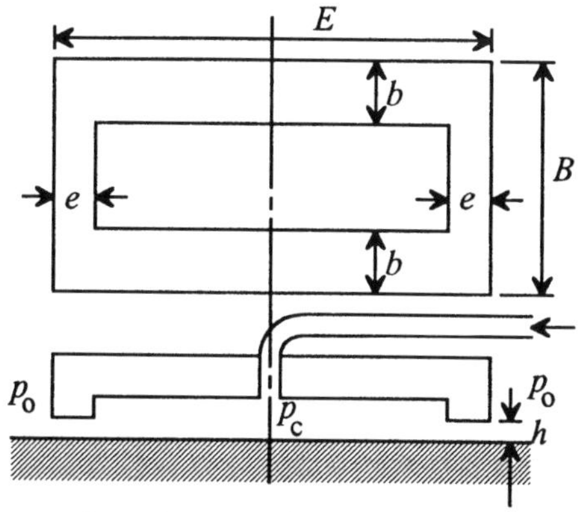

Figure 5.22

In a certain pad $E = 20$ cm, $e = b = 1$ cm, $B = 20$ cm, length $L = 2$ m, $D = 10$ mm, $p_s - p_o = 10$ bar. Determine the flow rate and load at a gap width $h = 2$ mm, and oil of viscosity 0.3 Ns/m^2.

The following relationships may be used:

effective area $A_e = \beta(1 - \alpha)^2 E^2$

$$W = \frac{A_e(p_s - p_o)}{1 + \bar{h}^3}$$

$$\left(\frac{\bar{h}}{h}\right)^3 = \frac{64(L - \alpha)(1 + \beta^2)}{3\pi\alpha\beta D^4}$$

where $\alpha = \frac{e}{E} = \frac{b}{B}$, $\beta = \frac{B}{E}$

Answer 1.69 l/s. 62.8 N.

16 A viscous, incompressible fluid flows through a convergent slot (as shown in Fig.5.23).

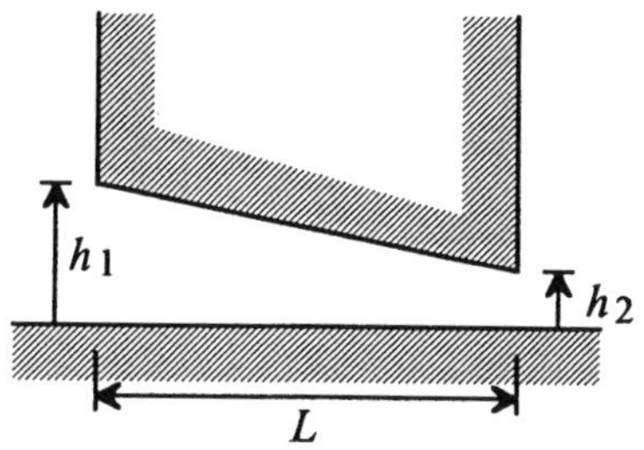

Figure 5.23

Show that the pressure distribution and flow rate/unit width, Q, are given by the equations

$$p = p_1 - \frac{h_2^2(h_1^2 - h^2)}{h^2(h_1^2 - h_2^2)}(p_1 - p_2)$$

$$Q = \frac{h_1^2 h_2^2(p_1 - p_2)}{6\mu L(h_1 + h_2)}$$

17 A slipper bearing is shown in Fig.5.24. The pressure distribution is given by the equation

$$p = \frac{6\mu L u_o (h - h_1)(h - h_2)}{h^2(h_1^2 - h_2^2)}$$

Show that, per unit width, the thrust W and drag F are given by the equations

$$W = \frac{6\mu L^2 u_o}{(h_1 - h_2)^2}\left(\ln\frac{h_1}{h_2} - \frac{2(h_1 - h_2)}{h_1 + h_2}\right)$$

$$F = \frac{W}{2L}(h_2 - h_1) + \frac{\mu L u_o}{h_1 - h_2}\ln\frac{h_1}{h_2}$$

If $\dfrac{h_1}{h_2} = 2$

determine the position of the hydrodynamic centre.

Answer $x_c = 0.256L$

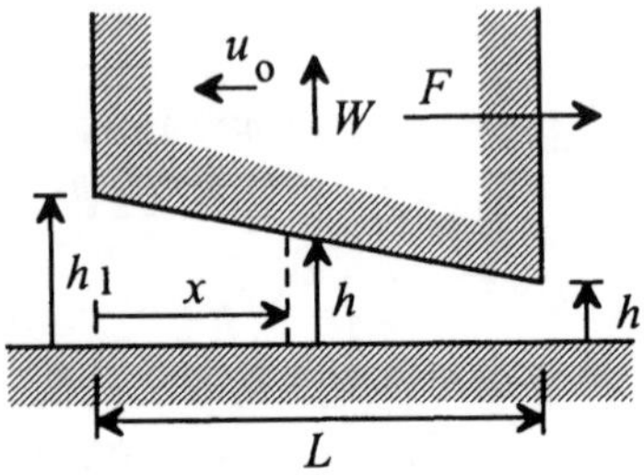

Figure 5.24

18 The fixed shoe of a slipper bearing is 50 mm long (in the direction of motion), and 100 mm wide. The moving plate is inclined at an angle of 0.05° to the shoe. The minimum thickness of the oil film is 0.05 mm. The viscosity of the oil = 0.04 Ns/m^2. The slider velocity is 10 m/s.

Calculate the load on the bearing, and the position of the hydrodynamic centre.

Answer 6.3 kN; 32 mm.

19 The fixed pad in a thrust bearing has a profile given by the equation

$$h = h_1 \exp(-\alpha x)$$

The bearing plate is plane and moves with a velocity u_o. Assuming that there is no side leakage show that where the pressure is a maximum the film thickness is

$$\frac{3}{2}h_1\left(\frac{a^2 - 1}{a^3 - 1}\right) \qquad \text{where } a = \frac{h_1}{h_2}$$

and h_1, h_2 are the maximum and film thickness respectively.

The Reynolds equation

$$\frac{dp}{dx} = \frac{6\mu u_0}{h^3}(h - \bar{h})$$

should be used: $\bar{h}$ = film thickness at the maximum pressure position.

In a particular bearing $u_o = 5$ m/s, $a = 2$, $h_2 = 0.01$ mm and the pad width = 10 cm. Calculate the flow rate between the pad and bearing plate.

Answer $3.2 \times 10^{-6}\,\text{m}^3/\text{s}$.

Hint. Show that the flow rate = $\frac{1}{2}u_o\bar{h}L$

20 The Reynolds equation for a lubricated journal bearing is

$$\frac{\partial}{\partial x}\left(h^3\frac{\partial p}{\partial x}\right) + \frac{\partial}{\partial z}\left(h^3\frac{\partial p}{\partial z}\right) = 6\mu u_o\frac{\partial h}{\partial x}$$

where $x = R\theta$, $-\frac{1}{2}L \le z \le \frac{1}{2}L$, $h = c(1 + \varepsilon\cos\theta)$.

If the length is small compared to the diameter show that the pressure distribution in a bearing is given by the equation

$$p = \frac{3\mu u_o\varepsilon\sin\theta}{Rc^2(1 + \varepsilon\cos\theta)^3}\left(\frac{L^2}{4} - z^2\right) + \frac{p_1}{L}\left(\frac{L}{2} - z\right)$$

where $p = 0$ at $z = \frac{1}{2}L$

$p = p_1$ at $z = -\frac{1}{2}L$

21 A viscous fluid is contained between two concentric cylinders: the outer cylinder rotates at a constant speed and the inner cylinder is stationary. There is no flow in the axial and radial directions. Assuming that the shear stress

$$\tau = \frac{A}{r^2}$$

show that the angular velocity of the fluid at radius r is given by

$$\Omega = B - \frac{A}{2\pi r^2}$$

The cylinder diameters are 10 cm and 20 cm. The outer cylinder rotates at a speed of 1000 rev/min. The length of the inner cylinder is 50 cm.

If the power required to rotate the outer cylinder is 300 W determine the fluid viscosity. Neglect end effects.

How can end effects be eliminated to give a more accurate determination of viscosity?

Answer $1.31\,\text{Ns/m}^2$.
Measurement of the power at various lengths of immersion.

22 A Newtonian fluid flows down a vertical wall as a film of constant thickness b.

Show that the mean fluid velocity in the film is

$$\frac{gb^2}{3\nu}$$

and is equal to 2/3 times the maximum velocity (at the free surface).

6

Boundary layer

The flow of a fluid over or around a body will generate a force, which can be resolved into two components: normal to the direction of the free (undisturbed) stream and termed the lift, and in the same direction as that of the free stream, and termed the drag.

The drag is made up of a pressure (or form) drag, and skin fraction drag. The pressure drag is due to the disturbance of the streamlines, and can be determined by potential flow theory (Chap.4): the fluid is inviscid (zero viscosity) and the force is due entirely to changes in static pressure. The skin friction drag is due to viscous forces that would be present in a real fluid.

The boundary layer concept, due to Prandtl, takes the flow over a solid surface to be in two regions:

(a) a layer, adjacent to the surface, in which *viscous* forces predominate, termed the boundary layer.

(b) a region outside the boundary layer in which viscous forces are negligible, so that potential flow theory can be used.

The general characteristics of the boundary layer are shown in Fig.6.1.

Boundary layer characteristics

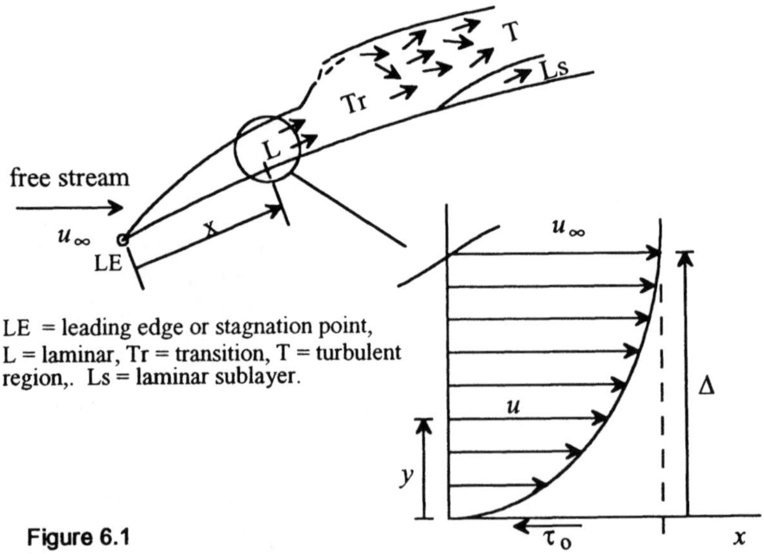

LE = leading edge or stagnation point, L = laminar, Tr = transition, T = turbulent region,. Ls = laminar sublayer.

Figure 6.1

The layer, starting from the leading edge, is initially laminar. The shear stress (for a Newtonian fluid) is proportional to the velocity gradient

$$\tau = \mu \frac{\partial u}{\partial y}$$

The fluid particles adjacent to the surface are stationary relative to the surface (the no-slip condition), and at the edge of the boundary layer ($y = \Delta$) the fluid velocity is equal to the free stream velocity at that *particular section*.

As the layer thickness Δ increases and the fluid velocity in the layer decreases a transition region is reached, where a significant increase in the thickness occurs. The layer then becomes turbulent, and mixing takes place so that there is momentum transfer *across* the layer (i.e. in the y direction). The shear stress is given by the equation

$$\tau = (\mu + \varepsilon)\frac{\partial u}{\partial y},\ \text{where } \varepsilon \text{ is termed the eddy viscosity.}$$

Pressure gradient and separation

The pressure gradient $\partial p/\partial x$ plays a major role in the growth of the boundary layer. A favourable gradient,

$$\frac{\partial p}{\partial x} < 0,$$

corresponding to accelerating free stream flow, retards the layer growth and produces a stable layer. On the other hand an adverse gradient

$$\left(\frac{\partial p}{\partial x} > 0\right),$$

corresponding to decelerating flow, causes the layer thickness to increase rapidly. The velocity gradient at the surface may decrease to zero, and then to a negative value (as shown in Fig .6.2). At these conditions the boundary layer *separates* from the surface, leading to *wake* formation and increase in the drag. Hence it is important, in practice, to avoid separation of the layer.

It is this influence that makes a turbine (expanding flow) inherently more efficient than a compressor (adverse pressure gradient).

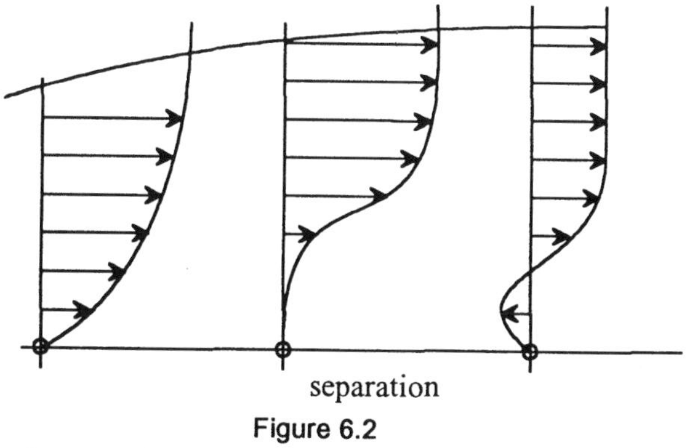

Figure 6.2

In general terms a laminar layer is more likely to separate than a turbulent layer, because of the cross-stream mixing in the latter. The slower particles near to the surface are energised by the faster, outer particles in the mixing process. However in many situations the laminar layer changes to a turbulent layer in a comparatively short distance.

Layer thickness

The layer thickness Δ is the value of the distance y where the local velocity u is equal to the free stream velocity u_∞. The velocity u approaches u_∞ asymptotically, so that the layer thickness is often taken as the value of y when $u = 0.99u_\infty$.

The *displacement* thickness Δ^* is defined by the equation

$$u_\infty \Delta^* = \int_0^\Delta (u_\infty - u)dy$$

The definite integral can be represented by the area ACD (Fig. 6.3), and is equal to the area ADEF. The displacement thickness is therefore a measure of the velocity deficit due to the boundary layer.

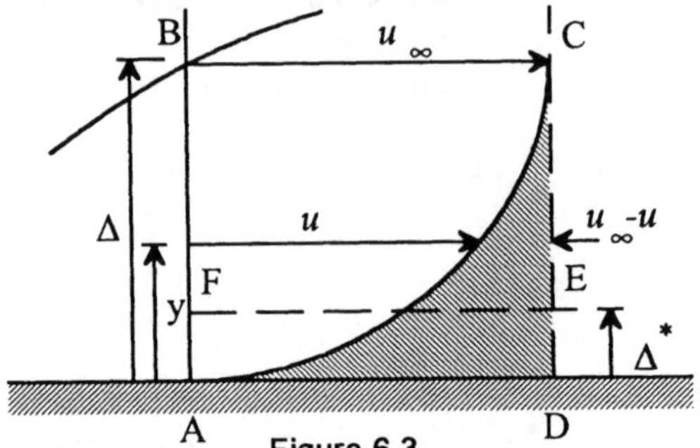

Figure 6.3

The *momentum* thickness θ is defined by the equation

$$\rho u_\infty^2 \theta = \int_0^\Delta \rho u(u_\infty - u)dy.$$

Considering a slice, thickness dy, the momentum in the layer is less than that of the free stream by an amount $\rho u dy.(u_\infty - u)$.

Hence the momentum thickness is a measure of the momentum deficit due to the boundary layer, at the section AB.

The *dissipation energy* thickness Δ^{**} is defined by the equation

$$\rho u_\infty^3 \Delta^{**} = \int_0^\Delta u\left(u_\infty^2 - u^2\right)dy.$$

The thickness Δ^* , θ, Δ^{**} represent the distance the surface would have to be displaced in the y direction to reduce the volume flow, momentum flow, and energy by an amount equal to the reduction caused by the boundary layer.

Boundary Layer equations

The Navier-Stokes equations for steady two-dimensional, incompressible flow reduce for a thin boundary layer to:

$$u\frac{\partial u}{\partial x} + v\frac{\partial u}{\partial y} = \frac{1}{\rho}\frac{\partial p}{\partial x} + \nu\frac{\partial^2 u}{\partial y^2}, \qquad \frac{\partial p}{\partial y} = 0$$

It should be noted that the equations apply to viscous (*laminar*) flow.

The first equation is often difficult to solve, and a good approximation can be given by the use of the *momentum integral* equation:

$$u_\infty \Delta^* \frac{\partial u_\infty}{\partial x} + \frac{\partial(u_\infty^2 \theta)}{\partial x} = \frac{\tau_o}{\rho}$$

or in non-dimensional form

$$\frac{1}{2}c_f = \frac{d\theta}{dx} + \frac{\theta}{u_\infty}(2 + H)\frac{dv_\infty}{dx}$$

where τ_o = shear stress at the surface $y = 0$

H = shape factor $= \dfrac{\Delta^*}{\theta}$

c_f = local skin friction coefficient $= \dfrac{\tau_o}{\frac{1}{2}\rho u_\infty^2}$

The energy integral equation can also be used:

$$\frac{d}{dx}(u_\infty^3\Delta^{**}) = 2\nu\int_0^\Delta\left(\frac{du}{dy}\right)^2 dy$$

Transition, turbulence

A characteristic of the laminar layer is that any disturbances in the layer are damped by viscous forces. At low values of the Reynolds number

$$Re_x = \frac{\rho u_\infty x}{\mu}$$

At higher values of Re_x (in the range 10^5 to 2×10^6) the disturbances are amplified, and spots of turbulence develop. The Reynolds number at this transition region depends upon many factors, such as the degree of turbulence in the free stream, surface roughness, surface temperature, and pressure gradient.

In a *turbulent* layer the velocity at a point in the layer varies with time, or the conditions are unsteady. At a particular point in time the velocity components can be written in the form

$$u = \bar{u} + u', \; v = \bar{v} + v'$$

where $\bar{u}, \bar{v}$ = time average components

u', v' = perturbances or deviation from the mean.

The shear stress is now given by the equation

$$\tau = \mu\frac{d\bar{u}}{dy} - \rho\overline{uv}$$

where the additional term represents the Reynolds stresses introduced by the momentum transfer (in mixing).

Mixing length

The mixing length theory assumes that an eddy (disturbance) retains its random velocity over a mixing length L before mixing with the surrounding fluid, and then

$$\rho\overline{uv} = -\rho L^2\left|\frac{\partial u}{\partial y}\right|\frac{\partial u}{\partial y}, \text{ hence } \tau = \left(\mu + \rho L^2\left|\frac{\partial u}{\partial y}\right|\right)\frac{\partial u}{\partial y}$$

Assumptions of the relationship between L and y then enable integration of the equation as shown in Ex. 6.8.

6.1 Laminar layer on a flat surface

An incompressible fluid flows over a flat plate which is at zero incidence, and the free stream velocity u_∞ is constant. The velocity profile in the boundary layer is of the form

$$\frac{u}{u_\infty} = a\eta + b\eta^3, \text{ where } \eta = \frac{y}{\Delta}$$

By use of the momentum integral equation derive an expression for the layer thickness in terms of u_∞, the kinematic viscosity of the fluid ν, and the distance from the leading edge x.

Also show that the drag coefficient per side is given by

$$C_D = \frac{0.646}{\sqrt{Re_x}}$$

Solution. Considering the free stream outside the boundary layer, and the Bernouilli equation $dp + \rho u_\infty du_\infty = 0$. Since u_∞ is constant

$$dp = 0 \text{ or } \frac{dp}{dx} = 0.$$

Inside the boundary layer any velocity profile must satisfy certain conditions, namely the no-slip condition at the plate ($u = 0$ at $y = 0$) and the continuous velocity condition at the edge of the layer ($u = u_\infty$ at $y = \Delta$). The no-slip condition is clearly satisfied for any values of a and b, and the edge condition gives

$$1 = a + b \qquad \left(\frac{u}{u_\infty} = 1 \text{ at } \eta = \frac{y}{\Delta} = 1\right)$$

Another condition is required to determine the values of a, b and this can be deduced from a consideration of the slope (or gradient) of the velocity profile at the layer edge. At this point a *smooth* merging of the velocity in the layer into the free stream velocity requires the condition

$$\frac{du}{dy} = 0, \text{ or using}$$

$$\eta = \frac{y}{\Delta}, \frac{du}{dy} = \frac{u_\infty}{\Delta}(a + 3b\eta^2) = 0 \text{ at } \eta = 1$$

Hence $a + 3b = 0$

Solving gives $a = \frac{3}{2}, b = -\frac{1}{2}$

$$\frac{u}{u_\infty} = \frac{3}{2}\eta - \frac{1}{2}\eta^3$$

The momentum integral (M.I.) equation is

$$u_\infty\Delta^* \frac{du_\infty}{dx} + \frac{d}{dx}(u_\infty^2\theta) = \frac{\tau_o}{\rho}$$

Now in this problem

$$\frac{du_\infty}{dx} = 0 \text{(constant free stream velocity).}$$

Also $\tau_o = \mu\left(\frac{\partial u}{\partial y}\right)$ with $y = 0$

$$= \frac{\mu u_\infty}{\Delta}\left(\frac{df}{dn}\right)_0 = \frac{\mu u_\infty}{\Delta}f'(0)$$

where the velocity profile, in general, is written in the form

$$\frac{u}{u_\infty} = f(\eta)$$

Hence $\tau_o = \frac{\mu u_\infty}{\Delta}\left(\frac{3}{2} - \frac{3}{2}\eta^2\right)_0 = \frac{3\mu u_\infty}{2\Delta}$

The momentum thickness θ is

$$\theta = \int_0^\Delta \frac{u}{u_\infty}\left(1 - \frac{u}{u_\infty}\right)dy = \Delta\int_0^1 f(1 - f)\,d\eta$$

$$= \Delta\int_0^1\left(\frac{3}{2}\eta - \frac{1}{2}\eta^3\right)\left(1 - \frac{3}{2}\eta + \frac{1}{2}\eta^3\right)d\eta = \frac{39\Delta}{280}$$

Substituting into the M.I. equation

$$\frac{d}{dx}\left(u_\infty^2\frac{39\Delta}{280}\right) = \frac{3\mu u_\infty}{2\Delta\rho}$$

$$\Delta\, d\Delta = \frac{140}{13}\frac{\nu}{u_\infty}dx$$

and integrating

$$\Delta^2 = \frac{280}{13}\frac{\nu x}{u_\infty} \text{ (taking } \Delta = 0 \text{ at } x = 0)$$

or $\Delta = 4.641\sqrt{\frac{\nu x}{u_\infty}}$

It is often convenient to express this in terms of the Reynolds number

$$Re_x = \frac{u_\infty x}{\nu} = \frac{\rho u_\infty x}{\mu}$$

$$\Delta = \frac{4.641x}{\sqrt{Re_x}}$$

On one side of the plate, per unit width, the skin friction drag force is

$$\int_0^x \tau_o \, dx = \frac{3\mu u_\infty}{2}\int_0^x \frac{dx}{\Delta} = \frac{3\mu u_\infty}{2}\int_0^x \frac{1}{4.641}\sqrt{\frac{u_\infty}{\nu x}}\, dx = 0.323 u_\infty^{\frac{3}{2}}\sqrt{\rho\mu x}$$

The drag coefficient

$$C_D = \frac{\text{drag force}}{\frac{1}{2}\rho u_\infty^2 x}$$

so that $$C_D = \frac{0.323 u_\infty^{\frac{3}{2}}\sqrt{\rho\mu x}}{\frac{1}{2}\rho u_\infty^2 x} = 0.646\sqrt{\frac{\mu}{\rho u_\infty x}} = \frac{0.646}{\sqrt{Re_x}}$$

Note. This flat plate, zero pressure gradient, problem was solved in exact terms by Blasius, the M.I. equation is an approximate solution, and the numerical values obtained are greatly dependent upon the velocity profile used. Any profile must, of course, satisfy the essential no-slip and edge conditions. However this still allows many possible profiles to be used as an approximation. For comparison some typical profiles and the results obtained are shown in the following table:

Velocity distribution	$\frac{\Delta^*}{\Delta}$	$\frac{\theta}{\Delta}$	$\frac{\tau_o \Delta}{\mu u_\infty}$	$\Delta\sqrt{\frac{u_\infty}{\nu x}}$	$C_D\sqrt{Re_x}$
Blasius (exact)	0.330	0.130		5.200	0.660
$\frac{3}{2}\eta - \frac{1}{2}\eta^3$	0.380	0.140	1.5	4.640	0.650
$2\eta - 2\eta^3 + \eta^4$	0.300	0.120	2.0	5.840	0.690
$\sin(\frac{1}{2}\pi\eta)$	0.360	0.140	1.570	4.790	0.660

The energy integral equation could be used instead of the M.I. equation. In this case

$$\Delta^{**} = \int_0^\Delta \frac{u}{u_\infty}\left(1 - \left(\frac{u}{u_\infty}\right)^2\right)dy$$

$$= \Delta\int_0^1 f(1 - f^2)\, d\eta$$

and substituting $f = \frac{3}{2}\eta - \frac{1}{2}\eta^3$ gives

$$\Delta^{**} = 0.216\Delta$$

$$\frac{d}{dx}(0.216\Delta u_\infty^3) = 2\nu\int_0^\Delta \left(\frac{du}{dy}\right)^2 dy$$

$$= 2\nu\Delta\int_0^1 \left(\frac{3u_\infty}{2\Delta}\right)^2\left(1 - \eta^2\right)^2 d\eta$$

since $\frac{du}{dy} = \frac{u_\infty}{\Delta}\frac{df}{d\eta} = \frac{3u_\infty}{2\Delta}(1 - \eta^2)$, $dy = \Delta\, d\eta$

Evaluating the integral gives, after simplification,

$$\Delta = 4.718\sqrt{\frac{\nu x}{u_\infty}}$$

6.2 Laminar boundary layer

An air stream flows over a flat plate, with a constant free stream velocity of 100 m/s. The kinematic velocity is $1.5 \times 10^{-5}\,m^2/s$.

Assuming that the velocity distribution is given by the equation

$$\frac{u}{u_\infty} = 2\eta - 2\eta^3 + \eta^4, \qquad \text{where } \eta = \frac{y}{\Delta}$$

determine the layer thickness momentum and displacement thickness at transition from a laminar layer.

It can be taken that transition occurs at a value of the Reynolds number (based on the distance x) equal to 5×10^5.

Solution. The M.I. equation, with a constant free stream velocity, is

$$u_\infty^2 \frac{d\theta}{dx} = \frac{\tau_o}{\rho}$$

Referring to Ex.6.1, in general terms

$$\frac{u}{u_\infty} = f(\eta), \qquad \frac{\tau_o}{\rho} = \frac{\nu u_\infty}{\Delta} f'(0)$$

and $\quad \theta = \Delta \int_0^1 f(1 - f)\, d\eta, \quad \Delta^* = \Delta \int_0^1 (1 - f)\, d\eta$

In this problem $f = 2\eta - 2\eta^3 + \eta^4$, and substituting

$$\frac{\tau_o}{\rho} = \frac{\nu u_\infty}{\Delta}(2 - 6\eta^2 + 4\eta^3\,)_{\eta=0} = \frac{2\nu u_\infty}{\Delta}$$

$$\frac{\theta}{\Delta} = \int_0^1 (2\eta - 2\eta^3 + \eta^4)(1 - 2\eta + 3\eta^3 - \eta^4)\, d\eta$$

$$= \int_0^1 (2\eta - 4\eta^2 - 3\eta^3 + 9\eta^4 - 4\eta^5 - 4\eta^6 + 4\eta^7 - \eta^8)\, d\eta$$

$$= 1 - \frac{4}{3} - \frac{2}{4} + \frac{9}{5} - \frac{4}{6} - \frac{4}{7} + \frac{4}{8} - \frac{1}{9} = \frac{37}{315}$$

Substituting into the M.I. equation gives

$$u_\infty^2 \frac{37}{315}\frac{d\Delta}{dx} = \frac{2\nu u_\infty}{\Delta}$$

$$\Delta\, d\Delta = \frac{630}{37}\frac{\nu}{u_\infty} dx$$

and integrating

$$\Delta^2 = \frac{1260}{37}\frac{\nu x}{u_\infty} \quad \text{or} \quad \Delta = 5.836\sqrt{\frac{\nu x}{u_\infty}}$$

Inserting the data given:

$$\Delta = 5.836\sqrt{\frac{1.5 \times 10^{-5} x}{100}} = \mathbf{0.00226}\sqrt{x}$$

Now at transition

$$Re_x = \frac{u_\infty x}{\nu} = 5 \times 10^5$$

hence $\quad x_t = \dfrac{5 \times 10^5 \times 1.5 \times 10^{-5}}{100} = 0.075\,\text{m}$

and $\quad \Delta_t = 6.19 \times 10^{-4}\,\text{m or } \mathbf{0.62}\,\text{mm}$

The momentum thickness at transition is

$$\theta_t = \frac{37}{315}\Delta_t = \mathbf{0.073}\,\text{mm}$$

The displacement thickness

$$\Delta^* = \Delta\int_0^1 (1 - 2\eta + 2\eta^3 - \eta^4)\,d\eta = \Delta(1 - 1 + \tfrac{1}{2} - \tfrac{1}{5}) = \tfrac{3}{10}\Delta$$

and at transition $\Delta_t^* = \mathbf{0.186}$ mm.

Note. The layer thickness up to transition is very small, reaching a value of 0.62 mm at the transition point, 75 mm from the leading edge (or stagnation point). The boundary layer effect is therefore low. The drag, per unit width, due to the laminar layer is

$$\int \tau_o\,dx = \int \frac{2\mu u_\infty}{\Delta}dx = 2\mu u_\infty \int_0^{x_t} \frac{dx}{0.00226\sqrt{x}} = 176991\mu\sqrt{x_t}$$

Assuming a value of $\rho = 1.2$ kg/m^3, $\mu = \rho\nu = 1.8 \times 10^{-5}$ kg/ms giving a drag force of 0.87 N.

6.3 Boundary layer equations

State the Prandtl boundary layer equation for steady, incompressible flow. Show, briefly, how for a flat plate at zero incidence the Blasius equation is derived.

Outline how the Falkner-Swan equation can be developed, and discuss its application.

Solution. The Navier-Stokes equations, as indicated in the introduction, reduce in this case to

$$u\frac{\partial u}{\partial x} + v\frac{\partial u}{\partial y} = -\frac{1}{\rho}\frac{\partial p}{\partial x} + \nu\frac{\partial^2 u}{\partial y^2}$$

Since $\dfrac{\partial p}{\partial y} = 0,\ \dfrac{\partial p}{\partial x} = \dfrac{dp}{dx}$

and from the Bernoulli equation

$$dp + \rho u_\infty\,du_\infty = 0$$

the first equation can be written as

$$u\frac{\partial u}{\partial x} + v\frac{\partial u}{\partial y} = u_\infty\frac{du_\infty}{dx} + \nu\frac{\partial^2 u}{\partial y^2}$$

This is known as the Prandtl equation.

For a flat plate, at zero incidence, the free stream velocity is constant. Also, introducing a new variable

$$\varepsilon = \frac{1}{2}y\sqrt{\frac{u_\infty}{\nu x}}$$

into the Prandtl equation with a function defined by the expression

$$u = \tfrac{1}{2}u_\infty f'$$

gives the differential equation

$$\mathbf{f f'' + f''' = 0}$$

where the dashes denote differentiation with respect to ε. This (Blasius) equation can be solved, giving the results quoted in Ex.6.1.

The Falkner-Swan equation is developed from the boundary layer equation to allow for the situation where the pressure gradient (in the external flow, outside the boundary layer) is not zero; and the free stream velocity can be expressed in terms of the distance x, in the form

$$u_\infty = kx^m$$

The boundary layer equation reduces to the Falkner-Swan equation

$$\mathbf{f''' + (m + 1)f f'' - 2m(f')^2 + 8m = 0}$$

The equation can be integrated by numerical methods to give the velocity profile: $u = \frac{1}{2}u_\infty f'$, $\quad v = -\frac{1}{2}\sqrt{\frac{u_\infty \nu}{x}}\left((m+1)f + (m-1)\varepsilon f'\right)$

The profiles at different points (i.e. different values of x) are identical to each other except for the change in the length scale. For this reason the solutions to f in the equation are termed *similar* solutions.

The shear stress at the surface is given by the expression

$$\tau_o = \frac{\mu u_\infty}{x}\sqrt{Re_x}\, f''(0)$$

Some examples of the flow field for different values of m are illustrated in the following table at a separation point $m = -0.0904$.

Flow type	m	$\frac{du_\infty}{dx}$	$\frac{dp}{dx}$
decelerating	$-0.09 < m < 0$	negative	positive
uniform	zero	zero	zero
accelerating	$0 < m < 1$	positive	negative
strongly accelerating	$1 < m < \infty$	positive	negative

6.4 Polhausen's method

> Outline the Pohlhausen method for the computation of a laminar boundary layer on a surface, in the steady flow of incompressible fluid subject to a pressure gradient.
>
> Briefly explain why the method was developed, and discuss its application.

Solution. The velocity profile in the layer is assumed, in this method, to be of the form

$$\frac{u}{u_\infty} = a\eta + b\eta^2 + cn^3 + d\eta^4 = f(\eta)$$

where, as before, $\eta = \frac{y}{\Delta}$.

Any profile must satisfy certain boundary conditions, namely:

at $y = 0$ (surface), $\quad u = 0 \quad$ or $\quad f(0) = 0$

at $y = \Delta$ (layer edge), $\quad u = u_\infty \quad$ or $\quad f(1) = 1$

$$\frac{du}{dy} = 0 \quad \text{or} \quad f'(1) = 0$$

$$\frac{d^2u}{dy^2} = 0 \quad \text{or} \quad f''(1) = 0$$

Using these conditions gives

$$a + b + c + d = 1$$

$$2b + 3c + 4d = 0$$

$$2b + 6c + 12d = 0$$

Some other relationship is now required to determine the four coefficients a, b, c, d. The relationship used involves the Pohlhausen parameter

$$\Lambda = \frac{\Delta^2}{\nu}\frac{du_\infty}{dx} = -f''(0) = -(2b + 6c\eta + 12d\eta^2\,)_{\eta=0} = -2b$$

Thus $b = -\frac{1}{2}\Lambda$

and from the boundary condition equations

$$a = 2 + \tfrac{1}{6}\Lambda, c = -2 + \tfrac{1}{2}\Lambda, d = 1 - \tfrac{1}{6}\Lambda.$$

Hence $\frac{u}{u_\infty} = f(\eta)$

$$= (2 + \frac{1}{6}\Lambda)\eta - \frac{1}{2}\Lambda\eta^2 + (\frac{1}{2}\Lambda - 2)\eta^3 + (1 - \frac{1}{6}\Lambda)\eta^4$$

$$= f_1 + \Lambda f_2 \text{ say}$$

where $f_1 = 2\eta - 2\eta^3 + \eta^4, f_2 = \tfrac{1}{6}\eta(1 - \eta)^3$.

The computation can now be carried out as in the previous examples: the displacement and momentum thickness can be determined *in terms of* the parameter Λ, and substituted into the M.I. equation. A differential equation is then obtained for the momentum thickness (as a function of Λ) and x:

$$\frac{d}{dx}\left(\frac{\theta^2}{\nu}\right) = \frac{F(\Lambda)}{u_\infty}$$

The equation can be integrated by numerical methods provided that the free stream velocity u_∞ and its derivative du_∞/dx are known, and the initial conditions are known. Schlichting shows that, at an initial stagnation point

$$\Lambda = 7.052 \qquad \frac{\theta^2}{\nu} = \frac{0.077}{\left(\frac{du_\infty}{dx}\right)}$$

and
$$\frac{d\left(\theta^2/\nu\right)}{dx} = -0.0652\left(\frac{d^2u_\infty}{dx^2}\right)/\left(\frac{du_\infty}{dx}\right)^2$$

At the *separation* point

$$\frac{\partial u}{\partial y} = 0 \text{ at } y = 0 \text{ or } f'(0) = 0.$$

Hence $a + 2b\eta + 3c\eta^2 + 4d\eta^3 = 0$ at $\eta = 0$

giving $a = 0$ and $\mathbf{\Lambda = -12}$

Further if $\Lambda > 12$ the local velocity u can exceed the free stream velocity u_∞, which is physically impossible. The values of Λ are therefore in the range $-12 \leq \Lambda \leq 12$.

The method is reasonably accurate in the computation of the layer thickness and drag coefficient, but is often less accurate in the prediction of the position of the separation point. It can also be a somewhat cumbersome method, although this can be considerably relieved by the use of a computer.

Note. The expression for the displacement and momentum thickness in terms of the parameter Λ can be obtained as follows:

$$\Delta^* = \Delta\int_0^1 (1 - f)\,d\eta = \frac{\Lambda}{120}(36 - \Lambda)$$

$$\theta = \Delta\int_0^1 f(1 - f)\,d\eta = \Delta\left(\frac{37}{315} - \frac{\Lambda}{945} - \frac{\Lambda^2}{9072}\right)$$

$$\tau_o = \frac{\mu u_\infty}{\Delta}\left(2 + \frac{\Lambda}{6}\right)$$

Also $F(\Lambda) = 2\left(\frac{37}{315} - \frac{\Lambda}{945} - \frac{\Lambda^2}{9072}\right)\left(2 - \frac{116\Lambda}{315} + \frac{79\Lambda^2}{7560} + \frac{\Lambda^3}{4536}\right)$

6.5 Thwaites method

The free stream velocity over a surface varies with the distance from the leading edge x, according to the equation $u_\infty = u_o(1 - x)$. It may be assumed that the layer thickness is zero at $x = 0$, and the layer is laminar.

By use of Thwaites approximation determine the position of the separation point. Show how the method was developed from the momentum integral equation.

Solution. The Thwaites approximation for a laminar boundary layer gives the equation

$$\frac{\theta^2}{\nu} = \frac{0.45}{u_\infty^6}\int u_\infty^5\, dx$$

with the separation at

$$\frac{\theta^2}{\nu}\frac{du_\infty}{dx} = -0.082.$$

In this problem $u_\infty = u_o(1 - x)$, and substituting

$$\frac{\theta^2}{\nu} = \frac{0.45}{u_o^6(1-x)^6}\int_0^x u_o^5(1-x)^5\, dx = \frac{0.45}{6u_o(1-x)^6}\left(1 - (1-x)^6\right)$$

$$= \frac{0.075}{u_o}\left(\frac{1}{(1-x)^6} - 1\right)$$

At separation

$$\frac{\theta^2}{\nu}\frac{du_\infty}{dx} = \frac{\theta^2}{\nu}(-u_o) = -0.082.$$

Hence $-0.075\left(\dfrac{1}{(1-x)^6} - 1\right) = -0.082$

giving $x = \mathbf{0.116}$

The method is derived as follows. Starting with the M.I. equation,

$$u_\infty \Delta^* \frac{du_\infty}{dx} + \frac{d}{dx}(u_\infty^2\theta) = \frac{\tau_o}{\rho}$$

$$u_\infty^2\frac{d\theta}{dx} + (2\theta + \Delta^*)u_\infty\frac{du_\infty}{dx} = \frac{\tau_o}{\rho}$$

$$\frac{d\theta}{dx} + (2 + H)\frac{\theta}{u_\infty}\frac{du_\infty}{dx} = \frac{\tau_o}{\rho u_\infty^2} = \frac{\nu l}{u_\infty \theta}$$

where $H = \dfrac{\Delta^*}{\theta}$ and is termed the *shape factor*, $l = \dfrac{\tau_o \theta}{\mu u_\infty}$

Hence $u_\infty \dfrac{d}{dx}(\theta^2) = 2u_\infty\dfrac{d\theta}{dx} = 2u_\infty\theta\left(\dfrac{\nu l}{u_\infty\theta} - (2 + H)\dfrac{\theta}{u_\infty}\dfrac{du_\infty}{dx}\right)$

$$= 2\nu l - 2(2 + H)\theta^2\frac{du_\infty}{dx}$$

Introducing the parameter

$$m = -\frac{\theta^2}{\nu}\frac{du_\infty}{dx}$$

gives $u_\infty \dfrac{d}{dx}(\theta^2) = 2\nu l + 2(2 + H)\nu m = \nu L$ say

where $L = 2l + 2m(2 + H)$

Experimental work carried out by Thwaites showed that a good approximation was given by the linear relationship $L = 0.45 + 6m$. Using this result gives

$$u_\infty \frac{d}{dx}(\theta^2) = (0.45 + 6m)\nu$$

or
$$u_\infty \frac{d}{dx}(\theta^2) + 6\theta^2 \frac{du_\infty}{dx} = 0.45\nu$$

Multiplying throughout by u_∞^5 then gives

$$\frac{d}{dx}(u_\infty^6 \theta^2) = 0.45\nu u_\infty^5$$

and integrating

$$u_\infty^6 \theta^2 = 0.45\nu \int u_\infty^5 \, dx$$

6.6 Layer control

Briefly outline the methods of boundary layer control, and their application.

A rectangular duct has porous wall, and the cross-sectional area varies with the axial distance from the inlet x, according to the equation $A = 0.1 + x/2$ (m^2).

Assuming two-dimensional, incompressible flow and a velocity profile in the laminar boundary layer of the form

$$\frac{u}{u_\infty} = 2\eta - 2\eta^3 + \eta^4$$

determine the suction velocity of fluid through the wall in terms of x if the boundary layer thickness is maintained at a constant value of 5 mm.

$\nu = 1.5 \times 10^{-5}\ m^2/s$, $u_\infty = 100$ m/s at the inlet.

Solution. The influence of the boundary layer, and particularly the onset of separation, on the lift and drag droves has led to the development of layer control. The maximum lift force on an aerofoil, for example, can also be increased substantially by the prevention of separation as well as any drag reduction.

The methods of layer control can be summarised as follows:

(a) removal of the low energy fluid in the layer through suction slots or a porous surface;

(b) blowing high energy fluid into the layer through slots;

(c) using a moving surface to reduce the relative velocity between the fluid and the surface, such as a rotating cylinder.

The basic principle underlying the methods is the maintenance of the fluid velocity at a sufficiently high value to avoid separation at the surface. If separation does occur the wake formation downstream produces a high increase in the drag and reduction in the lift.

The fluid flow through the suction or blowing slots can be carried through the aerofoil interior and the energy required supplied by a blower, or the pressure difference required can be obtained from the pressure variation about the aerofoil section. Examples of the latter include slotted flaps, slots, and leading edge slats.

The calculation is executed with the M.I. equation as the starting point. The equation is modified to allow for the suction velocity, v_s, of the fluid *through* the surface i.e. in the y-direction.

$$u_\infty^2 . \frac{dy}{dx} + \left(2 + H\right) u_\infty \theta \frac{du_\infty}{dx} + u_\infty v_s = \frac{\tau_0}{\rho}$$

The results from Ex. 6.2 give

$$\theta = \frac{37}{315}\Delta, \quad \Delta^* = \frac{3}{10}\Delta, \quad \frac{\tau_0}{\rho} = \frac{2\nu u_\infty}{\Delta}$$

hence $H = \frac{\Delta^*}{\theta} = \frac{3}{10}\left(\frac{315}{37}\right) = 2.554$

Substituting into the M.I. equation

$$\frac{37}{315}u_\infty^2 . \frac{d\Delta}{dx} + 4.554u_\infty\left(\frac{37}{315}\Delta\right)\frac{du_\infty}{dx} + u_\infty v_s = \frac{2\nu u_\infty}{\Delta}$$

In this problem Δ (and therefore Δ^*, θ) are constant; and the free stream velocity varies with the area. Neglecting the boundary layer thickness the volumetric flow rate

$$Q = Au_\infty = \left(0.1 + \frac{1}{2}x\right)u_\infty = \text{constant (incompressible flow)}$$

Hence $\frac{du_\infty}{dx} = -\frac{\frac{1}{2}Q}{\left(0.1 + \frac{1}{2}x\right)^2}$

and substituting gives

$$u_\infty v_s + 4.554u_\infty\left(\frac{37}{315}\Delta\right)u_\infty\left(\frac{-\frac{1}{2}Q}{\left(0.1 + \frac{1}{2}x\right)^2}\right) = \frac{2\nu u_\infty}{\Delta}$$

$$u_\infty v_s = \frac{2\nu}{\Delta} + \frac{0.267\Delta Q}{\left(0.1 + \frac{1}{2}x\right)^2}$$

Insertion of the numerical data gives

$$Q = 0.1(100) = 10\,\text{m}^3/\text{s}$$

$$v_s = \frac{2(1.5)10^{-5}}{0.005} + \frac{0.267(0.005)(10)}{\left(0.1 + \frac{1}{2}x\right)^2}$$

$$= \mathbf{0.006} + \frac{\mathbf{0.01335}}{\left(\mathbf{0.1} + \frac{1}{2}\mathbf{x}\right)^2}\ \text{m/s}$$

6.7 Transition and sub-layer

> Discuss the transition from a laminar to a turbulent layer, including the factors that influence transition.
> Explain what is meant by the terms sub-layer, transition layer, and outer layer in a turbulent boundary layer.

Solution. In simple terms a layer is laminar if the Reynolds number

$$Re_x = \frac{u_\infty x}{\nu}$$

is less than a certain critical value, and turbulent when Re_x exceeds this critical value. Unfortunately the transition from laminar to turbulent flow is not as sudden or clearly defined as this: the transition is gradual, although it may be fairly rapid. The major difficulty is in the determination of a precise value for the critical Reynolds number.

At low Reynolds numbers all *disturbances* are damped out by viscous stresses, and the flow is laminar regardless of the magnitude of any disturbance. As the Reynolds number (and layer thickness) increase a stage is reached where some disturbances are amplified and the layer becomes unstable: this value of the Reynolds number is termed the *lower critical*.

Further increase of the Reynolds number causes a greater range of disturbances to be amplified and an increase in the rate of amplification. Transition to a fully turbulent layer then occurs, over a small distance, to the *higher critical* value of the Reynolds number.

The onset of instability and the completion of transition are highly influenced by the following factors:

(a) Degree of turbulence in the free stream: increasing *initial* disturbances promote transition. For example in the classic Reynolds experiment in which the flow in a circular pipe enters from a large tank, through a bell-mouth entrance, the higher critical Reynolds number is about 2300 (based on the pipe diameter and mean velocity). However the use of baffles in the tank enables the critical value to be increased to 80 000! Another example is in the flow over a flat plate, where the critical Reynolds number (based on length x) is reduced from 3×10^6 for a turbulence-free flow to 0.5×10^6.

(b) The surface roughness, especially when the height of the roughness, ε, is of the same order as the layer thickness. A laminar layer can be *tripped* into turbulence with a wire across the surface, as demonstrated in Prandtl's experiments: in a low-turbulence stream

$$\varepsilon > \frac{820\nu}{u_{\infty I}} \text{ and } \varepsilon > 0.3\Delta^* .$$

(c) The free stream pressure gradient $\dfrac{dp}{dx}$.

A favourable gradient

$$\left(\frac{dp}{dx} < 0\right)$$

retards transition, and an adverse gradient

$$\left(\frac{dp}{dx} > 0\right)$$

advances it.

(d) Compressibility. At subsonic speeds the effect is small, and at supersonic speeds the situation becomes somewhat complicated due to the presence of shock waves, and the interactions between them and the boundary layer. Also at high Mach number flows the effect is modified by the associated thermal gradients.

(e) The curvature of the surface, since a radius of curvature in the free stream flow involves a transverse pressure gradient. For a convex surface the centrifugal force tending to move a fluid particle outwards is often less than the pressure force tending to return it: hence a convex surface stabilises the layer. A concave surface has the opposite effect.

A turbulent layer over a smooth surface is illustrated in Fig.6.4.

The layer consists of three regions: a viscous sublayer, a transition layer, and an outer layer. The sublayer and transition layer are influenced by the shear stress at the surface, the fluid properties (density and viscosity), and are almost independent of the free stream pressure gradient. The outer layer, which covers the bulk of the boundary layer, is fully turbulent and is strongly influenced by the pressure gradient.

Typical velocity distributions are of the form:

sublayer **AB** $\quad \dfrac{u}{u^*} = \dfrac{u^* y}{\nu}$

transition	**BC**	$\frac{u}{u^*} = c\left(\frac{u^* y}{\nu}\right)^{\frac{1}{n}}$
outer layer	**CD**	$\frac{u_\infty - u}{u^*} = c\left(1 - \frac{y}{\Delta}\right)^2$
	or	$\frac{u}{u^*} = c\left(\frac{y}{\Delta}\right)^{\frac{1}{n}}$

where c is a constant, n is an integer, and

$$u^* = \sqrt{\frac{\tau_0}{\rho}} = \text{friction velocity}$$

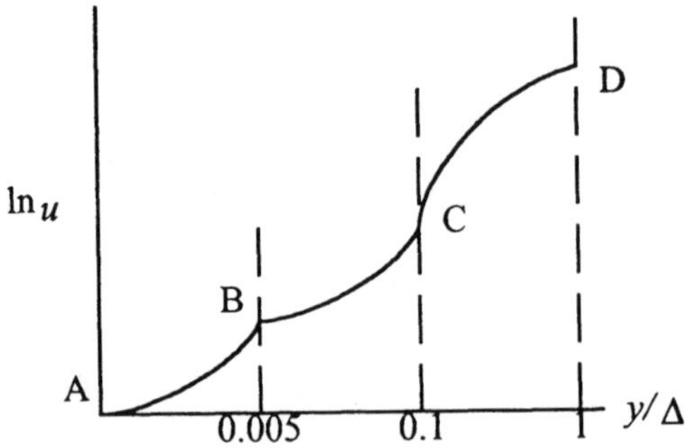

Figure 6.4

This name is given to the expression because it has *units* of velocity:

$$\sqrt{\frac{N}{m^2}\cdot\frac{m^3}{Kg}} = \sqrt{\frac{N}{m^2}} = \sqrt{\frac{Kg\,m}{s^2}\cdot\frac{m}{Kg}} = \frac{m}{s}$$

6.8 Turbulent layer: mixing length

Outline the concept of eddy viscosity, and show how it can be used in the boundary layer equations for a turbulent layer. Indicate how it may be derived in terms of a mixing length.

Briefly show how the Colebrook-White equation for a circular pipe can be obtained:

$$\frac{1}{\sqrt{4f}} = -4\log\left(\frac{\varepsilon}{7.4R} + \frac{1.255}{Re\sqrt{f}}\right)$$

where f = friction coefficient, R = pipe radius.

Solution. The primary characteristic of turbulent flow is that it is unsteady, so that the fluid velocity at a point depends upon the position and time. The velocity is therefore taken to consist of a *mean* velocity $\bar{u}$ (which is independent of time) plus a fluctuation (or perturbance) from the mean velocity u' which varies with time. Thus $u = \bar{u} + u'$, $v = \bar{v} + v'$.

The concept of eddy viscosity ε is that the fluctuations of velocity cause the actual viscosity of the mean velocity flow, μ, to be increased by a kind of viscosity.

Thus the total viscosity of the fluid is taken as

$$(\mu + \rho\varepsilon)\frac{\partial \bar{u}}{\partial y}.$$

The boundary layer equation now becomes

$$\bar{u}\frac{\partial \bar{u}}{\partial x} + \bar{v}\frac{\partial \bar{u}}{\partial y} = -\frac{1}{\rho}\frac{\partial \bar{p}}{\partial x} + \frac{\partial}{\partial y}\left((\nu + \varepsilon)\frac{\partial \bar{u}}{\partial y}\right).$$

Note. The continuity equation takes the form

$$\frac{\partial \bar{u}}{\partial x} + \frac{\partial \bar{v}}{\partial y} = 0.$$

Any calculations on the boundary layer need some knowledge of the way in which this eddy viscosity ε varies with the velocity, and various theories have been developed to establish some relationship. Since turbulent flow involves transverse motion across the layer, and mixing of the fluid particles in that direction (unlike laminar flow where the particles move along streamlines) it has been suggested that the viscosity ε depends upon a mixing length l, a measure of the mean transverse fluctuation.

Prandtl obtained the relationship

$$\tau \propto \rho l^2 \left|\frac{d\bar{u}}{dy}\right| \frac{d\bar{u}}{dy}.$$

where the absolute value

$$\left|\frac{d\bar{u}}{dy}\right|$$

is introduced to give the shear stress τ and velocity gradient the same sign.

von Karman, assuming that the fluctuations were similar at every point, obtained the result

$$l \propto \left|\frac{d\bar{u}}{dy} \Big/ \frac{d^2\bar{u}}{dy^2}\right|, \qquad \tau \propto \rho\left(\frac{d\bar{u}}{dy}\right)^4 \Big/ \left(\frac{d^2\bar{u}}{dy^2}\right)^2$$

Note. The unknown eddy viscosity has been replaced by another concept, mixing length. However it is easier to make reasonable assumptions for the latter than for the former.

For a *smooth* pipe Nikuradse obtained the following velocity distribution:

$$\frac{u_m - u}{u^*} = 5.75 \log \frac{R}{y}$$

where u_m = maximum velocity (at the pipe centre line). This equation does not apply close to the wall, where the flow is no longer turbulent. Allowing for the laminar sublayer, Nikuradse obtained from experimental results the law

$$\frac{u}{u^*} = 5.5 + 5.75 \log \frac{u^* y}{\nu}.$$

This can be expressed in terms of the friction coefficient

$$f = \frac{\tau_0}{\frac{1}{2}\rho\bar{u}^2}, \qquad \text{where } \bar{u} = \text{mean velocity.}$$

Thus $u^* = \sqrt{\dfrac{\tau_o}{\rho}} = \bar{u}\sqrt{\dfrac{1}{2}f}$

and substitution gives

$$\frac{1}{\sqrt{4f}} = 2.04 \log(Re\sqrt{4f}) - 0.91, \qquad \text{where } Re = \frac{\bar{u}D}{\nu} = \frac{2\bar{u}R}{\nu}.$$

Experimental work gives a modified law

$$\frac{1}{\sqrt{4f}} = 2 \log(Re\sqrt{4f}) - 0.8$$

In a *rough* pipe the effect of surface roughness depends upon whether the roughness $\in$ is greater than the sublayer thickness. If it is the eddy formation has an effect on the flow. Experimental work gave the law

$$\frac{1}{\sqrt{4f}} = 1.74 + 2\log\frac{R}{\epsilon}$$

The two equations can be combined in the Colebrook-White equation stated.

Note. Nikuradse found from experimental work on artificially roughened pipes, of relative roughness ε/D varying from 0.001 to 0.033

smooth pipe law $\quad 0 \le \frac{\epsilon u^*}{\nu} \le 5$

rough pipe law $\quad \frac{\epsilon u^*}{\nu} > 70$

6.9 Smooth pipe flow

Derive the relationship $f = c\,Re^m$ for the flow in a smooth pipe, radius R, when fully developed. Assume that a power law relationship of the form

$$\frac{u}{u^*} = c_1\left(\frac{u^* y}{\nu}\right)^{\frac{1}{n}} \text{ is valid:}$$

where u^* = friction velocity, and $Re = \frac{2\bar{u}R}{\nu}$.

If $n = 7$ and $c_1 = 8.56$ show that the

$$\text{pressure drop/unit length} = \frac{0.079\rho\bar{u}}{R(Re)^{0.25}}.$$

Solution. The flow is fully developed so that the boundary layer completely fills the section.

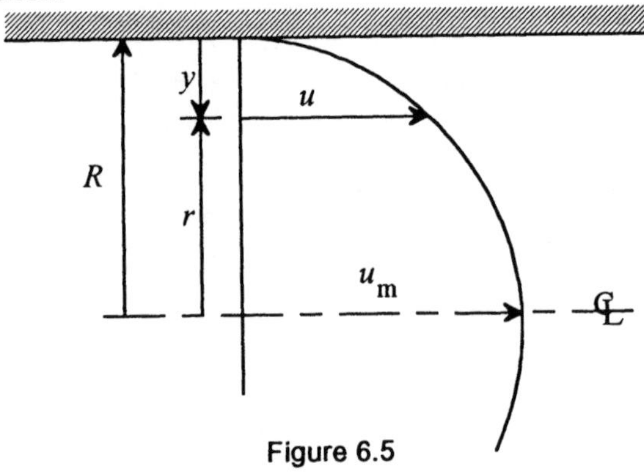

Figure 6.5

The distance y is measured from the pipe wall, $y = R - r$ (Fig. 6.5). u^m = maximum velocity at $y = R$.

$$\frac{u}{u_m} = \left(\frac{u^* y}{\nu}\right)^{\frac{1}{n}} / \left(\frac{y}{R}\right)^{\frac{1}{n}} = \left(\frac{y}{R}\right)^{\frac{1}{n}} = \left(1 - \frac{r}{R}\right)^{\frac{1}{n}}$$

The flow rate across the pipe section is

$$Q = \int_0^R 2\pi r u.dr = 2\pi u_m \int_0^R r\left(1 - \frac{r}{R}\right)^{\frac{1}{n}} dr$$

and substituting $r = R - y$, $dr = -dy$ gives

$$Q = -2\pi R^2 u_m . \frac{n^2}{(n+1)(2n+1)}$$

The mean velocity

$$\bar{u} = \frac{Q}{\pi R^2} = \frac{2n^2 u_m}{(n+1)(2n+1)}$$

Now $\frac{u}{u^*} = c_1\left(\frac{u^* y}{\nu}\right)^{\frac{1}{n}}$, $\quad \frac{u_m}{u^*} = c_1\left(\frac{u^* R}{\nu}\right)^{\frac{1}{n}}$, therefore

$$\frac{\bar{u}}{u^*} = \frac{2n^2}{(n+1)(2n+1)} c_1\left(\frac{u^* R}{\nu}\right)^{\frac{1}{n}} \ldots = c_2\left(\frac{u^* R}{\nu}\right)^{\frac{1}{n}} \quad \text{say}.$$

Rearranging gives

$$u^* = \left(\frac{\nu}{R}\right)^{\frac{1}{n+1}} \left(\frac{\bar{u}}{c_2}\right)^{\frac{n}{n+1}}$$

Finally the friction coefficient

$$f = \frac{\tau_0}{\frac{1}{2}\rho \bar{u}^2} = 2\left(\frac{u^*}{\bar{u}}\right)^2 = 2^{\frac{n+3}{n+1}}\left(\frac{1}{c_2}\right)^{\frac{2n}{n+1}}\left(\frac{2}{Re}\right)^{\frac{2}{n+1}}$$

or $\quad f = cRe^m$, where $c = 2c_2^{\frac{-2n}{n+1}}$, $c_2 = \frac{2n^2 c_1}{(n+1)(2n+1)}$, $m = -\left(\frac{2}{n+1}\right)$

With the values given $n = 7$, $c_1 = 8.56$

$m = -1/4$, $c_2 = 6.991$, $c = 0.079$.

Considering a control volume enclosing the pipe cross-section, length dx, the momentum equation for steady flow gives

$$dp.\pi R^2 = \tau_0 .2\pi R.dx$$

$$\frac{dp}{dx} = \frac{2\tau_0}{R} = \frac{2}{R}\left(f.\frac{1}{2}\rho\bar{u}^2\right) = \frac{\rho\bar{u}^2}{R}\left(0.079Re^{-0.25}\right)$$

Note. The relationship $f = 0.079Re^{-0.25}$ is known as the Blasius law, and is somewhat simpler (although less accurate) than the universal law derived in the previous example. This is to be expected, since the Blasius law is based on a *single* equation for the velocity distribution across the whole pipe section.

Values of the friction coefficient for a range of Reynolds numbers are tabulated below.

Re	1×10^2	1×10^3	1×10^4	1×10^5	5×10^5	1×10^6
Blasius	0.025	0.014	0.008	0.0044	0.0030	0.0025
Universal	0.042	0.016	0.0077	0.0045	0.0033	0.0029

6.10 Turbulent layer on a plane surface

The velocity distribution in a turbulent layer on a flat plate is given by the law

$$\frac{u}{u_\infty} = \left(\frac{y}{\Delta}\right)^{\frac{1}{n}}.$$

The pressure gradient is zero, and the friction coefficient f is given by the Blasius law, $f = 0.079Re^{-0.25}$.

Derive the following expressions for the boundary layer thickness, drag force and skin friction coefficient, for the value $n = 7$.

$\Delta = 0.38x\,Re_x^{-0.2}$

drag force $= 0.075\rho L u_\infty^2\, Re_L^{-0.2}$ /unit width

$c_f = 0.075\,Re_L^{-0.2}$, $\qquad$ where L = plate length.

Solution: The M.I. equation is

$$u_\infty.\Delta^*.\frac{du_\infty}{dx} + \frac{d}{dx}\left(u_\infty^2\theta\right) = \frac{\tau_0}{\rho}$$

and since the pressure gradient

$$\frac{dp}{dx} = -\rho u_\infty.\frac{du_\infty}{dx}$$

is zero, u_∞ is constant. Hence

$$u_\infty^2.\frac{d\theta}{dx} = \frac{\tau_0}{\rho}$$

Now the momentum thickness

$$\theta\int_0^\infty \frac{u}{u_\infty}\left(1 - \frac{u}{u_\infty}\right)dy = \Delta\int_0^1 \eta^{\frac{1}{n}}\left(1 - \eta^{\frac{1}{n}}\right)d\eta$$

where $\eta = \frac{y}{\Delta}$, $\frac{u}{u_\infty} = \eta^{\frac{1}{n}}$

Integrating gives $\theta = \frac{n\Delta}{(n+1)(n+2)}$

An *important* point in the computation of turbulent layers is that the shear stress is no longer given by the laminar flow equation.

$$\tau = \mu\left(\frac{du}{dy}\right).$$

The M.I. equation cannot be integrated without some knowledge of the relationship between shear stress and velocity gradient, or more precisely, without an equation relating the shear stress and layer thickness. This fact leads to some difficulties in the consideration of turbulent layers, and in many cases experimental relationships have to be used. In this problem the Blasius law is employed with some manipulation to obtain the necessary connection between shear stress and layer thickness: it is first derived for a circular pipe, and the pipe radius R replaced by Δ.

$$f = \frac{0.079}{Re^{0.25}} = \frac{\tau_0}{\frac{1}{2}\rho u_\infty^2}$$

$$\frac{\tau_0}{\rho u_\infty^2} = \frac{1}{2}(0.079)\left(\frac{\nu}{2u_\infty R}\right)^{0.25} = 0.0335\left(\frac{\nu}{u_\infty R}\right)^{0.25}$$

and for the plate $\frac{\tau_0}{\rho u_\infty^2} = 0.0335\left(\frac{\nu}{u_\infty\Delta}\right)^{0.25}$

Substituting into the M.I. equation

$$0.0335u_\infty^2\left(\frac{\nu}{u_\infty\Delta}\right)^{0.25} = u_\infty^2.\frac{d}{dx}\frac{n\Delta}{(n+1)(n+2)}$$

$$0.0335u_\infty^2\left(\frac{\nu}{u_\infty}\right)^{0.25}dx = \frac{n\Delta}{(n+1)(n+2)}.\Delta^{0.25}\,d\Delta$$

and integrating

$$\frac{0.0335}{n}(n+1)(n+2)\left(\frac{\nu}{u_\infty}\right)^{0.25}x = \frac{\Delta^{1.25}}{1.25}$$

giving $\Delta^{1.25} = \frac{0.0419}{n}(n+1)(n+2)\left(\frac{\nu}{u_\infty}\right)^{0.25}x$

or $\Delta = 0.079\left(\frac{(n+1)(n+2)}{n}\right)^{0.8}\left(\frac{\nu}{u_\infty}\right)^{0.2}x^{0.8}$

This can be expressed in terms of the Reynolds number

$$Re_x = \frac{u_\infty x}{\nu}, \qquad \Delta = 0.079\left(\frac{(n+1)(n+2)}{n}\right)^{0.8} x.Re_x^{-0.2}$$

Putting $n = 7$ gives $\Delta = 0.38x\,Re_x^{-0.2}$

The drag force/unit width is

$$D = 2\int_0^L \tau_0\,dx$$

$$= 2\int_0^L 0.0335\rho u_\infty^2\left(\frac{\nu}{u_\infty\Delta}\right)^{0.25} dx = 0.0853\rho u_\infty^2\left(\frac{\nu}{u_\infty}\right)^{0.2}\int_0^L x^{-0.2}\,dx$$

$$= 0.1066\rho u_\infty^2\left(\frac{\nu}{u_\infty}\right)^{0.2} L^{0.8} = \mathbf{0.1066} L u_\infty^2 Re_L^{-0.2}$$

The skin friction coefficient

$$c_f = \frac{D}{\frac{1}{2}\rho u_\infty^2 2L} = 0.1066 Re_L^{-0.2}$$

Note. The relationship between shear stress and layer thickness depends on experimental data, and many equations are available. Some of the equations involve the momentum thickness, as for example,

$$\frac{\tau_o}{\rho u_\infty^2} = 0.0128\left(\frac{u_\infty\theta}{\nu}\right)^{-0.25} \qquad \text{(Prandtl)}$$

$$= 0.0-65\left(\frac{u_\infty\theta}{\nu}\right)^{-0.167} \qquad \text{(Falkner)}$$

$$= \frac{0.0288}{\left(\log\frac{4.075u_\infty\theta}{\nu}\right)^2} \qquad \text{(Squire and Young)}$$

6.11 Layer partly laminar and partly turbulent

A flat plate is at zero incidence in an air stream, with no pressure gradient. The free stream velocity = 15 m/s, and the air density and viscosity are 1.20 kg/m^3 and 1.8×10^{-5} Kg/ms respectively.

The Reynolds number at transition from a laminar to a turbulent layer = 10^6. For the laminar layer $\Delta = 4.64x\,Re_x^{-0.5}$, $\theta = 0.139\Delta$. For the turbulent layer $\Delta = 0.38x\,Re_x^{-0.2}$, $\theta = 0.097\Delta$.

The drag coefficients are:

laminar layer $C_D = 0.646\,Re_x^{-0.5}$, turbulent layer $C_D = 0.074\,Re_x^{-0.2}$

Calculate the drag force on the plate, and drag coefficient, when the plate length = 2 m. Also determine the layer thickness at transition, and at the trailing edge.

Solution. To calculate the drag (and other parameters) in this situation where the boundary layer changes from laminar to turbulent, it is necessary to know the position of the transition point *and* the changes in boundary layer properties at transition. Different assumptions can be made about the changes at transition, but the one normally made is that the *momentum* thickness is unchanged. This means that the layer thickness and displacement thickness do change suddenly at the transition point, or there is a discontinuity in these thicknesses.

It is also normally assumed that the turbulent layer develops from a false or apparent origin, at x_o from the leading edge (Fig. 6.6).

At the transition point

$$Re = 10^6 = \frac{u_\infty x_t}{\nu}.$$

Hence $x_t = \frac{10^6}{15}\left(\frac{1.8\times10^{-5}}{1.2}\right) = 1.0\,\text{m}$

$$\Delta_t = 4.64x_o\,Re^{-0.5} = 4.64\left(\frac{1.5\times10^{-5}}{15\times1}\right)^{0.5} = \mathbf{0.00464}\,\text{m}$$

since $\nu = \frac{\mu}{\rho} = 1.5\times10^{-5}\,\text{m}^2/\text{s}$

$$\theta_t = 0.139\Delta_t = 0.000645\,\text{m}$$

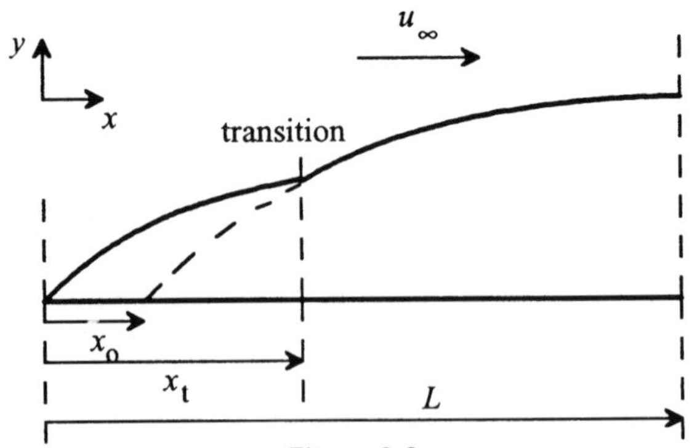

Figure 6.6

Now the momentum thickness of the turbulent layer is assumed to be equal to that of the laminar layer, so that

$$0.000645 = 0.097\Delta$$

$$\Delta = 0.00665\,\text{m} = 0.38x\,Re_x^{-0.2} = 0.38x\left(\frac{\nu}{u_\infty x}\right)^{0.2}$$

giving $x = 0.201\,\text{m}$

Thus $x_t - x_o = 0.201$, or $x_o = 0.799\,\text{m}$.

At the trailing edge the distance from the apparent origin is 2.0 – 0.799 = 1.201 m, and

$$\Delta = 0.38L\,Re_L^{-0.2} = 0.38(1.201)\left(\frac{1.5\times10^{-5}}{15\times1.201}\right)^{0.2} = \mathbf{0.02776}\,\text{m}$$

The drag force

$$D = C_D\tfrac{1}{2}\rho u_\infty^2 x$$

and is made up of two parts. Over the laminar layer length

$$D = \tfrac{1}{2}(1.2)(15)^2(1.0)\times0.646\left(\frac{1.5\times10^{-5}}{15\times1}\right)^{0.5} = 0.087\ \text{N/m width}$$

and over the turbulent layer length

$$D = \tfrac{1}{2}(1.2)(15)^2(1.799)\times0.074\left(\frac{1.5\times10^{-5}}{15\times1}\right)^{0.2} = 1.134\ \text{N/m width}$$

The total drag is 1.134 + 0.087 = **1.221** N and the overall drag coefficient is

$$C_D = \frac{D}{\frac{1}{2}\rho u_\infty^2 L} = \frac{1.221}{\frac{1}{2}(1.2)(15)^2(2)} = \mathbf{0.0045}$$

Note. At transition the layer thickness increases from 4.64 mm in the laminar layer to 6.65 mm in the turbulent layer: an increase of 43%. Also the drag due to the laminar layer is 7% of the total.

A formula (due to Prandtl) for the calculation of the drag coefficient is

$$C_D = 0.074 Re_L^{-0.2} - \frac{C}{Re_L}, \qquad \text{where } 10^5 < Re_L < 5\times10^6$$

and the constant C varies with the Reynolds number at transition:

Re_t	3×10⁵	5×10⁵	1×10⁶	3×10⁶
C	1,050	1,700	3,300	8,700

In this problem

$$Re_t = 10^6,\ Re_L = \frac{15\times2}{1.5\times10^{-5}} = 2\times10^6$$

and the Prandtl formula then gives

$$C_D = \frac{0.074}{(2\times10^6)^{0.2}} - \frac{3300}{2\times10^6} = 0.0024$$

Problems

The M.I. equation should be used unless stated otherwise.

1 A boundary layer traverse uses a small pitot tube to measure the velocity v across a boundary layer, on a flat plate at zero incidence. The free stream velocity = 16.5 m/s. The results of the traverse are shown in the following table:

y(mm)	2	4	6	8	10	12	14	16	18
v (m/s)	11.73	13.19	14.04	14.61	15.10	15.51	15.85	16.16	16.44

Assuming a power law velocity distribution of the form

$$\frac{u}{u_\infty} = \left(\frac{y}{\Delta}\right)^{\frac{1}{n}}$$

determine a value of the index n which best fits the results.

Answer 6.6

2 The velocity profile in a laminar boundary layer is given by the equation

$$\frac{u}{u_\infty} = a\frac{y}{\Delta} + b\left(\frac{y}{\Delta}\right)^2.$$

The pressure gradient is zero. Determine the layer thickness and skin friction coefficient in terms of the distance from the leading edge, x, and Reynolds number (based on the distance x).

Answer $a = 2, b = -1$

$\Delta = 5.477x Re_x^{-0.5}$, $c_f = 1.461\, Re_x^{-0.5}$

3 The velocity profile in a laminar boundary layer is given by the equation

$$\frac{u}{u_\infty} = \sin\frac{\pi y}{2\Delta}.$$

The pressure gradient is zero. Show that the layer and

displacement thickness are given by the expressions

$$\Delta = 4.789 x Re_x^{-0.5}, \Delta^* = 1.741 x Re_x^{-0.5}$$

4 The shear stress in a laminar layer varies linearly with the distance across the layer. The free stream velocity is constant.

Determine the velocity distribution, and hence

$$\Delta\sqrt{Re_x}, \Delta^*\sqrt{Re_x} \text{ and } \theta\sqrt{Re_x}.$$

Answer $\frac{u}{u_\infty} = 2\eta - \eta^2$, 5.47$x$, 1.82$x$, 0.73$x$

5 A flat plate is situated in a fluid stream at zero incidence, and the pressure gradient is zero. The free stream velocity = 50 cm/s. The velocity distribution in the layer is given by

$$\frac{u}{u_\infty} = 2\eta - 2\eta^3 + \eta^4$$

where $\eta = \frac{y}{\Delta}$

The fluid density and viscosity are 1000 kg/m^3 and 10^{-3} kg/ms respectively. The momentum thickness = 0.177Δ.

Calculate the boundary layer thickness at a distance 30 cm from the leading edge, and the drag force/m width on the plate up to that point; and the layer thickness at the transition point ($Re_x = 10^6$).

Also plot the shear stress distribution across the layer at the transition point.

Answer 3.68 mm, 0.33 N. 9.50 mm

6 The velocity profile in a laminar layer is given by the equation

$$\frac{u}{u_\infty} = \frac{5}{3}\eta - \frac{2}{3}\eta^3.$$

Calculate the layer thickness at a point 1m from the leading edge, and drag force/m width on the plate up to that point. The pressure gradient is zero, free stream velocity = 30 m/s, and the fluid viscosity = 1.5×10^{-5} m^2/s, density = 1.2 kg/m^3.

Answer 3.7 mm: 0.49 N

7 The velocity distribution in a laminar layer is linear, i.e.

$$\frac{u}{u_\infty} = \frac{y}{\Delta}.$$

Show that

$$\frac{d}{dx}\Delta^2 + \frac{10}{u_\infty}\Delta^2\frac{du_\infty}{dx} = \frac{12\nu}{u_\infty}$$

and hence

$$\Delta^2 = \frac{12\nu}{u_\infty^{10}}\int u_\infty^9\,dx.$$

8 The free stream velocity over a flat plate is given by the equation $u_\infty = 50(1 - x^2)$ m/s, where x is the distance from the leading edge. $\nu = 1.5 \times 10^{-5}$ m²/s.

Estimate the position of the separation point. Thwaites method should be used, assuming that separation occurs when

$$\frac{\theta^2}{\nu}\frac{du_\infty}{dx} = -0.090.$$

Calculate the Reynolds number at this point, and comment on the result.

Answer Approx. 27 cm. 0.8×10^6

9 The velocity distribution in a laminar layer is given by the equation

$$\frac{u}{u_\infty} = 2\eta - 2\eta^3 + \eta^4, \qquad \text{where } \eta = \frac{y}{\Delta}.$$

The displacement and momentum thickness are

$$\Delta^* = \frac{3}{10}\Delta, , \quad \theta = \frac{37}{315}\Delta.$$

The free stream velocity varies with the distance from the leading edge, x, according to the equation

$u_\infty = u_o(1 - kx)$, where k is a constant.

Derive an expression for the layer thickness in terms of k, u_o, x and ν; and show that separation occurs at $x = 1/k$.

Answer $$\Delta^2 = \frac{716\nu}{u_o}\left(1 - (1 - kx)^{\frac{21.03}{k}}\right)$$

10 Air flows over a circular cylinder, whose axis is normal to the flow direction. The free stream velocity over the cylinder is $u_\infty = 2u_0 \sin\beta$, where β is the angle measured from the stagnation point. Assuming that the layer is laminar estimate the position of the separation point. Thwaites approximation should be used.

Answer At $\beta = 110^o$.

11 A fluid flows over a porous flat place at zero incidence. The boundary layer is laminar, and the thickness is controlled by suction of the fluid through the plate at a constant velocity v_0. Show, by use of the Prandtl equation

$$u\frac{\partial u}{\partial x} + v\frac{\partial u}{\partial y} = -\frac{1}{\rho}\frac{\partial p}{\partial x} + \nu\frac{\partial^2 u}{\partial y^2},$$

that $u = u_\infty\left(1 - \exp\left(-\frac{v_0 y}{\nu}\right)\right)$,

and hence derive the results

$$\theta = \frac{\nu}{2v_0}, \qquad c_f = \frac{2v_0}{u_\infty}.$$

12 An incompressible fluid flows over a porous plate, and the free stream velocity is constant. Fluid is drawn through the surface at a constant velocity v_0, which is small compared to the free stream velocity.

Show that the skin friction coefficient is given by the equation

$$c_f = 2\frac{d\theta}{dx} + \frac{2v_0}{u_\infty}.$$

If $\rho = 1.2\,\text{g/m}^3$, $\nu = 1.5 \times 10^{-5}\,\text{m}^2/\text{s}$, $u_\infty = 40\,\text{m/s}$ and $v_0 = 0.1\,\text{m/s}$ determine the distance from the leading edge, x, at which the drag force is 4 N/m width.

Take $\frac{u}{u_\infty} = \frac{3}{2}\eta - \frac{1}{2}\eta^3$.

Answer 0.76 m.

13 The velocity distribution in a laminar layer is given by the equation

$$\frac{u}{u_\infty} = \frac{3}{2}\eta - \frac{1}{2}\eta^3.$$

The free stream velocity is constant, at 30 m/s. The fluid density and viscosity are 1.2 Kg/m^3, and 1.5×10^{-5} m^2/s respectively.

Determine the momentum loss /s per unit width up to a distance of 30 cm from the leading edge. Compare the momentum loss with that of a turbulent layer over the same area, given by the expression

$$\text{loss} = 0.037\rho x u_\infty^2\, Re_x^{-0.2}$$

Briefly comment on the values obtained.

Answer. 0.27 and 0.84 N.

14 (a) The velocity profile at a point on a surface was determined by the use of a small pitot tube, and gave the following results:

y (mm)	1.3	2.5	3.7	5.1	6.4	7.6	10.0
u (m/s)	11.0	18.0	23.0	27.0	29.0	30.0	34.0

y = distance from the surface, in a direction perpendicular to the surface

u = local velocity.

The fluid density = 1.2 Kg/m^3.

Estimate a value for the friction velocity, and hence the shear stress at the surface.

(b) Wind blows over an area of relatively flat ground, and the wind velocity was measured as 3.05 m/s at a height of 3.05 m above the ground. What would you expect the velocity to be at a height of 24.4 m?

In both parts a logarithmic velocity distribution should be assumed:

$$\frac{u}{u^*} = 2.5 \ln y + c$$

Answer (a) Approx. 4.5m/s; 24 N/m^2.
(b) 4.05 m/s.

15 The velocity distribution in a turbulent layer on a flat plate is of the form

$$\frac{u}{u^*} = c\left(\frac{u^* y}{\nu}\right)^{\frac{1}{n}}$$

However the distribution in the sublayer is of the form

$$\frac{u}{u^*} = A \ln\left(\frac{u^* y}{\nu}\right) + B$$

Show that at a common point a smooth merging of the profiles requires that

$$C = nA \exp\left(\frac{B}{nA} - 1\right),$$

and
$$\frac{u^* y}{\nu} = \exp\left(n - \frac{B}{A}\right).$$

If $A = 5$, $B = -3.05$, $n = 7$, $u^* = 5$ m/s, $\nu = 1.5 \times 10^{-5}$ m²/s calculate the distance from the plate at the common point, and the velocity at that point.

[*Hint.* At the common point u and du/dy have the same value.]

Answer. 6 mm, 175 m/s.

16 Water flows along a circular pipe, and at a certain section the free stream velocity is 3 m/s, the diameter is 60 cm, and the laminar layer thickness 12.5 mm. The velocity distribution in the layer is given the equation

$$\frac{u}{u_\infty} = \frac{1}{2}\left(1 - \cos \pi\eta\right), \text{ where } \eta = \frac{y}{\Delta}.$$

Compare the kinetic energy of the flow with that of an inviscid flow at the same mass flow rate. Determine the momentum loss /s due to the layer. The kinetic energy of the water in the layer should be neglected.

Answer. 3816, 3505 W. 28 W

17 The pressure gradient on a surface is zero. Show that the shear stress at the surface

$$\tau_o = \rho u_\infty^2 \frac{d\theta}{dx}.$$

The boundary layer is fully turbulent and the velocity distribution is given by the power law

$$\frac{u}{u_\infty} = \left(\frac{y}{\Delta}\right)^{\frac{1}{7}}.$$

Assuming that

$$\tau_o = 0.023 \rho u_\infty^2 Re_\Delta^{-0.25}$$

show that at a section, distance x from the leading edge, $\Delta = 0.38 x Re_x^{-0.20}$

Define the shape factor, H, and determine its value.

Express the shear stress at the surface in terms of Re_x

Answer $H = 1.286 \quad \tau_o = 0.029\rho u_\infty^2\, Re_\Delta^{-0.2}$

18 The velocity distribution (turbulent flow) in a smooth circular pipe, radius a, is given by the equation

$$\frac{u}{u^*} = 5.5 + 5.75 \log\left(\frac{u^* y}{\nu}\right)$$

except in the region close to the wall.

Show that $\frac{u}{u^*} = 5.75 \log \frac{\partial}{y}$,

where u_m = maximum velocity.

Water flows along a circular pipe radius 25 mm. The pressure drop = 1500 N/m^2 per metre length. The viscosity of the water = 10^{-3} kg/ms. The velocity distribution in the laminar sublayer is given by the equation

$$\frac{u}{u^*} = 5 \ln\left(\frac{u^* y}{\nu}\right) - 3.05$$

and in the buffer layer by the equation

$$\frac{u}{u^*} = 2.5 \ln\left(\frac{u^* y}{\nu}\right) + 5.5$$

Calculate the shear stress at the wall y = 0; the friction velocity u^*; the thickness of the sublayer and the velocity at the edge of the sublayer; the thickness of the buffer layer, the velocity and eddy viscosity at the edge of the buffer layer.

Answer. 18.75 N/m^2; 0.137 m/s; 0.036 mm, 0.69 m/s, 0.187 mm, 1.93 m/s, 5.07×10^{-3} kg/ms

19 Water flows through a circular pipe, diameter 90 cm. The pipe is laid at a slope of 1 (vertical): 100 (horizontal). Kinematic viscosity of water = 1×10^{-6} m^2/s.

Estimate the flow rate assuming

(a) a smooth pipe

$$\frac{1}{\sqrt{4f}} = 2 \log\left(\frac{Re\sqrt{4f}}{2.5}\right)$$

(b) a rough pipe, roughness K = 6 mm.

$$\frac{1}{\sqrt{f}} = 4 \log\left(\frac{D}{2}\right) + 3.48$$

Answer. (a) 2.72, (b) 1.47 m^3/s

20 Water flows over a flat plate, 3 m long, 1 m wide. The free stream velocity is constant at 2.5 m/s. $\nu = 1 \times 10^{-6}$ m/s.

Assuming that the entire boundary layer is turbulent, and the velocity distribution is given by the power law

$$\frac{u}{u_\infty} = \left(\frac{y}{\Delta}\right)^{\frac{1}{7}}$$

calculate the layer thickness at the trailing edge and the drag force on the plate.

Also calculate the drag coefficient, and comment on the value of the Reynolds number at the trailing edge.

Answer. 48 mm, 84.3 N. 0.003
$Re = 7.5 \times 10^6$, separation would have occurred upstream of the trailing edge.

21 Show that for a flat plate, length L, in a free stream of constant velocity u_∞, the drag force/unit width is

$$2\rho u_\infty^2 L\sqrt{\frac{a\nu}{u_\infty L}}, \qquad \text{where } \frac{u_\infty^2\theta}{\nu} = ax$$

A flat plate, width B, length L, experiences the same drag force when the width and the length are in the direction of flow. Assuming that the momentum thickness is given by

$$\theta = 0.083x\,Re_x^{-0.2}$$

determine the ratio of the free stream velocities.

Answer. $\left(\frac{L}{B}\right)^{1.5}$

22 Air flows over a smooth flat plate, at zero incidence, in a free stream of velocity u_∞. The velocity profiles in the boundary layer are given by

laminar layer $\quad \frac{u}{u_\infty} = \sin\left(\frac{1}{2}\pi\eta\right)$

turbulent layer $\quad \frac{u}{u_\infty} = \eta^{\frac{1}{7}}$

where $\quad \eta = \frac{y}{\Delta}$

In the turbulent layer the shear stress at the surface is given by

$$\tau_0 = 0.023\rho u_\infty^2 \,.\, Re_\Delta^{-0.25}$$

Determine the momentum thickness in terms of x and Re_x in each layer, where x = distance from the leading edge.

If x_e is the length of a fully turbulent layer equivalent to the laminar layer before the transition of x_t determine the ratio x_e/x_t

Transition occurs at $Re_x = 5\text{x}10^5$.

Answer. 0.009

23 A fluid flows over a surface in the presence of a pressure gradient

$$\frac{dp}{dx} = -2ax$$

Assuming that the layer is turbulent from the leading edge x = 0 show that

$$\frac{d\theta}{dx} + \left(H+2\right).\frac{2ax\theta}{\rho u_0^2 + 2ax^2} = \frac{1}{2}c$$

where $H = \Delta^*/\theta$, u_0 = free stream velocity at $x = 0$.

The velocity distribution follows a 1/7th power law, for which

$$\Delta^* \frac{1}{8}\Delta, \ \theta = \frac{7}{72}\Delta$$

Assuming that

$$c_f = 0.025 Re_\theta^{-0.25}$$

show that the equation becomes

$$\frac{d\theta}{dx} + \frac{46ax\theta}{7\rho u_0^2 + 14ax^2} = 0.0126\left(\frac{\left(u_0^2 + \frac{2ax^2}{\rho}\right)^{\frac{1}{2}}\theta}{\nu}\right)^{\frac{1}{4}}$$

24 The velocity distribution across a flow in a circular pipe, radius R is given by the power law

$$\frac{u}{u_m} = \left(1 - \frac{r}{R}\right)^{\frac{1}{n}}$$

where $u_m =$ velocity at the centre line $r = 0$.
Calculate the radius at which the local velocity is equal to the mean velocity for n = 5, 6, ..., 9; and comment on the result.

Answer 0.750, 0.755, 0.758, 0.760, 0.762 R.
Narrow variation from $0.75R$ is useful for flow measurement.

25 Water flows in a channel, and the depth of the stream is h. The velocity distribution in the vertical plane is given by the law

$$\frac{u}{u_0} = \left(\frac{y}{h}\right)^{\frac{1}{7}}$$

u_0 = the velocity at the surface.

Calculate the depth below the surface at which the local velocity is equal to the mean velocity; and the local velocity at a depth of $0.6h$. Also calculate the local velocity at depths of $0.2h$ and $0.8h$, and the arithmetic mean of these two velocities.

Comment on the values obtained.

Answer 0.39h; 0.93 u_0. $0.80u_0$, $0.88u_0$.
mean velocity = 0.875 u_0.

7

Non-Newtonian fluids: two-phase flow

Introduction: Non-Newtonian fluids

The discussion of viscous flow in previous chapters is based on Newtonian fluid behaviour, or one in which the shear stress τ is related to the velocity gradient by Newton's law:

$$\tau = \mu\left(\frac{du}{dy}\right)$$

Many fluids do obey this law, such as water, oil, gases: although in general the absolute (dynamic) viscosity μ does vary with temperature. This effect is significant in oils, and less so in gases.

A large number of fluids do not obey this simple law, and are termed non-Newtonian fluids: examples of such fluids include ink, paints, greases, sludges, emulsions, paper pulp, drilling mud, polymer solutions, and food products. The shear stress depends on the velocity gradient (shear strain), elastic properties, and in some fluids on time.

Fluid classification

Non-Newtonian fluids can be classified as follows: the characteristics are illustrated in Fig. 7.1.

Time-independent fluids

a	Newtonian	$\tau = \mu\left(\frac{du}{dy}\right)$
b	Bingham plastic	$\tau = \tau_y + \mu_p\left(\frac{du}{dy}\right)$
c	pseudoplastic	$\tau = K\left(\frac{dy}{dy}\right)^n, n < 1$
d	dilatant	$\tau = K\left(\frac{du}{dy}\right)^n, n > 1$

Time-dependent fluids

e	thixotropic	τ decreases with time
	rheopectic	τ increases with time
f	viscoelastic	$\mu_o\left(\frac{du}{dy}\right) = \tau + \left(\frac{\mu_o}{\lambda}\right)\frac{d\tau}{dt}$

where λ = rigidity modulus.

An example, familiar to a decorator, is 'jelly' paint: if stirred, or applied to a surface with several brush strokes, the paint rapidly thins becoming much less viscous.

Pseudoplastic fluids

Although many fluids do obey the simple power law quoted, it is often approximate. The index n is rarely constant over a wide range of shear, and many variations of the simple law have been developed to give a more accurate description of the fluid behaviour. Some empirical equations are:

Prandtl $$\tau = A \arcsin\left(C\frac{du}{dy}\right)$$

Ellis $$\mu_a = \mu_o \Big/ \left(1 + \left|\frac{\tau}{\tau_{0.5}}\right|^{\alpha-1}\right)$$

Meter $$\mu_a = \mu_\infty + (\mu_o - \mu_\infty) \Big/ \left(1 + \left|\frac{\tau}{\tau_m}\right|^{\alpha-1}\right)$$

Eyring $$\tau = A\frac{du}{dy} + B\sin\left(C\frac{du}{dy}\right)$$

where A, B, C are constants

μ_o = viscosity as τ approaches zero

μ_∞ = viscosity as τ approaches infinity

$\tau_{0.5}$ = shear stress when $\mu_a = 0.5\mu_o$

τ_m = shear stress when $\mu_a = 0.5(\mu_o + \mu_\infty)$

μ_a = apparent viscosity = $\tau \Big/ \left(\frac{du}{dy}\right)$

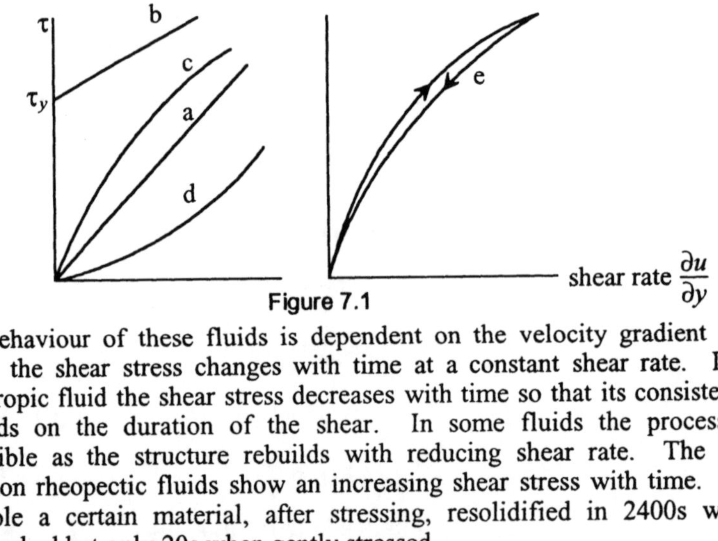

Figure 7.1

Time-dependent fluids

The behaviour of these fluids is dependent on the velocity gradient and time: the shear stress changes with time at a constant shear rate. In a thixotropic fluid the shear stress decreases with time so that its consistency depends on the duration of the shear. In some fluids the process is reversible as the structure rebuilds with reducing shear rate. The less common rheopectic fluids show an increasing shear stress with time. For example a certain material, after stressing, resolidified in 2400s when undisturbed but only 20s when gently stressed.

Viscoelastic fluids

These fluids have the viscous properties associated with a fluid, together with elastic properties. In the simplest type their behaviour can be described by a combination of Newton's law (viscous stress) and Hooke's law (elasticity), and since this was first proposed by Maxwell these fluids are often referred to as Maxwell fluids.

The fluids can be analogized to a mechanical system: the shear strain (viscosity) represented by a dashpot, and the elastic strain by a spring. The basic analogies are a spring and dashpot in parallel (known as a Voigt body), and a spring and dashpot in series (known as a Maxwell body). Combinations of the basic analogies can be developed to model the more complicated behaviours of viscoelastic fluids.

An example of this type of fluid is 'crazy putty', which can be easily deformed by moderate pressure but if dropped from a height onto a solid surface rebounds like an elastic ball.

Two-phase flow

In many practical applications a fluid consists of components in different phases, or a mixture of different fluids. Examples include liquid water/gaseous steam in a boiler tube; liquid oil/gas in a crude oil extraction pipe; pneumatic transport of coal; flow of slurry, liquid/solid.

The computation of the pressure drop and velocity in two-phase flow is very complex. In a similar manner to the analysis of non-Newtonian fluid behaviours the use of mathematical models and empirical data is needed to analyse the flow. The models used can be classified in broad terms as follow:

(a) *Homogeneous* model, in which the average properties of the mixture are used. The detailed flow patterns are ignored.

(b) *Separated flow* model, in which the equations of flow (continuity, momentum, energy) are applied to each phase or constituent of the fluid mixture. The interaction between phases or constituents is estimated by the use of semi-empirical factors..

(c) *Drift flux* model, in which the analysis is based on the relative motion between the phases or constituents.

Terms used in the study of two-phase flow include the following (gas/liquid fluid):

void fraction $\alpha = \dfrac{\text{gas flow rate (volume)}}{\text{fluid flow rate (volume)}}$

mass flow fraction $x = \dfrac{\text{gas flow rate (mass)}}{\text{fluid flow rate (mass)}}$

slip ratio $K = \dfrac{\text{gas phase velocity}}{\text{liquid phase velocity}}$

7.1 Bingham plastic

Briefly outline what is meant by a Bingham plastic, and a coaxial cylinder viscometer.

Show that in a viscometer of this type the fluid velocity at any radius r is given by the equation

$$u = \frac{C}{4\pi\mu_p}\left(\frac{r}{R_1^2} - \frac{1}{r}\right) - \frac{\tau_y r}{\mu_p}\ln\frac{r}{R_1}$$

where τ_y = yield stress

C = torque on the stationary cylinder (radius R_1)

Comment on the result. Derive a relationship between the torque and the angular velocity Ω.

Solution. A Bingham plastic is a fluid which under a shear stress shows no velocity gradient until a certain stress (the yield stress τ_y) is reached: thereafter flow commences and the shear stress is a linear function of the velocity gradient. Many real fluids approximate to this model, such as slurries, plastics, paint, emulsions and drilling mud.

A coaxial cylinder viscometer consists of two long coaxial cylinders (Fig. 7.2): one cylinder is held in a stationary position but free to twist about the common vertical axis. The other cylinder rotates at a measured value about the axis. The viscosity of the fluid can be determined from the measurement of the torque on the cylinder due to the viscous drag.

The outer cylinder (radius R_2) rotates at an angular velocity Ω, and the inner cylinder is stationary. The torque on the inner cylinder, C, is measured in the instrument.

At any radius $r, C = \tau(2\pi r)r = 2\pi r^2\tau$.

Also $\dfrac{du}{dy} = \dfrac{r\Omega}{dr} = r\dfrac{d}{dr}\left(\dfrac{u}{r}\right)$

Hence substituting in the equation for a Bingham plastic

$$\tau = \tau_y + \mu_p\left(\frac{du}{dy}\right)$$

gives $$\frac{C}{2\pi r^2} = \tau_y + \mu_p r\frac{d}{dr}\left(\frac{u}{r}\right)$$

$$\frac{d}{dr}\left(\frac{u}{r}\right) = \left(\frac{C}{2\pi r^3} - \frac{\tau_y}{r}\right)/\mu_p$$

and integrating

$$\frac{u}{r} = \left(-\frac{C}{4\pi r^2} - \tau_y \ln r\right)/\mu_p + A\text{, say}$$

$$u = -\left(\frac{C}{4\pi r} + \tau_y r \ln r\right)/\mu_p + Ar$$

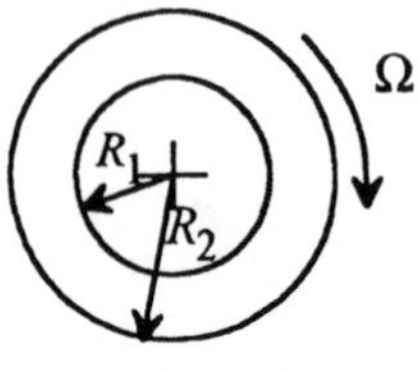

Figure 7.2

The boundary no-slip condition at the inner cylinder surface is that $u = 0$ at $r = R_1$. Substituting

$$0 = -\left(\frac{C}{4\pi R_1} + \tau_y R_1 \ln R_1\right)/\mu_p + AR_1$$

$$A = \left(\frac{C}{4\pi R_1} + \tau_y \ln R_1\right)/\mu_p$$

Hence $$u = \frac{C}{4\pi\mu_p}\left(\frac{r}{R_1^2} - \frac{1}{r}\right) - \frac{\tau_y r}{\mu_p}\ln\frac{r}{R_1}$$

This result applies only if $\tau > \tau_y$, since the fluid does not shear at a shear stress lower than the yield value, τ_y. The radius must therefore be in the range $R_1 \le r \le R_y$, where

$$\tau_y = \frac{C}{2\pi R_y^2}.$$

If $r > R_y$ then $u = \dfrac{ru_y}{Ry}$,

where u_y = velocity at radius $r = R_y$. Hence the fluid rotates as a rigid body with the outer cylinder.

The relationship between the torque C and angular velocity Ω also depends on whether $R_2 >$ or $< R_y$.

If $R_2 > R_y$ then $$\Omega = \frac{u_y}{R_y} = \frac{C}{4\pi\mu_p}\left(\frac{1}{R_1^2} - \frac{1}{R_y^2}\right) - \frac{\tau_y}{\mu_p}\ln\frac{R_y}{R_1}$$

$$= \frac{C}{4\pi\mu_p R_1^2} - \frac{\tau_y}{2\mu_p}\left(1 + \ln\frac{C}{2\pi R_1^2\tau_y}\right)$$

If $R_2 < R_y$ then $$\Omega = \frac{u_2}{R_2} = \frac{C}{4\pi\mu_p}\left(\frac{1}{R_1^2} - \frac{1}{R_2^2}\right) - \frac{\tau_y}{\mu_p}\ln\frac{R_2}{R_1}$$

Note. If $R_1^2 > \dfrac{C}{2\pi\tau_y}$

it can be shown that $\Omega = 0$, and the cylinder will not rotate!

7.2 Bingham plastic

> A Bingham plastic flows along a circular duct, of radius a (Fig. 7.3). Show that the pressure drop, Δp, over a length L is given by the equation
>
> $$Q = \frac{\pi a^4 \Delta p}{8L\mu_p}\left(1 - \frac{4}{3}\lambda + \frac{1}{3}\lambda^4\right)$$
>
> where Q = volumetric flow rate, $\lambda = \dfrac{2L\tau_y}{a\Delta p}$

Solution. The fluid does not begin to flow (or experience a velocity gradient) until the shear stress attains a value $T = \tau_y$: hence a central portion of the fluid moves along the duct as a *solid plug*. Since the shear stress distribution is linear, or

$$\tau = \frac{\tau_0 r}{a}$$

the plug radius

$$r_y = \frac{a\tau_y}{\tau_0}$$

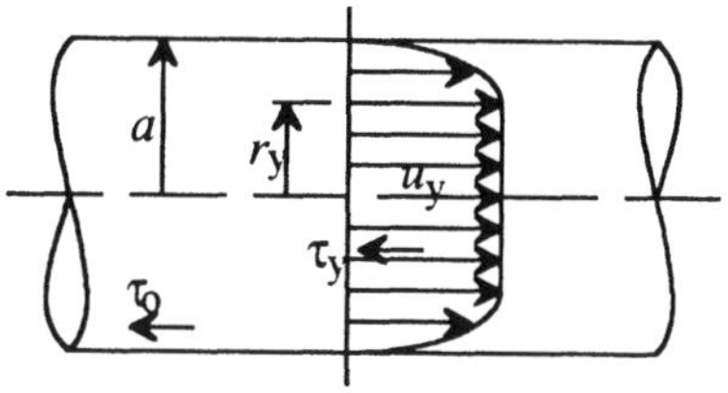

Figure 7.3

The pressure drop is related to the wall shear stress τ_0 by the equation

$$\frac{dp}{dx} = \frac{2\tau_0}{a} \qquad \text{(as shown in W.E.1.1).}$$

Thus $\tau = \dfrac{\tau_o r}{a} = \dfrac{1}{2} r \dfrac{dp}{dx} = -\dfrac{1}{2} P r$ say.

For a Bingham plastic

$$\tau = \tau_y + u_p\left(\frac{du}{dy}\right)$$

hence $-\dfrac{1}{2}Pr = \tau_y + u_p\left(\dfrac{du}{dy}\right)$ or $\dfrac{du}{dr} = \dfrac{-\frac{1}{2}Pr - \tau_y}{\mu_p}$

Integrating gives

$$u = -\frac{Pr^2}{4\mu_p} - \frac{\tau_y r}{\mu_p} + c$$

The integration constant, c, can be determined from the no-slip condition at the duct wall, i.e. $u = 0$ at $r = a$. This gives

$$c = \frac{Pa^2}{4\mu_p} + \frac{\tau_y a}{\mu_p}.$$

Substituting

$$u = \frac{P}{4\mu_p}(a^2 - r^2) + \frac{\tau_y a}{\mu_p}\left(1 - \frac{r}{a}\right)$$

At the central core $r_y = a\tau_y/\tau_o$ and

$$u_y = \frac{Pa^2}{4\mu_p}\left[1 - \left(\frac{\tau_y}{\tau_o}\right)^2\right] + \frac{\tau_y a}{\mu_p}\left(1 - \frac{\tau_y}{\tau_o}\right).$$

Substituting the relationship $\tau_y = -\frac{1}{2}Pr_y = -\frac{1}{2}Pa(\tau_y/\tau_o)$ gives the result

$$u_y = \frac{Pa^2}{4\mu_p}\left(1 - \frac{\tau_y}{\tau_o}\right)^2$$

The volumetric flow rate, Q, over the whole cross-section is made up of two parts: the central plug flow over a section of radius r_y plus the flow over the annulus $r_y \leq r \leq a$.

For the central plug

$$Q_1 = \pi r_y^2 u_y = \pi\left(\frac{a\tau_y}{\tau_0}\right)^2 \frac{Pa^2}{4\mu_p}\left(1 - \frac{\tau_y}{\tau_o}\right)^2 = \frac{\pi a^4 P}{4\mu_p}.\lambda^2\left(1 - \lambda\right)$$

$$\text{where } \lambda = \frac{\tau_y}{\tau_0} = \frac{\tau_y}{\frac{1}{2}Pa} = \frac{2\tau_y}{Pa}$$

For the annulus

$$u = \frac{P}{4\mu_p}\left(a^2 - r^2\right) + \frac{\tau_y a}{\mu_p}\left(1 - \frac{r}{a}\right) = \frac{P}{4\mu_p}\left[a^2 - r^2 - 2a\lambda(a - r)\right]$$

$$\text{Hence } Q_2 = \int_{r_y}^{a} 2\pi r u\, dr = \frac{2\pi P}{4\mu_p}\int_{a\lambda}^{a}\left[r(a^2 - r^2) - 2a\lambda(ar - r^2)\right]dr$$

$$= \frac{\pi Pa^4}{2\mu_p}\left(\frac{1}{4} - \frac{1}{3}\lambda - \frac{1}{2}\lambda^2 + \lambda^3 - \frac{5}{12}\lambda^4\right)$$

The total flow is

$$Q = Q_1 + Q_2 = \frac{\pi Pa^4}{2\mu_p}\left(1 - \frac{4}{3}\lambda + \frac{1}{3}\lambda^4\right), \qquad \text{where } P = \frac{dp}{dx} = \frac{\Delta p}{L}$$

Note. This equation is known as the *Buckingham* equation. As might be anticipated the equation is more complicated than the corresponding result for a Newtonian fluid. The determination of the pressure drop for a given flow rate involves the solution of a fifth order equation since $\lambda = 2\tau_y/Pa$ and requires an iterative approach.

7.3 Pseudoplastic fluid rotation

The viscosity of a pseudoplastic fluid is to be measured by a coaxial viscometer. The apparent viscosity of the fluid, μ_a, is known to satisfy a power law of the form

$$\mu_a = K\left(\frac{du}{dy}\right)^{n-1}.$$

Show that the angular velocity of the outer cylinder is given by the equation $\Omega = \frac{1}{2}n\alpha(R_1^{-2/n} - R_2^{-2/n})$

where $\alpha = \left(\frac{C}{2\pi K}\right)^{1/n}$, $C =$ the torque and

$R_1, R_2 =$ radii of the inner and outer cylinders respectively.

In a test with $R_1 = 3$ cm, $R_2 = 3.5$ cm, $n = 0.5$ the torque was measured as 0.2 Nm at an angular velocity of 100 rev/min. Determine the value of K, and the variation of the apparent viscosity with the radius.

Solution. At any radius r the torque due to the viscous drag is

$$C = \tau(2\pi r)r = 2\pi r^2\tau.$$

Also $\dfrac{du}{dy} = r\dfrac{d}{dr}\left(\dfrac{u}{r}\right).$

Substituting in the viscosity equation

$$\tau = \mu_o\left(\frac{du}{dy}\right) = K\left(\frac{du}{dy}\right)^n$$

$$\frac{C}{2\pi r^2} = Kr^n\left[\frac{d}{dr}\left(\frac{u}{r}\right)\right]^n \quad \text{or} \quad \left(\frac{C}{2\pi K r^2}\right)^{1/n} = r\frac{d}{dr}\left(\frac{u}{r}\right)$$

and $\left(\dfrac{C}{2\pi K}\right)^{1/n} r^{-1-\frac{2}{n}} = \dfrac{d}{dr}\left(\dfrac{u}{r}\right)$

Introducing the term α, $\dfrac{d}{dr}\left(\dfrac{u}{r}\right) = \alpha r^{-1-\frac{2}{n}}$

Integrating gives

$$\frac{u}{r} = -\frac{1}{2}n\alpha r^{-\frac{2}{n}} + c \quad \text{and} \quad u = cr - \frac{1}{2}n\alpha r^{1-\frac{2}{n}}$$

The integration constant, c, can be determined from the boundary condition of no-slip at the inner cylinder surface (which is stationary).

Thus $u = 0$ at $r = R_1$, giving $c = \frac{1}{2}n\alpha R_1^{-\frac{2}{n}}$

Hence $u = \frac{1}{2}n\alpha(R_1^{-\frac{2}{n}}r - r^{1-\frac{2}{n}})$.

At the outer cylinder radius R_2

$$u = R_2\Omega = \tfrac{1}{2}n\alpha(R_1^{-\frac{2}{n}}R_2 - R_2^{-\frac{2}{n}}) \quad \text{and} \quad \mathbf{\Omega = \tfrac{1}{2}n\alpha(R_1^{-\frac{2}{n}} - R_2^{-\frac{2}{n}})}$$

In the second part of the problem $R_1 = 0.03$ m, $R_2 = 0.035$ m, $n = ½$ and $\Omega = 100$ rev/min = 10.47 rad/s. Substituting in the previous equation

$$10.47 = \frac{1}{2}\left(\frac{1}{2}\right)\alpha(0.03^{-4} - 0.035^{-4}), \quad \alpha = 7.371\times10^{-5} = \left(\frac{C}{2\pi K}\right)^2$$

K = 3.708

The apparent viscosity varies with the radius, as follows:

$$\frac{du}{dr} = \frac{1}{2}n\alpha\left[R_1^{-\frac{2}{n}} - \left(1 - \frac{2}{n}\right)r^{-\frac{2}{n}}\right] = \tfrac{1}{4}\alpha\left[R_1^{-4} + 3r^{-4}\right] \quad \text{since } n = ½$$

$$\mu_a = \frac{\tau}{du/dr} = \frac{C}{2\pi r^2(du/dr)} = \frac{0.2}{2\pi r^2(\frac{1}{4}\alpha)(R_1^{-4} + 3r^{-4})} = \frac{1727\,r^2}{3 + (r/0.03)^4}$$

The values at various radii are tabulated below:

r (m)	0.030	0.031	0.032	0.033	0.034	0.035
μ_α (Ns/m²)	0.389	0.401	0.412	0.421	0.429	0.436

7.4 Pseudoplastic fluid flow in pipes

A non-Newtonian fluid follows the viscosity relationship

$$\tau = K\left(\frac{du}{dy}\right)^n.$$

It flows along a circular pipe, diameter D, which is horizontal. Derive an expression for the pressure drop per unit length in terms of the index n, coefficient K, diameter D and mean velocity $\bar{u}$.

Sketch the velocity profiles for different values of the index n, in the form of $u/\bar{u}$ plotted against r/a, where a = pipe radius.

Solution. Denoting the pressure gradient $(-dp/dx)$ by P then

$$\tau = \frac{1}{2}rP = K\left(-\frac{du}{dr}\right)^n, \quad -\frac{du}{dr} = \left(\frac{P}{2K}\right)^{1/n} r^{1/n}$$

and integrating

$$u = -\left(\frac{P}{2K}\right)^{1/n} \frac{r^{\frac{1}{n}+1}}{\frac{1}{n}+1} + c$$

The no-slip boundary condition at the pipe wall is $u = 0$ at $r = a$, giving

$$c = \left(\frac{P}{2K}\right)^{\frac{1}{n}} \frac{r^{\frac{1}{n}+1}}{\frac{1}{n}+1}$$

Hence $u = \left(\frac{P}{2K}\right)^{\frac{1}{n}} \frac{n}{n+1}\left(\alpha^{\frac{1}{n}+1} - r^{\frac{1}{n}+1}\right)$

The flow rate over the whole cross-section is

$$Q = \int_0^a 2\pi r u \, dr = 2\pi\left(\frac{P}{2K}\right)^{\frac{1}{n}} \int_0^a \frac{n}{n+1}\left(\alpha^{\frac{1}{n}+1} - r^{\frac{1}{n}+1}\right) dr$$

$$= \frac{2n}{n+1}\left(\frac{P}{2K}\right)^{1/n} \frac{n+1}{2(3n+1)} a^{\frac{3n+1}{n}} = \frac{n\pi}{3n+1}\left(\frac{P}{2K}\right)^{1/n} a^{\frac{3n+1}{n}}$$

Hence the mean velocity is

$$\bar{u} = \frac{Q}{\pi a^2} = \frac{n}{3n+1}\left(\frac{P}{2K}\right)^{1/n} a^{\frac{n+1}{n}}$$

This can be rearranged to give the required expression:

$$\left(\frac{P}{2K}\right)^{1/n} = \left(\frac{3n+1}{n}\right)\bar{u} / a^{\frac{n+1}{n}}$$

or $$P = 2K\left[\frac{3n+1}{n}\frac{\bar{u}}{a^{\frac{n+1}{n}}}\right]^n = K\beta\left(\frac{3n+1}{n}\frac{\bar{u}}{D^{\frac{n+1}{n}}}\right)^n$$

where $\beta = 2(2^{\frac{n+1}{n}})^n = 2^{n+2}$

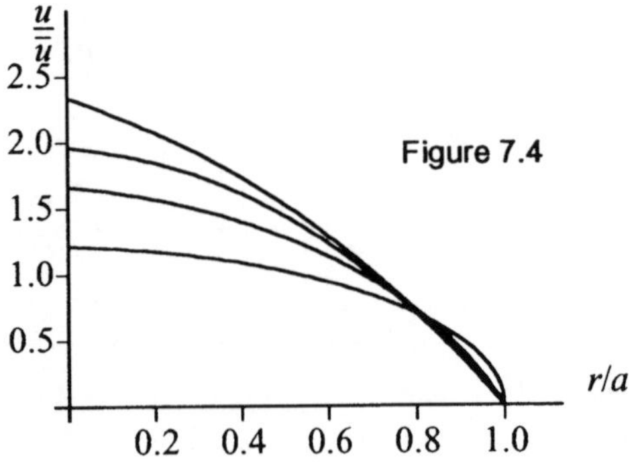

Figure 7.4

Note. For a Newtonian fluid

$$\tau = \mu\left(\frac{du}{dy}\right),$$

corresponding to $K = \mu$ and $n = 1$. Substituting these values into the previous equation gives

$$P = \mu(2)^3\left(\frac{4\bar{u}}{D^2}\right) = \frac{32\mu\bar{u}}{D^2}$$

which is the Poiseuille equation (see W.E.5.1). The velocity profiles can now be derived.

$$\frac{u}{\bar{u}} = \frac{\left(\frac{P}{2K}\right)^{1/n}\left(\frac{n}{n+1}\right)\left(\alpha^{\frac{n+1}{n}} - r^{\frac{n+1}{n}}\right)}{\frac{n}{3n+1}\left(\frac{P}{2K}\right)^{1/n} a^{\frac{n+1}{n}}} = \frac{3n+1}{n+1}\left[1 - \left(\frac{r}{a}\right)^{\frac{n+1}{n}}\right]$$

The profiles for various values of the index n are shown in Fig.7.4.

7.5 Generalised Reynolds number

> Discuss the method of estimating the pressure drop in a smooth circular pipe conveying a non-Newtonian fluid, using a friction coefficient and a generalised Reynolds number.

Solution. The determination of the pressure drop in a circular pipe conveying a Newtonian fluid has been considered in Chap.1 and 6. The pressure drop per unit length is

$\Delta p = 2\rho f u^2 / D$, where u = mean velocity, f = friction coefficient.

The friction coefficient, defined by

$$f = \tau_o / \tfrac{1}{2}\rho u^2$$

is a function of the Reynolds number

$$Re = \rho D u / \mu .$$

The nature of the function depends upon the character of the flow regime. Thus in viscous (or laminar) flow $f = 16/Re$; and in turbulent flow the relationship is less precise, various equations being used such as the

Blasius law	$f = 0.079 Re^{-0.25}$
'universal' law	$\frac{1}{\sqrt{4f}} = 2\log(Re\sqrt{4f}) - 0.8$

It has been proposed therefore that a similar method could be used for non-Newtonian fluids, employing a friction coefficient in the same way with some form of a Reynolds number, or an equivalent Reynolds number Re'. A method given by Metzner and Reed defines a friction factor, for both laminar and turbulent flow of time independent fluids.

In the laminar flow region $Re' = 8\rho u^2/\tau_o$ so that $f = 16/Re'$. The next step in the method is to use experimental data to determine the rheological constants, which can then be used to evaluate the generalised Reynolds number. The shear stress at the wall, τ_o, cannot be measured directly and is determined indirectly, from measurements of pressure drop Δp and mean velocity u.

The fluid constants are defined by the relations

$$\frac{\Delta p}{4L} = \tau_o = K'\left(\frac{8u}{D}\right)^{n'}$$

where K' is termed the consistency index, and n' is the flow behaviour index. The equation is based on an expression by Mooney for the wall shear rate

$$-\left(\frac{du}{dr}\right)_0 = \left(\frac{3n'+1}{4n'}\right)\frac{8u}{D} .$$

The indexes K', n' are not necessarily constants and can be used for any fluid. The generalised Reynolds number is then

$$Re' = \frac{\rho D^{n'} u^{2-n'}}{K' 8^{n'-1}} .$$

In the turbulent flow region Dodge and Metzner proposed an equation, for pseudoplastic (power law) fluids, of the form

$$\frac{1}{f} = \frac{4}{(n')^{0.75}}\log(Re' f^{1-\frac{1}{2}n'}) - \frac{0.4}{(n')^{1.2}}.$$

The friction factor, f, can be plotted against Re' to give an equivalent Moody diagram (Fig. 7.5): the various curves now corresponding to different values of n'.

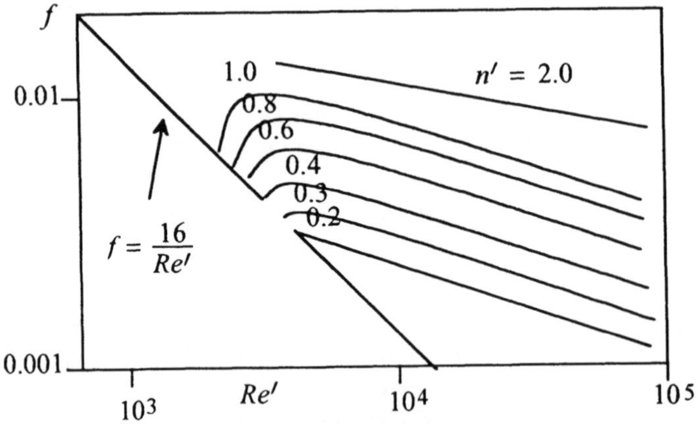

Figure 7.5

Many fluids do satisfy the generalised flow criteria, but some do not. For example some high molecular weight organic compounds (polymers) show friction factors much lower than those predicted by the turbulent flow equation. Slurries of solids in water may also show lower friction factors than for water only.

7.6 Non-power law pseudoplastic fluid

A non-Newtonian fluid can be described by an Ellis model, in which

$$\mu = \mu_o\left(1 + \left|\frac{\tau}{\tau_{0.5}}\right|^{\alpha-1}\right)^{-1}$$

where μ_o = viscosity as the shear stress $\tau \to 0$

$\tau_{0.5}$ = shear stress when $\mu = 0.5\mu_o$.

For the fluid $\mu_o = 0.4$ Ns/m², $\tau_{0.5} = 10$ N/m², density = 800 kg/m³, and $\alpha = 2.5$.

Calculate the flow rate of the fluid along a horizontal, circular pipe of diameter 80 mm under a pressure gradient of 1600 N/m² per metre length. Also determine the ratio of the mean velocity to maximum velocity.

Solution. For steady flow

$$\tau_o = \frac{1}{2}a\frac{dp}{dx},$$

where a = pipe radius. The shear stress distribution is linear, i.e.

$$\tau = \frac{\tau_o r}{a}.$$

Substituting the data given

$$\tau_o = \tfrac{1}{2}(0.04)(1600) = 32\ \text{N/m}^2$$

$$\tau = \frac{32r}{0.04} = 800r \text{ N/m}^2$$

Now $\tau = -\mu\left(\frac{du}{dr}\right)$

$$\frac{du}{dr} = -\frac{800r}{0.4}\left[1 + \left|\frac{800r}{10}\right|^{1.5}\right] = -2000r(1 + 715.5r^{1.5})$$

Integrating

$$u = -1000r^2 - 43143r^{3.5} + c$$

At the pipe wall, $r = 0.04$ m, $u = 0$ giving

$$c = 1000(0.04)^2 + 43143(0.04)^{3.5} = 2.15$$

The flow rate is

$$Q = \int_0^a 2\pi ru\,dr = 2\pi\int_0^{0.04}(2.15r - 1000r^3 - 43143r^{4.5})\,dr$$

$$= \mathbf{0.0068} \text{ m}^3\text{/s or } \mathbf{5.44} \text{ kg/s}$$

The maximum velocity is at the centre-line (since the flow is symmetric), and is

$$u_{max} = 2.15 \text{ m/s}$$

The mean velocity $\bar{u} = Q/\pi a^2 = 1.35$ m/s giving

$$\frac{\bar{u}}{u_{max}} = \mathbf{0.63}.$$

7.7 Fluid characteristics

A non-Newtonian fluid gave the following test results:

τ (N/m^2)	8	18	32	42	49	61	67
du/dr (s^{-1})	10	25	50	75	100	150	200

Determine the most appropriate model of the fluid behaviour, and the relevant fluid constants.

Solution. The results given are plotted, and give a smooth curve as shown in Fig.7.6. The shape of the curve suggests a short extrapolation to give $\tau = 0$ at $du/dr = 0$. Referring to Fig. 7.1 the curve is not a straight line, and $\tau_y = 0$ so that the fluid is not a Bingham plastic. It is probably a pseudoplastic, with an index $n < 1$. In this case the fluid characteristic would be given by an equation of the form

$$\tau = L\left(\frac{du}{dr}\right)^n.$$

The constants, K, and index n, can be determined from a plot of log τ against $\log(du/dr)$ and a straight line should be obtained. As can be seen from the plot a curve is produced. Regression analysis could be used to determine the 'best' straight line, but there would be some differences from the measured data at each end of the curve. The simple power law could be used over most of the range with, perhaps, an acceptable error at each end of the range.

The best line is found to give $K = 1.71$, $n = 0.72$ with 14% error at each end of the range.

A better model may be one satisfying one of the empirical equations. Considering the Ellis model, an initial investigation requires the values of the apparent viscosity

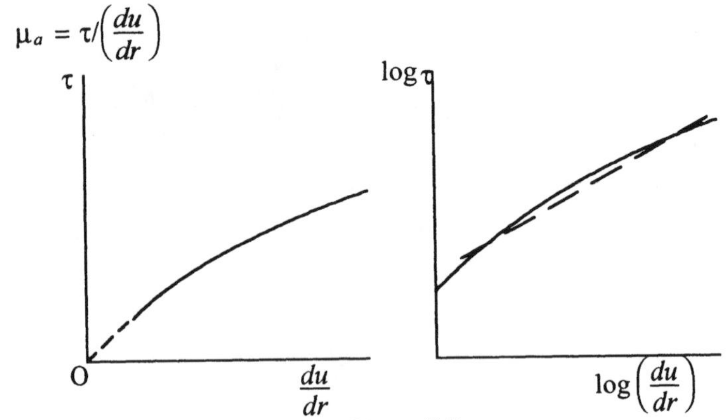

Figure 7.6

The plot of shear stress τ against apparent viscosity μ_a shows an approximate linear relationship,

$$\tau = 113 - 130\mu_a.$$

τ	8	18	32	42	49	61	67
μ_a	0.80	0.72	0.64	0.56	0.49	0.407	0.335

For the Ellis model

$$\frac{\mu_0}{\mu_a} = 1 + \left|\frac{\tau}{\tau_{0.5}}\right|^{\alpha-1}$$

where $\tau_{0.5}$ = shear stress when $\mu_a = 0.5\mu_0$

μ_0 = viscosity as the shear stress approaches zero.

From the plot of τ against μ_a, $\mu_0 = 0.87\,\text{Ns/m}^2$ and $\tau_{0.5} = 57\,\text{N/m}^2$

Hence $\frac{0.87}{\mu_a} = 1 + \left|\frac{\tau}{57}\right|^{\alpha-1}$

and from the values of τ and μ_a the values of α can be determined.

μ_a	0.8	0.72	0.64	0.56	0.49	0.407	0.335
α	2.24	2.36	2.77	2.93	2.67	3.41	3.90

It may be that the Meter model is a better one, but there is the problem of estimating the apparent viscosity as the shear stress approaches infinity.

The investigation emphasises the point that the fluid does not fall precisely into one of the models, and this is often the case. In some fluids the whole range may have to be split up into several parts and different values of the constants used, one set for a particular part. In this particular problem it appears that a power law gives an approximate model, or the particular model $\tau = 113 - 130\,\mu_0$ gives better agreement.

7.8 Viscoelastic fluids

Discuss the behaviour and properties of viscoelastic fluids. Outline how such fluids can be modelled by a mechanical system.

Solution. A viscoelastic fluid is a non-Newtonian fluid which exhibits elastic properties as well as viscous properties. They can be shown in many ways, such as the classic Weissenberg effect: a jet of fluid issuing from a tube does not show the contraction associated with a Newtonian fluid, but expands due to normal stress.

Another demonstration is in the behaviour of such a fluid when poured from a vessel. The fluid jet, or film, can be cut across the section to split into two portions. The lower portion continues to drop, but the upper portion may 'climb' back into the vessel.

Mechanical models of a viscoelastic fluid incorporate springs and dashpots, to represent the elastic and viscous forces.

The *Maxwell* model was a spring and dashpot in series. It can be defined by the equation

$$\tau + \left(\frac{\mu}{G}\right)\frac{d\tau}{dt} = \mu\left(\frac{du}{dy}\right) = \mu s \text{ say,}$$

where G = modulus of rigidity, s = shear strain.

Integrating gives

$$\tau = \exp\left(\frac{-Gt}{\mu}\right)\left[\tau_0 + G\int s \exp\left(\frac{Gt}{\mu}\right)dt\right]$$

The *Voigt* model uses a spring and dashpot in parallel, and can be defined by the equation

$$\tau = Gs + \mu s$$

which can be integrated to give

$$s = \exp\left(\frac{-Gt}{\mu}\right)\left[s_0 + \frac{1}{\mu}\int \tau \exp\left(\frac{Gt}{\mu}\right)dt\right]$$

These are basic models, and for many real fluids would be inadequate. It becomes necessary to use combinations of them to achieve more realistic models.

7.9 Two-phase flow patterns

A gas flows vertically upwards in a column of liquid. Outline the possible flow patterns, and sketch the form of bubble, slug, churn and annular flow.

Describe how the patterns would be modified if the flow was horizontal.

Solution. The possible flow patterns can be classified as shown in Fig. 7.7, and depend upon the gas velocity through the liquid. At low velocity the gas rises in the form of small bubbles, dispersed throughout the liquid.

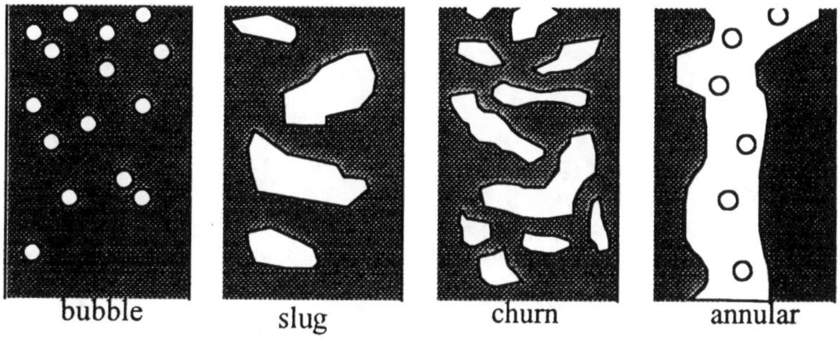

Figure 7.7

As the gas velocity increases the small bubbles coalesce to form larger bubbles, forming *slug* (or plug) flow. A further increase in the gas velocity causes the large bubbles to become unstable and break down, giving an oscillatory motion of the bubbles: this is known as *churn* flow. Finally as the gas velocity increases further the gas phase flows in a central core, often with small droplets of liquid entrained in it: this is termed *annular* flow.

In horizontal flow the effect of gravitational forces is to displace the heavier liquid towards the bottom of the duct. Another type of flow pattern can arise due to this effect, in which the flow is *stratified* into two layers. The flow patterns are illustrated in Fig. 7.8

bubble   plug   stratified

gas flow ⟶

slug   annular

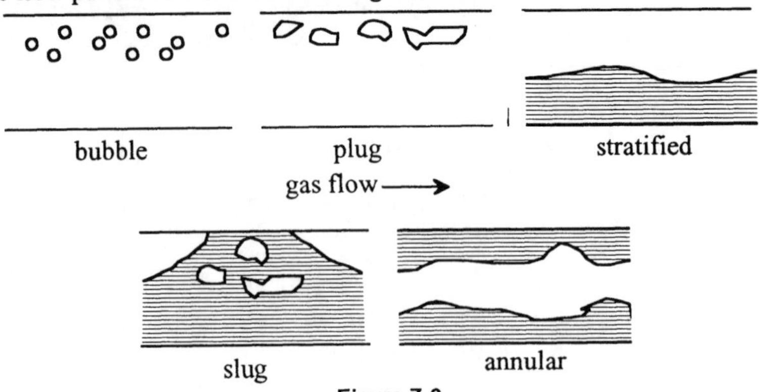

Figure 7.8

The pattern that occurs depends upon the mass flow rate, gas concentration in the mixture, and the physical properties (density, surface tension and viscosity) of the fluids. Clearly the situation is very complicated and, in practice, empirical data plays a very large part. A map can be drawn, from such data, as a general guide to the probable pattern: limited to a particular geometry and fluid pair. A typical map is shown in Fig. 7.9 for a horizontal flow.

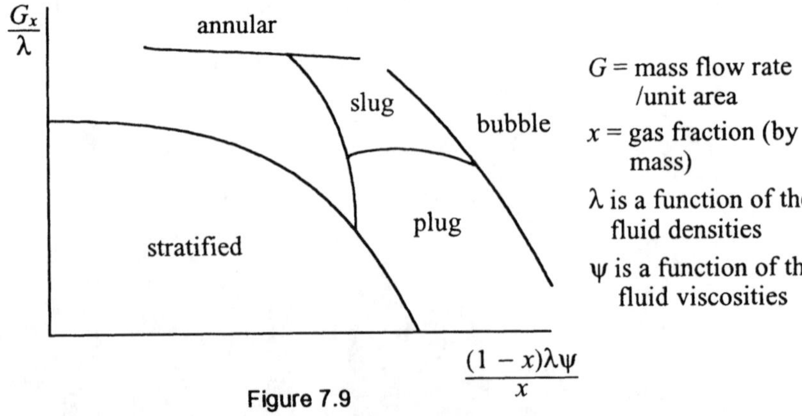

$\dfrac{G_x}{\lambda}$

annular

slug

bubble

plug

stratified

$\dfrac{(1-x)\lambda\psi}{x}$

Figure 7.9

G = mass flow rate /unit area

x = gas fraction (by mass)

λ is a function of the fluid densities

ψ is a function of the fluid viscosities

7.10 Homogeneous model

Outline the homogeneous model of gas-liquid flow. Define the terms void function α, quality x, and slip ratio K.

A mixture of air (at 20°C) and water flows up a vertical pipe, 25 mm diameter, 45 cm length. The mass flow rates of water and air are 0.42 and 0.01kg/s respectively. Estimate the pressure difference between the ends of the pipe, assuming that the friction coefficient is given by the equation

$$f = 0.079 / Re^{0.25}.$$

Handwritten margin notes:

Effect of gravity

homogeneous model more ↓ accuracy

Chisholm model.

Superficial velocity v_s

$u_s = \dfrac{Q}{A}$

mass flowrate

$G = \rho u A \leftarrow$ Area of what!

$\left[\dfrac{kg}{s}\right] = \left[\dfrac{kg}{m^3}\right] \cdot \left[\dfrac{m}{s}\right] \cdot \left(m^2\right)$

$G = $ mass flow rate per unit Area

$\hookrightarrow G = \dfrac{\dot{m}}{A}$

$\chi = \left(\dfrac{\rho_g \, \mu_\ell}{\rho_a \, \mu_w}\right)^{1/2}$

Holland & Bragg, Azbel, Milan.

Solution. The homogeneous model is a simple one, taking the mixture of the two fluids as a uniform one and therefore uses *average* properties. The variations in the fluid properties along the duct, and across any cross-section, are ignored. The model is clearly approximate but is easy to use, and with care, can give reasonable approximations.

The *void fraction* α is defined as the ratio of the cross-sectional area occupied by the gas A_g to the cross-sectional area of the channel, A.

Thus $\alpha = \dfrac{A_g}{A}$, or $1 - \alpha = \dfrac{A_L}{A}$

where A_L = cross-sectional area occupied by the liquid, and $A = A_g + A_L$. In the homogeneous model it can also be expressed in terms of the volumetric flow rate, Q:

$$\alpha = \frac{Q_g}{Q}$$

The gas phase fraction (mass flow) of the total mass flow rate of gas is termed the quality x:

$$x = \frac{\dot{m}_g}{\dot{m}}$$

$$\dot{m}_g = x\dot{m} = \int \rho_g u_g dA = \rho_g u_g A_g = \rho_g u_g \alpha A$$

Similarly the mass flow rate of liquid is

$$\dot{m}_L = \rho_L u_L (1 - \alpha) A$$

The *slip ratio* K is the ratio of the gas velocity to the liquid velocity, or $K = u_g/u_L$. This can be expressed in terms of the void fraction and quality:

$$K = \left(\frac{x}{1-x}\right)\left(\frac{1-\alpha}{\alpha}\right)\frac{\rho_L}{\rho_g}$$

In a homogeneous mixture the mixing is complete and the velocities of the phases are equal, i.e. $u_g = u_L$ and there is no slip $K = 1$. The equivalent density of the mixture, ρ, can be determined as follows:

$$\dot{m} = \dot{m}_g + \dot{m}_L$$

$$\rho u A = \rho_g u_g \alpha A + \rho_L u_L (1 - \alpha) A$$

and since $u = u_g = u_L$

$$\rho = \alpha\rho_g + (1 - \alpha)\rho_L$$

or in terms of the quality x,

$$\frac{1}{\rho} = \frac{x}{\rho_g} + \frac{1-x}{\rho_L}$$

The equivalent viscosity of the mixture, μ, can be determined from a similar expression

$$\frac{1}{\mu} = \frac{x}{\mu_g} + \frac{1-x}{\mu_L}$$

The calculation involves a mixture of air and water. At 20° C the properties of air and water are

air	$\rho_g = 1.20\,\text{Kg/m}^3$,	$\mu_g = 1.8 \times 10^{-5}\,\text{Kg/ms}$
water	$\rho_L = 1000\,\text{Kg/m}^3$,	$\mu_L = 1.0 \times 10^{-3}\,\text{Kg/ms}$

The mass flow rates are $\dot{m}_g = 0.01$, $\dot{m}_L = 0.042\text{Kg/s}$, so that the quality

$$x = \frac{\dot{m}_g}{\dot{m}} = \frac{0.01}{0.43} = 0.023.$$

$$\frac{1}{\rho} = \frac{0.023}{1.2} + \frac{0.977}{1000} = 0.020$$

homogeneous model the mixing is complete and velocities are equal $u_g = u_L$

giving the mixture density $\rho = 49.64\,\text{Kg/m}^3$.

The equivalent (or virtual) viscosity of the mixture can be calculated, knowing the quality.

$$\frac{1}{\mu} = \frac{0.023}{1.8\times10^{-5}} + \frac{0.977}{10^{-3}} = 2255, \qquad \mu = 4.435\times10^{-4}\ \text{kg/ms}$$

The mixture velocity (equal to the gas and liquid velocities)

$$u = \frac{\dot{m}}{\rho A} = \frac{0.43}{49.64\times\frac{\pi}{4}(0.025)^2} = 17.65\ \text{m/s}.$$

Reynolds number

$$Re = \frac{\rho D u}{\mu} = \frac{49.64\times0.025\times17.65}{4.435\times10^{-4}} = 49388$$

$$f = \frac{0.079}{Re^{0.25}} = 0.0053$$

The pressure difference due to friction is

$$\Delta p_f = \frac{4\rho f L u^2}{2D} = \frac{4\times49.64\times0.0053\times0.45\times(17.65)^2}{2\times0.025}$$

$$= 2950\ \text{N/m}^2$$

There is also a pressure difference due to the pipe being vertical,

$$\Delta p_z = \rho g z = 49.64\times9.81\times0.45 = 219\ \text{N/m}^2$$

would this be needed

giving a total pressure difference of

$$\Delta p = 2950 + 219 = \mathbf{3169}\ \text{N/m}^2$$

Note. The volumetric flow rates are

$$Q_g = \frac{\dot{m}_g}{\rho_g} = \frac{0.01}{1.20} = 0.00833\ \text{m}^3\text{/s}$$

$$Q_L = \frac{0.42}{1000} = 0.00042\ \text{m}^3\text{/s}$$

void fraction

$$\alpha = \frac{Q_g}{Q} = \frac{0.00833}{0.00875} = 0.952$$

$$u_g = \frac{\dot{m}_g}{\rho_g \alpha A} = \frac{0.01}{1.2\times0.952\times\frac{\pi}{4}(0.025)^2} = 17.65\ \text{m/s}$$

$$u_L = \frac{0.42}{1000\times0.048\times\frac{\pi}{4}(0.025)^2} = 17.65\ \text{m/s}$$

7.11 Energy and momentum equations

Derive forms of the momentum and energy equations for two-phase flow, in terms of the shear stress at the wall τ_o, the mass flow/unit area G, and the quality x, and void fraction α. Consider flow in a vertical pipe.

Under what conditions are the equations identical? What is meant by the critical flow rate?

Solution. Considering single phase flow the momentum equation can be derived from a force balance. On an element dz (Fig. 7.10),

$$G\,du = -\,dp - \rho g\,dz - \frac{\tau_o P}{A}\,dz$$

where p = perimeter of the pipe, A = cross-sectional area.

This can be written as

$$-\frac{dp}{dz} = \frac{\tau_o P}{A} + G\frac{du}{dz} + \rho g.$$

In two-phase flow the corresponding equation is

$$-\frac{dp}{dz} = \frac{\tau_o P}{A} + \frac{d}{dz}[\alpha G_g u_g + (1-\alpha)G_L u_L] + g[\alpha\rho_g + (1-\alpha)\rho_L]$$

where $\alpha\rho_g + (1-\alpha)\rho_L$ = mixture density ρ

$$G_g = \frac{\dot{m}_g}{A_g},\ G_L = \frac{\dot{m}_g}{A_L}$$

$$G = (\dot{m}_g u_g + \dot{m}_L u_L)/A = \alpha G_g u_g + (1-\alpha)G_L u_L$$

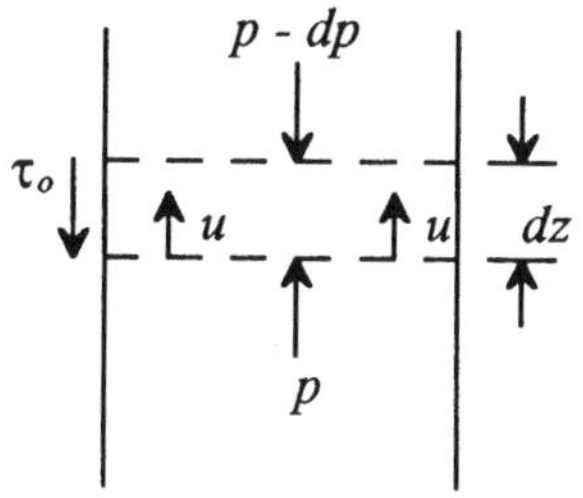

Figure 7.10

The quality x can be introduced:

$$x = \frac{\dot{m}_g}{\dot{m}}$$

and $$G_g = \frac{\dot{m}_g}{A_g} = \frac{x\dot{m}}{A_g} = \frac{x\dot{m}}{\alpha A} = \frac{xG}{\alpha}\ (\text{since } G = \frac{\dot{m}}{A}).$$

$$G_L = \frac{\dot{m}_L}{A_L} = \frac{(1-x)\dot{m}}{A_L} = \frac{(1-x)\dot{m}}{(1-\alpha)A} = \frac{(1-x)G}{1-\alpha}$$

and substituting into the equation

$$-\frac{\mathbf{dp}}{\mathbf{dz}} = \frac{\tau_o P}{A} + G^2\frac{d}{dz}\left[\frac{x^2}{\alpha\rho_g} + \frac{(1-x)^2}{(1-\alpha)\rho_L}\right] + g[\alpha\rho_g + (1-\alpha)\rho_L]$$

since $$\alpha G_g u_g = \alpha\left(\frac{xG}{\alpha}\right)\left(\frac{G_g}{\rho_g}\right) = xG\left(\frac{xG}{\alpha\rho_g}\right) = \frac{x^2G^2}{\alpha\rho_g}.$$

The energy equation for single-phase flow is

$$dp = \rho g\,dz + G\,du + \left(\frac{\tau_o P}{A}\right)dz = 0.$$

Putting the friction force

$$dF = \left(\frac{\tau_o P}{\rho A}\right)dz$$

for convenience gives the equation as

$$dp + \rho g\,dz + G\,du + \rho\,dF = 0$$

Now $\frac{1}{\rho} = \frac{x}{\rho_g} + \frac{1-x}{\rho_L}$

so that the equation for single-phase flow

$$\frac{dp}{\rho} + g\,dz + G\,d(\tfrac{1}{2}\rho u^2) + dF = 0$$

becomes, for two-phase flow,

$$d\left[\frac{xp}{\rho_g} + \frac{(1-x)p}{\rho_L}\right] - p\,d\left[\frac{x}{\rho_g} + \frac{1-x}{\rho_L}\right] + g\,dz + d\left[\frac{1}{2}xu_g^2 + \frac{1}{2}(1-x)u_L^2\right] + dF = 0$$

This can be rearranged to give

$$-\frac{dp}{dz} = \rho\frac{dF}{dz} + \frac{1}{2}\rho G^2\frac{d}{dz}\left[\frac{x^3}{\alpha^2\rho_g^2} + \frac{(1-x)^3}{(1-\alpha)^2\rho_L^2}\right] + \rho g$$

The momentum and energy equations are identical in the homogeneous model, where there is no slip (relative velocity) between the phases.

The *homogeneous model flow equation can be written in the form*

$$-\frac{dp}{dz} = \rho\frac{dF}{dz} + G\frac{du}{dz} + \rho g$$

since the homogeneous mixture is equivalent to a *single* phase fluid having average properties.

Now $G\frac{du}{dz} = G\frac{d}{dz}\left(\frac{G}{\rho}\right) = G^2\frac{d}{dz}\left(\frac{1}{\rho}\right)$

$$\frac{d}{dz}\left(\frac{1}{\rho}\right) = \frac{\partial}{\partial p}\left(\frac{1}{\rho}\right)\frac{dp}{dz} + \frac{\partial}{\partial x}\left(\frac{1}{\rho}\right)\frac{dx}{dz}$$

$$\frac{1}{\rho} = \frac{x}{\rho_g} + \frac{1-x}{\rho_L}, \qquad \frac{\partial}{\partial x}\left(\frac{1}{\rho}\right) = \frac{1}{\rho_g} - \frac{1}{\rho_L}.$$

Hence substituting

$$-\frac{dp}{dz} = \rho\frac{dF}{dz} + \rho g + G^2\left[\frac{\partial}{\partial p}\left(\frac{1}{\rho}\right)\frac{dp}{dz} + \left(\frac{1}{\rho_g} - \frac{1}{\rho_L}\right)\frac{dx}{dz}\right]$$

or

$$-\frac{dp}{dz} = \frac{\rho\frac{dF}{dz} + \rho g + G^2\left(\frac{1}{\rho_L} - \frac{1}{\rho_L}\right)\frac{dx}{dz}}{1 + G^2\frac{\partial}{\partial p}\left(\frac{1}{\rho}\right)}.$$

The interest in this equation is in the denominator: it can be seen that as $1/G^2$ approaches the value

$$-\frac{\partial}{\partial p}\left(\frac{1}{\rho}\right)$$

the pressure gradient dp/dz approaches an infinite value, as the denominator approaches zero. This condition is known as the *critical* flow rate.

7.12 Separated flow model

Outline the Lockhart-Martinelli method for the estimation of the pressure drop along a horizontal pipe conveying a two-phase fluid.

Estimate the pressure drop in a pipe, 50 mm diameter, 30 m length conveying a mixture of 0.7 l/s of oil and 0.15 m^3/s of gas. The friction coefficient $f = 0.079/Re^{0.25}$.

fluid	ρ kg/m^3	μ kg/ms
oil	800	6×10^{-4}
gas	0.8	1.5×10^{-5}

λ	0.04	0.07	0.10	0.20	0.40	0.70	1.00	2.00	4.00
α	-	0.96	0.95	0.91	0.86	0.81	0.77	0.69	0.60
ϕ_g	1.54	1.71	1.85	2.23	2.83	3.53	4.20	6.20	9.56

Solution. The separated flow model considers the two phases (or constituents) as separate fluids to which the normal single-phase equations can be applied. The interaction between the phases, which occurs in practice, is often difficult to analyse and is allowed for by the use of semi-empirical factors.

The Lockhart-Martinelli method correlates the two-phase pressure gradient with the single-phase gradients by the use of such factors. The pressure gradient (due to friction) is expressed in terms of the gradients

$$\left(\frac{dp}{dx}\right)_g, \left(\frac{dp}{dx}\right)_L$$

that would arise *if* the two phases flowed separately. The following parameters are defined:

$$\phi_L^2 = \frac{P}{P_L},\ \phi_g^2 = \frac{P}{P_g},\ \lambda^2 = \frac{P_L}{P_g},$$

$$\text{where } P = \frac{dp}{dx}.$$

The multiplier ϕ_g and void fraction α are correlated against the ratio λ: Lockhart and Martinelli separated the data into three sets, as shown in Fig. 7.11.

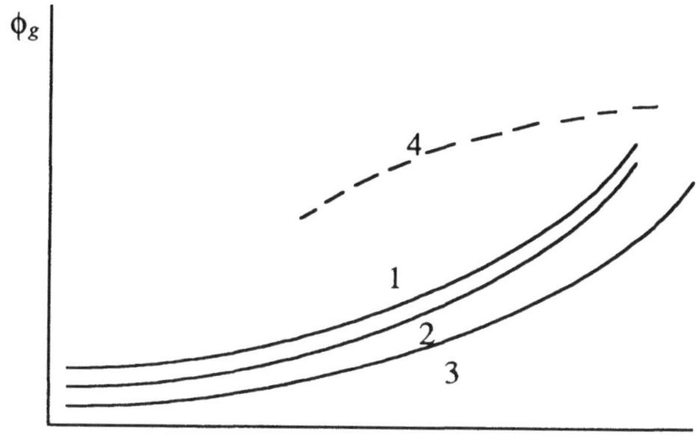

Curves: 1—turbulent flow (both phases)
2—viscous flow (liquid) with turbulent flow (gas)
3—viscous flow (both phases)
4—liquid fraction $1 - \alpha$

Figure 7.11

If a friction coefficient is used λ^2 can be expressed in terms of the physical properties of the fluids and the quality x. Thus,

$$Re_L = \left(\frac{\rho D u}{\mu}\right)_L = \left(\frac{GD}{\mu}\right)_L = \frac{(1-x)GD}{\mu_L}$$

$$f_L = \frac{0.079}{Re_L^{0.25}} = 0.079\left[\frac{\mu_L}{(1-x)GD}\right]^{0.25}$$

$$P_L = \left(\frac{4f\rho u^2}{2D}\right)_L = 2(0.079)\left[\frac{\mu_L}{(1-x(GD}\right]^{0.25}\frac{\rho_L}{D}\left[\frac{(1-x)G}{\rho_L}\right]^2$$

$$= \frac{0.158\mu_L^{0.25}(1-x)^{1.75}G^{1.75}}{\rho_L D^{1.25}}$$

Similarly

$$P_g = \frac{0.158\mu_g^{0.25}x^{1.75}G^{1.75}}{\rho_g D^{1.25}}$$

Hence $\lambda^2 = \frac{P_L}{P_g} = \left(\frac{1-x}{x}\right)^{1.75} \frac{\rho_g}{\rho_L}\left(\frac{\mu_L}{\mu_g}\right)^{0.25}$

In this particular problem, for the liquid only (oil)

$$u = \frac{0.7\times10^{-3}}{\frac{\pi}{4}(0.05)^2} = 0.357 \text{ m/s}$$

$$Re = 800\times0.05\times\frac{0.357}{6\times10^{-4}} = 23\,800, \qquad f = \frac{0.079}{Re^{0.25}} = 0.00636$$

$$P = 2\times800\times0.00636\times\frac{(0.357)^2}{0.05} = 26 \text{ N/m}^3$$

and for the gas only

$$u = \frac{0.15}{\frac{\pi}{4}(0.05)^2} = 76.39 \text{ m/s}$$

$$Re = 0.8\times0.05\times\frac{76.39}{1.5\times10^{-5}} = 203\,707, \qquad f = 0.00372$$

$$P = 2\times0.8\times0.00372\times\frac{(76.39)^2}{0.05} = 695 \text{ N/m}^3$$

Hence $\lambda^2 = \frac{P_L}{P_g} = 0.0374,\ \lambda = 0.193$.

Interpolation from the table of values of λ, α, ϕ_g gives

$\alpha = 0.914$, $\phi_g = 2.19$.

The pressure drop is

$$P = \phi_g^2 P_g = (2.19)^2(695) = 3\,333 \text{ N/m}^2 \text{ per m}$$
$$= 10^5 \text{ N/m}^2 \text{ over the 30m length.}$$

Note. $\alpha = 0.914$ which shows that the area occupied by the gas is 0.914 of the total area.

The calculation can be performed assuming a homogeneous model; the results are as follows:

$\alpha = 0.995$	$x = 0.176$
$\rho = 4.796$ kg/m³	$\mu = 7.63 \times 10^{-5}$ kg/ms
$u = 18.69$ m/s	$Re = 58\,740$
$f = 0.00507$	$P = 340$ N/m³

$\Delta p = 10\,190$ N/m².

The value of the pressure drop is about 1/10th of that predicted by the separated model. It is to be expected that the two models do not give the same value, but in this case there is a large difference. It should be remembered that both models are necessarily approximate and the simpler, homogeneous model is probably more inaccurate in this particular problem. In practice, therefore, the higher value would be used for design purposes.

7.13 Separated flow model

A horizontal pipe, 40 cm diameter, 100 m length, conveys a mixture of oil and gas. Assuming the Blasius formula (for the friction coefficient) and using the Martinelli curves provided, estimate the pressure drop.

	oil	*gas*	
flow rate	0.02	0.10	m³/s
density	800	6	kg/m³
viscosity	6×10^{-4}	1.5×10^{-5}	kg/ms

Solution. The Martinelli curves are shown in Fig. 7.11.

$$x = \frac{\dot{m}_g}{\dot{m}} = \frac{0.10\times 6}{0.6 + 0.02(800)} = \frac{0.6}{16.6} = 0.036$$

$$\lambda^2 = \left(\frac{1-x}{x}\right)^{1.75}\frac{\rho_g}{\rho_L}\left(\frac{\mu_L}{\mu_g}\right)^{0.25} = (315.2)(0.0075)(2.515) = 5.945$$

$$\lambda = 2.44$$

From the curves provided (assuming turbulent flow in both phases) $\phi_g = 9.5$, $1 - \alpha = 0.24$ or $\alpha = 0.86$. For gas only

$$u = \frac{0.10}{\frac{\pi}{4}(0.04)^2} = 80 \text{ m/s}$$

$$Re = 6\times 0.04\times\frac{80}{1.5\times 10^{-5}} = 1.27\times 10^6$$

$$f = \frac{0.079}{Re^{0.25}} \text{ (Blasius formula)} = 0.00235$$

$$P_g = 2\times 0.00235\times\frac{(80)^2}{0.04} = 753 \text{ N/m}^3$$

giving $P = \phi_g^2 P_g = (9.5)^2(753) = 67\,958$ N/m^3 and $\Delta p =$ **68** bar.

The gas flow is certainly turbulent. The type of oil flow can be classified by the Reynolds number.

$$u_L = \frac{0.02}{\frac{\pi}{4}(0.04)^2} = 15.92 \text{ m/s}$$

$$Re_L = 800\times 0.04\times\frac{15.92}{6\times 10^{-4}} = 8.5\times 10^5$$

and is turbulent. The assumption of turbulent flow in both phases is therefore valid.

7.14 Drift flux model

Outline the drift flux model for two-phase flow, of a gas-liquid mixture. Derive the following relationships:

$$u_1 = \frac{j}{1+\frac{j_{21}}{j_1}},\ u_2 = \frac{j}{1-\frac{j_{21}}{j_2}},\ \frac{j_1}{j_2} = \frac{u_1}{u_2}\left(\frac{1-\alpha}{\alpha}\right),$$

$$j_{12} = j_1\alpha - (1-a)j_2, j_{12} = \alpha(1-\alpha)u_{12}$$

where j is the volumetric flux, u is the phase velocity and subscripts 1,2 refer to the two phases. What is meant by flooding?

Solution. The drift flux model is based on the *relative* motion between the phases, in contrast to the separated flow model which is based on the motion of each phase. The model is closer to the actual flow pattern in that the two phases do normally move with different velocities, particularly in solid-liquid and solid-gas flows.

Some terms used in the model analysis are first defined as follows:

v = *superficial* velocity } = $\dfrac{\text{volumetric flow rat}}{\text{channel area}}$
j = volumetric flux
u = *phase* velocity
u' = *drift* velocity = phase velocity relative to the superficial velocity

The void fraction α is defined as the ratio of the cross-sectional area occupied by the gas to that of the channel A. The superficial velocities of the gas and liquid phases are

$$v_2 = \frac{Q_2}{A} = j_2 \text{ and } v_1 = \frac{Q_1}{A} = j_1 \text{ respectively:}$$

the total superficial velocity is clearly $v = v_1 + v_2$. The phase velocities are

$$u_2 = \frac{v_2}{\alpha} = \frac{j_2}{\alpha} \text{ and } u_1 = \frac{v_1}{1-\alpha} = \frac{j_1}{1-\alpha}.$$

The drift velocities of the phases are

$$u_1' = u_1 - v, \text{ and } u_2' = u_2 - v$$

The subscripts 1,2 refer to the gas and liquid phases respectively.

The concentration of the phases can be predicted if the value of the void fraction α is known. Additional information is provided by the relationship between the *drift* flux j_{12} and the void fraction, the physical properties of the fluids, and the nature of the flow pattern. The drift flux is a measure of the relative flow between the phases, and can be expressed in the following terms. Consider the gas phase flow/unit area, or flux, through a plane moving at a velocity v. Then by continuity $j_{21} = \alpha u_2'$. Similarly $j_{12} = (1-\alpha)u'$.

The relationship between j_{12} and α that is often used is one suggested by Wallis, namely

$$j_{12} = u_\infty \alpha (1-\alpha)^n$$

where u_∞ is the bubble rise velocity in an infinite fluid (i.e. with no corrections for the geometry of the system), and $0 \le n \le 2$. The types of solution are shown in Fig. 7.12.

The relationships stated for two-phase flow can be derived as follows:

$$j_1 = \frac{Q_1}{A} \text{ and } j_2 = \frac{Q_2}{A}, \text{ and } j = j_1 + j_2$$

The drift flux is

$$j_{21} = \alpha(u_2 - j), j_{12} = (1-\alpha)(u_1 - j)$$

$$\text{where } u_1 = \text{phase velocity} = \frac{j_1}{(1-\alpha)}, u_2 = \frac{j_2}{\alpha}$$

$$\text{Hence } \frac{j_{21}}{j_1} = -\frac{j_{12}}{j_1} = -\frac{(1-\alpha)(u_1 - j)}{(1-\alpha)u_1} = \frac{j}{u_1} - 1$$

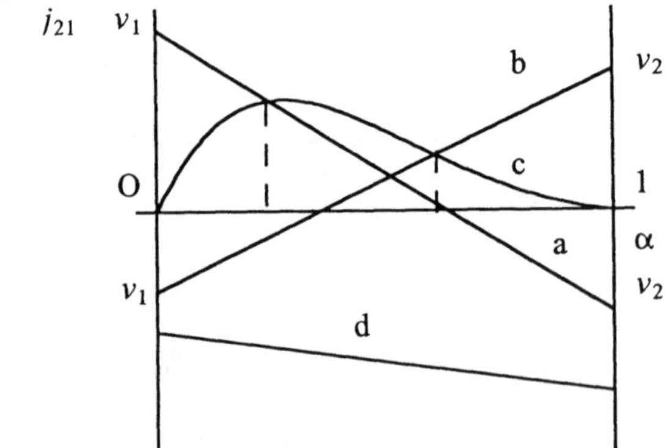

Curve: a—vertical cocurrent, up-flow
b—vertical cocurrent, down-flow
c—vertical contracurrent—liquid down, gas up
d—vertical contracurrent—liquid up, gas down

Figure 7.12

or $\quad \dfrac{j}{u_1} = 1 + \dfrac{j_{21}}{j_1}$

Similarly

$$\frac{j_{21}}{j_2} = \frac{\alpha(u_2 - j)}{\alpha u_2} = 1 - \frac{j}{u_2} \quad \text{or} \quad \frac{j}{u_2} = 1 - \frac{j_{21}}{j_2}$$

$$\frac{u_1}{u_2} = \frac{j_1}{1-\alpha}\frac{\alpha}{j_2} = \left(\frac{\alpha}{1-\alpha}\right)\frac{j_1}{j_2} \quad \text{or} \quad \frac{j_1}{j_2} = \left(\frac{1-\alpha}{\alpha}\right)\frac{u_1}{u_2}$$

$$j_{12} = -j_{21} = -\alpha(u_2 - j) = \alpha j - j_2 \quad (\text{since } j_2 = \alpha u_2)$$

$$= au_1\left(1 + \frac{j_{21}}{j_1}\right) - j_2 = \frac{\alpha j_1}{1-\alpha}\left(1 - \frac{j_{12}}{j_1}\right) - j_2$$

and rearranging gives

$$j_{12}\left(1 + \frac{\alpha}{1-\alpha}\right) = \frac{\alpha j_1}{1-\alpha} - j_2, \qquad j_{12} = \alpha j_1 - (1-\alpha)j_2$$

Finally $u_{12} = u_1 - u_2 = \dfrac{j_1}{1-\alpha} - \dfrac{j_2}{\alpha}$

or $\quad \boldsymbol{\alpha(1-\alpha)u_{12} = \alpha j_1 - (1-\alpha)j_2 = j_{12}}$

The term *flooding* is used to describe the situation where a reversal of the flow direction of a phase is about to occur. Consider for example the downward flow of a liquid film in a vertical tube against the upward flow of a gas. If the gas flow rate is increased the liquid velocity tends to decrease, and a point is reached at which the liquid film begins to be carried upwards: this point is termed the flooding point.

Wallis proposed that flooding could occur when

$$\sqrt{v_2^*} + \sqrt{v_1^*} = 1, \text{ where } v_2^* = v_2\sqrt{\rho_2}\left[gD(\rho_1 - \rho_2)\right]^{-1/2}$$

$$v_1^* = v_1\sqrt{\rho_1}\left[gD(\rho_1 - \rho_2)\right]^{-1/2}.$$

7.15 Drift flux model calculation

A mixture of liquid gas (in the form of bubbles) flows in a vertical pipe, diameter 15 cm. The drift flux and voidage fraction are related by the equation $j_{12} = 0.3\alpha(1-\alpha)^2$.

The flow rates of gas and liquid are $Q_2 = 880$ l/s, and $Q_1 = 750$ l/s respectively. Estimate the voidage fraction at the point of flooding.

Solution. The pipe cross-sectional area $A = \frac{\pi}{4}(0.15)^2 = 0.0177\ \text{m}^2$

and $\quad j_1 = \dfrac{Q_1}{A} = 0.0424\ \text{m/s}, j_2 = \dfrac{Q_2}{A} = 0.0500\ \text{m/s}.$

At the flooding point $j_{12} = 0.3\alpha(1-\alpha)^2$ and

$$j_2 = j_{21} - \alpha\left(\frac{dj_{21}}{d\alpha}\right) = 0.3\alpha(1-\alpha)^2 - 0.3\alpha[(1-\alpha)^2 - 2\alpha(1-\alpha)]$$

$$= 0.3\alpha(1-\alpha)[1 - \alpha - 1 + \alpha + 2\alpha] = 0.3\alpha(1-\alpha)(2\alpha)$$

$$= 0.6\alpha^2(1-\alpha)$$

$$j_1 = j_{21} + (1-\alpha)\left(\frac{dj_{21}}{d\alpha}\right)$$

$$= 0.3\alpha(1-\alpha)^2 + (1-\alpha)(0.3)[(1-\alpha)^2 - 2\alpha(1-\alpha)]$$

$$= 0.3(1-\alpha)^2[\alpha + 1 - \alpha - 2\alpha] = 0.3(1-2\alpha)(1-\alpha)^2$$

Now $j_1 + j_2 = 0.0924$

and solving gives

$\alpha = 0.32, j_1 = 0.0500, j_2 = 0.0424$ m/s (Fig. 7.13).

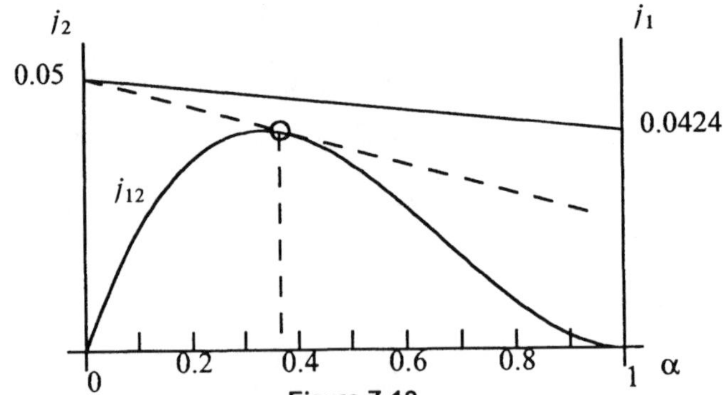

Figure 7.13

7.16 Annular flow model

> Briefly outline the annular flow model, and discuss the situations in which it may be more appropriate than other models.
> Discuss the importance of a reasonable prediction of the void fraction; and comment upon the models that have been proposed for gas-liquid flow systems.

Solution. The annular flow model assumes that, in a gas-liquid mixture flow, all the liquid is concentrated in an annulus around the tube wall. The gas (or vapour) constitutes the core.

It is a pertinent model in such situations as the riser tube in a steam boiler, where in the change from single-phase liquid (water) flow the flow pattern passes through the bubble flow and slug flow regimes before reaching the annular flow regime (Fig. 7.7).

The annular flow regime probably represents the conditions in the riser tube rather better than the simple homogeneous model, and is often adopted since it *should* be a desirable region of operation (where the heat transfer is most effective).

Considering an element, as shown in Fig. 7.14, the momentum equation gives

$$pA - (p + \delta p)A - dF - [\rho_f(A_f - \tfrac{1}{2}\delta A_g)\delta L + \rho_g(A_g + \tfrac{1}{2}A_g)\delta L]\cos\theta$$
$$= [(\dot{m}_g + \delta\dot{m}_g)(u_g + \delta u_g) + (\dot{m}_f - \delta\dot{m}_f)(u_f + \delta u_f) - \dot{m}_g u_g - \dot{m}_f u_f]$$

Introducing the void fraction $\alpha = A_g / A$ and neglecting second-order terms, this equation reduces to

$$-\frac{dp}{dL} = \frac{1}{A}\frac{dF}{dL} + \left[\frac{1-\alpha}{v_f} + \frac{\alpha}{v_g}\right]\cos\theta \quad + \frac{1}{A}\frac{d}{dL}\left[\dot{m}_g u_g + \dot{m}_f u_f\right]$$

where v = specific volume.

The drag force, F, can be expressed in the usual way in terms of a friction coefficient. For a single-phase liquid flow the friction drop is

$$\frac{dp_F}{dL} = \frac{4fu_\varepsilon^2}{2u_F D}$$

A similar equation can be used for the annular flow, with a factor ψ: where u_f = mean liquid velocity in two-phase flow. However experimental work indicates that ψ has a value between 0.8 and 1.2 in many cases, and can be taken as unity without serious error.

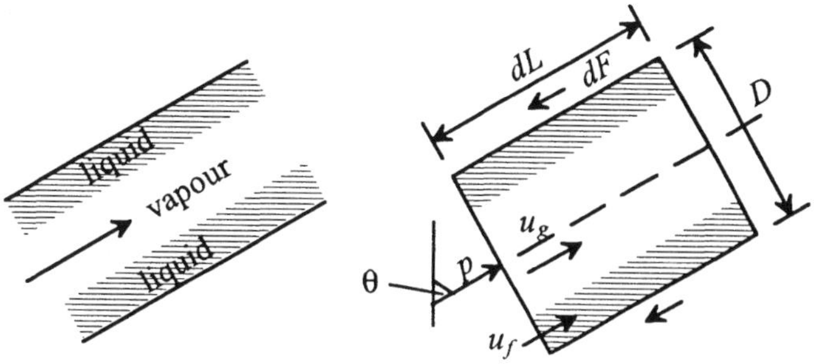

Figure 7.14

The momentum changes can be expressed in a more convenient form as follows:

$$\dot{m} = \dot{m}_f + \dot{m}_g = (1 - x)\dot{m} + x\dot{m}, \quad \text{where } x = \text{mass dryness fraction}$$

$$= \frac{u_f A_f}{v_f} + \frac{u_{fg} A_g}{v_g}, \qquad \text{since } u_g = \frac{x\dot{m}v_g}{A_g} = \frac{x}{\alpha}\frac{\dot{m}}{A}v_g$$

The slip factor

$$s = \frac{u_g}{u_f} = \frac{x}{1 - x} = \frac{(1 - \alpha)}{\alpha}\frac{v_g}{v_f}$$

and hence

$$u_g = \frac{\dot{m}}{A}\left[xv_g + s(1 - x)v_f\right], \qquad u_f = \frac{\dot{m}}{A}\left[\frac{xv_g}{s} + (1 - x)v_f\right]$$

Using these relationships, the momentum change is

$$\frac{\dot{m}^2}{A^2}\frac{dx}{dL}\left[s\left(\frac{x}{\alpha}.v_g - \frac{1 - x}{1 - \alpha}.v_f\right) - \frac{d\alpha}{dx}\left(\frac{x^2}{\alpha^2}.v_g - \left(\frac{1 - x}{1 - \alpha}\right)^2 v_f\right)\right].$$

In a practical situation the dryness fraction, x, varies along the tube length as the liquid is evaporated to steam. When the tube is heated uniformly, the dryness fraction can be assumed to vary linearly with the length, i.e. dx/dL is constant. The void fraction will also vary, and can be calculated by use of the previous relationships

$$\alpha = \frac{xv_g}{xv_g + s(1 - x)v_f}.$$

The prediction of the void fraction is necessary where gas and liquids flow together in the design of steam raising and chemical plant; for example a knowledge of the void fraction is required in the evaluation of mean fluid density, hydrostatic and acceleration pressure drops.

A generalised theory for two-phase flow is almost impossible because of the wide range of flow regimes encountered in practice. The earliest, and probably most widely used, method for prediction of the void fraction used empirical correlations (Martinelli and Nelson). More recent attempts to give a more generalised theory are based on a model for the bubble flow regime (Bankoff); a model which assumes equal frictional pressure drop for both phases (Levy); a model in which the velocity ratio of the two phases is constant (Thom); and a model in which the homogeneous mixture and liquid phase have the same velocity head in a stratified (annular) flow having a homogeneous mixture phase and a liquid phase (Smith).

Bankoff's model is only valid over a limited range of void fraction. Levy's momentum exchange model is inaccurate at low pressures. Thom's

Smith's method can be inaccurate where high viscous forces arise, and high dryness fractions.

Problems

1 A pseudoplastic fluid, for which the relationship between shear stress τ and velocity gradient is of the form

$$\tau = K\left(\frac{du}{dy}\right)^n,$$

flows along a pipe of diameter D. If the pressure drop is Δp over a length L show that the flow rate, Q, is given by the equation

$$Q = \frac{n\pi D^3}{8(3n+1)}\left(\frac{D\Delta p}{4KL}\right)^{\frac{1}{n}}$$

Also determine the ratio of the mean velocity to the maximum velocity at any cross-section.

Answer $\dfrac{(n+1)}{(3n+1)}$

2 The friction coefficient, f, is related to a Reynolds number $Re' = \rho D^n \bar{u}^{2-n}/K$ by the following equations:

$20 < Re' < 1000 \qquad f = 16/Re'$

$3000 < Re' < 10^5 \qquad f = 0.0014 + 0.125/\left(Re'\right)^{0.32}$

where $\bar{u}$ is the mean velocity, and D is the pipe diameter.

Calculate the pressure drop over a length of 10 m for a fluid flow rate of 0.1 m^3/s in the following situations:

(a) paper pulp in water, for which $n = 0.6$, $K = 6$, $D = 25$ cm, $\rho = 1050$ kg/m^3.

(b) clay suspension in water, for which $n = 0.13$, $K = 2.3$, $D = 10$ cm and $\rho = 1200$ kg/m^3.

Answer (a) 2580 N/m^2, (b) 3.15 bar.

3 A test on a non-Newtonian fluid gave the following results:

shear stress τ (N/m^2)	velocity gradient (s^{-1})	shear stress τ (N/m^2)	velocity gradient (s^{-1})
2.2	3.5	38.2	73.3
4.4	6.9	43.8	85.4
8.8	14.5	50.0	99.0
12.9	22.0	55.0	110.0
17.2	30.1	65.2	133.0
22.1	36.8	72.7	150.0
24.4	44.5	78.0	162.0
30.7	57.6	88.0	184.0
44.2	68.2		

Determine the nature of the fluid, and the relationship between the shear stress and velocity gradient.

The pressure drop when the fluid flowed at a rate of 9.8×10^{-4} m^3/s along a pipe, diameter 25 mm, length 2 m was measured as 3800 N/m^2. Is this value one that would be expected from the fluid relationship obtained from the previous test data?

The flow rate

$$Q = \frac{n\pi D^3}{8(3n+1)}\left(\frac{D\Delta p}{4KL}\right)^{1/n}$$

may be assumed without proof.

Answer From a plot of $\log\tau$ against $\log(du/dy)$ the fluid is a pseudoplastic:

$$\tau = 0.8\left(\frac{du}{dy}\right)^{0.4}.$$

4 A suspension of clay in water behaves as a Bingham plastic, with a yield stress of 10 N/m^2 and a density of 1440 kg/m^3. The shear stress at the wall of the pipe conveying the fluid is 100 N/m^2. Calculate the flow rate through the pipe, which is 25 mm diameter, 30 m length, when the pressure drop is 1 bar. $\mu_p = 0.4$ kg/ms.

The Buckingham equation is

$$Q = \frac{\pi a^4 \Delta p}{8L\mu_p}\left(1 - \frac{4}{3}K + \frac{1}{3}K^4\right), \quad \text{where } K = 2L\tau_y/(a\Delta p).$$

Calculate the plug radius and velocity; and the velocity of the fluid at a radius of 6 mm.

Answer 0.043 kg/s. 1.25 mm, 0.26 m/s. 0.217 m/s.

5 A fluid, characterised by a power law relationship, gave the following results in a test:

shear stress (N/m^2)	12.6	18.4	31.8	41.7	49.1	60.9	74.6	84.2
velocity grad. (s^{-1})	10	25	50	75	100	150	230	300

The fluid is pumped along a horizontal pipe, 25 mm diameter, 10 m long, at a rate of 0.001 m^3/s.

Determine the power law; ratio of the mean velocity to the maximum velocity at a cross-section; and the pumping power required.

Answer $K = 2.49$, $n = 0.62$. 0.57. 242 W.

6 A slurry gave the following results in a test where the pressure drop was measured at different flow rates:

(a) in a pipe, diameter 52 mm

flow (l/s)	760	965	1,290	1,795	2,525	3,160
dp/dx (N/m^3)	980	1,080	1,170	1,220	1,240	1,280

(b) in a pipe, diameter 20 mm

flow (l/s)	385	550	680	1,000	1,585
dp/dx (N/m^3)	3,850	4,270	4,550	5,010	5,620

It is known that the fluid is a pseudoplastic, following a law of the form

$$\tau = K\left(\frac{du}{dr}\right)^n.$$

Determine the value of K, n from the test data.

The flow rate is given by the equation

$$Q = \frac{n\pi a^3}{3n+1}\left(\frac{\tau_o}{K}\right)^{1/n}.$$

Answer (a) $K = 5.2$, $n = 0.20$
(b) $K = 4.6$, $n = 0.20$.

7 A test on a fluid gave the following results:

$\frac{\bar{u}}{a}$ (s^{-1})	44	96	168	300	410	500
τ_o (N/m^2)	140	188	238	316	360	402

Assuming that the fluid follows the power law

$$\tau = K\left(\frac{du}{dr}\right)^n$$

determine the best values of K and n.

State how the wall shear stress and pressure drop are related.

Answer $K = 12.2$, $n = 0.44$

$$\tau_o = \frac{1}{2}a\left(\frac{dp}{dx}\right)$$

8 A test on a polymer melt, known to be a pseudoplastic fluid, gave the following results for the pressure drop in a pipe 10 mm diameter:

$\bar{u}$ (m/s)	0.1	0.2	0.5	1.0	2.0	3.0	4.0	5.0	6.0
$\frac{dp}{dx}$ (bar/m)	45	62	87	115	150	166	195	209	220

Determine the values of K and n in the power law

$$\tau = K\left(\frac{du}{dr}\right)^n.$$

Answer $n = 0.39$, $K = 1900$.

9 A test on a non-Newtonian fluid gave the following results for the variation of shear stress τ (N/m^2) with the velocity gradient

du/dy (s^{-1}):

τ	$\frac{du}{dy}$	τ	$\frac{du}{dy}$	τ	$\frac{du}{dy}$
7	11	390	870	2,310	9,625
28	47	630	1,580	3,780	19,380
110	200	970	2,770	6,940	46,270
227	450	1,480	4,930	9,000	69,230

Assuming that the fluid can be modelled as a Meter type

$$\mu_a = \mu_\infty + \frac{(\mu_o - \mu_\infty)}{1 + \left|\frac{\tau}{\tau_m}\right|^{\alpha-1}}$$

determine the best value of the index α.

Answer $\mu_o = 0.65, \mu_\infty = 0.10$ Ns/m^2;
$\tau_m = 800$ N/m^2; $\alpha = 2.06$.

10 A drilling mud behaves as a Bingham plastic. The yield stress = 7 N/m^2, and the viscosity = 0.02 Ns/m^2. The mud flows along a pipe, diameter 20 cm, length 300 mm, at a flow rate of 170 kg/s. The density = 1400 kg/m^3. Estimate the pressure drop, using the Buckingham equation.

Also calculate the shear stress at the pipe wall; and plug radius and velocity.

Answer 71800 N/m^2. 12.0 N/m^2; 58 mm, 5.16 m/s.

11 A Bingham plastic flows along a pipe of diameter 25 mm. The fluid density = 1500 kg/m^3.

A test on the fluid gave the following results:

τ (N/m^2)	10	17	24	30	39	45	62	81
$\frac{du}{dy}$ (s^{-1})	0	20	40	60	80	100	150	200

The pressure gradient along the pipe is 3000 N/m^2 per m length. Calculate the shear stress at the wall; and the plug radius and velocity. Also calculate the flow rate, and mean velocity.

Answer $\tau_y = 10$ N/m^2, $\mu_p = 0.35$ Ns/m^2.
$\tau_o = 18.8$ N/m^2; 6.7 mm, 0.073 m/s.
0.03 l/s, 0.062 m/s.

12 A Bingham plastic is contained between two concentric cylinders. The inner cylinder is stationary and the diameter is 100 mm. The outer cylinder, free to rotate, has a diameter of 200 mm. The length of the annulus is 80 cm.

The yield stress = 30 N/m^2, and the velocity $\mu_p = 4$ Ns/m^2.

Determine the minimum torque required before the outer cylinder begins to rotate; and the power required to rotate the outer cylinder at a speed of 25 rev/min.

Answer 1.51 Nm; 9.2 W.

13 A pseudoplastic fluid, which follows a power law relationship between shear stress and velocity gradient, flows *along* an annulus of radii R_1 and R_2 (Fig. 7.15).

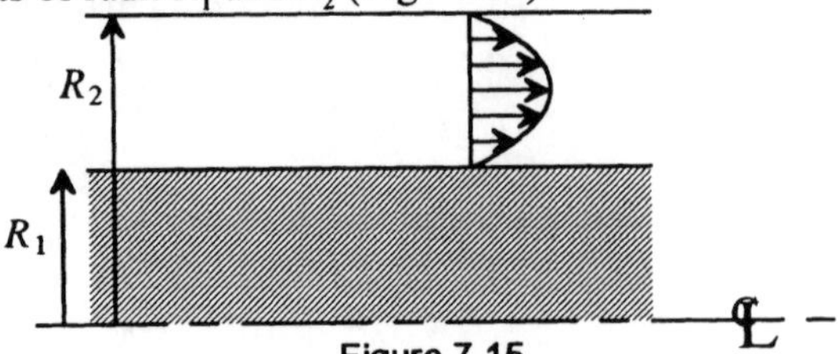

Figure 7.15

By consideration of the force balance on an element show that the velocity gradient is given by the equation

$$\frac{du}{dr} = \left(-\frac{P}{2K}\right)^{1/n}\left[r - \frac{(aR_2)^2}{r}\right]^{1/n} \qquad a \leq r \leq R_2$$

and
$$\frac{du}{dr} = \left(-\frac{P}{2K}\right)^{1/n}\left[\left(\frac{aR_2}{r}\right)^2 - r\right]^{1/n} \qquad R_2 \leq r \leq a$$

where the shear stress is zero at a radius $r = aR_2$.

Hence show that the value of a can be determined from the equation

$$\int_{R_1}^{aR_2}\left(\frac{a^2R_2}{r} - \frac{r}{R_2}\right)^{1/n} dr = \int_{aR_2}^{R_2}\left(\frac{r}{R_2} - \frac{a^2R_2}{r}\right)^{1/n} dr \ .$$

If $n = 0.07$, $K = 0.3$, $R_2 = 25$ mm, $R_1 = 10$ mm determine the flow rate. The pressure drop = 15 kN/m^2 per m length.

Answer 0.0026 m^3/s.

14 A pseudoplastic fluid flows along a circular pipe of radius a. A sudden expansion occurs in the pipe to a radius ba. Assuming that frictional effects are negligible show, by using the momentum equation, that the pressure drop due to the sudden enlargement is given by the equation

$$\Delta p = \frac{3n+1}{2(2n+1)}\left(\frac{Q}{\pi a^2}\right)^2\left(\frac{1}{b_4} - \frac{1}{b^2}\right)$$

The velocity profile is given by the equation

$$u = \bar{u}\left(\frac{3n+1}{n+1}\right)\left[1 - \left(\frac{r}{a}\right)^{\frac{n+1}{n}}\right]$$

where $\bar{u}$ = mean velocity = $\dfrac{Q}{\pi a^2}$.

Determine the 'loss' of kinetic energy across the enlargement, in terms of the density ρ and flow rate Q.

Answer $0.75\rho\frac{Q^2}{d^2}$.

15 A non-Newtonian fluid flows along a circular pipe of radius a. The shear stress at the wall, τ_o, and velocity gradient are related by the equation

$$\frac{du}{dr} = -\left(\frac{\tau_o}{K}\right)^{1/n}.$$

Show that the shear stress distribution across a radius is given by the equation

$$\frac{\tau}{\tau_o} = \frac{a}{r}.$$

For a particular fluid $n = 2$. Show that

$$\text{mean velocity} = \frac{1}{5}a\left(\frac{\tau_o}{K}\right)^2$$

$$\text{maximum velocity} = \frac{2}{3}a\left(\frac{\tau_o}{K}\right)^2.$$

The pressure drop in a pipe of diameter 30 m was measured as 8 kN/m^2 over a length of 50 cm. The flow rate was 1.22 l/s.

Determine the value of the coefficient K.

Answer 28.35.

16 A test on a non-Newtonian fluid gave the following results:

τ (N/m^2)	7.9	18.4	31.8	41.7	60.9	74.6	84.2	95.9	105.0
$\frac{du}{dr}$ (s^{-1})	10	25	50	75	150	230	300	400	600

Do these results conform with the models of a Bingham plastic, or pseudoplastic?

The fluid flows along a pipe of diameter 25 mm, length 10 m and the pressure drop = 165 kN/m^2. Determine the velocity profile, ratio of the mean velocity to the maximum velocity, and flow rate at a cross-section, by plotting du/dr against the radius r, and ru against r.

Answer Neither. Approx. 0.57 l/s.

17 A mixture of air and water flows up a vertical pipe, 25 cm diameter, 3 m length and is discharged into a vessel at a pressure of 1.0 bar. Density of air = 1.2 kg/m^3. The flow rates of air and water are 0.006 and 0.009 m^3/s respectively.

air viscosity = 1.8×10^{-5} kg/ms

water viscosity = 1×10^{-3} kg/ms.

Assuming the homogeneous model, and that

$$f = 0.079Re^{-0.25}$$

calculate the pressure at the pipe inlet.

Estimate the inlet pressure using the Martinelli curves (Fig. 7.11).

Answer 1.25 bar. 1.10 bar.

18 A slurry of coal and water is pumped along a pipe of diameter 10 cm length 20 m. The slurry contains 45%, by volume, of water.

flow rate of the slurry = 0.024 m^3/s
density of coal = 1360 kg/m^3
viscosity of the slurry = 0.015 kg/ms.

Estimate the pressure drop along the pipe, using
(a) a homogeneous model,
(b) the Lockhart-Martinelli curves.

Answer (a) 29140 N/m^2, (b) 38100 N/m^2.

19 A slurry contains equal proportions by volume of solid particles and water. The slurry required 1.9 kW power to pump it along a pipe, diameter 10 cm, length 30 m, at a flow rate of 0.030 m^3/s. Pump efficiency = 0.60.

Assuming a homogeneous model estimate the viscosity of the slurry.

Density of solid particles = 1400 kg/m^3

Friction coefficient $f = \dfrac{0.079}{Re^{0.25}}$.

Estimate the effective viscosity of the solids, using the relationship

$$\frac{1}{\mu} = \frac{x}{\mu_s} + \frac{1-x}{\mu_w}, \qquad \text{where } x = \text{quality}.$$

Hence estimate the pressure drop along the pipe using the Lockhart-Martinelli curves. $\mu_w = 10^{-3}$ kg/ms.

Answer 0.002 kg/ms. 0.007 kg/ms. 51800 N/m^2.

20 An off-shore pipeline conveys a mixture of oil and gas through a horizontal pipe, 20 cm diameter, 3500 m long. The flow rate is 0.01 m^3/s of oil, and 0.10 m^3/s of gas.

Estimate the power required to pump the mixture along the pipeline; (a) assuming a homogeneous model; (b) using the Martinelli curves.

The fluid properties are:

	oil	*gas*	
density	650	56	kg/m^3
viscosity	6×10^{-4}	1.5×10^{-5}	kg/ms

Assume the relationship $f = 0.079Re^{-0.25}$.

Answer (a) 0.94 bar, (b) 1.58 bar.

21 A mixture of air and water flows up a vertical pipe, of diameter 25 mm and length 100 m. The flow rates of air and water are 0.002 kg/s and 0.10 kg/s respectively. The mixture discharges from the pipe at a pressure of 1.0 bar. The air density is constant and equal to 1.2 kg/m^3. The kinematic viscosity of the air and water is 1.3×10^{-5} and 10^{-6} respectively. $f = 0.079Re^{-0.25}$.

The effective viscosity μ of the mixture can be determined from the equation

$$\frac{1}{\mu} = \frac{x}{\mu_g} + \frac{1-x}{\mu_f}, \qquad \text{where } x \text{ is the quality} = \frac{\dot{m}_g}{\dot{m}_g + \dot{m}_f}.$$

Estimate the pressure at the pipe inlet,

(a) assuming a homogeneous mixture,

(b) using the Lockhart-Martinelli curves.

Answer (a) 2.01 bar, (b) 1.72 bar.

22 Briefly outline the drift flux model of a gas-liquid flow. Define the terms drift flux j_{12}, and superficial velocity.

Derive the following expressions:

$$\text{void fraction } \alpha = \frac{j_2}{j}\left(1 - \frac{j_{21}}{j_2}\right)$$

$$\text{mean density } \rho_m = \frac{\rho_1 j_1 + \rho_2 j_2}{j} + \frac{(\rho_1 - \rho_2) j_{21}}{j}$$

where j = volumetric flux.

A mixture of gas and liquid flows up a vertical tube of diameter 50 mm. The densities are 1.2 and 800 kg/m^3. The flow rate of gas is 0.004 m^3/s. Assuming that flooding occurs when

$$\frac{(j_1\sqrt{\rho_1})^{1/2} + (j_2\sqrt{\rho_2})^{1/2}}{\left(gD(\rho_2 - \rho_1)\right)^{1/4}} = 1$$

determine the liquid flux at the flooding point. Using the alternative criterion that $j_{12} = 0.4\alpha(1-\alpha)^2$ determine the void fraction.

Answer 0.31 m/s. 0.15.

23 A mixture consists of two constant-phase incompressible fluids. The mass flow rates are $\dot{m}_1$ and $\dot{m}_2$. The mixture flows through a convergent nozzle, as shown in Fig. 7.16.

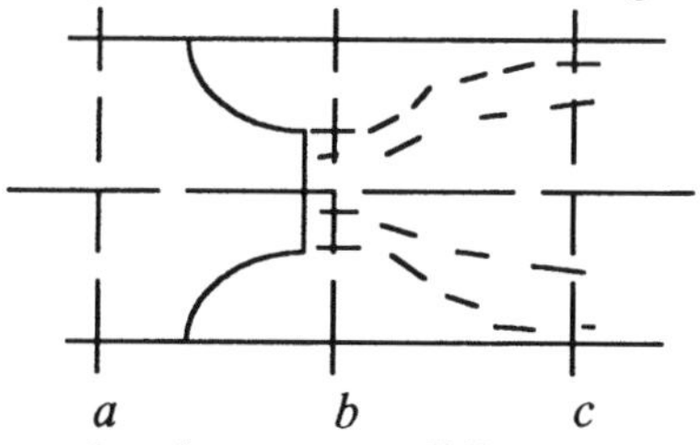

Figure 7.16

Show that the pressure differences are given by the equations

$$p_a - p_b = \frac{KG^2}{\rho_2}(K-1)\left[1 + x\left(\frac{\rho_2}{\rho_1} - 1\right)\right]$$

$$p_a - p_c = \frac{G^2}{2\rho_2}(K-1)^2\left[1 + x\left(\frac{\rho_2}{\rho_1} - 1\right)\right]$$

where G = mass flow/unit area

x = quality = $\dot{m}_1 / \dot{m}$

K = ratio of the area at section a to the area at section b.

Assume that the mixture is homogeneous.

8

Particle dynamics: Porous media: Fluidised beds

Introduction

The behaviour of solid particles in a fluid flow is of interest in many practical applications of fluid dynamics, such as the transport of solids in a river or sea, the treatment of sewage and effluents, the separation of solids from a fluid, the conveying of pulverised coal in a boiler plant, filtration and sedimentation, and in the use of fluidised beds for catalytic cracking of oil and the combustion of coal.

In many applications the particles are spherical in shape, but not necessarily all of the same diameter. In the case of non-spherical particles it is sometimes useful to compare them with an equivalent volume sphere: thus

$$\text{equivalent diameter} = \left(\frac{6V}{\pi}\right)^{1/3}, \text{ where } V = \text{volume of the particle.}$$

Size distribution

A bed of particles may consist of a mixture of different sizes. The side distribution may follow a *Gaussian* rule, in which the number of particles, n, of diameter D_p less than a diameter x is given by the equation

$$n = \frac{1}{2}N\left[1 + \operatorname{erf}\left(\frac{x}{\sigma\sqrt{2}}\right)\right]$$

where N = total number of particles

$$\sigma = \text{standard deviation} = \left[\frac{1}{N}\sum(D_p - \bar{D}_p)^2\right]^{1/2}$$

$\bar{D}_p$ = mean particle diameter

$$\operatorname{erf} y = 1 - \frac{1}{\sqrt{\pi}}\int_y^{\infty} \exp(-\tfrac{1}{4}y^2)\,dy$$

Another size distribution that is approached by materials that are ground or crushed (e.g. pulverised coal) is the *Rosin-Rammler* type. The distribution law is

$$R = 100\exp(-bx^n)$$

where R is the percentage of particles of size greater than x.

Particle drag

The drag force on an isolated sphere F can be expressed in terms of a drag coefficient, C_D, *projected* area A, and free stream kinetic energy. Thus

$$F = C_D A \tfrac{1}{2}\rho u^2, \text{ where } u = \text{fluid velocity relative to the sphere,}$$

and $$A = \frac{\pi D_p^2}{4}.$$

Reynolds number $Re = \rho u D_p/\mu$ is shown in Fig. 8.1.

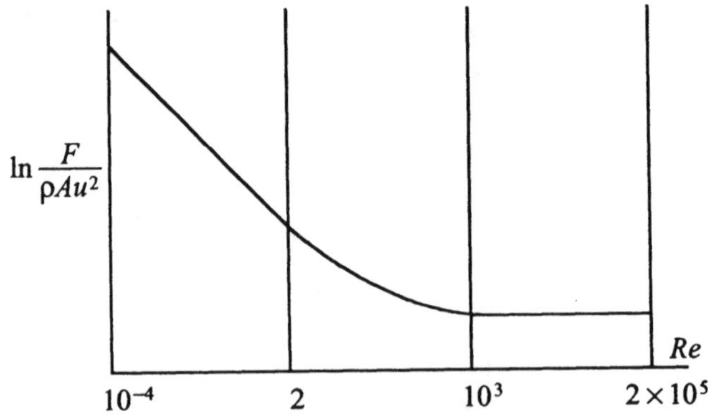

Figure 8.1

The relationships between the drag coefficient and Reynolds number are:

$Re < 2 \qquad C_D = 24/Re$

$2 < Re < 200 \qquad C_D = 18/Re^{0.6}$

$Re < 800 \qquad C_D = \frac{24}{Re}\left(1 + \frac{0.15}{Re^{0.687}}\right)$

$2000 < Re < 2\times10^5 \qquad C_D = 0.44$

The terminal velocity v_∞ of a particle, falling through a fluid under gravity, is determined from the equation

$$Re^2 C_D = \frac{4}{3} D_p^3 \frac{(s-1)g}{\nu^2}$$

where s = density of particle/density of fluid.

Fluidised bed

A fluidised bed is a bed of particles held in suspension by a fluid stream, as for example a bed of coal particles in a stream of air (fluidised bed combustion), or a bed of catalyst particles in a stream of petroleum product (cat. cracker).

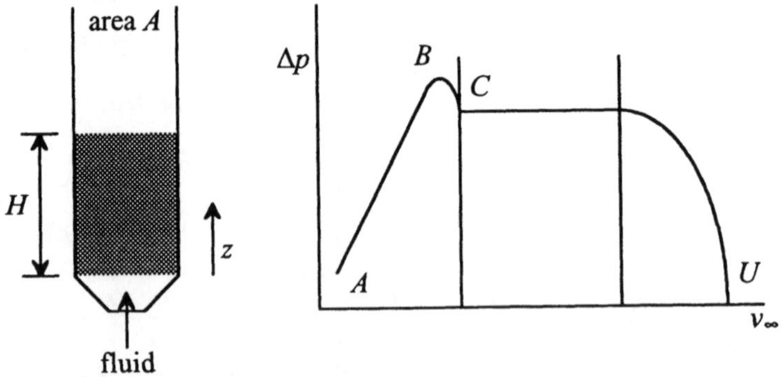

Figure 8.2

The upward flow of the fluid through the bed includes a static pressure drop due to the drag forces on the particles (in addition to the hydrostatic pressure drop). For a fixed bed the Carman-Kozeny or Ergun equations can be used to estimate the pressure drop:

$$-\frac{dp}{dz} = \frac{180(1-\varepsilon)^2}{\varepsilon^3}\frac{\mu U}{D_p^2}$$

or $$-\frac{dp}{dz} = \frac{180(1-\varepsilon)^2}{\varepsilon^3}\frac{\mu U}{D_p^2} + \frac{1.75\rho U^2(1-\varepsilon)}{\varepsilon^3 D_p}$$

where ε = porosity (void fraction) = volume of voids/total volume
U = superficial velocity of the fluid
= fluid flow rate/bed area A.

As the superficial velocity increases the pressure drop becomes equal to the weight of the particles and

$$A\,dp = AH(1-\varepsilon)(\rho_s - \rho)g$$

where ρ_s, ρ = solid and fluid density respectively.

This point (corresponding to C in Fig. 8.2) is known as the state of *incipient* fluidisation.

A further increase in the velocity causes a decrease in the porosity as the bed expands, and eventually the smallest particles may be swept out of the bed.

8.1 Steady settling of a particle

A spherical particle settles in a fluid. Show that the terminal velocity is given by the equation

$$v_\infty^2 = \frac{4gD_p(\rho_s - \rho)}{3\rho C_D}$$

where D_p = particle diameter, ρ_s = density of particle
ρ = fluid density.

Briefly outline how this result can be used to determine the viscosity of a fluid. A particle, of density 820 kg/m³, settles in a gas of density 1.2 kg/m³, viscosity 2 × 10⁻⁵ kg/ms. If the terminal velocity = 6 m/s determine the particle diameter.

$Re < 2$	$C_D = 24/Re$
$2 < Re < 200$	$C_D = 18/Re^{0.6}$
$200 < Re < 800$	$C_D = \frac{24}{Re}\left(1 + \frac{0.15}{Re^{0.7}}\right)$
$Re > 800$	$C_D = 0.44$

Solution. The momentum equation for *steady* conditions, ie. no acceleration of the particle and therefore at the terminal velocity, gives

$$W - B - F = 0$$

where W = weight of particle = $\frac{1}{6}\pi D_p^3 \rho_s g$

B = buoyancy force = $\frac{1}{6}\pi D_p^3 \rho g$

F = drag force = $C_D\left(\frac{\pi D_p^2}{4}\right)\left(\frac{1}{2}\rho v_\infty^2\right)$

Hence $W - B = F$

or $$= \frac{1}{6}\pi D_p^3\left(\rho_s - \rho\right)g = \frac{1}{4}\pi D_p^2 C_D \cdot \frac{1}{2}\rho v_I^2$$

giving $$v_\infty^2 = \frac{4}{3}\cdot\frac{gD_p\left(\rho_s - \rho\right)}{\rho C_D}$$

This result can be used in the *Stokes* tube to determine the viscosity of a fluid. If the particle falls at a low velocity, such that $Re < 2$,

then $C_D = \dfrac{24}{Re}$

and substituting gives

$$v_\infty = \frac{\left(\rho_s - \rho\right) g D_p^2}{18\mu}$$

Hence a measurement of the steady terminal velocity, and knowledge of the particle diameter and densities enables the viscosity to be determined. In practice the ratio of the particle diameter to the tube area may have a significant effect: if high there will be a blockage factor to take into consideration.

The numerical part of this problem can now be evaluated. Assuming laminar flow, $Re < 2$,

$$v_\infty = \frac{(\rho_s - \rho) g D_p^2}{18\mu}$$

and $$D_p = \sqrt{\frac{18\mu v_\infty}{(\rho_s - \rho) g}} = \sqrt{\frac{18 \times 2 \times 10^{-5} \times 6}{(820 - 1.2) \times 9.81}} = 0.52 \text{ mm}$$

The assumption that the flow is laminar must now be checked.

$$Re = \frac{\rho D_p v_\infty}{\mu} = \frac{1.2 \times 5.2 \times 10^{-4} \times 6}{2 \times 10^{-5}} = 187$$

which is greater than the value of Reynolds number, 2, corresponding to the limit: hence the flow is not laminar.

Assuming $2 < Re < 200$, $C_D = 18 / Re^{0.6}$

and $$v_\infty^2 = \frac{4}{3} g D_p \left(\frac{\rho_s - \rho}{\rho}\right) \frac{Re^{0.6}}{18} = \frac{2}{27} g D_p \left(\frac{\rho_s - \rho}{\rho}\right) \left(\frac{\rho D_p v_\infty}{\mu}\right)^{0.6}$$

giving $$D_p = 1.22 v_\infty^{0.875} \left(\frac{\rho}{\rho_s - \rho}\right)^{0.625} \left(\frac{\mu}{\rho}\right)^{0.375}$$

subst. $$D_p = 1.22(6)^{0.875} \left(\frac{1.2}{818.8}\right)^{0.625} \left(\frac{2 \times 10^{-5}}{1.2}\right)^{0.375} = 1.6 \text{ mm}$$

Again the value of the Reynolds number needs to be checked:

$$Re = \frac{1.2 \times 0.0016 \times 6}{2 \times 10^{-5}} = 576$$

and this is again outside the assumed range. Assume $200 < Re < 800$.

Then $$C_D = \frac{24}{Re}\left(1 + \frac{0.15}{Re^{0.7}}\right)$$

and $$v_\infty^2 = \frac{4 g D_p}{3}\left(\frac{\rho_s - \rho}{\rho}\right) \frac{Re}{24\left(1 + \frac{0.15}{Re^{0.7}}\right)}.$$

In this case it may be simpler to solve the equation for Re. Hence subst.

$$D_p = \frac{\mu Re}{\rho v_\infty}$$

gives $$\frac{32 v_\infty^3}{g}\left(\frac{\rho}{\rho_s - \rho}\right)\left(\frac{\rho}{\mu}\right) = \frac{Re^2}{1 + \frac{0.15}{Re^{0.7}}}$$

or $$Re^2 = 61\,960\left(1 + \frac{0.15}{Re^{0.7}}\right)$$

and solving by trial and error gives $Re \cong 250$.

Hence $D_p = \dfrac{2\times 10^{-5}\times 250}{1.2\times 6} = 6.9\times 10^{-4}$ m or **0.69 mm**

8.2 Unsteady settling

State Stokes law of drag on a spherical particle. A particle settles in stagnant fluid, starting from rest. Show that at time t the particle velocity is given by the equation

$$v = Kg\left[1 - \exp\left(-\frac{t}{K}\right)\right] \qquad \text{where } K = \frac{D_p^2}{18\mu}(\rho_s - \rho).$$

The particle is of diameter 10 mm, density 3000 kg/m^3 ; and the fluid of density 1200 kg/m^3, viscosity 0.2 Ns/m^2. Plot a graph of velocity and distance travelled against time, and estimate the time and distance taken to attain the terminal velocity.

Solution. See Fig. 8.3. Stokes law can be stated as follows: The drag force F on a spherical particle, diameter D_p, moving at a velocity v relative to the fluid is given by the equation

$$F = 3\pi\mu D_p v$$

This is equivalent to stating that the drag coefficient is

$$C_D = \frac{F}{A\frac{1}{2}\rho v^2} = \frac{3\pi\mu D_p v}{\frac{\pi}{4}D_p^2\frac{1}{2}\rho v^2} = \frac{24\mu}{\rho D_p v} \qquad \text{or} \qquad C_D = 24/Re$$

The momentum equation can be applied to a particle, giving

$$\frac{1}{6}\pi D_p^3(\rho_s - \rho)g - 3\pi\mu D_p v = \frac{1}{6}\pi D_p^3(\rho_s - \rho)\frac{dv}{dt}$$

Hence $\dfrac{dv}{dt} = g - \dfrac{18\mu}{(\rho_s - \rho)D_p^2}v = g - \dfrac{v}{K}$, $\qquad \dfrac{dv}{g - \frac{v}{K}} = dt$

and integrating

$$t = -K\ln\left(g - \frac{v}{K}\right) + \text{constant } c$$

At $t = 0$, $v = 0$ giving

$$c = K\ln g$$

and $\quad t = K\ln g - K\ln\left(g - \dfrac{v}{K}\right) = K\ln\left(\dfrac{g}{g - \frac{v}{K}}\right)$

$$v = gK\left[1 - \exp\left(-\frac{t}{K}\right)\right], \qquad \text{where } K = \frac{(\rho_s - \rho)}{18\mu}D_p^2.$$

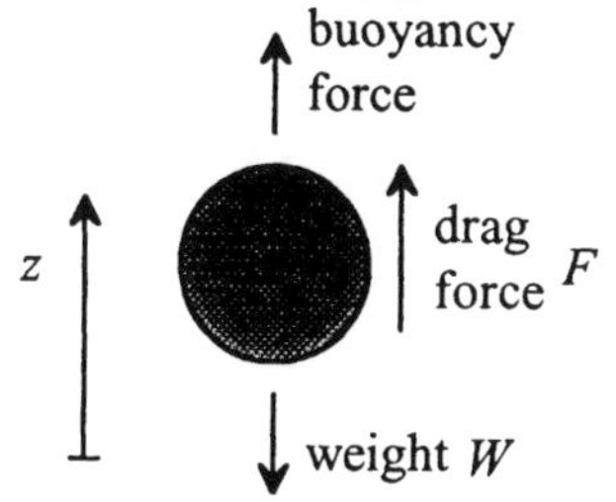

Figure 8.3

The terminal velocity (steady fall) is

$$v_\infty = \lim_{t\to\infty} v = gK = \frac{gD_p^2}{18\mu}(\rho_s - \rho).$$

The distance travelled can be obtained by a further integration.

$$v = \frac{dz}{dt} = Kg\left[1 - \exp\left(-\frac{t}{K}\right)\right]$$

$$z = Kg\int\left[1 - \exp\left(-\frac{t}{K}\right)\right]dt = Kg\left[t + K\exp\left(-\frac{t}{K}\right)\right] + c$$

At $t = 0$, $z = 0$ therefore $c = K^2g$

and $$z = Kg\left[t + K\left(1 - \frac{v}{Kg}\right) - K\right] = Kgt + K(Kg - v) - K^2g$$

$$= \boldsymbol{v_\infty t - Kv}$$

Substituting the numerical values

$$K = \frac{(0.01)^2(3000 - 1200)}{18(0.2)} = 0.05, \qquad v_\infty = gK = 0.49 \text{ m/s}$$

$$v = 0.49(1 - \exp(-20t)), \qquad z = 0.49t - 0.05v.$$

t (s)	v (m/s)	z (mm)	t (s)	v (m/s)	z (mm)
0.00	0.000	0.0	**0.10**	0.424	27.8
0.02	0.162	3.8	**0.11**	0.436	32.1
0.04	0.270	6.1	**0.12**	0.446	36.5
0.05	0.310	9.0	**0.13**	0.454	41.0
0.06	0.342	12.3	**0.14**	0.460	45.6
0.07	0.369	15.9	**0.15**	0.466	50.2
0.08	0.391	19.7	**0.20**	0.481	74.0
0.09	0.409	23.7	**0.30**	0.489	125.5

The particle therefore reaches a steady settling velocity of 0.49 m/s in about 0.3 s, after falling through a distance of about 130 mm.

8.3 Hindered settling

A suspension consists of uniform particles, of density 4000 kg/m^3, diameter 0.15 mm, in a liquid of density 1400 kg/m^3, viscosity 0.0013 kg/ms.

The volume of the particles is ¼ of the volume of the liquid. Determine the settling rate.

Assume laminar flow, and that the apparent viscosity of the suspension μ_c and fluid viscosity μ are related by the Steinour formula

$$\phi = \frac{\mu}{\mu_c} = \frac{\varepsilon}{10^{1.82(1-\varepsilon)}}$$ where ε is the voidage fraction.

Solution. The unhindered terminal velocity of a single particle can be determined from the previous equation (W.E.8.1)

$$v_\infty^2 = \frac{4}{3}\frac{gD_p(\rho_s - \rho)}{\rho C_D}$$

with $C_D = 24/Re$ for laminar flow. Under these conditions

$$v_\infty = \frac{(\rho_s - \rho)gD_p^2}{18\mu}.$$

In this problem the numerical value of v_∞ is

$$\frac{(4\,000 - 1\,400)g(0.15 \times 10^{-3})^2}{18 \times 0.0013} = \mathbf{0.0245\ m/s}$$

In a suspension the settling velocity of a particle is affected by the presence of neighbouring particles, and is clearly dependent upon the space between them, or particle concentration. The effect is difficult to predict from a theoretical analysis, and for practical purposes empirical expressions (such as that given) are used. The equation is modified,

$$v_\infty = \frac{(\rho_s - \rho_c)gD_p^2\varepsilon}{18\mu_c}$$

where ρ_c, μ_c are the density and apparent viscosity of the suspension.

The voidage fraction

$$\varepsilon = \frac{\text{volume of liquid}}{\text{volume of suspension}} = \frac{1}{1\frac{1}{4}} = 0.8$$

$$\rho_c = (1 - \varepsilon)\rho_S + \varepsilon\rho = 0.2(4\,000) + 0.8(1\,400) = 1\,920\ \text{kg/m}^3$$

$$\phi = \frac{0.8}{10^{1.82\times0.2}} = 0.346, \qquad \mu_c = \frac{\mu}{\phi} = \frac{0.0013}{0.346} = 0.00376$$

$$v_\infty = \frac{(4\,000 - 1\,920)g(0.15 \times 10^{-3})^2 \times 0.8}{18(0.00376)} = \mathbf{0.0054\ m/s}$$

thus the hindered particles attain a settling velocity of 5.4 mm/s, compared to a value of 24.5 mm/s for an isolated particle.

Note. The effect of the concentration is shown by a calculation of the settling velocity at difference voidage fractions.

ε	1.0	0.9	0.8	0.7	0.6	0.5	0.4	0.3	0.2
ρ_c (kg/m^3)	1,400	1,660	1,920	2,180	2,440	2,700	2,960	3,220	3,480
ϕ	1.000	0.592	0.346	0.199	0.112	0.062	0.032	0.016	0.007
μ_c (kg/ms)	0.0013	0.0022	0.0038	0.0065	0.0116	0.0211	0.0402	0.0814	0.1857
v_∞ (mm/s)	24.5	11.7	5.4	2.4	1.0	0.4	0.13	0.03	0.008

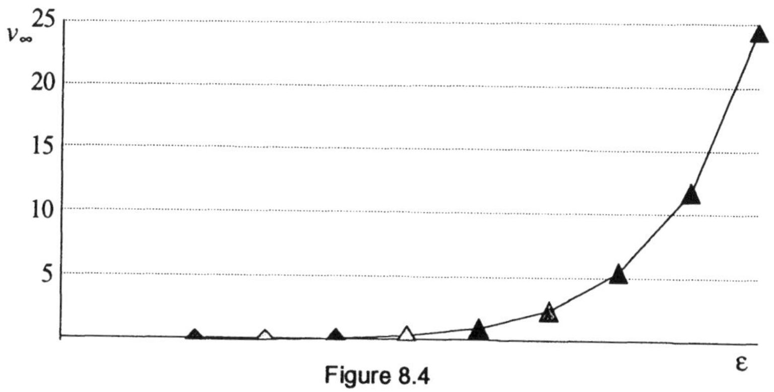

Figure 8.4

8.4 Cyclone separator

A cyclone separator is 30 cm diameter, 1.3 m height. The inlet and outlet sections are both circular, of diameter 95 mm. The cyclone is required to remove spherical particles down to a particle diameter of 2 μm from an air stream.

density of particle material	= 2600 kg/m^3
density of air	= 1.2 kg/m^3
viscosity of air	= 1.8×10^{-5} kg/ms

Calculate the minimum air flow rate into the cyclone required.

Solution. A cyclone separator is widely used for the separation of particles from a gas stream, as, for example, in the cleaning of a gas stream from a boiler. The gas flows through the cyclone in a helical pattern, forming a vortex or cyclone. The centrifugal force on the particles, due to their rotation about the centre-line, causes the heavier particles to move radially outwards and they collect at the wall. Their motion is resisted by drag forces, and gravitational forces also affect the motion. The motion of the gas is ideally that of a free vortex, with an axial velocity superimposed: similar to a helical path.

Consider a spherical particle, diameter D_p, rotating with a tangential velocity v_t at a radius r. At low radial velocities, steady conditions and no slip between the gas and the particle a balance of the centrifugal and drag forces gives

$$\frac{mv_t^2}{r} = 3\pi\mu D_p v_r \qquad \text{where } v_r = \text{radial velocity of the particle.}$$

For a spherical particle, the mass $m = \frac{1}{6}\pi D_p^3 \rho_s$ and substituting gives

$$\frac{v_t^2}{r} = \frac{18\mu v_r}{\rho_s D_p^2}.$$

The free-fall terminal velocity of a particle is

$$v_\infty = \frac{\rho_s g D_p^2}{18\mu}$$

and introducing it into the previous expression gives

$$\frac{v_t^2}{r} = \frac{g v_r}{v_\infty} \text{ or } v_\infty = \frac{v_r g r}{v_t^2}.$$

Experimental work indicates that particles tend to separate if they rotate outside a central core of radius $0.2D_o$ (where D_o = diameter of the outlet pipe), and

$$v_r = \frac{\dot{m}_g}{2\pi\rho r H}, \quad v_t = v_i\sqrt{\frac{D}{2r}}$$

where v_i = the velocity of the gas stream at the separator inlet
H = depth of separator, D = chamber diameter.

Substituting gives

$$v_\infty = \frac{g v_r r}{v_t^2} = g\left(\frac{\dot{m}_g}{2\pi\rho r H}\right)\frac{r}{v_t^2} \text{ at } r = 0.2D_o$$

$$= \frac{\dot{m}_g}{2\pi\rho H(0.2D_o)} \frac{g(0.2D_o)}{v_i^2 D} 2(0.2D_o) = \frac{0.2D_o g\dot{m}_g}{\pi\rho H D v_i^2}$$

Finally $\dot{m}_g = \rho A_i v_i$ where A_i = inlet area, and substituting gives

$$v_\infty = \frac{0.2\rho g D_o A_i^2}{\pi H D \dot{m}_g} \quad \text{or} \quad \dot{m}_g = \frac{0.2\rho g D_o A_i^2}{\pi H D v_\infty}$$

Inserting the data given:

$$\dot{m}_g = \frac{0.2(1.2)(9.81)(0.095) \times \frac{1}{4}\pi(0.095)^2}{\pi(1.3)(0.3)v_\infty} = \frac{0.00129}{v_\infty}$$

Now $v_\infty = \dfrac{\rho_s g D_p^2}{18\mu} = \dfrac{2600(9.81)(2 \times 10^{-6})^2}{18(1.8 \times 10^{-5})} = 0.157 \times 10^{-3}$ m/s

hence $\dfrac{0.00129}{0.157 \times 10^{-3}} = 8.217$ kg/s or $6.85\,\text{m}^3/\text{s}$

Note. A small inlet and outlet result in the separation of smaller particles, but the pressure drop through the separator varies with v_i^l. Also outside the central core, the particles move continuously downwards and are normally removed continuously from the base to avoid entrainment into the gas stream.

8.5 Cyclone separator efficiency

> The efficiency of a cyclone separator, η, is given by the equation
>
> $$\eta = 1 - \exp(-44600D)$$
>
> The separator passes a gas stream, in which the particle size varies. The distribution of the particle diameters is given by the Rosin-Rammler law
>
> $$R = 100\exp(19800D_p),$$
>
> where R = percentage, by *mass*, of particles of diameter greater than D.
> Determine the overall efficiency of the cyclone.

Solution. Let x = *mass fraction* of particles of diameter less than D.
Then the separator efficiency for particles in the size range D to $D + \partial D$ is

$$\eta = \frac{dm_c}{d(xm)}$$

where m = the total mass particles, m_c = the mass of particles separated.

Hence $m_c = m\int_0^1 \eta\, dx$

or the overall efficiency,

$$\eta_0 = \frac{m_c}{m} = m\int_0^1 \eta\, dx$$

Now $x = 1 - \exp(-19800D) = 1 - \exp(bD)$ say
and $\eta = 1 - \exp(-44600D) = 1 - \exp(-aD)$ say
Substituting

$$\eta_0 = b\int [1 - \exp(-aD)]\exp(-bD)\,dD$$

with the integration limits

$$D = 0 \;\; at \;\; x = 0, \qquad D = \infty \;\; at \;\; x = 1.$$

Hence $\eta_0 = b\int [\exp(-bD)] - \exp[(-a+b)dD]$

$$= b\left[-\frac{1}{b}\exp(-bD)\right] - \frac{1}{a+b}\exp[(-a+b)dD]_0^\infty$$

$$= b\left[-\frac{1}{b} + \frac{1}{a+b}\right] = \frac{a}{a+b} = \frac{44\,600}{44\,600 + 19\,800} = \mathbf{0.69}$$

8.6 Centrifugal separator

Particles are separated from a liquid in a centrifugal separator (centrifuge), which rotates at an angular velocity Ω. Derive an expression for the critical diameter.

Calculate the critical diameter when a solution, at a throughput of 6×10^{-4} kg/s, is cleared of particles in a centrifuge, of bowl depth 200 mm, outer diameter 45 mm.

density of solution	= 800 kg/m^3
viscosity of solution	= 0.1 kg/ms
density of particles	= 1460 kg/m^3
centrifuge velocity	= 10000 rev/min

Assume that the liquid layer thickness = 15 mm.

Solution. A force balance on a particle gives

$$m\frac{dv}{dt} = mr\Omega^2\left(\frac{\rho_s - \rho}{\rho_s}\right) - \frac{1}{2}\rho v^2 C_D A$$

where v = velocity, t = time, r = radius.

The separation of the particles is limited by the particle fall rate, and in many cases the flow is laminar so that $C_D = 24/Re$. Hence

$$\frac{1}{6}\pi D^3\rho_s\frac{dv}{dt} = \frac{1}{6}\pi D^3\rho_s r\Omega^2\left(\frac{\rho_s - \rho}{\rho_s}\right) - \frac{1}{2}\rho v^2\frac{24\mu}{\rho D v}\frac{\pi D^2}{4}$$

or $$\frac{dv}{dt} = \left(\frac{\rho_s - \rho}{\rho_s}\right)r\Omega^2 - \frac{18\mu v}{\rho_s D^2}.$$

At radius r the terminal velocity v_∞ is given by the condition

$$\frac{dv}{dt} = 0 \quad \text{or} \quad v_\infty = \frac{r\Omega^2(\rho_s - \rho)D^2}{18\mu}$$

in a *radial* direction.

The distance travelled by a particle, in a radial direction, is in time dt

$$x = \frac{r\Omega^2(\rho_s - \rho)D^2}{18\mu}dt$$

and integrating

$$\ln\frac{r_2}{r_1} = \frac{(\rho_s - \rho)\Omega^2 D^2 t}{18\mu}$$

where t = time interval V/Q

V = volume of material in the centrifuge

Q = volumetric feed rate (throughput).

There are two possible situations to consider. If the liquid layer is *thin* compared to the radius the centrifugal force can be considered as constant, and

$$x = \frac{r\Omega^2(\rho_s - \rho)D^2}{18\mu}\frac{V}{Q}$$

Taking $x = (r_2 - r_1)/2 = 1/2 \times$ liquid layer thickness, then half of the particles of some diameter D_c will settle to the wall when the fluid leaves the centrifuge. The other half of the particles remain in the suspension. This diameter is termed the *critical diameter*, and its importance is in the fact that particles whose diameter is greater than this critical diameter will settle. The value of the critical diameter is given by the rearranged equation (with $x = \frac{1}{2}(r_2 - r_1)$)

$$D_c^2 = \frac{9\mu Q(r_2 - r_1)}{(\rho_s - \rho)V\Omega^2 r}$$

The second situation is one in which the layer thickness is large compared to the radius. In this case the term $(r_2 - r_1)/r$ is replaced by the term $2\ln(r_2/r_1)$.

In this problem

$$Q = \frac{6\times10^{-4}}{800} = 7.5\times10^{-7}\,\mathrm{m^3/s}, \qquad \Omega = 10\,000\times\frac{2\pi}{60} = 1\,047\,\mathrm{rad/s}$$

$$V = \frac{1}{4}\pi(0.045^2 - 0.015^2)(0.2) = 2.827\times10^{-4}\,\mathrm{m^3}$$

$$D_c = \frac{9\times0.1\times7.5\times10^{-7}}{(1\,460 - 800)\times2.827\times10^{-4}\times(1\,047)^2}\times2\ln\frac{0.045}{0.013}$$

$$= 7.25\times10^{-11}$$

$D_c = 8.5\times10^{-6}$ m or **8.5 μm**

8.7 Bed of particles: fluidisation

Outline the way in which the pressure drop across a bed of particles changes as the velocity of a fluid, passing through the bed, varies.

A bed of particles, at rest, has a porosity = 0.35 and a height of 1.0 m. A hot gas is passed through the bed. The particles are of density 1650 kg/m^3, diameter 50 μm. The gas density = 3.5 kg/m^3, viscosity = 2×10^{-5} kg/ms.

Calculate the superficial gas velocity required to fluidise the bed, the gas velocity at which the bed would begin to flow with the gas and the bed expansion when the gas velocity is 0.05 m/s.

The porosity at the minimum fluidisation velocity = 0.42.

Solution. The pressure drop across a bed of particles, Δp, varies with the superficial velocity U, defined as the gas or fluid flow rate/cross-sectional area of the bed. The pressure drop is also a function of the particle diameter, D_p, and fluid properties. The form of the variation is shown in Fig. 8.5, as a plot of Δp against $Re = \rho D_p U/\mu$. Initially the bed is stable, and the relationship is given by the Carman-Kozeny equation (line AB). As the velocity increases a point (B) is reached where the pressure drop balances the weight of the bed solids. A further increase produces an unstable bed (BC), where the particles adjust their position to present the minimum resistance to the fluid flow. The point C is termed the *fluidisation point*. As the velocity increases further, the particles begin to move with some freedom, rather similar to hindered settling (CD). The bed continues to expand (DE) with a small increase in the pressure drop, until the bed ceases to exist at point E.

The fluidisation can take different forms. If the densities of the fluid and solids are of the same order, the particles are small, and the flow velocity is relatively low, the bed fluidises evenly: this is known as *particulate fluidisation*.

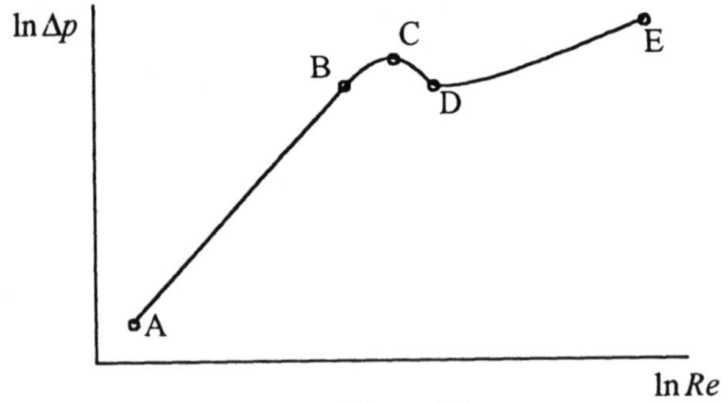

Figure 8.5

The criterion is that $Fr\,Re\left(\frac{\rho_s - \rho}{\rho}\right)\frac{H}{d} < 100$

where Fr = Froude number $= U^2/gD_p$, H = bed depth

taken at point C, where $\Delta p = gH(1-\varepsilon)(\rho_s - \rho)$, ε = porosity.

If, however, there is a substantial difference in the densities or the particles are of a large diameter, a relatively high fluid flow velocity is necessary. The fluidisation then becomes uneven, with the fluid passing through the bed in large bubbles, bursting at the surface. This is termed *aggregative* fluidisation. The criterion is

$$Fr.\,Re\left(\frac{\rho_s - \rho}{\rho}\right)\frac{H}{d} > 100$$

The Carman-Kozeny equation (q.v. Intro.) is

$$-\frac{dp}{dz} = \frac{180(1-\varepsilon)^2}{\varepsilon^3}\cdot\frac{\mu U}{D_p^2}$$

Hence, at the beginning of fluidisation

$$(1-\varepsilon)(\rho_s - \rho)Hg = \frac{180(1-\varepsilon)^2}{\varepsilon^3}\cdot\frac{\mu U H}{D_p^2}$$

or $$U = \frac{\varepsilon^3}{1-\varepsilon}\,\frac{(\rho_s - \rho)gD_p^2}{180\mu}$$

Substituting the data given the superficial gas velocity required to fluidise the bed, at $\varepsilon = 0.42$, is

$$U = \frac{(0.42)^2}{0.58}\times\frac{(1\,650 - 3.5)g(50\times10^{-6})^2}{180(2\times10^{-5})} = \mathbf{14.33\times10^{-4}\ m/s}$$

The bed begins to flow with the gas, i.e. to disintegrate, when the gas velocity is equal to the free fall velocity of the particles. Thus

$$U = \frac{(\rho_s - \rho)gD_p^2}{18\mu} = \frac{(1\,650 - 3.5)g(50\times10^{-6})^2}{18(2\times10^{-5})} = \mathbf{0.112\ m/s}$$

The bed expansion can be determined from the relationship between the gas velocity, porosity and physical properties:

$$\frac{\varepsilon^3}{1-\varepsilon} = \frac{180\mu U}{(\rho_s - \rho)gD_p^2}$$

Denoting the conditions at the start of the fluidisation by the subscript o, then

$$\frac{\varepsilon^3}{1-\varepsilon} - \frac{\varepsilon_o^3}{1-e_o} = \frac{180\mu}{(\rho_s - \rho)gD_p^2}(U - U_o)$$

Also $\frac{H}{H_o} = \frac{1-\varepsilon_o}{1-\varepsilon}$.

Substituting the data given, at $U = 0.05$ m/s

$$\frac{\varepsilon^3}{1-\varepsilon} - \frac{(0.42)^3}{0.58} = \frac{180(2\times10^{-5})}{(1\,650 - 3.5)g(50\times10^{-6})^2}(0.05 - 0.0043)$$
$$= 4.33$$

$$\frac{\varepsilon^3}{1-\varepsilon} = 4.458$$

giving $\varepsilon =$ **0.858** and $\frac{H}{1.0} = \frac{1-0.42}{1-0.858}$ or $H =$ **4.08 m**

Note. The expansion of the bed from a depth of 1.0 m to 4.08 m would almost certainly incur by-passing and slugging; and the bed height would be rather less than the calculated value.

Also, at the beginning of fluidisation, the criterion of particular fluidisation is

$$Fr\,Re\left(\frac{\rho_s - \rho}{\rho}\right)\frac{H}{D} < 100$$

or
$$\frac{(0.00143)^2}{g(50\times10^{-6})}\;\frac{3.5(50\times10^{-6})(0.00143)}{2\times10^{-5}}\;\frac{1\,646.5}{3.5D} < 100$$

$$\frac{(4.17\times10^{-3})(58.8)}{D} < 100$$

giving $D > 0.00245$ m where D is the bed diameter.

8.8 Carman-Kozeny equation

Outline the Kozeny model of a fluidised bed and derive the Carman-Kozeny equation

$$-\frac{dp}{dz} = \frac{180(1-\varepsilon)^2}{\varepsilon^3}\frac{\mu U}{D_p^2}$$

What is the basis of the Ergun factor added to the Carman-Kozeny term? Show how the Carman-Kozeny equation can be derived using the drift-flux approach. It may be assumed that the drift flux is given by the equation

$$j_{fs} = v_\infty \varepsilon^n (1-\varepsilon)$$

Solution. The Kozeny model of the fluid flow through a bed of solid particles is a set of channels formed by capillary tubes, parallel to the direction of flow (Fig.8.6).

If the number of channels $= n$, the voidage fraction ε is

$$\varepsilon = \frac{\text{volume of voids}}{\text{total volume}} = \frac{nd^2H}{D^2H} = n\left(\frac{d}{D}\right)^2$$

If the mean velocity through the channels is $\bar{v}$, then

$$D^2 = n\bar{v}d^2 \text{ or } n = \frac{U}{\bar{v}}\left(\frac{D}{d}\right)^2, \text{ and } U = \varepsilon\bar{v}.$$

Consider a uniformly sized bed, containing N particles each of volume V_p, surface area A_p. The total volume of *voids* is then

$$\frac{NV_p\varepsilon}{1-\varepsilon}$$

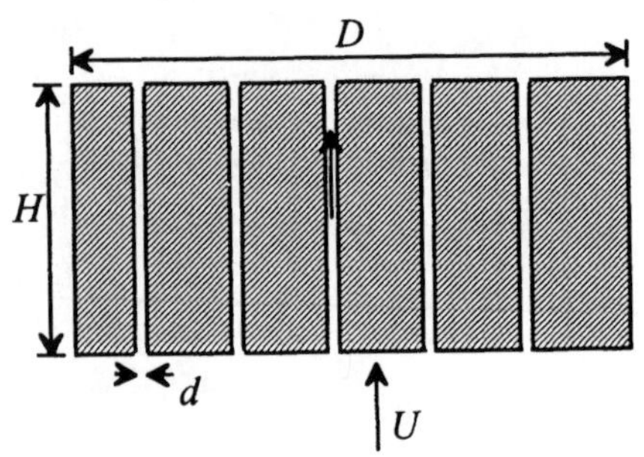

Figure 8.6

The hydraulic mean radius is

$$R_h = \frac{\text{total volume of voids}}{\text{total surface area of particles}} = \frac{NV_p\varepsilon}{1-\varepsilon}\cdot\frac{1}{NA_p} = \frac{\varepsilon V_p}{(1-\varepsilon)A_p}$$

Now the Darcy equation for the pressure drop is

$$\Delta p = \frac{4fH\rho U^2}{2D_p}$$

where U = superficial velocity = flow rate / $(\frac{1}{4}\pi D^2)$. In the Kozeny model this basic equation is used, with U replaced by $\bar{v}$ and D_p by R_h giving

$$\Delta p = \frac{4\rho fH\bar{v}^2}{2R_h} = 2\rho fH\left(\frac{U}{\varepsilon}\right)^2\frac{(1-\varepsilon)A_p}{\varepsilon V_p} = \frac{2\rho fH(1-\varepsilon)U^2}{e^3}\frac{A_p}{V_p}$$

$$= 2fU^2(\rho HS_{p)}\left(\frac{1-\varepsilon}{\varepsilon^3}\right)$$

where S_p = specific area of a particle = A_p / V_p.

The friction coefficient f is a function of the Reynolds number

$$Re = \frac{\rho R_h\bar{v}}{\mu} = \frac{\rho}{\mu}\frac{\varepsilon}{(1-\varepsilon)S_p}\frac{U}{\varepsilon} = \frac{U}{(1-\varepsilon)S_p\nu}$$

In the laminar range, $Re \le 4, f = K/Re$ say, giving

$$\Delta p = 2\frac{K(1-\varepsilon)S_p\nu}{U}U^2\rho HS_p\left(\frac{1-\varepsilon}{\varepsilon^3}\right) = 2KUH\mu S_p^2\frac{(1-\varepsilon)^2}{\varepsilon^3}$$

In the case of *spherical* particles

$$S_p = \frac{\pi D_p^2}{\frac{1}{6}\pi D_p^3} = \frac{6}{D_p}$$

and $$\Delta p = 2KUH\mu\left(\frac{36}{D_p^2}\right)\frac{(1-\varepsilon)^2}{\varepsilon^3} = 72K\left(\frac{\mu U}{D_p^2}\right)\frac{(1-\varepsilon)^2}{\varepsilon^3}$$

A value of $K = 2\frac{1}{2}$ gives the *Carman-Kozeny* equation. If the kinetic energy is significant, an additional term (following *Ergun*) is introduced. The extra pressure drop is

$$\Delta p' = \frac{1}{2}\rho\bar{v}^2NH = K'\frac{\rho\bar{v}^2}{D} \text{ say}$$

Now $\frac{1}{4}N\pi D^2 = \varepsilon\frac{1}{4}\pi D^2$ and $S_p = \frac{NH\pi D_o}{\frac{1}{4}\pi D^2H(1-\varepsilon)} = \frac{6}{D_p}$

hence $D = \frac{4\varepsilon D_p}{6(1-\varepsilon)}$.

Substituting

$$\Delta p' = K'\rho\left(\frac{U}{\varepsilon}\right)^2\frac{6(1-\varepsilon)}{4\varepsilon D_p} = K'\left(\frac{1-\varepsilon}{\varepsilon^3}\right)\frac{\rho U^2}{D_p}$$

Ergun obtained a value $K' = 1.75$ from experimental data.

Drift flux model

The pressure gradient is

$$-\frac{dp}{dz} = f\frac{1}{2}\rho v_f^2\frac{A}{V}$$

where A = the total surface area of the particles

V = *available* flow volume.

For spherical particles $\frac{A}{V} = \left(\frac{1-\varepsilon}{\varepsilon}\right)\frac{6}{D_p}$

Also $v_f = \frac{U}{\varepsilon}$, and $f = \frac{K}{Re}$ where $Re = \frac{\rho U D_p}{(1-\varepsilon)\mu}$.

Hence substituting gives

$$-\frac{dp}{dz} = \frac{K\mu(1-\varepsilon)}{\rho U D_p}\frac{\rho}{2}\left(\frac{U}{\varepsilon}\right)^2\frac{1-\varepsilon}{\varepsilon}\frac{6}{D_p} = \frac{3K\mu U}{D_p^2}\frac{(1-\varepsilon)^2}{\varepsilon^3}$$

Taking $K = 60$ then gives the Carman-Kozeny equation.

8.9 Darcy's law, permeability

> A bed of particles, of depth 50 mm, contains uniform particles. The bed is circular, of diameter 1.0 m. Air flows through the bed at a flow rate of 0.035 m^3/s, and the pressure drop is 10 kN/m^2. The particles are of diameter 2 mm.
>
> State Darcy's law, and determine the permeability of the bed. Estimate the bed porosity, using the Carman-Kozeny equation.
>
> Air density = 1.2 kg/m^3, viscosity = 1.8×10^{-5} kg/ms.

Solution. Darcy's law can be stated as follows:

$$U = \frac{K}{\mu}\frac{\Delta p}{H}$$

where U is the superficial fluid velocity, and K is the *permeability* of the bed. The permeability is often expressed in Darcy, where the Darcy unit is the permeability which allows a flow of 1 cm^3/s cm^3 for a fluid of viscosity 1 cP (0.001 Ns/m^2) under a pressure gradient of 1 atm/cm. Thus

1 Darcy $\equiv 9.87 \times 10^{-8}$ cm^2 unit.

Substituting, $U = \frac{K}{1.8\times10^{-5}}\times\frac{10\,000}{0.05} = 0.111\times10^{11}K$ m/s

The air flow rate = 0.035 m^3/s and $U = \frac{0.035}{\frac{1}{4}\pi(1)^2} = 0.0446$ m/s

giving the permeability,

$$K = \frac{0.0446}{0.111\times10^{11}} = 0.419\times10^{-11}\,\text{m}^2$$

$$= 0.419\times10^{-7}\,\text{cm}^2 = \mathbf{4.19\times10^{-8}\,cm^2} \text{ or } \mathbf{0.425\,Darcy}$$

The Carman-Kozeny equation can now be used to determine the bed porosity (or voidage fraction) ε.

$$\frac{dp}{dz} = \frac{180\mu U}{D_p^2}\frac{(1-\varepsilon)^2}{\varepsilon^3}, \quad \frac{10\,000}{0.05} = \frac{180(1.8\times10^{-5})(0.0446)}{(0.002)^2}\frac{(1-\varepsilon)^2}{\varepsilon^3}$$

hence $\frac{(1-\varepsilon)^2}{\varepsilon^3} = 5\,536$

Solving by trial-and-error gives ε = **0.055**. Thus the solid particles occupy $1 - \varepsilon = 0.945$ of the total volume.

Note. The bed permeability and Darcy's law were developed by Darcy from experimental work in the early 19th century.

8.10 Bed of non-spherical particles

A bed consists of cubes of material, of density 1500 kg/m^3, side 6 mm, and has a depth 3 m. Air flows through the bed at a rate of 1.35 kg/s per m^2 bed area. Bed diameter = 1.0 m.

Air density = 6.5 kg/m^3, viscosity = 2.2×10^{-5} kg/ms. Estimate the pressure drop across the bed.

The sphericity varies with porosity as follows:

porosity ε	0.34	0.44	0.49	0.55	0.61	0.69	0.76	0.85	0.96
sphericity ψ	1.0	0.8	0.7	0.6	0.5	0.4	0.3	0.2	0.1

Solution. The sphericity ψ is defined as the ratio of the surface area of an equal volume sphere to the surface area of the particle. Thus for a spherical particle of diameter D_p the sphericity = 1. Considering a cube, of side 6 mm, the diameter of the equal volume sphere D_s is given by

$$\frac{1}{6}\pi D_s^3 = 6^3 \text{ and } D_s = 7.43\,\text{mm}.$$

Hence $\psi = \dfrac{\pi D_s^2}{6(6)^2} = 0.80$

and from the table $\varepsilon = 0.44$. The superficial velocity $U = 1.35/6.5 = 0.208$ m/s and substituting into the Carman-Kozeny equation

$$\frac{\Delta p}{3} = \frac{180(0.56)^2}{(0.44)^3} \times \frac{2.2 \times 10^{-5}(0.208)}{(0.00743)^2}$$

giving Δp = **165 N/m²**.

If the Ergun correction is added,

$$\text{pressure drop} = 165 + \frac{1.75\rho U^2 H(1-\varepsilon)}{\varepsilon^3 D_p}$$

$$= 165 + \frac{1.75(6.5)(0.208)^2(3)(0.56)}{(0.44)^3(0.00743)} = \mathbf{1471\,N/m^2}$$

8.11 Fluidisation

Water flows vertically upwards in a cylinder of diameter 3 cm, at a rate of 2.5×10^{-6} m^3/s. The tube contains solid particles, spherical in shape, and each of diameter 0.25 mm. The density of the solid is 8900 kg/m^3.

Determine the state of fluidisation of the bed; the pressure drop and voidage fraction. Assume that the minimum fluidisation velocity of the water is given by the equation $C_D Re^2 = 0.018 Gr^2$,

where $Re = \dfrac{\rho D_p U}{\mu}$, $Gr^2 = \dfrac{\rho g D_p^3(\rho_s - \rho)}{\mu^2}$, $C_D = \dfrac{24}{Re}(1 + 0.15Re^{0.7})$,

$$\varepsilon^{4.7} = \frac{0.75 C_D Re^2}{Gr^2}$$

Viscosity of water = 10^{-3} kg/ms.

Solution. Gr is the Grashof number, and inserting the data given

$$Gr^2 = \frac{1\,000(9.81)(0.25\times10^{-3})^3(8\,900-1\,000)}{10^{-6}} = 1\,211$$

Hence $C_D Re^2 = 0.0.18(1\,211) = 21.8$
at the minimum fluidisation velocity.

Now $$Re = \frac{1\,000(0.25\times10^{-3})U}{(10^{-3})} = 250U$$

and substituting gives

$$\frac{24}{250U}\left[1 + 0.15(250U)^{0.7}\right](250U)^2 = 21.8$$

$$U + 7.155U^{1.7} = 0.0036 = \mathrm{F}(U) \text{ say}$$

Solving by trial-and-error, or a plot of F() against U, gives the value of U.

U (m/s)	0.0030	0.0031	0.0032
F	0.0034	0.0035	0.0036

Hence U = **0.0032 m/s**.

The actual superficial water velocity is

$$\frac{2.5\times10^{-6}}{\frac{1}{4}\pi(0.03)^2} = 0.0035\ \mathrm{m/s}$$

so that the bed has just become fluidised.

The voidage fraction ε can be calculated from the semi-empirical relationship quoted,

$$\varepsilon^{4.7} = \frac{0.75 C_D Re^2}{Gr^2}$$

In this case $Re = 250U = 0.875$

$$C_D = \frac{24}{0.875}(1 + 0.15(0.875)^{0.7}) = 31.18$$

giving $$\varepsilon^{4.7} = 0.75(31.18)\frac{(0.875)^2}{1\,211} = 0.0148$$

$$\varepsilon = \mathbf{0.408}$$

Note. The voidage fraction is approximately 0.40 at the point of incipient fluidisation.

The pressure drop can be calculated from the Carman-Kozeny equation:

$$\Delta p = \frac{\mu U}{D_p^2}\frac{180(1-\varepsilon)^2}{\varepsilon^3} = \frac{10^{-3}(0.0035)}{(0.25\times10^{-3})^2}\times\frac{180(0.592)^2}{(0.408)^3}$$

$$= 52\,014\ \mathrm{N/m^2}$$

The hydrostatic pressure gradient is

$$\Delta p = \rho g = 9\,810\ \mathrm{N/m^2}$$

giving a total pressure drop of **61824 N/m²**.

Note. The Ergun correction gives an additional pressure drop term of

$$\frac{1.75\rho U^2}{D_p}\frac{1-\varepsilon}{\varepsilon^3} = 750\ \mathrm{N/m^2}.$$

The kinetic energy effect is therefore relatively small.

8.12 Filtration

A solid is separated from a fluid by filtration. Briefly outline the factors on which the filtration rate depends.

Assuming the basic filtration equation

$$\frac{\Delta p}{\mu H r} = \frac{1}{A}\frac{dV}{dt},$$

where V = fluid volume,

r = specific resistance = $\frac{5(1-\varepsilon)^2 S^2}{\varepsilon^3}$,

S = specific surface area of the particles
= specific area/volume

show that

$$\frac{dV}{dt} = \frac{A^2 \Delta p}{v r \mu (V + AL/v)}$$

where v = volume of cake (solid) deposited by unit volume of filtrate,

L = cake thickness during filtration equivalent to the filter cloth and initial layer of cake, in resistance to the fluid flow.

A slurry contains 2.8% of solid material (by *mass*), and is filtered through a set of 15 frames, each 1.25 m thick, 70 cm wide. The rate of filtration is 0.08 m^3/s.

density of solid material	= 2230 kg/m^3
density of dry filter cake	= 1320 kg/m^3
viscosity of water	= 10^{-3} kg/ms

The pressure drop is measured as 3200 N/m^2 after 120 s, and 6500 N/m^2 after 300 s of filtration. What value would be expected after

(a) 1000 s,
(b) 1500 s?

Solution. Filtration is the process in which a solid is separated from a fluid by means of a porous medium, which retains the solid while passing the fluid (Fig. 8.7). The behaviour of the fluid is similar to that of a fluid flow through a fixed bed; but differs in that in filtration the bed thickness steadily increases. At a constant filtration pressure the flow rate will progressively decrease, whereas a constant flow rate requires a gradually increasing pressure.

The resistance is a minimum (and therefore the flow rate a maximum) at the beginning of filtration, and increases with time. The filter cakes can be incompressible or compressible: in the former the resistance to flow of a given volume of cake is not affected by the pressure difference across the cake, or the material deposition rate so that ε can be taken as constant.

The cake thickness H and volume of filtrate V in the equation given are related to each other.

The mass of solids in the cake = $(1-\varepsilon)AH\rho_s$, and the mass of liquid retained in the cake = $\varepsilon AH\rho$. Hence

$$\frac{\text{mass of solids in the cake}}{\text{mass of filtrate + mass of liquid retained in the cake}} = \frac{F}{1 - F}$$
$$= \frac{(1 - \varepsilon)AH\rho_s}{(V + \varepsilon AH)\rho}$$

where F = fraction of solids to liquid (by *mass*) in the original suspension

Hence $(1 - F)(1 - \varepsilon)AH\rho_s = FV\rho + \varepsilon AFH\rho$

giving $H = \dfrac{FV\rho}{A[(1 - F)(1 - \varepsilon)\rho_s - F\varepsilon\rho]}$

Let v = volume of cake deposited per unit volume of filtrate passed.

Then $v = \dfrac{F\rho}{(1 - F)(1 - \varepsilon)\rho_s - F\varepsilon\rho}$, and $H = \dfrac{vV}{A}$.

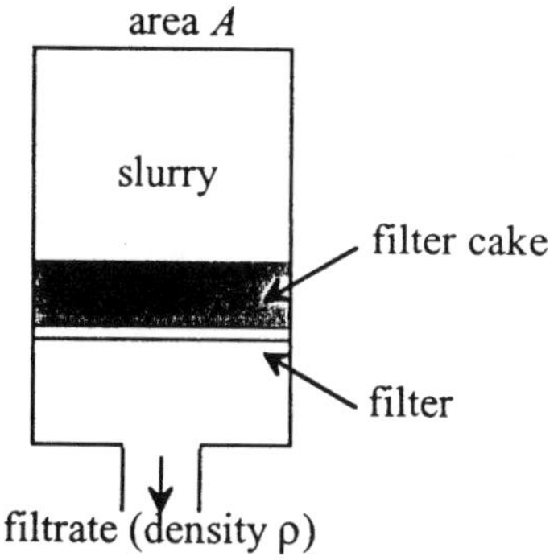

Figure 8.7

The basic filtration equation can now be written as

$$\frac{dV}{dt} = \frac{A^2\Delta p}{\mu rvV}$$

The equation can be integrated if the relationship between Δp, V and time t is known. Also the pressure drop arises across the cake *and* the filter cloth: this can be allowed for by introducing an equivalent thickness L. Then the basic equation becomes

$$\frac{1}{A}\frac{dV}{dt} = \frac{\Delta p}{\mu r(H + L)}$$

or $$\frac{dV}{dt} = \frac{A\Delta p}{\mu r(\frac{vV}{A} + L)} = \frac{A^2\Delta p}{\mu rv(V + AL/v)}$$

The equation can be integrated if the relationship between Δp, V, t is known. Thus, for *constant rate* filtration

$$\frac{dV}{dt} = \text{constant}, \quad \text{and } \frac{V}{t} = \frac{A^2\Delta p}{v r\mu(V + AL/v)}$$

or $$V^2 + \frac{ALV}{v} = \frac{A^2\Delta p\,.\,t}{\mu vr}$$

For *constant pressure* filtration, integration gives between limits $V = V_1$ at $t = t_1$, $V = V_2$ at $t = t_2$,

$$\frac{1}{2}(V_2^2 - V_1^2) + \frac{AL}{v}(V_2 - V_1) = \frac{A^2\Delta p}{\mu vr}(t_2 - t_1)$$

Then numerical calculation is performed by a slightly different method. For constant rate filtration

$$\frac{dV}{dt} = \frac{V}{t} \text{ or } V = t\left(\frac{dV}{dt}\right)$$

and substituting gives

$$\Delta p = \frac{\mu v r}{A^2} t\left(\frac{dV}{dt}\right)^2 + \frac{\mu r L}{A}\left(\frac{dV}{dt}\right) = \alpha t\left(\frac{dV}{dt}\right)^2 + \beta\left(\frac{dV}{dt}\right) \text{ say}$$

Now $\Delta p = 3200$ N/m² at $t = 120$ s, and 6500 N/m² at $t = 300$ s.

Hence $3200 = \alpha(120)(0.08)^2 + \beta(0.08)$

$6500 = \alpha(300)(0.08)^2 + \beta(0.08)$

giving $\alpha = 2\,865$, $\beta = 12\,496$, $\Delta p = 18.336t + 1\,000$

(a) At $t = 1000$ s, $\Delta p =$ **19340 N/m²**

(b) At $t = 1500$ s, $\Delta p =$ **28500 N/m²**.

Note: The cake thickness and equivalent thickness can be calculated as follows. Taking the situation after 1000 s:

$V = 0.08 \times 1000 \qquad = 80\ \text{m}^3$

$A = 1.25 \times 0.7 \times 15 \qquad = 13.125\ \text{m}^2$

$\varepsilon = 1 - 1320/2230 \qquad = 0.408$

$F \qquad = 0.028$

$$v = \frac{\rho F}{(1 - F)(1 - \varepsilon)\rho_s - F\varepsilon\rho}$$

$$= \frac{1\,000(0.028)}{0.972(0.592)(2\,230) - 0.028(0.408)(1\,000)} = 0.022$$

giving the cake thickness

$$H = \frac{vV}{A} = \mathbf{0.134\ m}$$

The specific cake resistance is

$$\frac{\alpha A^2}{\mu v} = \frac{2\,865(13.125)^2}{10^{-3}(0.022)} = 2.24 \times 10^{10}$$

and the equivalent thickness

$$L = \frac{\beta A}{\mu(2.24 \times 10^{10})} = \mathbf{0.0073\ m}$$

8.13 Pneumatic transport

Solid, spherical particles, of diameter 1 mm and density 500 kg/m³ are transported pneumatically up a vertical pipe of diameter 25 cm, at a rate of 0.35 kg/s.

Air density = 1.2 kg/m³, viscosity = 1.7×10^{-5} kg/ms.

Estimate the air velocity at transition from a dense phase flow to moving bed flow. Assume that the porosity at incipient fluidisation = 0.40.

Investigate whether choking is likely to occur, using Yang's criterion that for no choking

$v_\infty < 0.35\sqrt{gD}$, where D = pipe diameter.

$C_D = \dfrac{24}{Re}$ $\qquad Re < 2$

$C_D = \dfrac{24}{Re}(1 + 0.15Re^{0.69})$ $\qquad 200 < Re < 800$

Solution. Pneumatic conveyance is used extensively for the transport of solid materials in many areas. It can be operated under suction or positive pressure. Vertical conveyance depends upon the balance between the weight of the particles and the drag force on them. The velocity of the gas relative to the particles is close to the vertical terminal velocity v_∞. Dense phase conveyance implies that the slip velocity between the gas and the solid particle is greater than that at incipient fluidisation. Transition to moving bed flow will be at

$$v_f - v_s = v_o$$

where $v_f = \text{gas velocity} = \dfrac{U}{\varepsilon}$, $v_s = \text{particle velocity} = \dfrac{U_s}{1-\varepsilon}$

v_o = fluid velocity at the point of incipient fluidisation $= \dfrac{U_o}{\varepsilon_o}$

and U, U_s = superficial fluid and solids velocity resp.

The subscript o is used to denote conditions at incipient fluidisation, i.e. $\varepsilon_o = 0.40$.

Substituting gives

$$\frac{U}{\varepsilon_o} - \frac{U_s}{1-\varepsilon_o} = \frac{U_o}{\varepsilon_o} \quad \text{or} \quad (1-\varepsilon_o)U - \varepsilon_o U_s = (1-\varepsilon_o)U_o$$

Also at the incipient fluidisation point

$$\Delta p = (1-\varepsilon_o)(\rho_s - \rho)g = \frac{180(1-\varepsilon_o)^2\mu U_o}{\varepsilon_o^3 D_p^2}$$

(Carman-Kozeny equation)

$$\text{Hence } (1-0.4)(500-1.2)g = \frac{180(0.6)^2(1.7\times10^{-5})U_o}{(0.4)^3(10^{-3})^2}$$

and $U_o = 0.17\,\text{m/s}$

$$\text{Now } U_s = \frac{\dot{m}_s}{\rho_s A} = \frac{0.35}{500\times\frac{1}{4}\pi(0.25)^2} = 0.0143\,\text{m/s}$$

and using the equation

$$(1-\varepsilon_o)U - \varepsilon_o U_s = (1-\varepsilon_o)U_o$$

gives $0.6U - 0.4(0.0143) = 0.6(0.170)$ or $U = 0.18\,\text{m/s}$

Hence the air velocity at transition $= \dfrac{U}{\varepsilon_o} = \mathbf{0.45\,m/s}$

Note. If the kinetic energy of the particles is taken into consideration, the additional Ergun factor gives:

$$0.6(498.8)g = 17213U_o + \frac{1.75(1-\varepsilon_o)\rho U_o^2}{\varepsilon_o^3 D_p}$$

$$= 17213U_o + 19688U_o^2$$

or $U_o^2 + 0.874U_o - 0.149 = 0$

and $U_o = \frac{1}{2}(-0.874 \pm 1.166) = \mathbf{0.15\,m/s}$

The amended values are now

$$U = \frac{0.4(0.0143) + 0.6(0.15)}{0.6} = 0.15\,\text{m/s}$$

$$v_f = \frac{0.16}{0.4} = \mathbf{0.40\,m/s}$$

The choking condition given is that for no choking

$$v_\infty < 0.35\sqrt{gD}\text{, where } v_\infty^2 = \frac{4}{3}\frac{(\rho_s - \rho)}{\rho C_D} g D_p$$

(q.v. W.E.8.1) The drag coefficient is a function of the Reynolds number

$$Re = \frac{\rho D_p v_\infty}{\mu} = 70.59 v_\infty$$

The value cannot be calculated unless v_∞ is known, and v_∞ depends on C_D i.e. on Re. Hence a trial-and-error approach is required.

Assume $Re < 2$ then $C_D = \frac{24}{Re} = \frac{24\mu}{\rho D_p v_\infty} = \frac{0.34}{v_\infty}$

and substituting

$$v_\infty^2 = \frac{4}{3}\frac{(500 - 1.2)g(10^{-3})}{1.2 C_D} = \frac{5.437}{C_D} = 15.99 v_\infty$$

$$v_\infty = 15.99 \text{ m/s}$$

and this gives $Re = 1129$, which is well above the range assumed.

Assume $Re < 800$ then $C_D = \frac{24}{Re}(1 + 0.15 Re^{0.69}) = \frac{0.34}{v_\infty}(1 + 2.83 v_\infty^{0.69})$

and substituting into the equation

$$v_\infty^2 = \frac{5.437}{C_D}$$

gives $0.34 v_\infty (1 + 2.83 v_\infty^{0.69}) = 5.437$ or $v_\infty (1 + 2.83 v_\infty^{0.69}) = 15.99$

Solving by trial-and-error gives $v_\infty = 2.52$ m/s.

The corresponding value of Reynolds number is $Re = 178$, which is in the range assumed. Hence $v_\infty = 2.52$ m/s. Yang's criterion can now be applied:

$$\frac{v_\infty}{\sqrt{gD}} = \frac{2.52}{\sqrt{g(0.25)}} = 1.61$$

and hence choking is *likely* to occur.

8.14 Horizontal transport

Discuss the pneumatic transport of solid particles in a horizontal pipe. Coal, in the form of spherical particles each of diameter 0.75 mm, is transported along a pipe by air. The pipe is 65 mm diameter, 50 m length. Flow rate of coal = 1.0 kg/s. Density of coal = 1400 kg/m^3. Air density = 1.2 kg/m^3, viscosity = 1.7×10^{-5} kg/ms. The ratio of solids to air, by mass = 10. $v_\infty = 2.8$ m/s.

Estimate the pressure drop along the duct. Assume that the additional drop due to the solids is given by the equation

$$\Delta p = \frac{575 \dot{m}_s}{v_\infty v_s^2} \times \Delta p \text{ (air only).}$$

Solution. The transport of solid particles is a complicated situation, involving many effects. The manner in which the particles are suspended is clearly related to the flow pattern: the factors involved include the degree of turbulence, the drag forces on the particles, the shape of the particles which may generate lift forces, and the gravitational forces. The concentration of particles in the fluid is important, affecting the drag forces and the degree of collisions between particles. The nature of the material can be important in that particles may, on contact with each other, stick together or coagulate forming larger particles (e.g. in the transport of sweets); and also some materials become charged (electrostatic) during transport. In general the dominant factors are the fluid velocity and the terminal velocity of a particle.

Ideally the particles are evenly distributed over the pipe cross-section, along the whole of the pipe length. However particles tend to flow in the lower half of the pipe, and in a size distribution of particles the larger sizes move towards the bottom. As the particles enter the pipe they may settle before being fully accelerated, forming dunes or a continuous bed on the pipe bottom. The bed can develop along the pipe length, moving slowly forward.

The superficial solids velocity

$$U_s = \frac{\dot{m}_s}{\rho_s A} = \frac{1.0}{1400} \times \frac{1}{\frac{1}{4}\pi(0.065)^2} = 0.215\,\text{m/s}$$

particle velocity $v_s = U - v_\infty$

$$\text{where } U = \frac{0.1}{1.2 \times \frac{1}{4}\pi(0.065)^2} = 25.10\,\text{m/s}$$

Hence $v_s = 25.10 - 2.8 = 22.3\,\text{m/s}$

$$\varepsilon = \frac{v_s - U_s}{v_s} = \frac{22.3 - 0.215}{22.3} = 0.99$$

The pressure drop is taken as the sum of the drops due to air only and due to the presence of the solids.

Air only:

$$Re = \frac{\rho D U}{\mu} = \frac{1.2(0.065)(25.1)}{1.7 \times 10^{-5}} = 1.15 \times 10^5$$

$$f = \frac{0.079}{Re^{0.25}} = 0.0043$$

$$\Delta p_a = \frac{2\rho f L U^2}{D} = \frac{2(1.2)(0.0043)(50)(25.1)^2}{0.065} = 5001\,\text{N/m}^2$$

Due to the solids the additional pressure drop is

$$\Delta p_s = \frac{575\dot{m}_s}{v_\infty v_s^2}\Delta p_a = \frac{575(1)}{(2.8)(22.3)^2} \times 5001 = 2\,065\,\text{N/m}^2$$

giving $\Delta p = \mathbf{7\,066\,N/m^2}$.

8.15 Size distributions

The size distribution of a dust was measured and gave the following results:

size range (μm)	0-2	2-4	4-8	8-12	12-16
no. of particles in range	2,000	600	140	40	20

The particles are spherical, of density 2650 kg/m^3. Determine the distribution by mass; the volume mean and surface mean diameters.

Solution. In general terms, let 1 kg of dust contain n_i particles of diameter D_i, constituting a *mass fraction* x_i.

$$x_i = \pi n_i \rho \frac{D_i^3}{6} \text{ for spherical particles.}$$

Also $\sum x_i = 1$, and $\sum D_i x_i = \sum \pi n_i D^4 \frac{\rho}{6}$

The *volume mean diameter*

$$D_{mv} = \frac{\Sigma D_i x_i}{\Sigma x_i} = \frac{\Sigma n_i D_i^4}{\Sigma n_i D_i^3}$$

The mean diameter may be based on the surface, instead of the total volume (or mass).

The *surface mean diameter* (or Sauter mean diameter) is

$$D_{ms} = \frac{\Sigma n_i D_i^3}{\Sigma n_i D_i^2}$$

It is the size of particle with the same specific surface (surface area per unit volume) as the mixture.

In this problem the mean diameter in an interval is used for the calculation.

D (μm)	1	3	6	10	14	
no. particles, n	2,000	600	140	40	20	
mass (kg)	2.8	224.8	42.0	55.5	76.1	$\times 10^{-12}$
x	0.007	0.560	0.105	0.138	0.190	

(total mass = 401.2×10^{-12} kg)

Volume mean diameter

$$= \frac{\Sigma D_i x_i}{\Sigma x_i} = \frac{\Sigma n_i D_i^4}{\Sigma n_i D_i^3}$$

$$= \frac{2000(1)^4 + 600(3)^4 + 140(6)^4 + 40(10)^4 + 20(14)^4}{2000(1)^3 + 600(3)^3 + 140(6)^3 + 40(10)^3 + 20(14)^3}$$

$$= \frac{1\,400\,360}{143\,320} = \mathbf{9.77\,\mu m}$$

Sauter mean diameter

$$= \frac{\Sigma n_i D_i^3}{\Sigma n_i D_i^2} = \frac{143\,320}{20\,360} = \mathbf{7.04\,\mu m}$$

Note: The Sauter mean diameter is used in applications where the specific surface is important, as, for example in the combustion of liquid or solid fuels as jets or sprays of fuel.

Problems

1 A steel ball, 5 mm diameter, falls vertically downwards in a column of oil. The terminal velocity is measured as 6 cm/s. Determine the viscosity of the oil.

Assuming that the ball starts from rest determine the time taken for the ball to attain 99% of the terminal velocity.

density of steel = 7900 kg/m^3

density of oil = 950 kg/m^3

If the ball diameter is 10mm would you expect the terminal velocity to be quadrupled?

Answer 1.58 kg/ms. 26 ms.
Yes—provided the column diameter is large compared to the ball diameter.

2 A sample of coal particles gave the following size analysis.

Estimate the volume mean and surface mean diameters of the sample. Determine whether the size distribution follows the Rosin-Rammler law $R = 100\exp(-aD^n)$, and, if so, the numerical value of a, and n.

% by mass	dia. < (mm)	% by mass	dia. < (mm)
0	0.40	58	0.77
7	0.56	74	0.78
20	0.66	85	0.80
30	0.68	100	0.90
47	0.72		

Answer 0.715 mm, 0.700 mm

Approx. $a = 15$, $n = 9.8$ where D = dia. (mm)

3 A sample of crushed ore gave the following size analysis:

% by mass	dia. < (mm)	% by mass	dia. < (mm)
7.5	1.41	10.6	0.26
13.6	1.00	8.2	0.18
15.8	0.71	5.6	0.13
15.4	0.50	10.0	0.09
13.3	0.36		

Assuming a Rosin-Rammler distribution determine the numerical values of the constant, and index.

The particle density = 1500 Kg/m^3 .

Estimate the total number of particles in 1 gram of the sample, and the surface mean diameter.

Answer $a = 1.65$, $n = 1.32$

238 040. 0.4 mm.

4 A dust sample gave the following analysis:

size range (μm)	0-1	1-2	2-4	4-6	6-10	10-14
no. of particles	2,000	1,000	500	200	100	40

The density of the dust = 2600 Kg/m^3

Determine the volume mean and surface mean diameters.

Answer 8.7, 6.6 mm.

5 A sphere falls freely, in a vertical direction, through a liquid of density 1200 Kg/m^3, viscosity 1.5 Kg/m^s. The sphere reaches a steady terminal velocity of 40 mm/s.

Density of sphere material = 2280 Kg/m^3.

Determine the sphere diameter.

$$C_D = 24/Re \qquad Re < 2$$
$$= 18/Re^{0.6} \qquad 2 < Re < 200$$
$$= \frac{24}{Re}(1 + 0.15Re^{0.7}) \qquad 200 < Re < 800$$

Calculate the time taken and distance travelled by the sphere when it reaches 99 % of the terminal velocity.

Answer 10 mm. 18 ms, 0.56 mm

6 An experiment determined the terminal velocities of spherical particles, of different diameters, in water.

density of sphere material = 2000 Kg/m^3

viscosity of water = 0.001 Kg/m^3

The following results were obtained

particle dia. (mm)	0.01	0.10	0.5	1.0	3.3	8	15
terminal velocity (mm/s)	0.055	5	60	150	330	540	710

Plot a graph of drag coefficient C_D against the Reynolds number $Re = \rho D_p v_\infty/\mu$.

The equation

$$Re^2 . C_D = \frac{4}{3} D_p^3 \frac{(\rho_s - \rho)g\rho}{\mu^2}$$

may be used without derivation.

7 A spherical particle of diameter D, travels in a gas (which is stationary) with velocity components u, v in the horizontal (x) and vertical (y) directions respectively. Initially at time $t = 0$, the velocity components are u_o, v_o.

The drag coefficient = $24/Re$, where

$$Re = \frac{\rho D(u^2 + v^2)^{1/2}}{\mu}$$

By application of the momentum equation in the x and y directions show that the displacements from the initial positions are given by the equations:

$$x = \frac{u_o}{K}[1 - \exp(-Kt)]$$
$$y = \frac{1}{K^2}(Kv_o - c) + \frac{ct}{K} + \frac{1}{K^2}(c - Kv_o)\exp(-Kt)$$
$$\text{where } K = \frac{18\mu}{\rho_s D^2},\ c = \left(1 - \frac{\rho}{\rho_s}\right)g$$

The vertical component of the velocity is in a downwards direction.

8 A spherical particle, 10 mm diameter, enters a stationary column of water with a vertical, upward velocity of 5 m/s.

kinematic viscosity of water $= 10^{-6}\ m^2/s$
density of sphere material $= 2500\ kg/m^3$

Assuming that the drag coefficient is constant and equal to 0.44, estimate the time taken for the particle to attain a velocity such that the Reynolds number = 800, and the distance travelled during that time.

Indicate how the calculation would be affected after this period of time.

Answer 0.21 s, 0.57 m.
The drag coefficient is no longer constant.

9 Distinguish between free and hindered settling of a particle in a fluid.

Particles, of spherical shape, settle in a liquid of density 2500 kg/m^3. The particle density = 7500 kg/m^3. Calculate the settling velocity of particles of diameter 1 mm, assuming the Steinour formula for the apparent viscosity of the suspension μ_c:

$$\frac{\mu}{\mu_c} = \varepsilon\, 10^{-1.82(1-\varepsilon)}$$

where ε is the voidage fraction.

The volume of the particles is 1/5th of the liquid volume. Assume laminar flow. $\mu = 10^{-3}$ kg/ms.

Also calculate the free settling velocity of the particles.

Answer 0.95, 2.73 m/s.

10 A suspension of spherical particles in water contains, by *mass*, 40% of particles.

density of particle material $= 2500\ kg/m^3$
viscosity of water $= 0.001$ kg/ms
diameter of particles $= 0.05$ mm

Calculate the steady terminal velocity of the particles

(a) assuming free fall

(b) considering hindered settling, assuming the Steinour correction.

$C_D = 24/Re$

Answer (a) 2.04, (b) 0.53 mm/s.

11 A sample of material has the following size distribution:

dia. D (μm)	30	21	17	16	15	12	9
R (%)	5	12	20	24	28	38	48

where R is the percentage, by mass, of the sample containing particles of diameter $> D$.

Plot a graph of R against D (μm).

A slurry contains 50 kg of the sample per m³ of water, and is allowed to settle. The particles are spherical and can be assumed to settle freely.

density of material = 2500 kg/m³
viscosity of water = 0.001 kg/ms

Determine the density of the slurry, 25 cm from the surface, after a settling time of 15 minutes.

Assume that the mass of particles, kg/m³ of suspension is given by the equation

$$m = \frac{\rho_s(\rho_c - \rho)}{\rho_s - \rho}$$

at the given depth which has a diameter corresponding to the settling time.

If the vessel is 1 m depth determine the percentage of the material that has settled to the base of the vessel after (a) 60 min, (b) 120 min.

Answer 1025 kg/m³ (a) 80, (b) 62%.

12 A flue gas, containing grit, is cleared by passing it through a cyclone separator.

The size distribution of the grit particles is as follows:

dia. D (μm)	5	10	18	23	34	40	50	70
R%, by mass, of particles with a dia. $< D$	4	9	20	30	50	60	70	80

The cyclone efficiency

$$\eta = \frac{\text{mass of separated particles}}{\text{total mass of particles}}$$

varies with the particle diameter as follows:

D (μm)	2	4.5	6	7.5	8.5	9.5	12	17	24	40	50	70
η (%)	10	25	35	45	55	65	75	85	92	96	98	99

Plot a graph of efficiency and R against the particle diameter. Hence estimate the percentage, by mass, of the particles separated from the flue gas (i.e. overall cyclone efficiency).

Answer 64%.

13 A dusty gas gave the following data in a cyclone separator:

dia. (μm)	2.5	7.5	15	30	60	120
% by mass	10	15	35	20	10	10
cyclone efficiency	20	40	80	90	95	100

Estimate the overall efficiency of the separator.

Answer 69%.

14 A spherical particle, diameter D, travels in a rotation about a vertical axis. Initially the particle is at a radius r_o and the radial velocity is zero (ie. tangential injection into the fluid).

Density of particle ρ_s > density of fluid ρ.

Assuming that the effect of gravity is negligible show that the radius of rotation r, at time t, is given by the equation

$$r = \left[A\exp(-Kt) + B\exp(Kt)\right]\exp(-\tfrac{1}{2}at)$$

$$\text{where } a = \frac{18\mu}{\rho_s D^2},\ n = \frac{(\rho_s - \rho)\Omega^2}{\rho_s},\ K^2 = n + \frac{1}{4}a^2$$

$$\text{and} \quad A = \frac{r_o}{2K}(K - \frac{1}{2}a),\ B = \frac{r_o}{2K}(K + \frac{1}{2}a)$$

The particle density = 2000 kg/m^3, fluid density = 1.2 kg/m^3. Fluid viscosity = 1.8x10^{-5} kg/ms. The angular velocity Ω = 20 rad/s. The particle diameter = 0.1 mm. Estimate the time taken for the particle to attain a radius of $5r_o$.

Answer Approx. 4½ ms.

15 A centrifugal clarifier is used to separate particles from water. The classifier bowl is cylindrical, of diameter 60 cm, and rotates at a steady speed of 500 rev/min. The water occupies 2/3 of the volume of the bowl.

particle diameter, D = 0.01 mm,
particle density = 2500 kg/m^3
viscosity of water = 0.001 kg/ms

Assuming free settling and laminar flow, show that the radial velocity is

$$\frac{dr}{dt} = \left(\frac{\rho_s - \rho}{18\mu}\right) rD^2\Omega^2$$

Hence determine the time taken to separate the particles to the wall of the bowl.

Answer 24s.

Note: *In the remaining problems the Carman-Kozeny equation (C.K.) and Ergun equation (C.K.E.) can be used, unless stated otherwise.*

16 A cylindrical bed, 15 cm diameter, 20 cm depth, contains spheres of diameter 0.5 mm. Air passes through the bed at a rate of 0.02 kg/s. The air density = 8 kg/m^3. The void fraction = 0.30.

Determine the pressure drop across the bed using

(a) the C.K. equation,

(b) the C.K.E. equation.

Comment on the different values obtained.

viscosity of air = 2×10^{-5} kg/ms

Answer (a) 7370, (b) 10260 N/m^2
Difference is due to significant kinetic energy effect.

Note. The C.K. equation is applicable if

$$Re = \frac{\rho U D_p}{(1 - \varepsilon)\mu} < 10$$

In this problem $Re = 40.3$.

17 A tube, diameter 10 cm, is filled with spheres of diameter 1.0 mm, and material density 2500 kg/m^3.

air density = 1.3 kg/m^3

air viscosity = 1.7×10^{-5} kg/ms

Calculate the air flow rate at the point of incipient fluidisation (when $\varepsilon = 0.40$).

Estimate the pressure drop when the air flow rate is

(a) 0.0025,

(b) 0.007 m^3/s.

Answer 6270, 10945 N/m^3.

18 A material, of density 3000 kg/m^3, is packed to form a bed of particles, 30 mm thick, 25 mm diameter. The mass of material in the bed = 0.025 kg. Calculate the voidage fraction.

The pressure drop across the bed is 20 kN/m^2 at an air flow rate of 1.5×10^{-5} m^3/s through the bed.

viscosity of air = 1.8×10^{-5} kg/ms

density = 1.2 kg/m^3.

Assuming that the particles are spherical, and all of the same diameter, calculate the particle diameter using the C.K. equation.

Answer 0.434. 2.5 μm.

19 A bed of particles, diameter 0.3 mm, is contained in a cylindrical vessel of diameter 1.2 m. Density of particle material = 2600 kg/m^3. The bed is fluidised by a gas of density 105 kg/m^3, viscosity 2×10^{-5} kg/ms. At the minimum fluidising conditions the bed height is 3 m, and the superficial gas velocity is 20 mm/s.

Determine the bed porosity at the minimum fluidising conditions. Use the criterion

$$Fr\,Re\left(\frac{\rho_s - \rho}{\rho}\right)\frac{H}{D} > 100$$

to determine whether aggregative fluidisation is likely.

The superficial gas velocity is increased to 0.2 m/s. Determine the bed porosity and height. Calculate the pressure drop at each condition.

Answer 0.32. Yes. 0.54, 4.43 m. 4903, 1791 N/m^2.

20 A bed of particles, diameter 0.1 mm, density 2000 kg/m^3, is fluidised by a liquid of density 900 kg/m^3, viscosity 0.003 kg/ms. The bed, at rest, has a height of 1.4 m. Bed diameter = 1.0 m.

Calculate the liquid flow rate and superficial liquid velocity when fluidisation commences (at ε = 0.40); and when the particles begin to flow out of the bed with the liquid. Determine the pressure drop at the commencement of fluidisation. Calculate the bed height and pressure drop when the voidage increases to 0.60.

Answer 0.015 kg/s, 2.13×10^{-5} m/s. 1.41 kg/s, 0.002 m/s.
9060 N/m^2. 2.1 m, 850 N/m^2.

21 The size distribution of an ore sample is as follows:

R %	0	8	20	40	60	80	90	100
D_p (μm)	400	500	560	620	700	800	850	100

where R = % material, by mass, of diameter < D.

Calculate the surface mean diameter of the sample.

A bed of the ore is contained in a cylindrical vessel of diameter 30 cm. Bed depth = 2 m. It is fluidised by an air stream.

Density of ore = 2000 kg/ms

Air density = 1.2 kg/m^3, viscosity = 1.8×10^{-5} kg/ms

Calculate the air flow rate at which fluidisation begins to occur (based on the S.M.D.), where e = 0.40; and the air flow rate at which the smallest particles will be carried out of the bed.

Answer 0.65 mm, 0.017 m^3/s; 0.172 m^3/s

22 A bed consists of 100 kg of spherical particles, density 1500 kg/m^3, diameter 0.5 mm. The bed is fluidised by a liquid, of density 850 kg/m^3, viscosity 0.002 kg/ms, at a flow rate of 0.04 kg/s. The porosity = 0.55.

The liquid flow rate to achieve incipient fluidisation is 0.02 kg/s. Determine the bed diameter; minimum depth and depth at the operating conditions given.

Answer 0.604 m; 0.438 m, 0.516 m. $\varepsilon_0 = 0.47$.

23 A gas flow through a fluidised bed which contains 20kg catalyst (a catalytic reactor). The catalyst is in the form of a spherical particles, 5 mm diameter, of density 1500 kg/m^3. The gas flow rate is 0.15 m^3/s, corresponding to a superficial gas velocity = 3 U_0.

Gas density = 2 kg/m^3, viscosity = 1×10^{-5} kg/ms

U_0 = superficial gas velocity at incipient fluidisation, at which point the void fraction = 0.40.

Calculate the reactor vessel diameter; the bed porosity and height at the operating conditions.

Answer 0.237 m; 0.82, 1.01 m.

24 The pressure drop across a bed of granular material, h (head) depends upon the superficial fluid velocity U, bed depth L, particle diameter d, container diameter D, bed porosity ε, and fluid properties. Show, by dimensional analysis, that

$$\frac{h}{d} = \phi\left(\frac{\rho dU}{\mu}, \frac{gd}{U^2}\frac{L}{d}, \frac{D}{d}, \varepsilon\right)$$

Briefly discuss the significance of each ratio, or number.

The Leva equation relating these parameters is

$$\Delta p = \frac{2f\dot{m}^2}{g\rho} \cdot \frac{L}{d} \cdot \lambda^{3-n} \cdot \frac{(1-\varepsilon)^{3-n}}{\varepsilon^3}$$

where f is the friction factor, λ is a shape factor defined as the surface area of a particle/surface area of a sphere of equivalent volume, and n is an index.

Using this equation calculate the pressure drop when a gas, of density 1.2 kg/m^3, viscosity 18×10^{-4} kg/ms flow at a rate $\dot{m} = 0.70\, kg/m^2s$ through a bed of alumina, depth 18 m. Density of alumina = 1250 kg/m^3. Mean particle diameter = 8 mm. The mass of the particles = 18 kg. Volume of the packed bed = 0.03 m^3. $\lambda = 1.30$, $f = 1.5$, $n = 1.90$

Answer $\rho du/\mu$ = Reynolds number. $\frac{U^2}{gd}$ = Froude number.

119 N/m^2

25 The Galileo number

$$Ga = \frac{\rho(\rho_s - \rho)gD_p^3}{\mu^2}.$$

The relationship between Ga and the Reynolds number

$$Re_\infty = \rho D_p \frac{v_\infty}{\mu}$$

is as follows:

$Ga = 18Re_\infty$	$Ga < 3.6$
$Ga = 18Re_\infty + 2.7Re_\infty^{1.69}$	$3.6 < Ga < 10^5$
$Ga = 0.33Re_\infty^2$	$Ga > 10^5$

where v_∞ is the terminal settling velocity of the particle.

Using the C.K.E. equation, and assuming that $\varepsilon_o = 0.40$ at incipient fluidisation, derive the relationship

$$Re_o^2 + 61.7Re_o - 0.037Ga = 0$$

where $Re_o = \dfrac{\rho D_p U_o}{\mu}$.

Plot a curve of Re_∞ / Re_o against Ga, over the range $10^{-2} \le Ga \le 10^6$. Comment on the curve obtained.

Answer Since $\dfrac{Re_\infty}{Re_o} = \dfrac{v_\infty}{U_o}$, the range of velocities over which particulate fluidisation can be obtained is much greater in the streamline (laminar) region than in the turbulent region.

26 A bed of particles, 1 mm diameter, density 2250 kg/m^3, is washed in a cylindrical vessel 2 m diameter, by a fluid of density 1040 kg/m^3, viscosity 8×10^{-4} kg/ms.

Show that the mass flow rates at the flooding condition are related by the equation

$$3.244\dot{m}_f - \dot{m}_s = 118.$$

Assume that

$$C_D Re_\infty^2 = \frac{4}{3}Gr^2 \quad \text{where } Re_\infty = v_\infty \frac{D_p}{\nu}$$

$$C_D = \frac{24}{Re_\infty}(1 + 0.15Re_\infty^{0.69})$$

$$Gr^2 = \rho g D_p^3 \frac{(\rho_s - \rho)}{\mu^2}$$

and at flooding (where $\varepsilon = 0.4$)

$$j_{fs} = v_\infty \varepsilon^{2.7}(1 - \varepsilon) = (1 - \varepsilon)j_f - \varepsilon j_s$$

where j = volumetric flux.

27 Show that the height H and superficial velocity U in an *aggregate* fluidised bed are related by the equation

$$U - U_o = U_b\left(\frac{H}{H_o} - 1\right)$$

where the subscript o refers to incipient fluidisation, U_b is the velocity of a bubble relative to the material immediately above it.

The incipient fluidisation velocity in a bed is 5½ cm/s, and the mean bed height is 22 cm. If the velocity is increased to 26 cm/s the bed height increases to 40 cm.

Assuming that the bubbles are of the same diameter d, and $U_b = 0.71\sqrt{gd}$ calculate the bubble diameter, and number of bubbles.

Take $\varepsilon_o = 0.40$.

Answer 12.7 mm; 839 140.

28 A slurry is filtered, and the initial filtration rate is 250 cm^3/s. After a period of 200 s the pressure drop across the filter is 5 kN/m^2, and after 500 s it is 9 kN/m^2. The filtration rate is constant.

Calculate the time taken for the pressure drop to reach a value of 15 kNm^2, and the volume of filtrate collected at this time.

The filtration continues at a constant pressure drop. Calculate the time taken to collect 0.5 m^3 of filtrate.

The equation

$$\frac{dV}{dt} = \frac{A^2 \Delta p}{\mu r v(V + AL/v)}$$

should be used.

V = volume of filtrate

v = volume of cake deposited /m^3 filtrate passed.

Answer 950 s, 0.238 m^3. 1536 s.

29 Particles, of mean diameter 2 mm, are transported pneumatically along a pipe, 15 cm diameter, 20 m length, at a rate of 1.5 kg/s.

density of particle material	= 1100 kg/m^3
density of air	= 1.2 kg/m^3
viscosity of air	= 2×10^{-5} kg/ms
air flow rate	= 0.4 m^3/s

Assume the relationships

$$v_\infty^2 = \frac{4(\rho_s - \rho)gD_p}{3\rho C_D}$$

$$Re_\infty < 2 \qquad C_D = \frac{24}{Re_\infty}$$

$$2 < Re_\infty < 2000 \qquad C_D = \frac{24}{Re_\infty}(1 + 0.15Re_\infty^{0.69})$$

where $Re_\infty = \rho D_p v_\infty/\mu$

$$\Delta p = \rho_s(1 - \varepsilon)v_s^2 + \rho_f \varepsilon U_f^2$$

$$+L\left(\frac{2\rho f U_f^2}{D} + \frac{2f_s(1-\varepsilon)\rho_s v_s^2)}{D}\right)$$

$$\text{where } \varepsilon = 1 - \frac{U_s}{v_s}, f = \frac{0.079}{Re_f^{0.25}}$$

$$v_s = U_f - v_\infty, f_s = \frac{0.05}{v_s}$$

Calculate the terminal velocity v_∞, the voidage fraction ε, and pressure drop.

Answer 6.7 m/s; 0.995; 4870 N/m^2.

30 Particles, of diameter 0.2 mm, density 1600 kg/m^3, are conveyed along a horizontal pipe of diameter 5 cm, length 10 m. The flow rate of the particles is 0.5 kg/s. Air density = 1.2 kg/m^3, viscosity = 1.7×10^5 kg/ms. Settling velocity of particles, v_∞ = 2.0 m/s.

Assuming that

$$U - U_s = \frac{v_\infty}{1.57 + 3.33\sqrt{v_\infty/\rho_s}}$$

$$f = \frac{0.079}{Re^{0.25}}$$

$$\Delta p = \Delta p_o\left(1 + \frac{6130\dot{m}_s}{vU_s^2}\right)$$

where Δp_a is the pressure drop due to air only, calculate the air flow rate and pressure drop.

Answer 0.0026 m^3/s; 5.03 bar.

31 Spheres, of diameter 5 mm, density 50 kg/m^3, are transported pneumatically up a vertical tube of diameter 7 cm, length 12 m.

density of air = 1.2 kg/m^3

viscosity = 1.8×10^{-5} kg/ms

Determine the terminal settling velocity of the particles in still air; and the minimum air velocity required to ensure that moving bed flow does not occur (i.e. the void fraction = 0.4). The C.K.E. equation should be used.

Assume that $C_D = 0.44$.

Calculate the flow rate of material at this minimum condition. Also determine the maximum capacity (of particle transport), using the Yang equations:

$$U_s = (v_f - v_\infty)(1 - \varepsilon)$$

$$(v_f - v_\infty)^2 = 200gD(\varepsilon^{-4.7} - 1)$$

Answer 2.46 m/s. 0.19 m/s. 0.056 kg/s. 0.102 kg/s.

9

Turbulence and mixing: jets, plumes, wakes

Turbulence

Turbulence in fluid motion is often present, and gives rise to the most important and the most complicated kind of fluid motion. It is impossible to obtain a full analysis of many turbulent motions, and, in many situations empirical information is required. Nevertheless much work can be achieved by using mean quantities and methods of estimating the additional effects produced by turbulence.

Turbulent flow involves unsteady, random motion of the fluid in which the velocity at a point (fixed) shows fluctuations which vary with time. Thus the velocity components u, v, w in the x, y, z directions can be expressed as

$$u = \bar{u} + u', v = \bar{v} + v', w = \bar{w} + w'$$

where the components $\bar{u}$, $\bar{v}$, $\bar{w}$ are the mean values (independent of time) and u', v', w' perturbations (varying with time). The intensity of the turbulence can be measured, or represented, by the root mean squares of the perturbations:

$$\tfrac{1}{2}((\overline{u'^2})^{\frac{1}{2}} + (\overline{v'^2})^{\frac{1}{2}}) \text{ in two-dimensional flow}$$

$$\tfrac{1}{3}((\overline{u'^2})^{\frac{1}{2}} + (\overline{v'^2})^{\frac{1}{2}} + (\overline{w'^2})^{\frac{1}{2}}) \text{ in three-dimensional flow.}$$

Large changes in flow resistance, and other properties can be produced by quite small velocity fluctuations. For example, considering an elementary control volume in the form of a box of sides dx, dy, dz the momentum flux through the face $dy\,dz$ is

$$\rho(\bar{u} + u')^2\, dy\, dz = \rho\left(\bar{u}^2 + 2\bar{u}u' + u'^2\right) dy\, dz\ .$$

The mean value of this flux (the component in the x- direction) is

$$\rho(\bar{u}^2 + \overline{u'^2})\, dy\, dz,$$

since $\bar{u}' = 0$. Hence a fluctuation with zero mean produces a mean momentum flux $\rho\overline{u'^2}$ additional to that of the steady velocity momentum flux. These additional momentum fluxes lead to an extra turbulent stress (Reynolds stresses) added on to the viscous stresses. The Navier-Stokes equations can be used by introducing an *eddy viscosity*.

The random motion of fluid elements in turbulent motion can be regarded as analogous to the random motion, on a smaller scale, of molecules in a gas. A *mixing length* can then be postulated, analogous to the mean free path of molecules. The theories developed include the momentum transport theory (due to Prandtl), vorticity transport theory (due to Taylor) and similarity theory (due to Karman): in general leading to semi-empirical equations.

These are discussed in Chap. 6 (worked example 6.8).

Wakes

When a body is placed in a fluid flow a disturbance is created, producing a region downstream of the body known as the *wake*. It spreads in a direction perpendicular to the flow until it blends into the free (or undisturbed) stream.

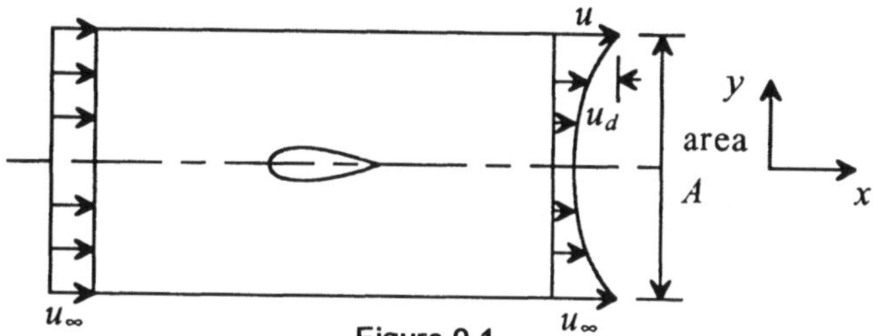

Figure 9.1

Referring to Fig. 9.1, if a *large* control volume is considered around the body,

$$\text{drag force } F = \int \rho u(u_\infty - u)\,dA = \int \rho u_d(u_\infty - u_d)\,dA$$

and the drag coefficient is, per unit width,

$$C_D = \frac{F}{\frac{1}{2}\rho u_\infty^2} = 2\int \frac{u}{u_\infty}\left(1 - \frac{u}{u_\infty}\right)dy = 2\theta$$

where θ = momentum thickness.

In wakes and jets the gradient $\partial u/\partial y$ can be large and therefore the shear stress associated with it. Also, in a wake the transverse dimension (y) is small compared to the distance from the body (x): this is not so in the case of jets. The boundary layer equations can be applied to wakes and jets, downstream of the core, with the boundary conditions $u = u_\infty$ or $u = u_o$ at the edge (Fig. 9.2): the no-slip condition at a surface becomes

$$\frac{\partial u}{\partial y} = 0 \text{ at } y = 0.$$

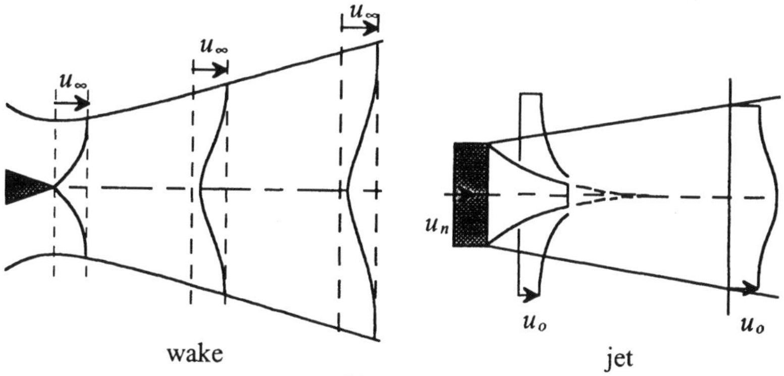

Figure 9.2

For laminar wakes

$$u_d = u_\infty - u \propto \frac{1}{x} \text{ (round) or } x^{-1/2} \text{ (plane)}$$

For turbulent wakes

$$u_d \propto x^{-1/3} \text{ (round) or } x^{-1/2} \text{ (plane).}$$

Jets, plumes and wakes are interactions within a fluid; and in the simplest situations their form is determined by viscous forces. A jet is a momentum and energy source (in a reservoir), and a plume is a buoyancy source; whereas a wake is a momentum and energy deficit downstream of a body in a fluid flow, conditioned by the boundary layer growth on the body surface. In many applications the fluid can be considered incompressible.

Jets can be classified as

(a) plane or axisymmetric (round)

(b) with or without swirl

(c) submerged: a fluid jet entering a reservoir containing the same fluid (e.g. an air whistle)

wall: a fluid jet, impinging on or parallel to a surface

plume: a jet in which the jet fluid density is less than that of the surrounding fluid (e.g. a chimney emission)

confined: a fluid jet which is contained in a fixed space (e.g. an injector, or combustor).

9.1 Statistical approach

Briefly explain what is meant by turbulent flow, and describe some natural examples.

Outline the statistical approach to the description of turbulent motion, using the one-dimensional continuity equation as an illustration.

What is meant by the Reynolds (or turbulent) stresses?

Solution. Turbulent fluid motion is one in which the flow is irregular, and properties of the flow (e.g. pressure, velocity) vary with time and space in a random manner; and statistically distinct average values can be observed.

This kind of motion is very common in most real flows, and often it is found that a fluctuating motion is superimposed on the main (or steady mean) flow. It is characterised by the presence of unsteady eddies or vortices; the determination of the apparent mean stresses by the velocity fluctuations; and the swamping of viscous stresses by the turbulent stresses.

Examples occur in almost every situation where a body moves through an enclosure such as a pipe or turbomachine, or in the earth's atmosphere. The wakes behind the bars of a grid or screen are turbulent, forming homogeneous turbulence downstream of the plane of the screen (e.g. wind tunnel inlet screens). The presence of the bends, branches, section changes in a duct introduce disturbances to the flow which may take some considerable time to decay.

Wall turbulence is turbulent flow which is influenced by the presence of a solid boundary: which may be external (boundary layer) or internal (pipe or duct). For example the flow along a flat plate is influenced by the boundary layer on the plate.

Free turbulence arises when the fluid motion is not directly influenced by a solid boundary. Examples include the wake downstream of a body, and a jet issuing from a nozzle.

The statistical approach considers the equations of motion of a fluid in terms of time average quantities. The velocity at a fixed point varies with time, and is expressed as the sum of an average velocity $\bar{u}$ and a perturbation (or fluctuation u'). Thus

$$u = \bar{u} + u' \text{ (Fig. 9.3).}$$

It should be noted that time averages are used, i.e.

$$\bar{u} = \frac{1}{T}\int_0^T u\,dt$$

where T is a large time interval.

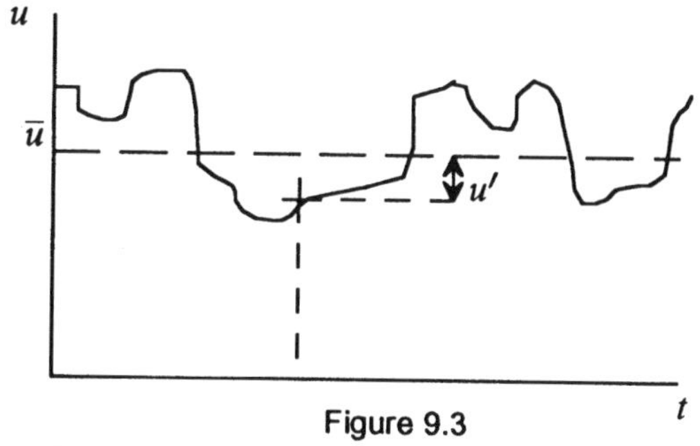

Figure 9.3

The equations of motion are written for instantaneous quantities. The time average of both sides of the equation is then taken, and the equation then simplified so that only the mean quantities remain. The equality, if valid for instantaneous quantities, is also valid *on average* for some period of time.

Consider, for example, the continuity equation

$$\frac{\partial \rho}{\partial t} + \frac{\partial}{\partial x}(\rho u) = 0$$

Taking the time average

$$\overline{\frac{\partial \rho}{\partial t} + \frac{\partial}{\partial x}(\rho u)} = 0$$

and putting $u = \bar{u} + u'$, and using the rules of averages

$$\overline{ab} = \bar{a}\bar{b} + \overline{a'b'}, \qquad \overline{a+b} = \bar{a} + \bar{b}$$

$$\overline{\frac{\partial a}{\partial x}} = \frac{\partial \bar{a}}{\partial x}, \qquad \overline{a'} = \overline{b'} = 0$$

where $a = \bar{a} + a'$, $b = \bar{b} + b'$,

gives $$\overline{\frac{\partial \rho}{\partial t}} + \overline{\frac{\partial}{\partial x}(\rho u)} = 0$$

and $$\overline{\frac{\partial}{\partial x}(\rho u)} = \overline{\frac{\partial}{\partial x}(\rho\bar{u} + \rho u')} = \overline{\frac{\partial}{\partial x}(\rho\bar{u})} + \overline{\frac{\partial}{\partial x}(\rho u')}$$

$$= \frac{\partial}{\partial x}\overline{(\rho\bar{u})} + \frac{\partial}{\partial x}\overline{(\rho u')}$$

Substituting $\rho = \bar{\rho} + \rho'$, and simplifying gives

$$\frac{\partial \bar{\rho}}{\partial t} + \frac{\partial}{\partial x}(\bar{\rho}\bar{u}) + \frac{\partial}{\partial x}\overline{(\rho' u')} = 0$$

In the case of incompressible flow this reduces to

$$\frac{\partial \bar{u}}{\partial x} = 0$$

The momentum equation can be treated in the same manner, although it is more complicated. The result is that an extra term appears in the instantaneous quantities equation, of the form

$$-\frac{\partial}{\partial y}(\rho u' v')$$

This extra term is referred to as the *Reynolds* or *turbulent* stresses; although it is not really a stress but a momentum exchange effect.

9.2 Turbulence measurement

The velocity at a point in a fluid flow varied with time, as follows:

u (m/s)	1.50	1.61	1.70	0.86	0.97	1.21	1.44	1.56	1.22	0.97	0.85
t (m/s)	0	1	2	3	4	5	6	7	8	9	10

Estimate the mean velocity over the period of time shown; and the turbulence intensity.

Solution

$$\bar{u} = \frac{1}{10}\int_0^{10} u\,dt$$

By plotting the velocity, u, against time t, the mean value can then be obtained from a measurement of the area under the curve: the result is

$$\mathbf{u = 1.27\ m/s}$$

Note. The arithmetic mean velocity

$$\Sigma \frac{u}{10} = 1.39 \text{ m/s}$$

The turbulence intensity = $(\overline{u'^2})^{1/2}$:

t (m/s)	0	1	2	3	4	5	6	7	8	9	10
u' (m/s	0.23	0.34	0.43	0.41	0.30	0.06	0.17	0.29	0.05	0.30	0.42
u'^2	0.053	0.116	0.185	0.168	0.090	0.004	0.029	0.084	0.002	0.090	0.176

The mean value can be obtained from a plot of u'^2 against time t giving

$$\overline{u'^2} = 0.087 \text{ m}^2/\text{s}^2$$

and the turbulence intensity = $\sqrt{0.087}$ = **0.295 m/s**.

The *degree* of turbulence is sometimes expressed as the intensity/mean velocity, and in this case is equal to 0.295/1.27 = 0.232 or **23.2%**.

9.3 Reynolds stresses

Show how the Navier-Stokes equations for unsteady flow can be modified in the case of unsteady, turbulent flow. Consider incompressible flow.

Comment on the difficulty of turbulence theory.

Solution. The Navier-Stokes equations for unsteady, incompressible flow are

$$\rho\left(\frac{\partial u}{\partial t} + \frac{\partial u^2}{\partial x} + \frac{\partial (uv)}{\partial y} + \frac{\partial (uw)}{\partial z}\right) = -\frac{\partial p}{\partial x} + \mu \nabla^2 u$$

$$\rho\left(\frac{\partial v}{\partial t} + \frac{\partial (vu)}{\partial x} + \frac{\partial v^2}{\partial y} + \frac{\partial (vw)}{\partial z}\right) = -\frac{\partial p}{\partial y} + \mu \nabla^2 v$$

$$\rho\left(\frac{\partial w}{\partial t} + \frac{\partial (wu)}{\partial x} + \frac{\partial (wv)}{\partial y} + \frac{\partial w^2}{\partial z}\right) = -\frac{\partial p}{\partial z} + \mu \nabla^2 w$$

where u, v, w are the velocity components in the x, y, z directions.

In turbulent flow the velocity components can be expressed in the form

$$u = \bar{u} + u',\ v = \bar{v} + v',\ w = \bar{w} + w'$$

Substituting these into the equations and using the rules of averages,

(a) terms which are linear in the turbulent components,

e.g. $\dfrac{\partial u'}{\partial t}, \dfrac{\partial^2 u'}{\partial x^2}$, are zero.

(b) $\overline{u'} = \overline{v'} = \overline{w'} = 0$

(c) mixed terms (e.g. $\bar{u}.u'$) are zero

gives the result

$$\rho\left(\bar{u}\frac{\partial \bar{u}}{\partial x} + \bar{v}\frac{\partial \bar{u}}{\partial y} + \bar{w}\frac{\partial \bar{u}}{\partial z} + \frac{\partial(\overline{u'^2})}{\partial x} + \frac{\partial(\overline{u'v'})}{\partial y} + \frac{\partial(\overline{u'w'})}{\partial z}\right)$$
$$= -\frac{\partial \bar{p}}{\partial x} + \mu\nabla^2\bar{u}$$

$$\rho\left(\bar{u}\frac{\partial \bar{v}}{\partial x} + \bar{v}\frac{\partial \bar{v}}{\partial y} + \bar{w}\frac{\partial \bar{v}}{\partial z} + \frac{\partial(\overline{u'w'})}{\partial x} + \frac{\partial(\overline{v'w'})}{\partial y} + \frac{\partial(\overline{w'^2})}{\partial z}\right)$$
$$= -\frac{\partial \bar{p}}{dy} + \mu\nabla^2\bar{v}$$

$$\rho\left(\bar{u}\frac{\partial \bar{w}}{\partial x} + \bar{v}\frac{\partial \bar{w}}{\partial y} + \bar{w}\frac{\partial \bar{w}}{\partial z} + \frac{\partial(\overline{u'w'})}{\partial x} + \frac{\partial(\overline{v'w'})}{\partial y} + \frac{\partial(\overline{w'^2})}{\partial z}\right)$$
$$= -\frac{\partial \bar{p}}{\partial z} + \mu\nabla^2\bar{w}$$

These are similar to the original equations with the time-average components $\bar{u}$, $\bar{v}$, $\bar{w}$ replacing u, v, w: the additional expressions can be regarded as stress components or *Reynolds* stresses. These affect the pressure and shear stresses, and

$$\begin{bmatrix} p'_{xx} & \tau'_{xy} & \tau'_{xz} \\ \tau'_{xy} & p'_{yy} & \tau'_{yz} \\ \tau'_{xz} & \tau'_{yz} & p'_{zz} \end{bmatrix} = \begin{bmatrix} \rho\overline{u'^2} & \rho\overline{u'v'} & \rho\overline{u'w'} \\ \rho\overline{u'v'} & \rho\overline{u'^2} & \rho\overline{v'w'} \\ \rho\overline{u'w'} & \rho\overline{v'w'} & \rho\overline{w'^2} \end{bmatrix}$$

Thus the total stresses become

$$p_{xx} = -p + 2\mu\frac{\partial \bar{u}}{\partial x} - \rho\overline{u'^2}, \qquad \tau_{xy} = \mu\left(\frac{\partial \bar{u}}{\partial y} + \frac{\partial \bar{v}}{\partial x}\right) - \rho\overline{u'v'} \quad \text{etc.}$$

The theoretical analysis of turbulent flow is limited in that quantitative solutions still rely on empirical data; and statistical approaches to the equations of motion (as above) lead to more unknowns than equations.

One approach to turbulence theory is to use an *eddy viscosity* and *mixing length*; analogous to fluid viscosity in that the momentum exchange in turbulent flow can be thought of as similar to the molecular momentum transport which gives rise to viscosity is a property of the *fluid*, but turbulence is a characteristic of the fluid *flow*. Thus, the analogy may be satisfactory in simple flows but needs to be used with care. A further point is that consideration of a 'turbulent fluid' with an eddy viscosity may need to take into account the memory effects, making the fluid behave like a viscoelastic type.

9.4 Mixing length theories

Explain what is meant by the Boussinesq mixing coefficient. Discuss how Prandtl's mixing length, Taylor's vorticity transfer, and von Karman's similarity theories relate to the coefficient.

Solution. The Newton equation of viscosity is

$$\tau_L = \mu\frac{\partial u}{\partial y}$$

for laminar (streamline, or viscous) flow. A comparable equation for the Reynolds stresses in turbulent flow can be written (according to Boussinesq) as

$$\tau_t = K_t\frac{\partial \bar{u}}{\partial y}$$

where K_t is termed a *mixing* coefficient. This name is used because a fundamental characteristic of turbulent flow, as compared to laminar flow, in that momentum is transferred normal to the direction of flow at a high rate. Thus mixing is more pronounced and faster. The difference can be seen in the velocity profile across a pipe cross-section, or the mixing of two fluid streams (as in a fuel burner).

The *eddy* viscosity (or apparent viscosity) ε is defined as K_t/ρ, and is then analogous to the kinematic viscosity $\nu = \mu/\rho$. It can then be introduced into the Navier-Stokes equations, for example, in incompressible two-dimensional flow

$$\bar{u}\frac{\partial \bar{u}}{\partial x} + \bar{v}\frac{\partial \bar{u}}{\partial y} = -\frac{1}{\rho}\frac{d\bar{p}}{dx} + \frac{\partial}{\partial y}\left[(\nu + \varepsilon)\frac{\partial \bar{u}}{\partial y}\right]$$

The question now arises 'how can the eddy viscosity be determined, or related to the velocity?' The *mixing length* theory, due to Prandtl, was developed to answer this question.

Consider two-dimensional parallel flow, in the x-direction. Thus $\bar{u}$ is a function of the y coordinate and $\bar{v} = \bar{w} = 0$. Also

$$\tau_{xy} = \tau = -\rho\overline{u'v'} = \rho\varepsilon\frac{d\bar{u}}{dy}$$

and all other stress components are zero.

Suppose that as the fluid flows over a surface the particles coalesce into 'lumps', which cling together and move bodily for a certain length whilst retaining their momentum in the x-direction. Assume that such a lump is displaced from a layer at $y_1 - l$ over a distance l in the transverse (y) direction (Fig. 9.4).

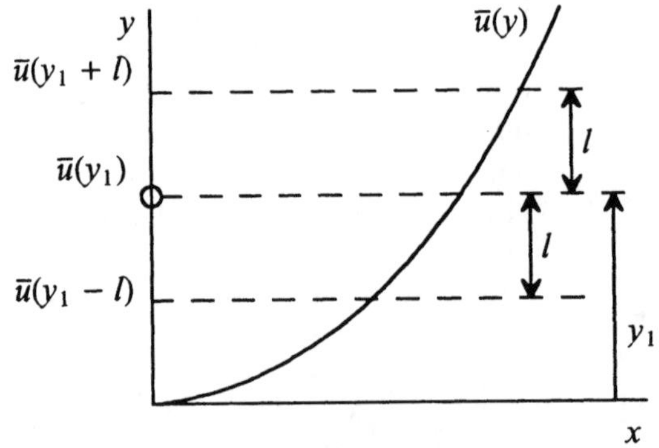

Figure 9.4

$$\Delta u_1 = \bar{u}(y_1) - \bar{u}(y_1 - l)$$

$$= \bar{u}(y_1) - \left[\bar{u}(y_1) - l\left(\frac{d\bar{u}}{dy}\right)_1 + \ldots\right] \text{ using Taylor's theorem}$$

$$= l\left(\frac{d\bar{u}}{dy}\right), \text{ neglecting second-order terms}$$

Similarly $\quad \Delta u_2 = \bar{u}(y + l) - \bar{u}(y_1) = l\left(\frac{d\bar{u}}{dy}\right)_1$

Now regarding the velocity differences as turbulence velocity components at $y = y_1$, the time average of the absolute can be obtained:

$$\overline{|u'|} = \frac{1}{2}(|\Delta u_1| + |\Delta u_2|) = l\left|\left(\frac{d\bar{u}}{dy}\right)_1\right|$$

Hence the mixing length l is the distance covered in the transverse direction, by a lump (or agglomeration) of fluid particles travelling with its original mean velocity so that the difference between its velocity and the new velocity (after displacement) is equal to the mean transverse fluctuation.

Now $\overline{|v'|} = cl\frac{d\bar{u}}{dy}$

and it can be assumed that $\overline{u'v'} = c\overline{|u'|}\,\overline{|v'|}$, where c is a constant.

Hence $\overline{u'v'} = cl^2\left(\frac{d\bar{u}}{dy}\right)^2$

or incorporating the constant into the mixing length

$$\tau = \rho l^2\left(\frac{d\bar{u}}{dy}\right)^2$$

Alternatively, since τ changes sign with $d\bar{u}/dy$

$$\tau = \rho l^2\left|\frac{d\bar{u}}{dy}\right|\frac{d\bar{u}}{dy}$$

This is Prandtl's mixing layer theory, and the result obtained can be expressed in terms of the eddy viscosity:

$$\varepsilon = l^2\left|\frac{d\bar{u}}{dy}\right|$$

The *vorticity transfer* theory (due to Taylor) assumes that the vorticity remained constant during turbulent mixing in contrast to Prandtl's theory of constant momentum in the principal flow direction.

Neglecting viscous forces, and introducing the vorticity

$$\zeta = \frac{1}{2}\left(\frac{\partial u}{\partial y} - \frac{\partial v}{\partial x}\right)$$

into the equation of motion

$$\frac{\partial u}{\partial t} + u\frac{\partial u}{\partial x} + v\frac{\partial u}{\partial y} = -\frac{1}{\rho}\frac{\partial p}{\partial x}$$

gives $\quad \frac{\partial u}{\partial t} + \frac{\partial}{\partial x}\left(\frac{u^2 + v^2}{2}\right) + 2v\zeta = -\frac{1}{\rho}\frac{\partial p}{\partial x}$

Now in fully developed motion,

$$\overline{\frac{\partial}{\partial x}(u^2 + v^2)} \text{ and } \overline{\frac{d\bar{u}}{dy}} = 0$$

Also $\overline{2\zeta} = \frac{d\bar{u}}{dy}$

and the vorticity can be written in terms of a mixing length L:

$$\overline{2\zeta} = \frac{d\bar{u}}{dy} + L\frac{d^2\bar{u}}{dy^2}$$

In this case the mixing length can vary with time, and from one lump to another.

Since $\bar{v} = 0$, $v = v'$ and $-\dfrac{1}{\rho}\dfrac{\partial \bar{p}}{\partial x} = \overline{Lv'}\dfrac{d^2\bar{u}}{dy^2}$

Putting $v' = L_1 \dfrac{d\bar{u}}{dy}$

gives $\overline{Lv'} = -\left|\overline{LL_1}\dfrac{d\bar{u}}{dy}\right|$

and hence

$$-\frac{1}{\rho}\frac{\partial \bar{p}}{\partial x} = l_w^2\left|\frac{d\bar{u}}{dy}\right|\frac{d^2\bar{u}}{dy^2} \qquad \text{where } l_w^2 = \overline{LL_1}$$

$$\frac{\partial \tau}{\partial y} = \frac{\partial \bar{p}}{\partial x} = \rho l_w^2\left|\frac{d\bar{u}}{dy}\right|\frac{d^2\bar{u}}{dy^2}$$

Finally, assuming that l_w is independent of y, integration gives

$$\tau = \frac{1}{2}\rho l_w^2\left|\frac{d\bar{u}}{dy}\right|\frac{d\bar{u}}{dy}$$

Von Karman attempted to determine the relationship between the mixing length and the spatial coordinate by assuming that the turbulent fluctuations were *similar* at every point in the flow. This led to the results

$$l \propto \left(\frac{d\bar{u}}{dy}\right)\Big/\left(\frac{d^2\bar{u}}{dy^2}\right)$$

$$\tau = \rho\lambda^2\left(\frac{d\bar{u}}{dy}\right)^4\Big/\left(\frac{d^2\bar{u}}{dy^2}\right)^2$$

where λ is an empirical constant.

Note. The vorticity transfer theory can only be applied to *free* turbulence (i.e. no wall effects), whereas the Prandtl mixing length theory can be applied to both free turbulence and turbulent flow along a wall.

It may also appear that little has been achieved in replacing an unknown eddy viscosity ε by a further unknown mixing length l. However it has been found simpler to make reasonable assumptions about l than about ε. For example, in pipe flow, a simple assumption is that

$$l = ky \qquad \text{where } k \text{ is a constant}$$

Hence, for $\dfrac{d\bar{u}}{dy} > 0$, $\quad \tau_o = \rho k^2 y^2\left(\dfrac{d\bar{u}}{dy}\right)^2$

or $\quad \dfrac{d\bar{u}}{dy} = \dfrac{u^* k}{y}$

and integrating

$$\bar{u} = \frac{u^*}{k}\ln y + \text{constant}, \text{ where } u^* = \left(\frac{\tau_o}{\rho}\right)^{1/2} = \text{friction velocity}$$

Reference can be made to W.E.6.8.

9.5 Free turbulence: wake

What is meant by free turbulence? Briefly outline how a wake is formed, and the importance of wake studies.

Describe how the half-width and drag coefficient can be obtained for a turbulent wake of a circular cylinder.

Solution. *Free turbulence* is turbulent fluid motion which is not *directly* influenced by a solid boundary, as for example the wake downstream of a body or a jet issuing from a nozzle into a fluid, or shear (mixing) layers.

Consider a sphere over which a fluid flows. At low fluid velocities (or low Reynolds numbers) the streamlines divide as shown in Fig. 9.5. As the velocity increases, the boundary layer on the spherical surface thickens to a situation where it separates from the surface; eddies (vortices) are formed just downstream of the sphere. The separation point moves forward as the velocity increases further (or due to surface roughness), the eddies become larger and unsteady as they are shed from the sphere. They are carried downstream (vortex streets from cylindrical surfaces) forming the wake shown.

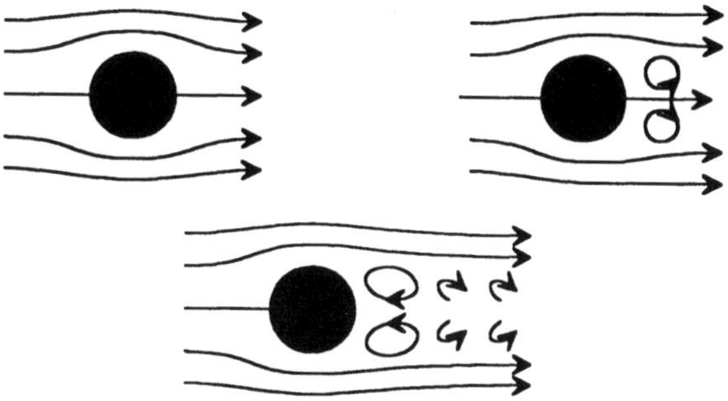

Figure 9.5

The formation of the wake produces a drag force, and an analysis of the wake is required to determine this force. Hence it is necessary to investigate the geometry of the wake, the mean velocity, and the momentum and energy transport during mixing (with the surrounding fluid).

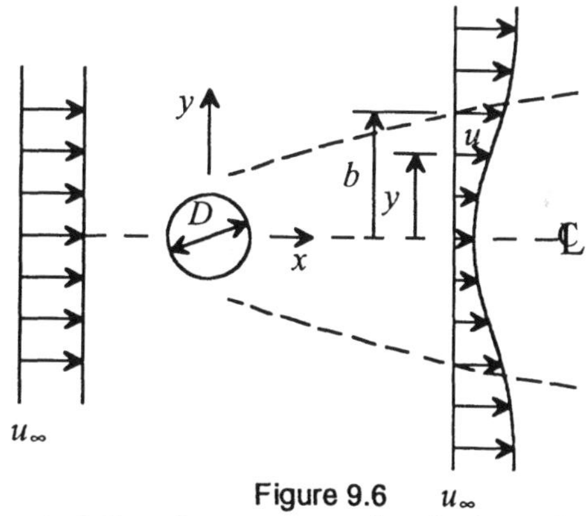

Figure 9.6

It should be noted that the mean motion is dependent on the turbulent eddies, similar to the outer portion of a turbulent boundary layer. Viscous forces do have an effect, but only in the *final* stage of the energy dissipation of the turbulent energy.

Consider a circular cylinder, diameter D, in a fluid stream of undisturbed velocity u_∞ (Fig. 9.6).

At a large distance from the cylinder the momentum equations, assuming that $\bar{v}$ is small, the transverse gradient $\partial/\partial y$ is large compared to the gradient $\partial/\partial x$, and viscous forces are negligible, become

$$u_\infty \frac{d\bar{u}}{dx} = -\frac{\partial}{\partial y}(\overline{u'v'}), \qquad 0 = \frac{\partial \bar{p}}{\partial y} + \rho\frac{\partial}{\partial y}(\overline{v'^2})$$

Assuming similar velocity profiles, i.e.

$$\frac{\bar{u}}{u_\infty} = f\left(\frac{y}{b}\right)$$

and that the Prandtl mixing length is proportional to the wake width b, the momentum integral equation gives

$$b = c_1\sqrt{xDC_D} \quad \text{and} \quad \frac{u_\infty - \bar{u}}{u_\infty} = c_2\left(\frac{x}{DC_D}\right)^{-1/2}\left[1 - \left(\frac{y}{b}\right)^{3/2}\right]^2$$

where c_1, c_2 are constants and C_D is the drag coefficient.

9.6 Wake thickness calculation

An aerofoil, of chord 30 cm, is at zero incidence in a uniform airstream of velocity 30 m/s.

The minimum velocity in the wake, at a station 2.4 m downstream from the trailing edge, is measured as 27 m/s at the centre.

Estimate the wake thickness at this station, assuming a cubic profile in each half wake. The wake and momentum thickness at the trailing edge are 15 mm and 1.5 mm respectively.

Air density = 1.2 kg/m^3.

Also calculate the drag coefficient.

Solution

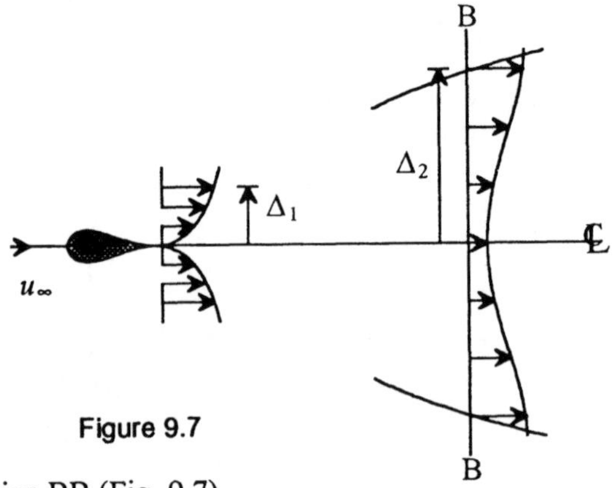

Figure 9.7

At the station BB (Fig. 9.7),

$$u = 27,\ \frac{\partial u}{\partial y} = 0 \text{ at } y = 0 \text{ and } u = 30,\ \frac{\partial u}{\partial y} = 0 \text{ at } y = \Delta$$

Assuming (as stated) that

$$\frac{u}{u_\infty} = a\left(\frac{y}{\Delta}\right)^3 + b\left(\frac{y}{\Delta}\right)^2 + c\left(\frac{y}{\Delta}\right) + d$$

and substituting

$$0.9 = d,\ 0 = c,\ 1.0 = a + b + c + d,\ 0 = 3a + 2b + c$$

Hence $a = -0.2$, $b = 0.3$, $c = 0$, $d = 0.9$

The momentum thickness is

$$\theta = \Delta\int_0^1 \frac{u}{u_\infty}\left(1 - \frac{u}{u_\infty}\right)d\eta \quad \text{where } \eta = \frac{y}{\Delta}$$

$$= \Delta\int_0^1(-0.2\eta^3 + 0.3\eta^2 + 0.9)(1 + 0.2\eta^3 + 0.3\eta^2 - 0.9)\,d\eta$$

$$= 0.046\Delta$$

Now $\dfrac{\theta_2}{\theta_1} = \dfrac{I_1}{I_2} = \dfrac{\Delta_2}{\Delta_1}$ where $I = \int_0^1 u(1 - u)\,dy = \dfrac{\theta}{\Delta}$

Hence $I_1 = \dfrac{1.3}{13} = \dfrac{1}{10}$, $I_2 = 0.046$, $\dfrac{\Delta_2}{\Delta_1} = \dfrac{0.10}{0.046} = 2.174$

giving $\Delta_2 = 2.174(15) = \mathbf{32.6\ mm}$

$$\text{The drag} = 2\rho b\int_0^\Delta u(u_\infty - u)\,dy = 2\rho u_\infty^2\theta \text{ per unit width (span)}$$

$$= 2\rho(30)^2(0.046)(0.0326) = 3.24 \text{ N/m width}$$

and the drag coefficient

$$= \frac{3.24}{\frac{1}{2}\rho u_\infty^2 \times \text{chord}} = \frac{3.24}{162} = \mathbf{0.020}$$

9.7 Mixing length in wakes and jets

Show how the mixing length theory can be applied to free turbulence in wakes and jets to obtain relationships for the width and fluid velocity in terms of the axial length x.

Solution. Free turbulence refers to the situation where there is no surface present to affect the flow pattern (as distinct from wall turbulence). The static pressure, p_∞, is constant and the flow equations become

$$u\frac{\partial u}{\partial x} + v\frac{\partial u}{\partial y} = \frac{1}{\rho}\frac{\partial \tau}{\partial y} \qquad \text{(momentum)}$$

and $$\frac{\partial u}{\partial x} + \frac{\partial v}{\partial y} = 0 \qquad \text{(continuity)}$$

where $\tau = \mu\dfrac{\partial u}{\partial y} - \rho\overline{u'v'} = (\mu + \varepsilon)\dfrac{\partial u}{\partial y}$

At a section XX (Fig. 9.8), the mixing length is proportional to the width b. Also the rate at which the width increases, db/dx, will be dependent upon the turbulence level, or we can put

$$\frac{db}{dx} = \frac{(\overline{v'^2})^{1/2}}{u_{\max}}$$

Now the mixing length theories put

$$(\overline{v'^2})^{1/2} = cl\frac{\partial \bar{u}}{\partial y}$$

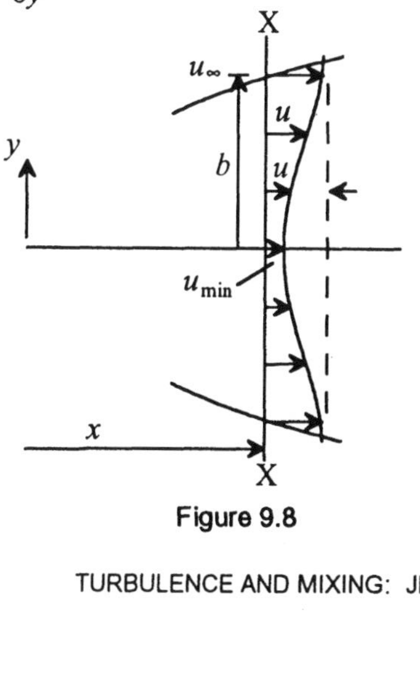

Figure 9.8

and hence

$$\frac{db}{dx} = \frac{cl(\partial\bar{u}/\partial y)}{u_{max}}$$

Also $b(\partial\bar{u}/\partial y)$ is proportional to $u_{max} - u_{min}$, so that

$$\frac{db}{dx} \propto \left(1 - \frac{u_{min}}{u_{max}}\right)$$

In the case of a *wake*, $u_{max} = u_\infty$ (Fig. 9.8)

and $$\frac{db}{dx} \propto \left(1 - \frac{u_{min}}{u_\infty}\right)$$

Introducing the drag coefficient

$$C_D = 2\int_0^b \frac{u}{u_\infty}\left(1 - \frac{u}{u_\infty}\right)dy \propto b\left(1 - \frac{u_{min}}{u_\infty}\right)$$

Hence $b\dfrac{db}{dx} \propto C_D$ or $b \propto (C_D x)^{1/2}$ and $1 - \dfrac{u_{min}}{u_\infty} \propto \sqrt{\dfrac{C_D}{x}}$

In the case of a *jet* emerging into stationary fluid, $u_{min} = 0$.

Thus $\dfrac{db}{dx}$ = constant.

It follows that

$$\mathbf{b} \propto \mathbf{x}, \quad \mathbf{u}_{max} \propto \mathbf{x}^{-1/2} \qquad \text{(plane jet)}$$

$$\mathbf{b} \propto \mathbf{x}, \quad \mathbf{u}_{max} \propto \mathbf{x}^{-1} \qquad \text{(circular jet)}$$

Note. In the case of a circular wake, the width is proportional to $x^{1/3}$, and $(u_{min} - u_\infty)$ to $x^{-1/3}$. It should also be pointed out that these results are not valid in the wake close to the body, or in a jet close to the nozzle.

9.8 Axisymmetric jet

> An axisymmetric jet issues from a nozzle into a reservoir of stagnant fluid; the jet and reservoir fluids have the same physical properties.
>
> Outline the manner in which the jet develops, and discuss its characteristics. Discuss the effect of swirl.

Solution. The fluid jet leaves the nozzle at a mean velocity u_o and is *submerged* in the reservoir fluid. There are no *external* forces involved in the development of the jet, and to begin with the jet is laminar changing to turbulent flow at some critical Reynolds number

$$Re_c = \frac{2u_o r_o}{\nu}$$

In the case of an axisymmetric (round) jet Re_c = approximately 1000, but as usual the value is very dependent on the nature of any entry disturbances. The initial region $x \leq x_1$ consists of a potential (inviscid) core surrounded by a turbulent shear layer (or mixing layer), which is bounded by fluid of mean velocity u_s. x_1 is of the order of $8\text{-}10r_o$.

The turbulent eddies in the mixing layer then begin to dominate the core flow, which begins to vanish. In this region $x_1 < x < x_2$ the potential core disappears, and the mean velocity distribution is dissimilar. Approximately $x_2 = 16r_o$.

Fully developed flow is realised from this station, and the velocity profiles become similar.

It should be noted that the surface between the jet and reservoir fluids is not a smooth curve as shown in Fig. 9.9, although it is often reasonably defined. There are always unsteady fluctuations associated with turbulent flow (or turbulence in the fluid), and the boundary shown should be regarded as a time mean surface.

The *axial momentum* of the jet is constant (since no external forces are involved), and is independent of the manner in which the jet disperses. The continuity (conservation of mass) also holds, and these two conditions show that fluid must be *entrained* into the jet from the surroundings.

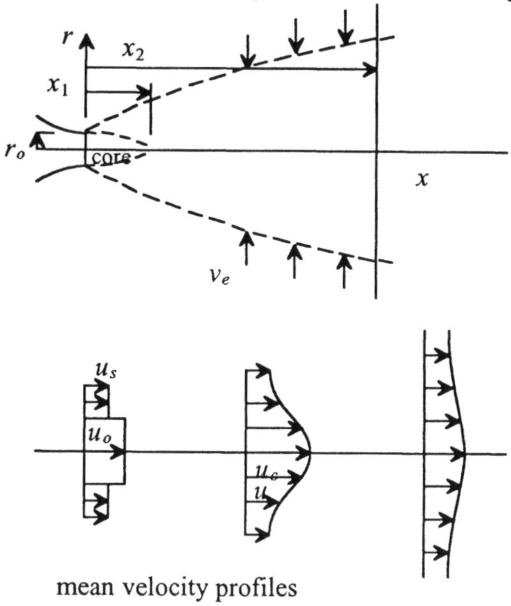

Figure 9.9

Hence $u_o^2 A_o = \int u^2 \, dA$ (momentum)

and $u_o A_o + 2 v_e A_s = \int u \, dA$ (continuity)

For a round jet

centre-line velocity $u_c \propto \dfrac{u_o r_o}{x}$

width $b \propto x$

velocity $u \propto \exp\left(\dfrac{r}{x}\right)^2$

[For a plane jet $b \propto x$, and $u_c \propto x^{-1/2}$]

In some situations there may be chemical species or a fluid property (such as heat) carried into the reservoir by the jet, and, in general, follows similar relationships. Also the jet and reservoir fluid densities may differ appreciably and the jet geometry will then be affected by buoyancy forces. Examples of this type of jet are jets of combustion products from a burner, the exhaust jet of hot gases into the surrounding atmosphere, and the jet of hot gases issuing from a stack (chimney).

Axisymmetric (round) jets are often subject to rotation (or swirl) about the x-axis, as, for example, in jet engine exhausts and fuel burners. The degree of swirl is measured by means of a *swirl number* S = angular momentum of the jet/ ($r_o \times$ axial momentum of jet) i.e. $$S = \frac{\int r^2 uw\,dr}{r_o \int r(u^2 - \frac{1}{2}w^2)\,dr}$$

where w = the tangential component of the velocity.

The effect of swirl is to make u_c decrease more rapidly, the jet width b to increase more rapidly, and the entrained volume of reservoir fluid to increase more rapidly along the x-axis, than in a jet without swirl. The high increase in the mixing rate of the jet and reservoir fluids is an important factor in the design of high intensity fuel burners, giving short, intense flames.

9.9 Axisymmetric jet

A submerged axisymmetric jet of fluid issues from a nozzle, radius r_o, into a stagnant fluid having the same properties as the jet fluid.

At a large distance from the nozzle the velocity distribution across the jet is given by the equation

$$\frac{u}{u_c} = \exp\left[-k\left(\frac{r}{x}\right)^2\right] \qquad \text{(as shown in Fig. 9.10)}$$

Derive expressions for u_c, radius b at which $u = u_c/2$, and the volumetric flow rate Q in terms of u_o, r_o, k and x.

The entrainment velocity v_e is defined by the equation

$$5\pi v_e b = \frac{dQ}{dx}$$

Show that $v_e = \dfrac{0.48u_c}{\sqrt{k}}$.

Solution. The continuity and momentum equations can be applied to the control volume CCXX shown: the continuity equation involves the volume of entrained fluid, and in the absence of any external forces the axial momentum is constant. Also the density of the jet and reservoir (entrained) fluids are equal.

Hence $u_o A_o + 2v_e A_s = \int u\,dA$ (continuity)

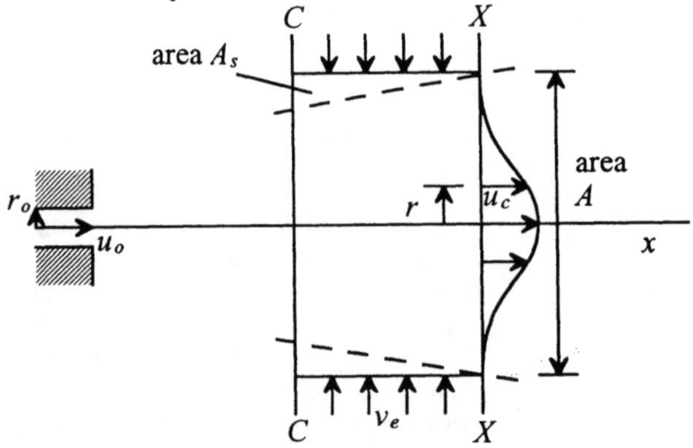

Figure 9.10

$$u_o^2 A_o = \int u^2\,dA \qquad \text{(momentum)}$$

Now $\dfrac{u}{u_c} = \exp\left[-k\left(\dfrac{r}{x}\right)^2\right] = f(x)$ say and $u_o^2 A_o = \int_0^\infty u_m^2 f^2 \, 2\pi r \, dr = 2\pi u_c^2 \int_0^\infty r f^2 \, dr$

Let $\frac{r}{x} = t, z = -2kt^2$

Then $dz = -4kt\,dt = \frac{-4kt\,dr}{x}$

$$u_o^2 A_o = 2\pi u_c^2 \int_0^\infty r \exp\left[-2k\left(\frac{r}{x}\right)^2\right] dr = 2\pi u_c^2 \int tx \exp(-z) \frac{x\,dz}{-4kt}$$

$$= -\frac{\pi u_c^2 x^2}{2k} \int \exp(-z)\,dz$$

$$\pi t_o^2 u_o^2 = -\frac{\pi u_c^2 x^2}{2k} \quad \text{giving} \quad u_c = \frac{u_o r_o}{x}\sqrt{2k}$$

b = radius at which the local velocity $u = \frac{1}{2}u_c$. Hence

$$\frac{1}{2} = \exp\left[-k\left(\frac{b}{x}\right)^2\right], \quad -0.693 = -k\left(\frac{b}{x}\right)^2$$

and $b = x\sqrt{\frac{0.693}{k}}$ or $b = \frac{0.833x}{\sqrt{k}}$

The volumetric flow rate is

$$Q = 2\pi \int_0^\infty ur\,dr = 2\pi \int_0^\infty r u_c \exp\left[-k\left(\frac{r}{x}\right)^2\right] dr$$

$$= 2\pi u_c \int tx \exp\left(\frac{1}{2}z\right) \frac{x\,dz}{-4kt} = \frac{\pi u_c x^2}{2k} \int \exp\left(\frac{1}{2}z\right) dz$$

$$= -\frac{\pi u_c x^2}{2k}\left[2\exp\left(\frac{1}{2}z\right)\right]_0^\infty$$

and $Q = \frac{\pi u_c x^2}{k}$ or $Q = \frac{4.443 x u_o r_o}{\sqrt{k}}$

The entrainment velocity is given by the equation

$$v_e = \frac{1}{5\pi b}\frac{dQ}{dx} = \frac{1}{5\pi}\left(\frac{\sqrt{k}}{0.833x}\right)\left(\frac{2\pi u_c x}{k}\right) = 0.48\frac{u_c}{\sqrt{k}}$$

Note. The equations quoted hold for both laminar and turbulent flow in regions where $x > 10r_o$. The laminar flow persists up to a Reynolds number

$$Re_o = \frac{2u_o r_o}{\nu}$$

of approximately 1000, and becomes fully turbulent at $Re_o > 3000$.

9.10 Coaxial and perpendicular

> Discuss the behaviour of a fluid jet issuing into
> (a) fluid flowing in the same direction,
> (b) fluid flowing in a direction perpendicular to the jet fluid direction
> (c) a confined fluid flowing in the same direction.

Solution. (a) The situation in a compound or coaxial jet is illustrated in Fig. 9.11. The expansion of the jet is clearly dependent on the ratio of the velocities u_s/u_o: as this ratio increases the jet weakens, and becomes a wake when $u_s > u_o$. Thus

$$b = xf\left(\frac{u_s}{u_o}\right)$$

compared to $b \propto x$ in a stagnant reservoir fluid.

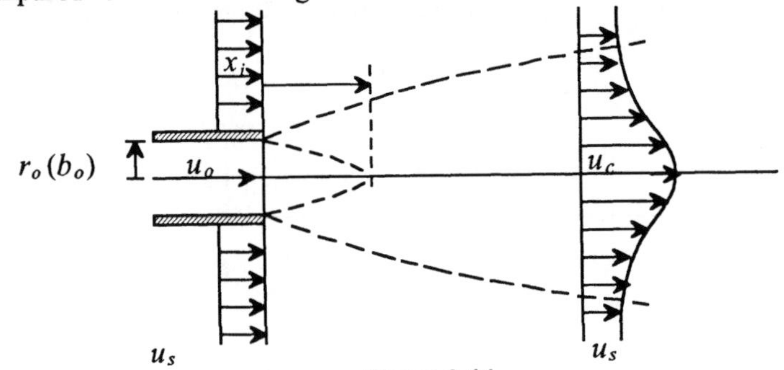

Figure 9.11

Note. Experimental data, for $0 < u_s/u_o < 0.5$, is shown in the following table. b is the width (or radius) of the jet at which

$$u = \tfrac{1}{2}(u_c + u_s).$$

	plane jet	round jet
x_i	$\left(12 + \dfrac{40u_s}{u_o}\right)x$	$\left(10 + \dfrac{24u_s}{u_o}\right)r_o$
$u_c - u_s$	$3.5\sqrt{\dfrac{b_o}{x}}\,\sqrt{u_o(u_o - u_s)}$	$12\dfrac{r_o}{x}\sqrt{u_o(u_o - u_s)}$
$\dfrac{u - u_s}{u_c - u_s}$	$\exp\left[-0.69\left(\dfrac{y}{b}\right)^2\right]$	$\exp\left[-0.69\left(\dfrac{r}{b}\right)^2\right]$

(b) If the reservoir fluid flows across the jet fluid direction the situation becomes rather complicated and, in fact, the analysis is somewhat limited. The jet geometry is again dependent on the velocity ratio $= u_s/u_o$.

The core length decreases as this ratio decreases. The flow beyond the core becomes irrotational and vortices are created in the cross-flow wake behind the jet. Pressure forces deform the circular cross-section of the jet, and a vortex pair is formed in the jet cross-section. The situation is illustrated in Fig. 9.12.

In general the jet profile is given by an equation of the form

$$\frac{y}{r_o} \propto \left(\frac{u_o}{u_s}\right)^m \left(\frac{x}{r}\right)^n$$

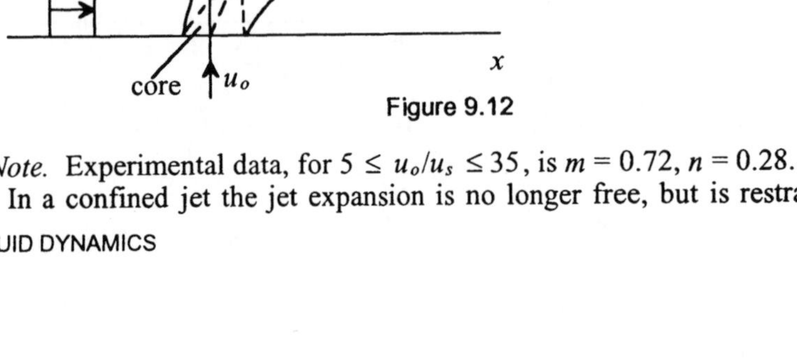

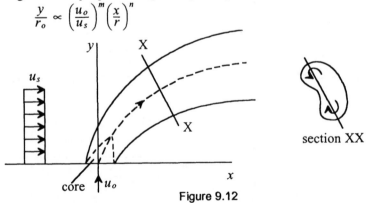

Figure 9.12

Note. Experimental data, for $5 \le u_o/u_s \le 35$, is $m = 0.72$, $n = 0.28$.

In a confined jet the jet expansion is no longer free, but is restrained by the surface. The effect of the wall is to compensate for the prevention of free jet expansion by promoting recirculation, as shown in Fig. 9.13.

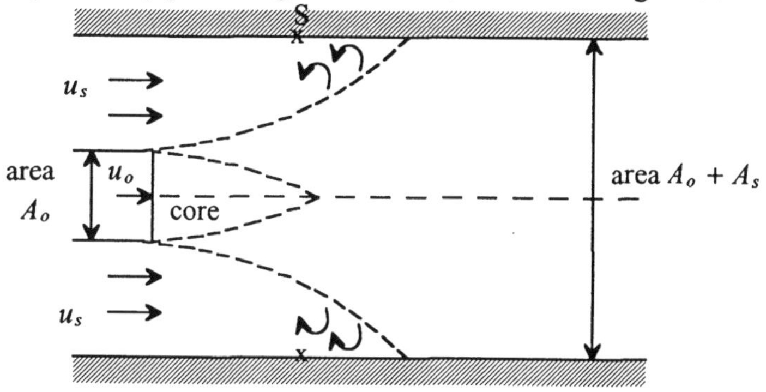

Figure 9.13

Thus, a laminar jet entering a laminar stream becomes turbulent (as the potential core vanishes) at x = approximately 10 r_o and the surrounding fluid stagnates at some point S on the wall.

If u is the mean velocity of the mixture,

$$A_o u_o + A_s u_s = (A_o + A_s)u \qquad \text{(continuity)}$$

and $$A_o u_o^2 + A_s u_s^2 = (A_o + A_s)\left(\frac{A_o u_o + A_s u_s}{A_o + A_s}\right)^2 + (A_o + A_s)\frac{\Delta p}{\rho}$$

Hence $$\frac{\Delta p}{\rho} = \frac{A_o u_o^2 + A_s u_s^2}{A_o + A_s} - \left(\frac{A_o u_o + A_s u_s}{A_o + A_s}\right)^2$$

$$= \frac{(A_o u_o^2 + A_s u_s^2)(A_o + A_s) - (A_o u_o + A_s u_s)^2}{(A_o + A_s)^2}$$

$$= \frac{A_o A_s)u_s - u_o)^2}{(A_o + A_s)^2}$$

There is therefore a pressure *increase* between the station where the two streams are mixed, and the nozzle exit provided $u_o \neq u_s$. Also, this pressure rise will stagnate the surrounding fluid when

$$\Delta p > \frac{1}{2}\rho u_s^2 \quad \text{or} \quad \frac{u_o}{u_s} > \frac{A_o^2 + A_s^2}{2A_o A_s}$$

9.11 Plumes

What is meant by a plume? A stack (chimney) discharges flue gases into the atmosphere. Briefly outline the types of plume that can arise, and particularly in the presence of a cross wind.

A stack, of height 100 m, discharges flue gas (density 0.7 kg/m^3) at a velocity v_s = 20 m/s. Stack diameter = 3 m. Calculate the effective stack height when the cross-wind velocity U is (a) 5 m/s, (b) 10 m/s. Air density = 1.2 kg/m^3.

The Briggs formulae should be used:

$$z_\infty = \frac{1.6F^{1/3}(3.5x_\infty)^{2/3}}{U}$$

where $$F = \frac{1}{4}gv_s D^2\left(1 - \frac{\rho_s}{\rho_a}\right)$$

$$x_\infty = 14F^{5/8} \quad (F < 55) \qquad = 34F^{0.4} \quad (F > 55)$$

Solution. A plume is a vertical jet of fluid which is produced by a steady source of buoyancy, i.e. a difference in the densities of the jet and surrounding fluids $(\rho_a - \rho_s)g$.

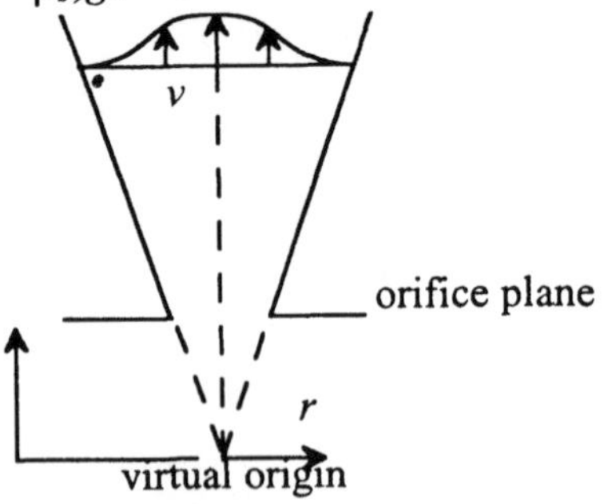

Figure 9.14

An axisymmetric plume (Fig. 9.14), with a constant buoyancy flux B (in the z-direction), is subject to an increase in momentum flux equal to the buoyancy force.

Hence vBr^2 = constant and $d(v^2r^2) \propto Br^2\,dz$

If viscous effects are negligible, $r \propto z$ and it follows that

$$v \propto z^{-1/3}, \quad B \propto z^{-5/3}.$$

A plume slows down less rapidly than a jet (for which $v \propto z^{-1}$), because of the continuous effect of the buoyancy force; and is diluted more rapidly due to the different fluid densities.

The presence of a *cross-wind* can affect the plume shape considerably. The various types of plume are shown in Fig. 9.15.

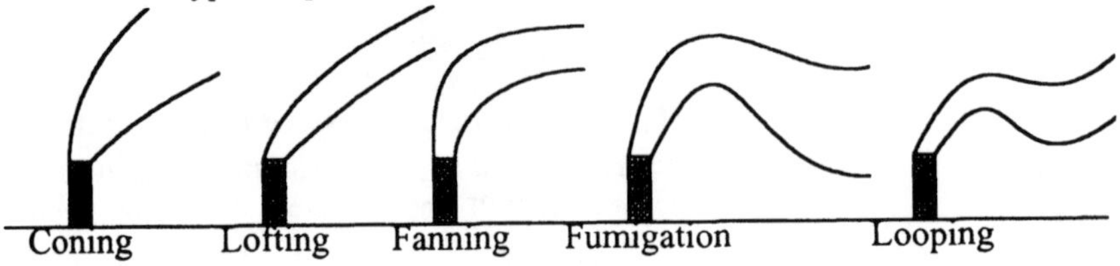

Figure 9.15

In the Fanning type the plume spreads in a horizontal fan. The Fumigation type arises when an inversion above the plume promotes downward mixing. The Looping type occurs when the vertical mixing is pronounced, due to atmospheric thermal gradients. The Coning type is probably the commonest form of plume, and if downward spreading is prevented by a low level inversion it becomes a Lofting plume.

The plume type is important in the study of pollution, such as the deposition of grit, dust, and pollutant gases (CO_2, SO_2, NO_x etc). The effective stack height $(H + z_\infty)$ is used in the estimation of the horizontal travel of pollutants.

$$F = \frac{1}{4}gv_sD^2\left(1 - \frac{\rho_s}{\rho_a}\right) = \frac{1}{4}(9.81)(20)(3)^2\left(1 - \frac{0.7}{1.2}\right) = 184$$

$$x_\infty = 34F^{0.4} = 274 \text{ m}$$

$$z_\infty = \frac{1.6(184)^{1/3}(3.5 \times 274)^{2/3}}{U} = \frac{883.5}{U} \text{ m}$$

9.12 Ejector

Outline the construction and application of an ejector, indicating the problems involved in the analysis of the device.

A jet pump (ejector) is shown in Fig. 9.16. Show that the efficiency $\frac{p_{od} - p_{os}}{p_{on} - p_{os}}$ is given by the equation

$$\eta = \frac{2R(1 - R)(1 - R - \alpha R)^2 + (1 - R)^2[(1 + \alpha)^2 R^2 - 1]}{(1 - R)^2 - (\alpha R)^2}$$

where $R = \frac{A_n}{A_m}$, $\alpha = \frac{Q_s}{Q_n}$

Assume that the fluids are of the same density.

Solution

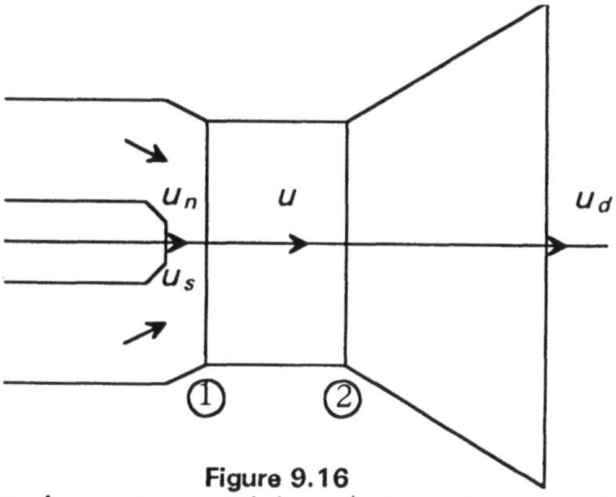

Figure 9.16

An ejector (or jet pump, or injector) is a device which uses a high velocity jet of fluid to entrain another fluid, and discharge the mixture of the fluids. It is widely used in engineering practice, examples including vacuum pumps in steam condensers, fuel burners, aerated gas burners, mixers, boiler draught inducers.

An important application is in the use of gaseous fuels; as a device to produce sufficient pressure to drive a fuel-air mixture through a burner port, and as a means of controlling the fuel:air ratio.

The analysis of the device is difficult because the *mixing* of two fluid streams is a complex situation: the process is often turbulent and ill-defined. In particular the mixing length, or length of tube required to obtain complete mixing of the fluids, is difficult to calculate; and semi-empirical data is usually required.

The ejector is a simple device, has no moving parts, has low initial and maintenance costs, and relatively small size.

In the following analysis the subscripts n, s, m, d refer to the nozzle, secondary (suction) fluids, mixture of fluids, and diffuser exit respectively.

Assuming one-directional flow, incompressible fluids, and neglecting frictional effects the continuity and momentum equations give:

$$A_n u_n + A_s u_s = A_m u_m \qquad \text{(continuity)}$$

$$(p_1 - p_2)A_m = \rho u_m^2 A_m - \rho(A_n u_n^2 + A_s u_s^2) \qquad \text{(momentum)}$$

The fluids are of equal density, and $\rho = \rho_n = \rho_s = \rho_m$.
Introducing the parameters

$$\alpha = \frac{Q_s}{Q_n} = \frac{u_s A_s}{u_n A_n} \quad \text{and} \quad R = \frac{A_n}{A_m}$$

gives $$\frac{p_2 - p_1}{\rho} = \frac{A_n u_n^2 + A_s u_s^2}{A_m} - u_m^2 = R u_n^2 + \left(\frac{A_s}{A_m}\right) u_s^2 - u_m^2$$

and $$u_m = \frac{A_n u_n + A_s u_s}{A_m} = R u_n + \left(\frac{A_s}{A_m}\right) u_s$$

Assuming that $A_s = A_m - A_n$, $A_s/A_m = 1 - R$ and

$$\begin{aligned}\frac{p_2 - p_1}{\rho} &= R u_n^2 + (1 - R) u_s^2 - [R u_n + (1 - R) u_s]^2 \\ &= R(1 - R) u_n^2 - 2R(1 - R) u_n u_s - R(1 - R) u_s^2 \\ &= R(1 - R)(u_n - u_s)^2 = \frac{R u_n^2 (1 - R - \alpha R)^2}{(1 - R)}\end{aligned}$$

since $$\alpha = \frac{u_s}{u_n}\left(\frac{1 - R}{R}\right)$$

The efficiency η is given by

$$\eta = \frac{h_{od} - hos}{h_{on} - h_{os}}, \qquad \text{where } h_o = \text{stagnation head} = \frac{p}{\rho g} + \frac{u^2}{2g}$$

Thus $h_{on} = \dfrac{p_1}{\rho g} + \dfrac{u_n^2}{2g}$, $h_{os} = \dfrac{p_1}{\rho g} + \dfrac{u_s^2}{2g}$, $h_{od} = \dfrac{p_2}{\rho g} + \dfrac{u_m^2}{2g}$

Substituting

$$\begin{aligned}\eta &= \left(\frac{p_2 - p_1}{\rho g} + \frac{u_m^2}{2g} - \frac{u_s^2}{2g}\right) \Big/ \left(\frac{u_n^2 - u_s^2}{2g}\right) \\ &= \frac{2R(1 - R)(u_n - u_s)^2 + (u_m^2 - u_n^2)}{u_n^2 - u_s^2}\end{aligned}$$

Now $u_m = R u_n + (1 - R) u_s$, $u_n = \left(\dfrac{1 - R}{\alpha R}\right) u_s$

or $$u_s = \left(\frac{\alpha R}{1 - R}\right) u_n, \quad \frac{u_m}{u_n} = R + (1 - R)\frac{u_s}{u_n} = (1 + \alpha) R$$

and substituting gives

$$\eta = \frac{2R(1 - R)\left(1 - \frac{\alpha R}{1 - R}\right)^2 + (1 + \alpha)^2 R^2 - 1}{1 - \left(\frac{\alpha R}{1 - R}\right)^2}$$

or $$\eta = \frac{2R(1 - R)(1 - R - \alpha R)^2 + (1 - R)^2[(1 + \alpha)^2 R^2 - 1]}{(1 - R)^2 - (\alpha R)^2}$$

Note. Since $u_n >> u_s$, and $A_n/A_m << 1$, $p_2 - p_1 > 0$ and there is a pressure rise in the mixing chamber between sections 1 and 2. The efficiency is then a measure of the fraction of the pressure energy available $(p_{on} - p_{os})$ converted to pressure energy of the mixture $(p_{od} - p_{os})$. Also, in the diffuser

$$h_{od} = \frac{p_2}{\rho g} + \frac{u_m^2}{2g} = \frac{p_d}{\rho g} + \frac{u_d^2}{2g}$$

Sometimes the efficiency is based on the static pressure differences rather than stagnation pressures.

The ratio of the flow rates,

$$\frac{Q_s}{Q_n} = \alpha$$

is often referred to as the *augmentation ratio.*

The effect of friction may be appreciable, particularly in some geometries where rapid changes of section occur: they can be allowed for by the use of the well-known k factors. Thus the friction pressure drop in the mixing chamber can be expressed as

$$\Delta p = k\left(\tfrac{1}{2}\rho u_m^2\right)$$

The inlet geometry can be significant in the approach of the fluids to the mixing chamber, such as whether the fluid streams are concentric, or cross-flow (the secondary stream drawn in via a perpendicular passage).

9.13 Mixing in

Outline the Thring-Newby approach to the problem of mixing of jets, and the determination of the mixing length in a chamber.

Briefly discuss mixing index, and the Craya-Curtet number. Indicate the application of these parameters in the aerodynamics of a confined jet.

Solution. Mixing between two fluids leaving concentric tubes and mixing in an enclosure tube occurs frequently in engineering practice, and the mixing length L to give complete mixing of the fluids is often required.

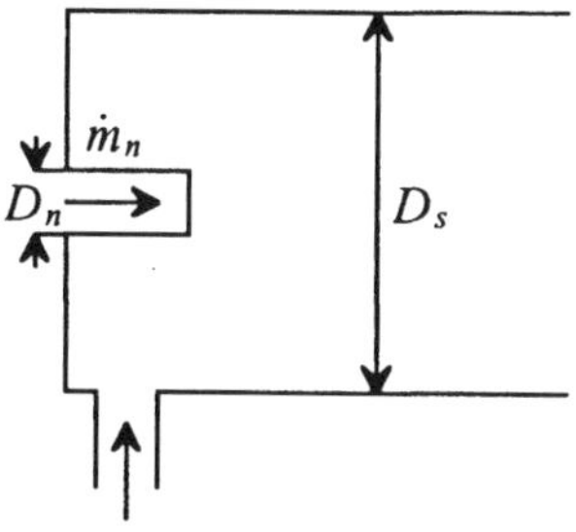

Figure 9.17

One approach is to assume a hypothetical enclosed single jet which has the same mixing length as the double concentric jet. Thring and Newby showed that the axial concentration of the nozzle fluid (isothermal constant density jet) C follows the simple equation

$$\frac{1}{C} \propto \frac{L}{D_n}$$

The hypothetical single jet assumed is of diameter D_n' given by

$$D_n' = \frac{2\dot{m}_n}{\sqrt{\pi\rho M}}, \quad \text{where } M = \text{total momentum} = \dot{m}_n u_n + \dot{m}_s u_s$$

Now the length L at which the nozzle fluid flow $\dot{m}_n$ (Fig. 9.17) entrains $R\dot{m}_n$ of secondary fluid is given by the equation

$$\frac{1}{C} = k\left(\frac{L}{D_n'}\right), \quad \text{where } C = 1/(1 + R), \text{ and } k \text{ is a constant.}$$

Substituting for D_n' gives

$$1 + R = kL\frac{\sqrt{\pi\rho M}}{2\dot{m}_n}$$

or $$L = 2(1 + R)\dot{m}_n\frac{\sqrt{\pi\rho M}}{k} = \frac{k'(1 + R)\dot{m}_n}{\sqrt{\rho M}} \text{ say}$$

The constant k' can be obtained from experimental data. It should be noted, however, that the geometry of the system (which is a function of the ratio $D_n/(D_s - D_n)$) is an important factor; the ratio of the fluid flow rates $\dot{m}_s/\dot{m}_n$ is of importance; and the intensity of mixing is relevant, in the form of a parameter

$$N = \frac{\dot{m}_s}{R\dot{m}_n}$$

which allows for excess secondary fluid over the ideal ratio of the flow rates.

Another approach is that of a *mixing correlation*. In this the mixing process is described by a mixing index, and uses a modified Prandtl mixing length which can take swirl into account. The mixing index is defined as

$$M.I. = 1 - \frac{I}{I_o}$$

where $I = \int |c - c_\infty| \rho u y \, dy$

c = local mass fraction

c_∞ = complete mixing mass fraction

I_o = the integral evaluated at the beginning of mixing.

The modified mixing length (Prandtl) is modified to allow for the curvature in the form

$$\tau = \rho l^2 \left|\frac{du}{dy}\right| \left(\frac{du}{dy} - \frac{ku}{r}\right)$$

A relationship can be derived between the mixing index and distance from the nozzle, in dimensionless form, independent of the nozzle geometry and the presence of swirl.

The mixing and flow pattern of a confirmed turbulent jet when the densities of the fluids are *different* is important in fuel burners: and also when the densities vary due to combustion (temperature effects). Craya and Curtet analysed the isothermal, incompressible confined jet. Assuming that radial and tangential velocity components were negligible they derived a similarity parameter (originally proposed by Thring and Newby)

$$C = \frac{F\left(\frac{q}{Q}\right)^2}{\left(\frac{r_m}{r_2}\right)^2} + \left(\frac{g}{Q}\right) - \frac{3}{2}\left(\frac{q}{Q}\right)^2$$

where Q = total volumetric flow rate /s

q = an excess volumetric flow rate in the jet stream

r_m = an effective jet width = $\sqrt{\dfrac{q}{\pi w_o}}$

w_o = excess velocity at the jet axis

F = a shape factor for a jet.

Experimental work showed that the flow and mixing characteristics are unique functions of the *Craya-Curtet* number, Ct, defined as

$$Ct = C^{-1/2}$$

This group could be expressed in terms of two velocities, termed the

$$\text{kinematic mean velocity } u_k = \frac{Q}{\pi r_2^2}$$

$$\text{dynamic mean velocity } u_d = \sqrt{\frac{u_1^2 r_1^2 + u_2^2(r_2^2 - r_1^2)}{r_2^2} - \frac{1}{2}u_2^2}$$

The result is

$$Ct = \frac{u_k}{\sqrt{u_d^2 - \frac{1}{2}u_k^2}}$$

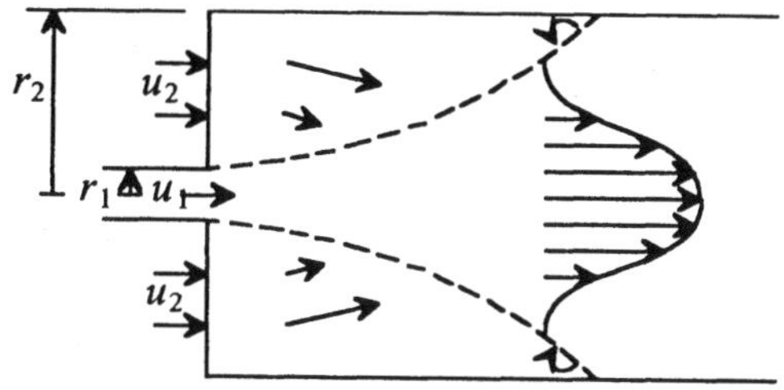

Figure 9.18

The analysis can be developed to develop a similarity parameter for a variable density confined jet (Fig. 9.18), using modified kinematic and dynamic mean velocities u_k', u_d' defined as

$$u_k' = \frac{\rho_1 u_1 r_1^2 + \rho_2 u_2 (r_2^2 - r_1^2)}{\rho_o r_2^2}$$

$$u_d' = \frac{\rho_1 u_1^2 r_1^2 + \rho_2 u_2^2 (r_2^2 - r_1^2)}{\rho_o r_2^2} - \frac{1}{2}\left(\frac{\rho_2}{\rho_o}\right)u_2^2$$

where ρ_o = mean density of the exit fluid

$$= \frac{\rho_1 u_1 r_1^2 + \rho_2 u_2 (r_2^2 - r_1^2)}{u_1 r_1^2 + u_2 (r_2^2 - r_1^2)}$$

9.14 Wake drag

Outline how the boundary layer drag on a body can be determined from a pitot tube traverse across the wake.

A cylinder is mounted (in a wind tunnel) with its axis normal to the direction of a uniform air stream, of velocity 50 m/s and static pressure 1.0 bar. The cylinder diameter = 50 mm, and the rectangular working section is 30 cm height, 22.5 cm width.

At a section downstream of the cylinder the velocity in the wake is given by the equation

$$u = u_m\left(0.8 - 0.2\cos\frac{2y}{D}\right)$$

where u_m = the velocity outside the wake.

Solution. The traverse across a wake is normally made at a distance well downstream of the body, so that the static pressure is nearly equal to the free stream pressure p_∞.

Assuming incompressible flow,

$$p_o = p_\infty + \tfrac{1}{2}\rho u^2 \qquad \text{and} \qquad \frac{u}{u_\infty} = \sqrt{\frac{2(p_o - p_\infty)}{\rho u_\infty^2}} = \sqrt{\phi} \text{ say}$$

The drag force $F = \int \rho u(u_\infty - u)\,dy$ over the control volume section YY (Fig. 9.19).

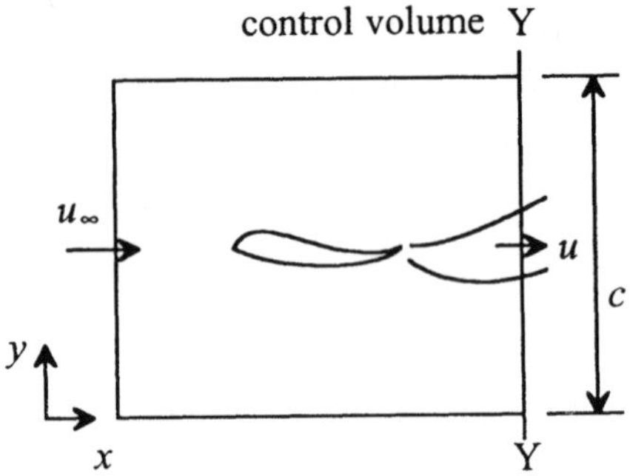

Figure 9.19

The drag coefficient $C_D = \dfrac{F}{\frac{1}{2}\rho c u_\infty^2} = \dfrac{2}{c}\displaystyle\int \frac{u}{u_\infty}\left(1 - \frac{u}{u_\infty}\right)dy = \dfrac{2\theta}{c}$

where c = width of control volume

θ = momentum thickness of the wake.

Hence $C_D = \dfrac{2}{c}\displaystyle\int \sqrt{\phi}\,(1 - \sqrt{\phi})\,dy$

It may not be possible to make a traverse at a distance sufficiently far downstream to neglect the pressure difference. In this case the Jones method can be used (Fig. 9.20), in which the plane of the measurements is *normal* to the local centre-line. Assuming that the stagnations pressure is constant then gives the result

$$C_D = \frac{2}{c}\int \sqrt{\phi - C_p}\,\sqrt{1 - \phi}\,dy$$

where C_p = pressure coefficient = $\dfrac{p - p_\infty}{\frac{1}{2}\rho u_\infty^2}$

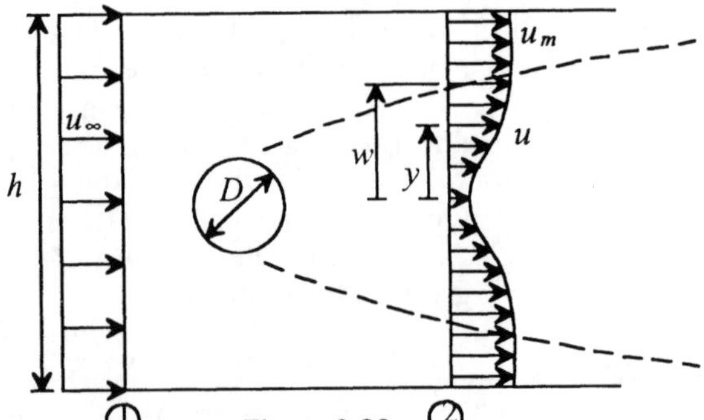

Figure 9.20

The continuity equation gives

$$\dot{m} = \rho u_\infty bh = 2\int_0^w \rho ub\,dy + \rho u_m b(h - 2w)$$

Now $u_z = u_m\left(a - b\cos\frac{2y}{D}\right)$ say, and $u_z = u_m$ at $y = w$.

Hence $1 = a - b\cos\frac{2w}{D}$

and $w = \frac{1}{2}D\arccos\left(\frac{a-1}{D}\right) = \frac{1}{2}(0.05)\arccos\left(\frac{0.8-1}{0.225}\right) = \mathbf{0.067\ m}$

Substituting

$$u_\infty h = u_m(h - 2w) + 2u_m\int_0^w\left(a - b\cos\frac{2y}{D}\right)dy$$

$$= u_m(h - 2w) + 2u_m\left(aw - \frac{bD}{2}\sin\frac{2w}{D}\right)$$

giving $\frac{u_\infty}{u_m} = \left(1 - \frac{2w}{h}\right) + 2\left(\frac{aw}{h} - \frac{bD}{2h}\sin\frac{2w}{D}\right)$

Inserting the values $a = 0.8$, $b = 0.2$, $h = 0.3$ m.

$$\frac{50}{u_m} = 1 - \frac{0.134}{0.3} + 2\left(\frac{0.8\times0.067}{0.3} - \frac{0.2\times0.05}{2\times0.3}\sin\frac{0.134}{0.05}\right) = 0.896$$

$$u_m = 55.8\ \text{m/s}$$

Assuming that the static pressure at station 2 is uniform

$$p_\infty + \tfrac{1}{2}\rho u_\infty^2 = p_2 + \tfrac{1}{2}\rho u_m^2$$

$$p_\infty - p_2 = \tfrac{1}{2}\rho(u_m^2 - u_\infty^2) = 306.8\rho$$

Applying the momentum equation to the stations 1 and 2 gives

$$(p_\infty - p_2)bh - bF = 2\int_0^w \rho u_2^2 b\,dy + \rho b u_m^2(h - 2w)$$

$$F = (p_\infty - p_2)h - \rho u_m^2(h - 2w) - 2\rho\int_0^w u_2^2\,dy$$

or $$\frac{F}{\rho} = 306.8(0.3) - (55.8)^2(0.3 - 0.134)$$

$$-2\int_0^w (55.8)^2\left(0.8 - 0.2\cos\frac{y}{0.025}\right)^2 dy$$

$$= 67.3\ \text{N/m span.}$$

and $$C_D = \frac{F}{\frac{1}{2}\rho u_\infty^2 D} = \frac{67.3}{\frac{1}{2}(50)^2(0.05)} = \mathbf{1.08}$$

Note. In many cases the velocity profile would not follow a simple relationship such as that given in this problem, and a numerical integration would be required.

Also the wall effect is, in this problem, negligible since the cylinder diameter is small compared to the tunnel height. $D/h = 0.167$.

Problems

1 The velocity at a point in a fluid flow varied with time as given in the following table:

u (m/s)	t (m/s)
2.010	0
1.986	1
1.940	2

u(m/s)	t (m/s)
1.988	6
1.952	7
1.950	8

u(m/s)	t (m/s)
2.012	12
2.008	13
1.980	14

1.980	3		1.960	9		1.946	15
2.026	4		2.002	10			
2.034	5		2.010	11			

Estimate the turbulence intensity.

Answer 12.8%.

2 Air flows over a flat plate, and at a certain section the boundary layer thickness = 72 mm, and the shear stress at the surface τ_o = 0.39 N/m². The velocity distribution in the region

$$20 < \frac{yu^*}{\nu} < 1000$$

is given by

$$\frac{\bar{u}}{u^*} = 2.44 \ln\left(\frac{yu^*}{\nu}\right) + 4.9$$

Air density = 1.2 kg/m³, viscosity = 1.4×10^{-5} m²/s.

Assuming that the shear stress is constant calculate the Prandtl mixing length and the ratio of the eddy viscosity to the kinematic viscosity at y = 1.3 mm and y = 2.6 mm.

Answer 0.17 mm, 2.90×10^{-4} m²/s;
1.07 mm, 5.93×10^{-4} m²/s.

3 The results of a pitot tube traverse across a symmetrical wake, of width 50 mm, normal to the wake centre line gave the following results:

y (mm)	0	5	10	15	20	25
u (m/s)	14	16	21	30	37	40

Determine the drag coefficient.

Answer 0.22.

4 A jet of fluid issues from a nozzle, diameter D_o, at a mean velocity u_o into a large reservoir containing a fluid having the same properties.

The axial velocity distribution in the jet is given by the equation

$$\frac{u}{u_m} = \left(1 + \frac{1}{4}\theta^2\right)^{-2}, \quad \text{where } \theta = \frac{0.24u_o}{\nu}\sqrt{A_o}\left(\frac{r}{x}\right).$$

Show that the centre-line velocity u_m is given by the equation

$$u_m = \frac{0.117u_o^2}{\nu x}$$

and determine the mass flow rate in terms of x.

Answer 25.6μx.

5 A submerged jet issues from a rectangular orifice into a fluid of similar properties. The velocity distribution in the jet is given by the equation

$$\frac{u}{u_m} = \exp\left[-57\left(\frac{y}{x}\right)^2\right]$$

The orifice depth = $2b_o$.

Determine the centre-line velocity, u_m; Q, the volumetric flow rate /unit width; the jet width at which the local velocity is equal to one half of the centre-line velocity; and the entrainment velocity

$$v_e = \frac{1}{2}\left(\frac{dQ}{dx}\right).$$

Assume that $\int_0^\infty \exp(-x^2)\,dx = \sqrt{\pi}$.

Answer $u_m = 3.47u_o\sqrt{\frac{b_o}{x}}$; $Q = 0.82u_o\sqrt{b_o x}$; $0.11x$; $0.203u_o\sqrt{\frac{b_o}{x}}$ or $0.058u_m$.

6 A jet issues from a circular nozzle, of diameter 2 cm, at a uniform velocity of 20 m/s. The local velocity is measure at a station beyond the initial core, and gave the following results:

radius r (mm)	velocity u (m/s)
5	8.90
10	8.23
15	7.23
20	6.02
25	4.76
30	3.57
35	2.54

radius r (mm)	velocity u (m/s)
40	1.72
45	1.10
50	0.67
55	0.39
60	0.21
65	0.11
70	0.05

Assuming that the jet is axisymmetric, show, by plotting u^2r against r, that the axial momentum is nearly equal to the axial momentum of the jet leaving the nozzle.

Determine the volumetric flow rate at the station, Q, and hence the *entrained* flow in terms of the nozzle flow rate Q_o.

Answer 0.028 m^3/s; $3.4Q_o$.

7 A jet of air issues from a circular nozzle, diameter 12.5 mm, at a mean velocity of 190 m/s, into stagnant air. The velocity distribution across the jet (beyond the core) is given by the equation

$$\frac{u}{u_m} = \frac{1}{2}\left(1 + \cos\frac{\pi r}{R}\right)$$

where R = jet radius.

At a section of jet radius 75 mm the centre-line velocity u_m = 36 m/s. Determine the volumetric flow rate at this section, and the entrained volume /m² jet surface area.

If $u_m = \dfrac{12u_o r_o}{x}$

and volumetric flow rate = $\dfrac{cQ_o x}{r_o}$

determine the position of the section x and the constant c. Also calculate the angle of the jet.

Answer 0.188 m³/s; 1.63 m³/m²s. 40 cm; 0.13. 10.9°.

8 The exhaust gas from a jet engineer issues as an axisymmetric jet, centre-line 5.0 m above the ground level. The nozzle is 85 cm diameter, and the gas leaves at a uniform velocity of 90 m/s.

The velocity in a round jet is given by the equations:

$$\text{centre-line velocity } u_m = \exp\left[-94\left(\frac{r}{x}\right)^2\right]$$

$$\text{local velocity} = \frac{12u_o r_o u_m}{x}$$

where x = horizontal distance measured from the plane of the engine exhaust nozzle.

Determine the distance x at which the jet would contact the ground; and the maximum distance at which a person of height 2 m would find his head experiencing little disturbance due to the jet.

Ground effects can be neglected.

Answer Approx. 16 m; 10 m.

9 Define the term 'swirl number, S'. Using the data given show the effect of the swirl number on the previous problem.

$$u_m = \frac{kr_o u_o}{x}, \quad u = u_m \exp\left[-\alpha\left(\frac{r}{x}\right)^2\right], \quad \alpha = \frac{92}{1 + 6S}$$

S	0.2	0.4	0.6	0.8	1.0
k	9	6	4	2.8	2.0

10 A single stage ejector (or jet pump) is shown in Fig. 9.21.

Assuming that the nozzle (primary) and secondary (entrained) fluids are of the same density, and one-dimensional, incompressible flow, show that the efficiency η is given by the expression

$$\eta = \frac{R + n(2 - R)}{n^2(1 - R) + n(1 + R)}$$

The efficiency, in this problem, is defined as

$$\eta = \frac{Q_s p_d}{Q_n(p_n - p_d)}, \qquad \text{where } n = \frac{u_n}{u_s}, \quad R = \frac{A_n}{A_m}$$

and the subscripts n, s, m, d refer to the nozzle, secondary fluid, mixture chamber and diffuser exit respectively.

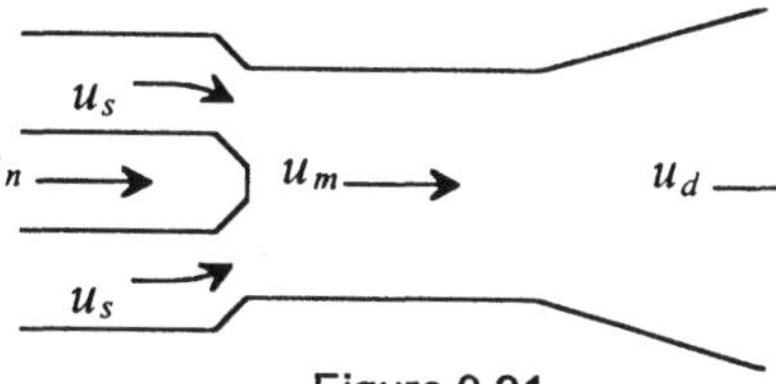

Figure 9.21

Frictional effects can be neglected.

11 Two rectangular ducts, of cross-sectional areas A, and $4A$, discharge flow rates $3Q$, $4Q$ respectively, at the same static pressure, into another rectangular duct of area $5A$.

Derive expressions for the static pressure increase in the single duct; and the energy dissipated. Neglect frictional effects. Why is there an energy dissipation in the mixing chamber?

Answer $\quad \dfrac{16Q^2}{5A}; \quad \dfrac{16Q^2}{5A} - \dfrac{201}{2}\left(\dfrac{Q}{A}\right)^2$

12 An air blast injector is shown in Fig. 9.22. The nozzle fluid (air) issues as a high velocity jet, entraining the secondary fluid (gaseous fuel).

Neglecting frictional effects show that the efficiency, defined as

$$\eta = \frac{p_d - p_n}{(\rho_n Q_n^2)/(2A_n^2)}$$

is given by the expression

$$\eta = \frac{2A_n}{A_m} - (1 + R)^2\left(\frac{\rho_1}{\rho_2}\right)\left(\frac{A_n}{A_m}\right)^2$$

where subscripts n, m refer to the nozzle exit and the end of the mixture tube respectively, and

$$R = \frac{\rho_s Q_s}{\rho_n Q_n}.$$

Show that, for a given value of R, the maximum efficiency is

$$\frac{1}{(1 + R)^2}\left(\frac{\rho_2}{\rho_1}\right).$$

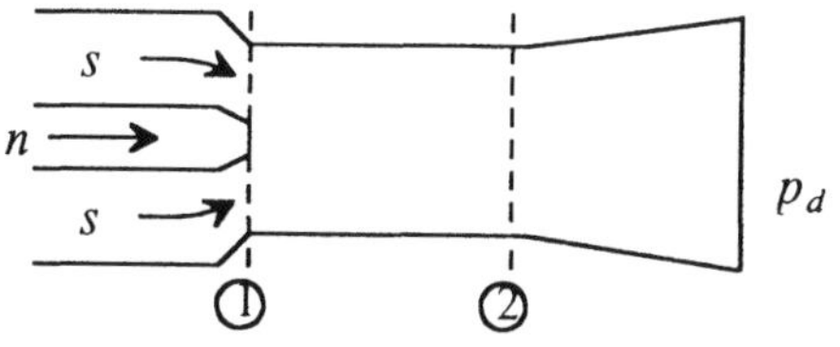

Figure 9.22

13 In the previous problem the frictional effects can be allowed for by the introduction of the coefficients k_{12}, k_d where the pressure loss is expressed in terms of velocity heads of mixed fluid at station 2.

Show that the efficiency is then given by

$$\eta = \frac{2A_n}{A_m} - (1 + k_{12} + k_d)(1 + R)^2\left(\frac{\rho_1}{\rho_2}\right)\left(\frac{A_n}{A_m}\right)^2$$

14 In an *equal velocity* injector entrainment is not produced by shearing between the jet (primary) and entrained fluids, but as a result of a negative pressure around the nozzle outlet.

In such an injector the primary fluid is fuel gas, entraining air.

nozzle diameter = 7 mm
mixture tube diameter = 20 mm
density of air = 1.2 kg/m^3
density of gas = 0.66 kg/m^3
diffuser exit diameter = 50 mm
loss coefficients: k_{12} = 0.10
k_d = 0.15
gas supply pressure = 3400 N/m^2

The flow rates of gas and air are 0.0017 and 0.013 m^3/s respectively.

Assuming that both fluids enter in the axial direction, incompressible flow, show by the application of the continuity, momentum and energy equations that the efficiency is given by

$$\eta = \frac{p_d - p_s}{p_n - p_s} = \frac{(R = s)(1 - k_d - k_{12}) - (R + 1)s}{(R + 1)(1 - s)}$$

where $s = \dfrac{\rho_n}{\rho_i}$

$R = \dfrac{A_i}{A_n}$

Calculate the efficiency; and the static pressure at the diffuser exit and mixing tube exit.

Answer 0.35; 5570, 4510 N/m^2.

15 A gas burner is shown in Fig. 9.23. The nozzle diameter = 10 mm.

volume of air/volume of gas[§] = 9.5
vol. of combustion products/vol. of gas[§] = 10.5
temperature of combustion products = 2200 K
gas density, relative to air = 0.55
pressure loss coefficients (friction) k = 0.3
(i.e. friction pressure loss = $k\frac{1}{2}\rho u^2$)
([§] at 273 K)

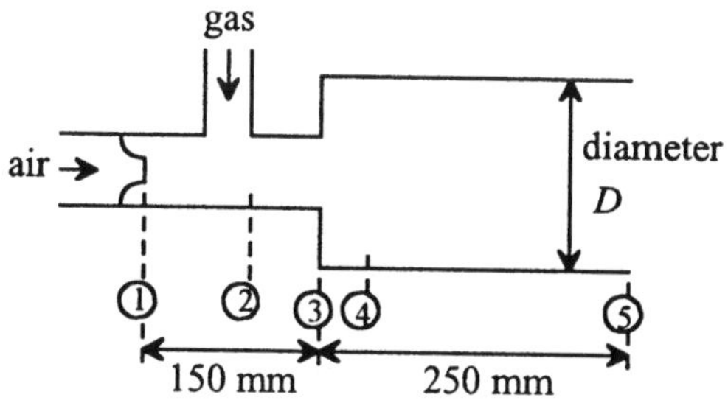

Figure 9.23

The air and gas mix completely in the mixing chamber 2-3, and combustion takes place at the sudden expansion 3-4.

Assuming that $p_1 = p_5$, incompressible flow (except for temperature effects) and uniform conditions over any cross-section determine the area ration A_5/A_1 in terms of the area ratio A_2/A_5.

Hence calculate the diameters D_2 and D_5 for the ratio A_5/A_1 to be a minimum.

Answer 16.8 mm, 25.4 mm.

10

Flow over aerofoils: through cascades

Introduction

The basic theory of isentropic flow (including linearised flow), shock waves, Prandtl-Meyer flow, and boundary layer have been covered in previous chapters. This chapter deals with the practical aspects of flow around aerofoils, and the fluid flow through turbomachine guide and rotor assemblies.

Isolated aerofoil

The terms used in the description of an aerofoil are shown in Fig. 10.1. The characteristics can be shown in the form of lift and drag coefficients (C_L, C_D); lift force/drag force ratio (L/D); and pitching moment coefficient C_M plotted against the angle of attack α or C_M, C_D against C_L. A complete plot would include the curves at various values of the Reynolds number (Fig. 10.2).

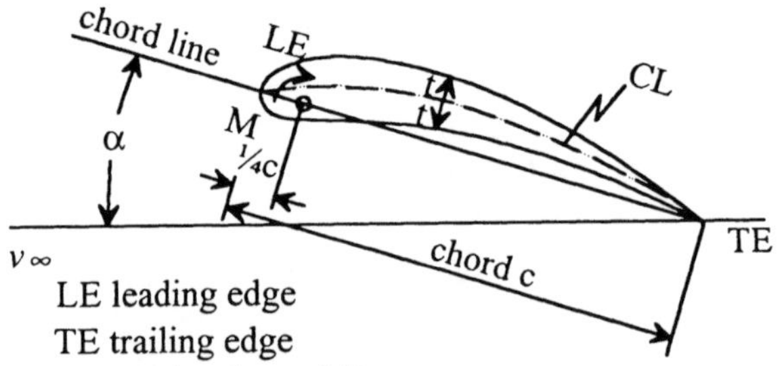

LE leading edge
TE trailing edge
CL camber (mean) line
t half-thickness

Figure 10.1

The lift force, L, is the component of the force on the aerofoil in a direction perpendicular to the direction of the free stream v_∞ (or line of flight) and the drag force D, the force component in the direction of the free stream.

$$L = \tfrac{1}{2}\rho v_\infty^2 A C_L, \qquad D = \tfrac{1}{2}\rho v_\infty^2 A C_D$$

where A = wing area (projected) = bc (constant cross-section)
b = span.

The lift and drag forces may be considered to act at a fixed point (with respect to the aerofoil). A complete specification of the forces on the aerofoil requires a knowledge of the moment about this fixed point:

$$\text{pitching moment } M = \tfrac{1}{2}\rho v_\infty^2 A c\, C_M$$

The two components and pitching moment are important in the study of aircraft performance and stability.

The rates of change of C_L, C_D with angle of attack are strongly affected by the *aspect ratio AR*, which is defined as the ratio of the span squared to the wing area (b^2/A).

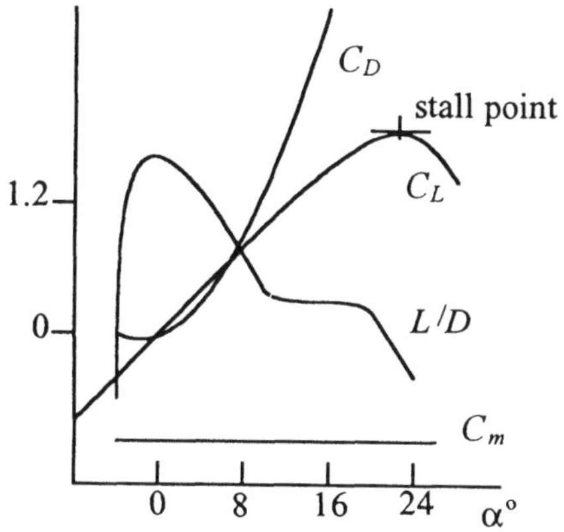

Figure 10.2

In the case of a rectangular wing, $AR = b/c$. The effect is shown in Fig.10.3.

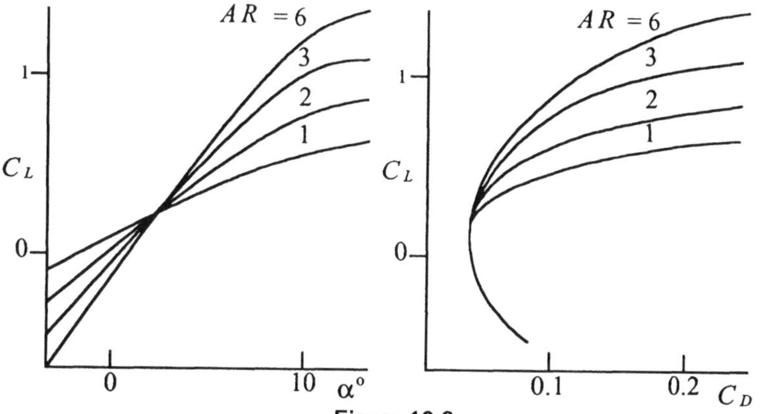

Figure 10.3

Cascades

The analysis of the flow through a cascade of blades is dependent upon the blade *solidity* σ, defined as the chord:pitch ratio, c/s. In a high solidity (low pitch) cascade the flow between the blades can be considered as bounded; in a low solidity (high pitch) cascade the blades can be considered as isolated with factors to allow for mutual interference. The former is more appropriate in turbomachine cascades (compressors, turbines) and the latter in fans, windmills.

Straight cascade

A *stationary* cascade is shown in Fig. 10.4. It should be noted that the following *notation* is used in this chapter:

v	velocity (absolute)
v_f, v_w	axial and tangential components of velocity
v_r	velocity (relative)
α, θ	angle between the direction of the absolute and relative velocity, respectively, and the *tangential* direction
F_a, F_t	axial and tangential components of the force on a blade
ξ	stagger angle

subscripts:

1-2, 3-4 refer to stationary (fixed) cascades (stator, guide vanes)

2-3 refer to moving (rotor) cascade.

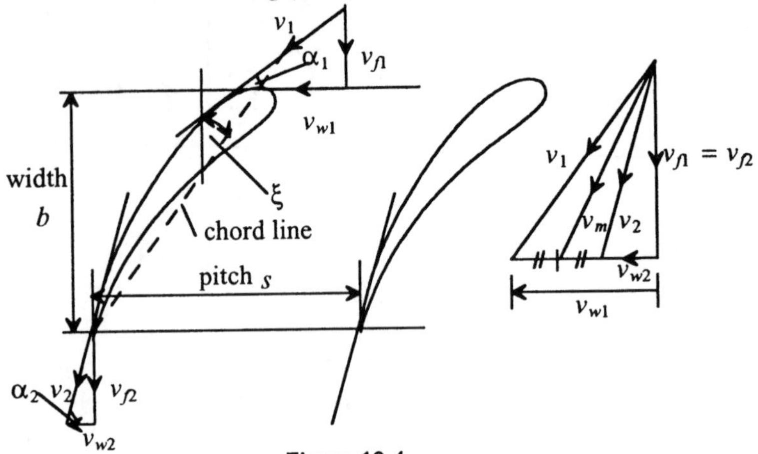

Figure 10.4

In many cascades the axial component (*flow*) v_f is constant. The mean *whirl* velocity (tangential component) is the vector mean, or

$$v_{wm} = \frac{1}{2}(v_m + v_{w2}) = \frac{1}{2}v_f(\cot\alpha_1 + \cot\alpha_2).$$

In a *moving* cascade the absolute velocity is replaced by the *relative* velocity over the blade. The combined velocity triangles are shown in Fig. 10.5.

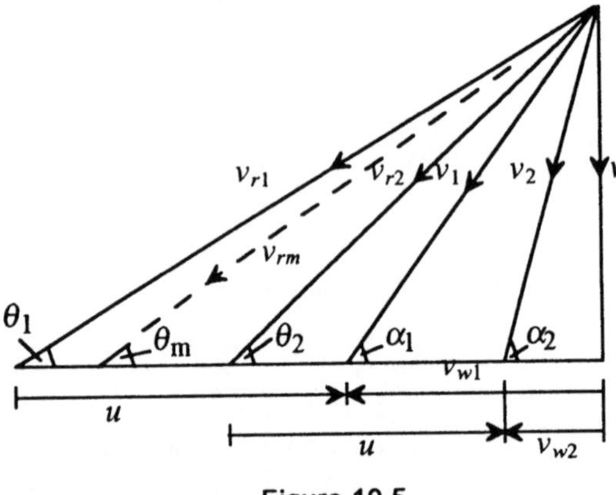

Figure 10.5

$$\cot\alpha_m = \frac{1}{2}(\cot\alpha_1 + \cot\alpha_2), \quad \cot\theta_m = \frac{1}{2}(\cot\theta_1 + \cot\theta_2)$$

$$v_{wm} = v_f \cot\alpha_m, \quad v_{rm} = v_f \cot\theta_m$$

u = blade velocity

Note. In the construction of velocity triangles it is useful to insert the arrows denoting directions, and hence to check that *relative* + *blade* = *absolute* velocity *vectors*.

Cascade performance

The fluid angles and blade angles are not always the same, as assumed in Figs. 10.4, 10.5. In fact they would only be equal at *one* set of conditions: for example a change in flow rate (and hence v_f) only gives different values for θ (fluid angle). Thus, if the blade angle is fixed there will be a difference in the fluid and blade angles. It is often the case that the fluid approaches the blade at an angle of *incidence*, i (Fig. 10.6). Further, a boundary layer develops on the blade surface so that, without separation, the fluid leaves the blade at an angle different to the blade angle. This difference is known as the *deviation*, δ. The effect is greater in a compressor than in a turbine due to the boundary layer thickness increasing more rapidly against a pressure rise, although modified by the greater curvature of a turbine blade.

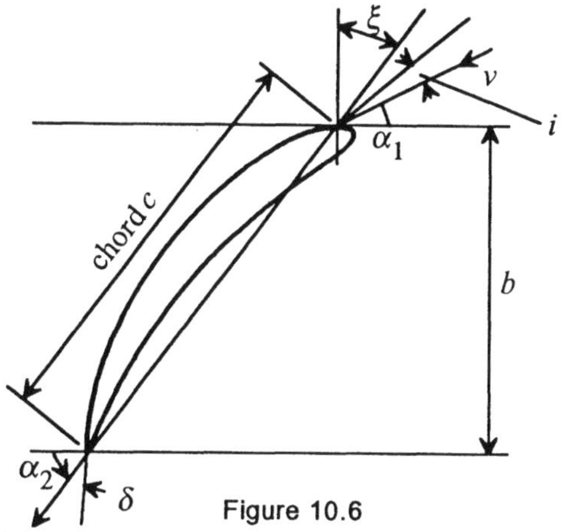

Figure 10.6

In a turbomachine the cascade of blades is enclosed in a casing so that the fluid flow into, through and out of the cascade is modified by the presence of the wall boundary layer, and contraction of the streamlines. The performance of a cascade can be described by the use of a loss coefficient

$$\xi = \frac{\Delta p_o}{\frac{1}{2}\rho v_f^2}$$

Δp_o is the decrease in *stagnation* pressure, which remains constant in isentropic flow. The coefficient is determined from experimental data.

10.1 Pressure distribution over an aerofoil

A wind-tunnel test on a NACA 4412 aerofoil, at an angle of attack of 8°, gave the following results for the pressure coefficient C_p:

$\frac{x}{c}$(%)	C_p lower surface	C_p upper surface	$\frac{x}{c}$(%)	C_p lower surface	C_p upper surface	$\frac{x}{c}$(%)	C_p lower surface	C_p upper surface
0.0	0.16	−1.00	10	0.40	−1.39	65	0.24	−0.46
0.5	0.90	−1.74	15	0.35	−1.31	75	0.23	−0.29
0.9	1.01	−1.79	20	0.32	−1.24	90	0.20	−0.01
1.7	0.92	−1.74	30	0.29	−1.07	95	0.18	0.08
2.9	0.75	−1.65	40	0.27	−0.88	98	0.17	0.12
4.9	0.57	−1.55	50	0.25	−0.69	100	0.13	0.13

Estimate the lift coefficient.

Solution. The pressure coefficient, C_p, is defined as

$$C_p = \frac{(p - p_\infty)}{\frac{1}{2}\rho v_\infty^2}$$

where p_∞, v_∞ refer to the undisturbed stream (approach velocity). The distance x is measured along the chord line, and expressed in terms of the chord length c. The lift force is due to the net pressure force on the wing surfaces, and is equal to the component of that force in a direction perpendicular to the free stream direction. The pressure is measured relative to the free stream pressure, and

since $C_L = \dfrac{L}{\frac{1}{2}\rho c v_\infty^2}$

then $C_L = (\text{mean } C_p) \cos\alpha$.

The pressure coefficient is plotted against x/c, and the mean value can then be estimated from the area *between* the curves. The value is approximately 0.98 (see Fig. 10.7)

giving $C_L = 0.98 \cos 8 = \mathbf{0.97}$.

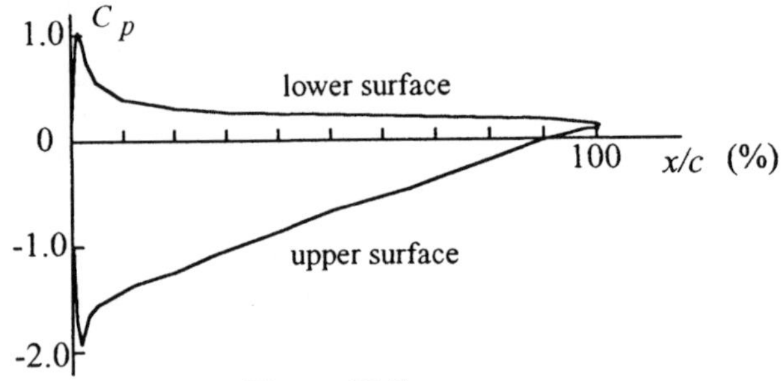

Figure 10.7

Note. On the lower surface $C_p > 0$, and the pressure is *greater* than the free stream pressure over the whole length. On the upper surface $C_p < 0$, and the pressure is *less* than the free stream pressure except over the last 10% of the chord length.

The NACA 4412 aerofoil is one of a series based on the section geometry. The first integer indicates the maximum mean line ordinate (measured from the chord line) in % chord. The second integer indicates the distance from the leading edge to the location of the maximum camber, in tenths of a chord. The last two integers indicate the section thickness in % chord. Thus the NACA 4412 has 4% camber at 0.4 of the chord, and is 12% thick.

10.2 Aerofoil characteristic

An aerofoil of span 30 cm, constant chord 5 cm, gave the following results for the measurement of the lift and drag forces:

α°	L (N)	D (N)	α°	L (N)	D (N)
−3.4	−16.0	0.9	11.8	119.5	1.8
−1.7	−2.3	0.8	13.4	131.1	2.3
−0.4	12.0	0.8	15.0	140.9	3.1

1.1	25.9	0.8	15.8	143.0	3.8
2.6	39.5	0.9	19.8	117.6	20.4
5.6	67.0	1.0	26.8	90.3	37.7
8.7	94.4	1.3			

The free stream velocity = 100 m/s. Air density = 1.2 kg/m^3.

Plot C_L, C_D against the angle of attack α; the ratio C_L/C_D against α; and the polar diagram.

Comment on the curves obtained.

Solution. The lift and drag coefficients are calculated from the definitions

$$C_L = \frac{L}{\frac{1}{2}\rho v_\infty^2 A}, \qquad C_D = \frac{D}{\frac{1}{2}\rho v_\infty^2 A}.$$

In this case the denominator is

$$\tfrac{1}{2}(1.2)(100)^2(0.3)(0.05) = 90.$$

α	C_L	C_D	C_L/C_D	α	C_L	C_D	C_L/C_D
−3.4	−0.178	0.010	−17.8	11.8	1.328	0.020	66.40
−1.7	−0.026	0.009	−2.89	13.4	1.457	0.026	56.04
−0.4	0.133	0.009	14.78	15.0	1.566	0.034	46.06
1.1	0.288	0.009	32.0	15.8	1.589	0.042	37.83
2.6	0.439	0.010	43.9	19.8	1.307	0.227	5.76
5.6	0.744	0.011	67.64	26.8	1.003	0.419	2.39
8.7	1.049	0.014	74.93				

The graphs are shown in Fig. 10.9.

The lift coefficient increases almost linearly with α to a maximum value of 1.60 at α = 15.5°: the *stall* point. These values are typical of a wing without high-lift devices (plain and slotted flaps). Thereafter C_L decreases as the boundary layer separates. The drag coefficient is almost constant to about α = 12° and then begins to increase, especially at α = 16°. The ratio C_L/C_D peaks rapidly to a maximum at α = 9°, and then decreases rapidly.

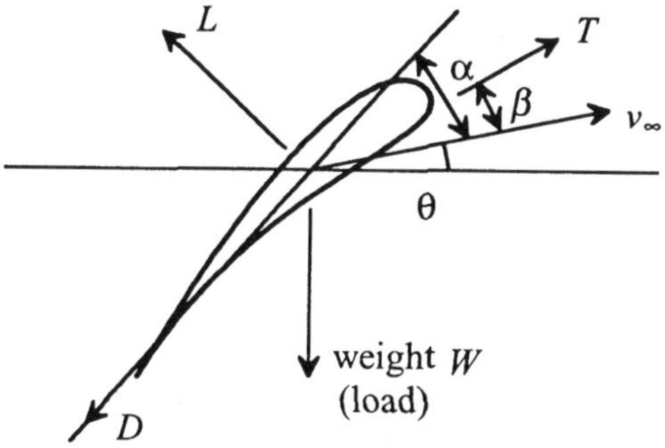

Figure 10.8

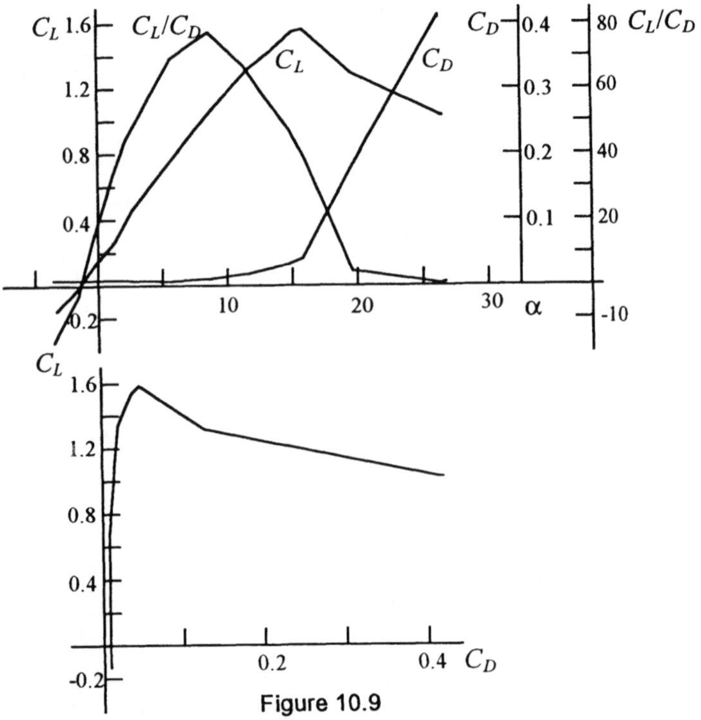

Figure 10.9

10.3 Aerofoil performance

Show that the power required to propel an aerofoil which supports a load is proportional to $C_D/C_L^{1.5}$.

The characteristics of an aerofoil are:

α	C_L	C_D	α	C_L	C_D
–6	0.00	0.013	8	0.93	0.075
–4	0.12	0.011	10	1.08	0.091
–2	0.29	0.017	12	1.15	0.112
0	0.40	0.020	14	1.21	0.140
2	0.52	0.030	16	1.22	0.165
4	0.67	0.040	18	1.21	0.210
6	0.80	0.058			

Solution. The thrust, T, is at an angle β to the free stream velocity. The propulsive power is $P = Tv_\infty$ (see Fig. 10.8).

For steady, level flight ($\theta = 0$) we have

$$T\cos\beta = D, \qquad L + T\sin\beta = W$$

Now for a small angle β, $\cos\beta = 1$, $\sin\beta = 0$ and

$$T = D, \qquad L = W \quad \text{or} \quad \frac{T}{W} = \frac{D}{L} = \frac{C_D}{C_L}$$

hence $P = \dfrac{WC_D}{C_L}v_\infty$.

Further $W = L = \frac{1}{2}\rho v_\infty^2 AC_L$ or $v_\infty = \sqrt{\dfrac{2W}{\rho AC_L}}$

hence $P = \dfrac{WC_D}{C_L}\sqrt{\dfrac{2W}{\rho AC_L}} = \sqrt{\dfrac{2W^3}{\rho A}\dfrac{C_D^2}{C_L^3}}$ or $P \propto \dfrac{C_D}{C_L^{3/2}}$

The graphs are now plotted from the data given (Fig. 10.10).

α	$\dfrac{C_L^{3/2}}{C_D}$	$\dfrac{C_L}{C_D}$	α	$\dfrac{C_L^{3/2}}{C_D}$	$\dfrac{C_L}{C_D}$
–6	0.00	0.00	8	11.96	12.40
–4	3.78	10.91	10	12.34	11.87
–2	9.19	17.06	12	11.01	10.27
0	12.65	20.00	14	9.51	8.64
2	12.50	17.33	16	8.17	7.39
4	13.71	16.75	18	6.34	5.76
6	12.34	13.79			

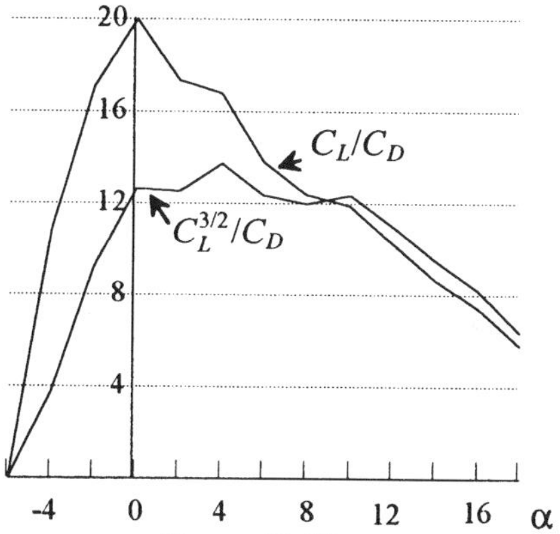

Figure 10.10

The propulsion power is a minimum when the ratio $C_L^{3/2}/C_D$ is a maximum, i.e. at $\boldsymbol{\alpha} = \mathbf{3°}$.

Note. The power at maximum lift-drag ratio C_L/C_D is, at $\alpha = 0$,

$$\frac{13.8}{12.8} = 1.08 \times \text{minimum.}$$

10.4 Thin aerofoil sections

Discuss the theory of thin aerofoil sections, as developed by Glauert. Show how the lift coefficient can be derived. Take the mean line as the curve

$$y = kx(1 - x/c)^2$$

Solution. Many properties of wing sections are functions of the *mean line* shape, the mean line being the locus of points situated midway between the upper and lower surfaces: distances are measured normal to the mean line. The commonest family of wing sections are obtained by combining a mean line and a thickness distribution.

The properties mainly associated with the mean line shape are the load distribution (along the chord), angle of zero lift, pitching-moment coefficient, the lift curve slope.

The *thin section* theory replaces the aerofoil by its mean line, and the load distribution along the chord is taken as a chordwise distribution of vortices. Let Δ be the difference in velocity between the upper and lower surfaces. (See Fig. 10.11.) Then, for a *small* camber (so that distances along the chord line are nearly equal to those along the mean line) the total circulation around the section is

$$\Gamma = \int_0^c \Delta\, dx$$

The vertical component of velocity, v_n, caused by an *element* of the vortex distribution along the mean line is

$$\frac{\Delta\, dx}{2\pi}\frac{1}{x - x_1}$$

where x = abscissa of the element

x_1 = abscissa of the point at which the velocity is to be calculated.

Hence $v_n = \int_0^c \frac{\Delta\, dx}{2\pi(x - x_1)}$

normal to the chord line.

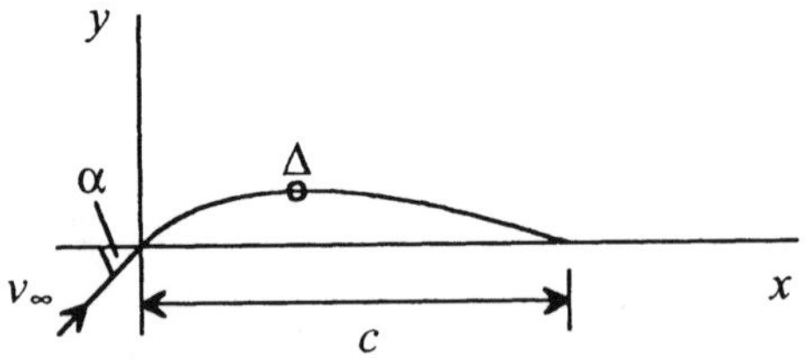

Figure 10.11

Also, the thin section must be a streamline, and for small angles

$$\alpha + \frac{v_n}{v_\infty} = \frac{dy}{dx}.$$

These two equations give the fundamental relations between the mean line shape and its characteristics. The *Fourier* method of analysis can now be applied to these equations.

Let $x = \frac{1}{2}c(1 - \cos\theta)$

and assume that

$$\Delta = 2v_\infty\left(A_o \cot\frac{\theta}{2} + \sum_0^\infty A_n \sin n\theta\right)$$

Now $dx = \frac{1}{2}c \sin\theta\, d\theta, \qquad \cot\frac{\theta}{2} = \frac{1 + \cos\theta}{\sin\theta}$

hence $\Delta\, dx = cv_\infty\left[A_o(1 + \cos\theta) + \left(\sum_1^\infty A_n \sin n\theta\right)\sin\theta\right]d\theta$

The lift is therefore

$$L = \int_0^c \rho v_\infty \Delta\, dx = \pi\rho c v_\infty^2\left(A_o + \frac{1}{2}A_1\right)$$

and the lift coefficient is

$$C_L = \frac{L}{\frac{1}{2}\rho c v_\infty^2} = 2\pi(A_o + \tfrac{1}{2}A_1)$$

It now remains to determine the relations between the Fourier coefficients and the mean line shape. Substituting for x and Δ gives

$$v_n = \frac{v_\infty}{\pi}\int_0^\pi\left[\frac{A_o(1 + \cos\theta)}{\cos\theta_1 - \cos\theta} + \frac{\frac{1}{2}\sum_1^\infty A_n[\cos(n-1)\theta - \cos(n+1)\theta]}{\cos\theta_1 - \cos\theta}\right]d\theta$$

since $\cos(n-1)\theta - \cos(n+1)\theta = 2\sin n\theta \sin\theta$.

Glauert showed that

$$\int_0^\pi \frac{\cos n\theta}{\cos\theta - \cos\phi}\,d\theta = \frac{\pi \sin n\phi}{\sin\phi} \quad \text{and hence} \quad \frac{v_n}{v_\infty} = -A_o + \sum_1^\infty A_n \cos n\theta$$

Substituting

$$\frac{dy}{dx} = \alpha + \frac{v_n}{v_\infty} = \alpha - A_o + \sum_1^\infty A_n \cos n\theta$$

and the standard expressions for the Fourier series coefficients are then

$$\alpha - A_o = \frac{1}{\pi}\int_0^\pi\left(\frac{dy}{dx}\right)d\theta, \qquad A_n = \frac{2}{\pi}\int_0^\pi\left(\frac{dy}{dx}\right)\cos n\theta\, d\theta$$

For the given mean line $y = kx(1 - x/c)^2$:

Substituting $x = \frac{1}{2}c(1 - \cos\theta)$ gives

$$y = \tfrac{1}{8}kc(1 - \cos\theta)(1 + \cos\theta)^2$$

$$\frac{dy}{dx} = \frac{dy}{d\theta}\frac{d\theta}{dx} = \frac{1}{4}k(1 + \cos\theta)(3\cos\theta - 1)$$

$$\alpha - A_o = \frac{k}{4\pi}\int_0^\pi(1 + \cos\theta)(3\cos\theta - 1)\,d\theta = \frac{1}{8}k$$

$$A_1 = \frac{2}{\pi}\frac{k}{4}\int_0^\pi(1 + \cos\theta)(3\cos\theta - 1)\cos\theta\,d\theta = \frac{1}{2}k$$

and $\quad C_L = 2\pi(A_o + \frac{1}{2}A_1) = 2\pi\alpha + \frac{1}{4}\pi k$

Note. The angle of zero lift is

$$\alpha_o = \frac{1}{\pi}\int_0^\pi\left(\frac{dy}{dx}\right)(1 - \cos\theta)\,d\theta = \alpha - A_o - \frac{1}{2}A_1 = -\frac{1}{8}k$$

The pitching moment about the leading edge is

$$M = -\int_0^c \rho\Delta v_\infty x\,dx = -\frac{1}{4}\pi c^2\rho v_\infty^2(A_o + A_1 - \frac{1}{2}A_2)$$

or the pitching moment coefficient

$$C_m = \frac{M}{\frac{1}{2}\rho c^2 v_\infty^2} = \frac{1}{2}\pi(A_o + A_1 - \frac{1}{2}A_2) = \frac{1}{4}C_L - \frac{1}{4}\pi(A_2 - A_1)$$

In this particular case $A_2 = 3/8\,k$, giving

$$C_m = \tfrac{1}{2}\pi\alpha + \tfrac{3}{32}\pi k.$$

10.5 Downwash and induced drag

Briefly outline the manner in which the total drag of an aerofoil is made up; and explain what is meant by downwash.

Discuss the lifting-line theory, indicating the effect of downwash. Outline how the induced drag can be determined from a known lift distribution (and consequently the circulation along the aerofoil).

Solution. The total drag of an aerofoil can be divided into three parts:

(a) due to skin friction (boundary layer), which depends upon the smoothness of the surface;
(b) due to eddies in the wake (part of the pressure drag), which is greater for thick sections than for thin ones;
(c) due to *downward* flow of the air near the aerofoil as a consequence of the lift, known as *induced* drag.

The simplest three-dimensional theory is based on the concept of the *lifting line* (Glauert and Prandtl), in which the aerofoil is replaced by a straight line (Fig. 10.12). The circulation about the wing (associated with the lift, $\rho v_\infty \Gamma$) is replaced by a vortex filament, whose strength is proportional to the local lift intensity.

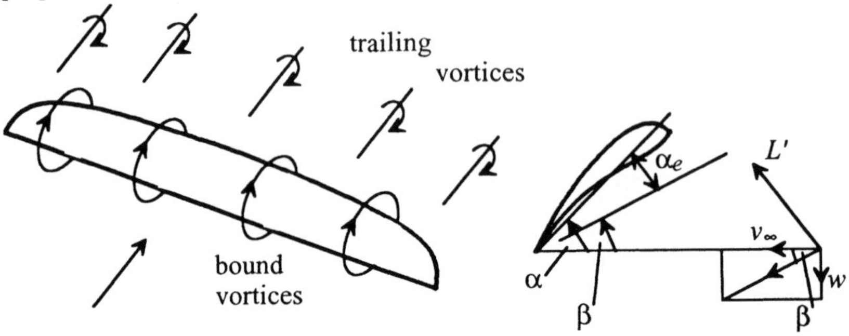

Figure 10.12

Now a vortex filament cannot end in a fluid (Helmholtz's theorem) and therefore the variation of vortex strength along the line is assumed to result from the superposition of horseshoe-shaped vortices. The effect of the trailing vortices, corresponding to a positive lift, is to induce a downward component of velocity behind the aerofoil: it is termed the *downwash*. The sheet of trailing vortices progresses downstream and tends to roll up into two discrete vortices.

The effect of downwash is to reduce the angle of attack, and reduce the slope of the lift curve; and produce induced drag.

Consider an aerofoil of constant cross-section, and no sweepback (Fig. 10.13). The span = b.

At a point P on the trailing edge, the trailing vortex induces a downwash at point P_1 (normal to the xy plane) of

$$w = \frac{1}{4\pi}\frac{d\Gamma}{dx}\frac{dx}{x_1 - x}$$

Hence the total downwash at point P_1 due to the contribution from all points on the aerofoil is

$$w_1 = \frac{1}{4\pi}\int_{-b/2}^{b/2}\frac{\frac{d\Gamma}{dx}dx}{x_1 - x}$$

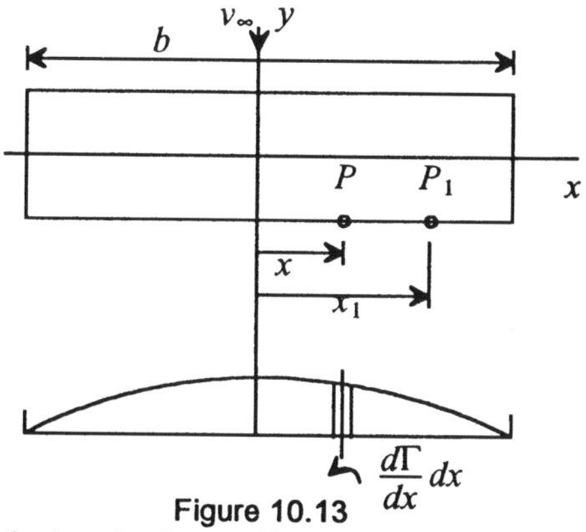

Figure 10.13

For small values of w/v_∞ the *local* effective angle of attack is then

$$\alpha_{e1} = \alpha - \frac{1}{4\pi}\int_{-b/2}^{b/2} \frac{\frac{d\Gamma}{dx}dx}{x_1 - x}$$

The lift/unit span

$$L' = \rho v_\infty \Gamma_1 = \tfrac{1}{2}\rho v_\infty^2 C_{L1}$$

where $C_{L1} = \lambda\alpha_{e1}$

$$\lambda = \frac{dC_L}{d\alpha} \text{ (for an infinite aspect ratio)}$$

Hence $\Gamma = \frac{1}{2}cv_\infty\lambda\alpha_e$, and $w = v_\infty(\alpha - \alpha_e)$

giving $$\frac{1}{4\pi}\int_{-b/2}^{b/2}\frac{\frac{d\Gamma}{dx}dx}{x_1 - x} = \left(v_\infty\alpha - \frac{2\Gamma}{\lambda c}\right)_{x=x_1}$$

Introducing a parameter θ in the form $x = -\frac{1}{2}b\cos\theta$, and putting the circulation as

$$\Gamma = 2bv_\infty\sum_1^\infty \gamma_n \sin n\theta$$

gives $$w_1 = \frac{v_\infty}{\pi}\int_0^\pi \sum_1^\infty \frac{n\gamma_n \cos n\theta}{\cos\theta - \cos\theta_1}d\theta$$

Using the result of Glauert quoted in the previous example this becomes

$$w_1 = v_\infty\sum_1^\infty \frac{n\gamma_n \sin n\theta_1}{\sin\theta_1} = v_\infty\alpha - \frac{4b}{\lambda c}\sum_1^\infty \gamma_n \sin n\theta_1$$

The lift force is

$$\int^{b/2} \rho v_\infty \Gamma\, dx = \frac{1}{2}\pi\rho v_\infty^2 b^2\gamma_1$$

$$\text{lift coefficient} = \frac{\text{lift force}}{\frac{1}{2}\rho v_\infty^2 bc} = \pi\gamma_1 AR$$

where AR = aspect ratio = b/c (in this case).

The total induced drag is

$$D_i = \int_{-b/2}^{b/2}\frac{L'w}{v_\infty}dx = \int_{-b/2}^{b/2}\rho w\Gamma\, dx$$

$$= \rho v_\infty^2 b^2\int_0^\pi\left(\sum_1^\infty \gamma_n \sin n\theta\right)\left(\sum_1^\infty n\gamma_n \sin n\theta\right)d\theta = \frac{1}{2}\pi\rho v_\infty^2 b^2\sum_1^\infty n\gamma_n^2$$

Note. A semi-elliptic lift distribution gives a simple solution and also a *minimum* induced drag. Thus putting

$$\Gamma = \Gamma_o\sqrt{1-\left(\frac{2x}{b}\right)^2} = \Gamma_o\sqrt{1-t^2} \text{ say}$$

$$\frac{d\Gamma}{dx} = \frac{d\Gamma}{dt}\frac{dt}{dx} = \frac{1}{2}\Gamma_o\frac{-2t}{\sqrt{1-t^2}}\frac{2}{b} = \frac{-2\Gamma_o t}{b\sqrt{1-t^2}}$$

$$w_1 = \frac{1}{4\pi}\int_{-b/2}^{b/2}\frac{\frac{d\Gamma}{dx}dx}{x_1 - x} = -\frac{\Gamma_o}{2\pi b}\int_{-1}^{1}\frac{t\,dt}{(t_1-t)\sqrt{1-t^2}} = -\frac{\Gamma_o}{2\pi b}(-\pi) = \frac{\Gamma_o}{2b}$$

The downwash is therefore *constant* along the span. The lift,

$$L = \rho v_\infty\int_{-b/2}^{b/2} dx = \rho v_\infty\Gamma_o b\frac{\pi}{4} \quad\text{and hence}\quad w = \frac{2L}{\rho\pi b^2 v_\infty^2}$$

The induced drag is then

$$\frac{wL}{v_\infty} = \frac{L^2}{\frac{1}{2}\pi b^2\rho v_\infty^2}.$$

10.6 Prandtl-Glauert law

> Derive the Prandtl-Glauert law used in linearised potential *subsonic* flow. Two-diemensional flow should be considered, and the general equation for irrotational isentropic flow can be used without proof:
>
> $$\frac{\partial^2\phi}{\partial x^2}\left[1-\frac{1}{a^2}\left(\frac{\partial\phi}{\partial x}\right)^2\right] + \frac{\partial^2\phi}{\partial y^2}\left[1-\frac{1}{a^2}\left(\frac{\partial\phi}{\partial y}\right)^2\right] + \frac{\partial^2\phi}{\partial z^2}\left[1-\frac{1}{a^2}\left(\frac{\partial\phi}{\partial z}\right)^2\right] = 0$$
>
> Show how it can be applied to estimate an aerofoil's characteristics in compressible flow from the incompressible flow characteristics.

Solution. Linearised flow assumes that the disturbances produced by a body are small, or 'first order' effects (see Ex.1.12). Hence, if u_∞ is the free stream velocity in the x-direction and the velocity components are u, v, w in the x, y, z directions respectively then the quantities u/u_∞, v/u_∞, w/u_∞ are small enough to neglect second order terms. The equation given then reduces to

$$\frac{\partial^2\phi}{\partial x^2}\left[1-\frac{1}{a^2}\left(\frac{\partial\phi}{\partial x}\right)^2\right] + \frac{\partial^2\phi}{\partial y^2} + \frac{\partial^2\phi}{\partial z^2} = 0$$

It should be noted that in this equation a is the acoustic velocity, and $a^2 = \gamma RT$.

For an ideal gas (i.e. constant specific heat) the energy equation for isentropic flow is

$$\frac{\gamma}{\gamma-1}\frac{p}{\rho} + \frac{1}{2}\mathrm{v}^2 = \text{constant}$$

or

$$\frac{\gamma}{\gamma-1}RT + \frac{1}{2}(u^2+v^2+w^2) = \text{constant}$$

$$\frac{a^2}{\gamma-1} + \frac{1}{2}\left[\left(\frac{\partial\phi}{dx}\right)^2 + \left(\frac{\partial\phi}{\partial y}\right)^2 + \left(\frac{\partial\phi}{\partial z}\right)^2\right] = \text{constant}$$

Hence $a^2 = a_\infty^2 - u_\infty u(\gamma-1)$

and substituting gives

$$\frac{\partial^2\phi}{\partial x^2}\left[1 - \frac{M_\infty^2(1 + 2u/u_\infty)}{1 - M_\infty^2 u(\gamma - 1)/u_\infty}\right] + \frac{\partial^2\phi}{\partial y^2} + \frac{\partial^2\phi}{\partial z^2} = 0$$

where the Mach number (free stream) $M_\infty = u_\infty/a_\infty$.

Finally if u/u_∞ is small compared to $(1 - M_\infty^2)$, and $M_\infty^2(u/u_\infty) << 1$ the equation reduces to

$$(1 - M_\infty^2)\frac{\partial^2\phi}{\partial x^2} + \frac{\partial^2\phi}{\partial y^2} + \frac{\partial^2\phi}{\partial z^2} = 0$$

or in two-dimensional flow

$$(1 - M_\infty^2)\frac{\partial^2\phi}{\partial x^2} + \frac{\partial^2\phi}{\partial z^2} = 0$$

The corresponding equation for incompressible flow is

$$\frac{\partial^2\phi}{\partial x^2} + \frac{\partial^2\phi}{\partial z^2} = 0$$

Thus a simple *transformation* from compressible to incompressible flow is provided by

$$\phi_c = \frac{f(x, \beta z)}{\beta^n} \qquad \text{where } \phi_i = f(x, z)$$

The subscripts c, i refer to compressible and incompressible flow respectively, and $\beta^2 = 1 - M_\infty^2$.

At the aerofoil surface

$$\left(\frac{dz}{dx}\right)_c = \frac{1}{\beta^{n-1}}\left(\frac{dz}{dx}\right)_i$$

and at corresponding values of x the section ordinates

$$z_c = \frac{z_i}{\beta^{n-1}}:$$

The pressure coefficients are in the ratio

$$\frac{C_{pc}}{C_{pi}} = \frac{1}{\beta^n}$$

To summarise:

	compressible	equivalent in incompressible flow
ordinate	z	$z\beta^{n-1}$
incidence	α	$\alpha\beta^{n-1}$
potential function	$\frac{f(x, \beta z)}{z^n}$	$f(x, z)$
pressure coefficient	C_p	$C_p\beta^n$

If the value of the index n is taken as 1, the *sections* are *identical* and

$$C_{pc} = \frac{C_{pi}}{\beta}$$

This result is known as the *Prandtl-Glauert law*. The result can be applied equally well to the lift coefficient and moment coefficient.

The law agrees quite well with experimental data, considering the assumptions made in its derivation. These amount to thin sections with small camber, at low lift coefficients and low Mach numbers. An example is shown in Fig. 10.14.

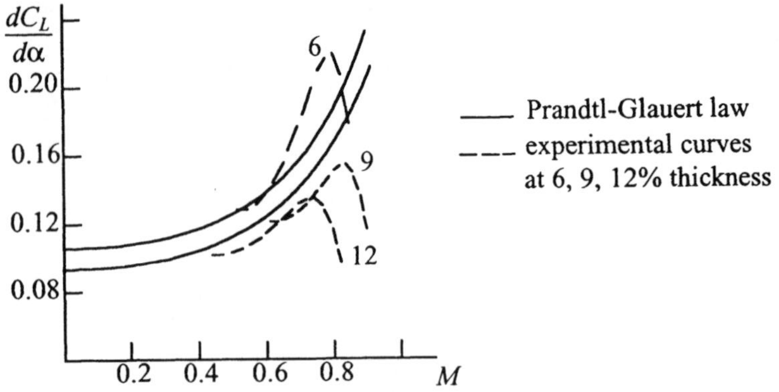

Figure 10.14

Note. Many attempts have been made to obtain more accurate expressions. One that is widely used is the Karman-Tsien relation

$$\frac{C_{pc}}{C_{pi}} = \left(\beta + \frac{M^2}{1+\beta}\frac{C_{pi}}{2}\right)^{-1}$$

10.7 Ackeret's law

> Discuss the application of linearised theory to *supersonic* flow, and derive Ackeret's law.
>
> Outline how the lift and wave drag coefficients can be determined in terms of the angle of attack of the surface, the slope of the surface and the free stream Mach number.
>
> Determine the coefficients for a flat plate aerofoil.

Solution

Note. A discussion of linearised flow theory has been considered in Chap.1 (W.E.1.12, 1.13), and therefore the results will be quoted directly.

Linearised theory can be usefully applied to flow around a corner, to determine the lift and drag forces on an aerofoil. It should be noted however that expansion around a convex corner can be analysed by Prandtl-Meyer theory; and compression around a concave corner involves shock wave theory at substantial angles of deflection.

The potential equation, from the previous example, is

$$(M_\infty^2 - 1)\frac{\partial^2\phi}{\partial x} - \frac{\partial^2\phi}{\partial z^2} = 0$$

The general solution is of the form

$$\phi - f_1(x - Bz) + f_2(x + Bz)$$

where $B^2 = M_\infty^2 - 1$

The lines $x \pm Bz$ are the lines of action of the two families of Mach waves, and since the disturbances are always propagated in the downstream direction the functions $f_1(x - Bz)$ and $f_2(x + Bz)$ are those of the family of waves generated from the lower and upper boundaries respectively (Fig. 10.15).

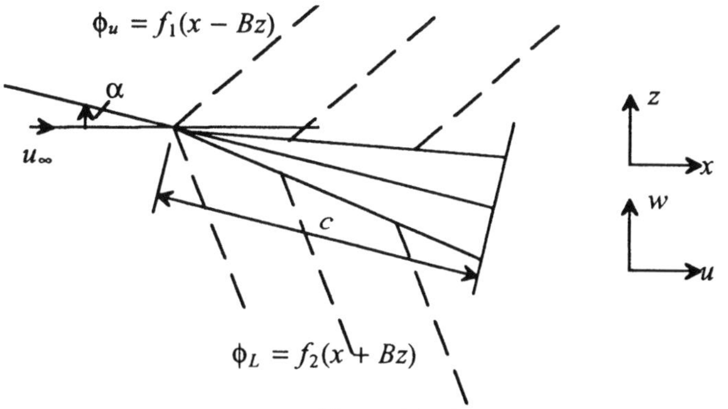

Figure 10.15

For the upper surface the boundary condition on the surface is that

$$\left(\frac{dz}{dx}\right)_u = \frac{w}{u_\infty} = -\frac{1}{u_\infty}\left(\frac{\partial f_1}{\partial z}\right) = \frac{Bf_1'}{u_\infty}$$

where f_1' denotes differentiation with respect to $(x - Bz)$. The pressure coefficient is

$$C_p = \frac{p - p_\infty}{\frac{1}{2}\rho_\infty u_\infty^2} = \frac{2(p/p_\infty - 1)}{\gamma M_\infty^2} = -\frac{2u}{u_\infty}$$

since $\dfrac{p}{p_\infty} = 1 - \dfrac{\gamma M_\infty^2 u}{u_\infty}$

Hence for the upper surface

$$C_{pu} = \frac{2f_1'}{u_\infty} = \frac{2}{B}\left(\frac{dz}{dx}\right)_u$$

Similarly for the lower surface

$$C_{pL} = -\frac{2}{B}\left(\frac{dz}{dx}\right)_L$$

This result is known as *Ackeret's* law.

The lift coefficient

$$C_L = -\frac{1}{c}\int(C_{pu} - C_{pL})\,dx$$

or

$$C_L = -\frac{2}{Bc}\left[\int_0^c\left(\frac{dz}{dx}\right)_u dx + \int_0^c\left(\frac{dz}{dx}\right)_L dx\right]$$

$$C_L = \frac{4\alpha}{B}$$

The drag coefficient (due to the *waves*) is

$$C_{Dw} = \frac{2}{Bc}\left|\int_0^c\left(\frac{dz}{dx}\right)_u dx + \int_0^c\left(\frac{dz}{dx}\right)_L dx\right| = \frac{2}{B}(2\alpha^2 + \overline{s_u^2} + \overline{s_L^2})$$

where $\overline{s^2}$ is the mean square slope of the surface. For a *flat plate* it immediately follows that

$$C_L = \frac{4\alpha}{B} = \frac{4\alpha}{\sqrt{M_\infty^2 - 1}}$$

and

$$C^{Dw} = \frac{2}{B}(2\alpha^2 + \alpha^2 + \alpha^2) = \frac{4\alpha^2}{\sqrt{M_\infty^2 - 1}}$$

10.8 Cascade performance

A stationary cascade of blades is shown in Fig. 10.16. Assuming steady, incompressible flow and constant flow velocity in the axial direction derive expressions for the lift and drag coefficients, and cascade efficiency in terms of the blade angles, solidity, axial flow velocity and decrease in *stagnation* pressure.

Solution

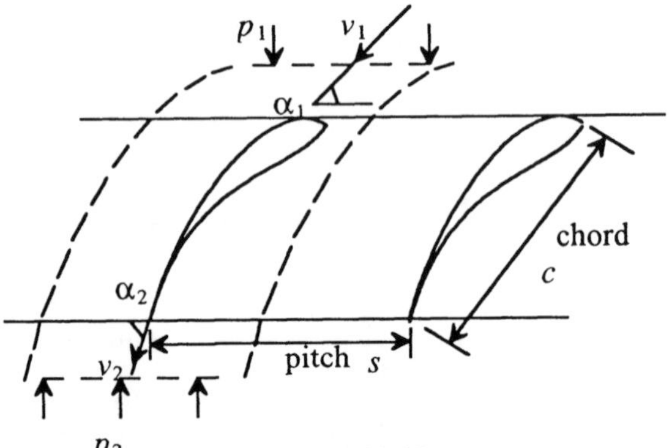

Figure 10.16

Consider the forces on the control surface (shown by the dotted lines) in which the side boundaries are taken as the median streamlines. The velocity is made up of two components, in the axial and tangential directions. The forces, X, Y, in the axial and tangential directions are shown (Fig. 10.17) together with the corresponding lift and drag forces, acting at some point P.

Per unit span, the *continuity* equation gives

$$v_f = v_1 \sin\alpha_1 = v_2 \sin\alpha_2$$

The *momentum* equation gives, for steady flow,

$$X = (p_2 - p_1)s$$

$$Y = \dot{m}(v_{w1} - v_{w2}) = \rho s v_f(v_{w1} - v_{w2}) = \rho s v_f^2(\cot\alpha_1 - \cot\alpha_2)$$

since $v_w = v_f \cot\alpha$

The *energy* (Bernoulli) equation gives

$$p_1 + \tfrac{1}{2}\rho v_1^2 = p_2 + \tfrac{1}{2}\rho v_2^2 + \Delta p_o$$

where the stagnation pressure decrease Δp_o arises due to frictional and other effects. Hence:

$$p_2 - p_1 = \tfrac{1}{2}\rho(v_1^2 - v_2^2) - \Delta p_o$$

Now $v^2 = v_f^2 + v_w^2 = v_f^2 + v_f^2 \cot^2\alpha$

giving $X = s(p_2 - p_1) = \tfrac{1}{2}\rho s v_f^2(\cot^2\alpha_1 - \cot^2\alpha_2) - s\Delta p_o$

The mean angle can be introduced:

$$v_{wm} = \tfrac{1}{2}(v_{w1} + v_{w2})$$

and $\quad v_f \cot\alpha_m = \tfrac{1}{2}(v_f \cot\alpha_1 + v_f \cot\alpha_2)$

or $\quad \boldsymbol{\cot\alpha_m = \tfrac{1}{2}(\cot\alpha_1 + \cot\alpha_2)}$

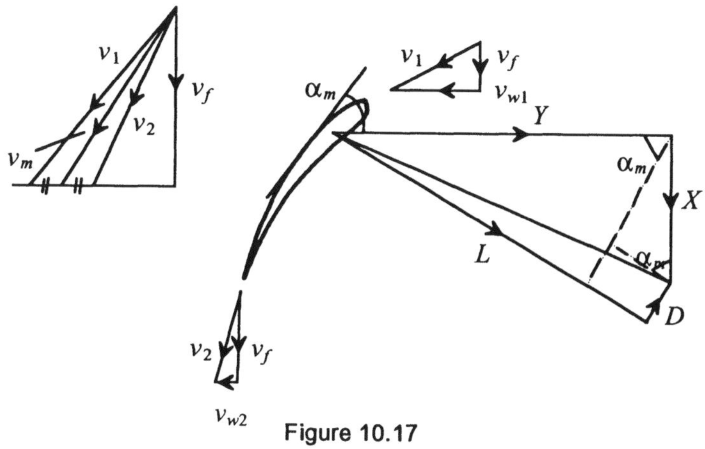

Figure 10.17

$$X = \rho s v_f^2(\cot\alpha_1 - \cot\alpha_2)\cot\alpha_m - s\,\Delta p_o$$

Turning to the tangential force

$$Y = \rho s v_f^2(\cot\alpha_1 - \cot\alpha_2)$$

The lift and drag forces can be expressed in terms of the axial and tangential forces. Referring to Fig. 10.16

$$L = X\cos\alpha_m + Y\sin\alpha_m, \qquad D = Y\cos\alpha_m - X\sin\alpha_m$$

Substituting for X, Y gives

$$\begin{aligned} D &= \rho s v_f^2(\cot\alpha_1 - \cot\alpha_2)\cos\alpha_m - \rho s v_f^2(\cot\alpha_1 - \cot\alpha_2)\cos\alpha_m \\ &\quad + s\,\Delta p_o \sin\alpha_m \\ &= s\,\Delta p_o \sin\alpha_m \end{aligned}$$

$$\begin{aligned} L &= \rho s v_f^2(\cot\alpha_1 - \cot\alpha_2)\sin\alpha_m \\ &\quad + \rho s v_f^2(\cot\alpha_1 - \cot\alpha_2)\cot\alpha_m\cos\alpha_m - s\,\Delta p_o \cos\alpha_m \\ &= \rho s v_f^2\frac{(\cot\alpha_1 - \cot\alpha_2)}{\sin\alpha_m} - s\,\Delta p_o \cos\alpha_m \end{aligned}$$

The lift and drag coefficients are based upon the mean velocity and projected area

$$\frac{1}{2}\rho v_m^2 c = \frac{\frac{1}{2}\rho c v_f^2}{\sin^2\alpha_m}$$

Hence $C_D = \dfrac{s\,\Delta p_o \sin^3\alpha_m}{\frac{1}{2}\rho c v_f^2}$ or $C_D = \dfrac{2\,\Delta p_o \sin^3\alpha_m}{\sigma\rho v_f^2}$

where σ = chord/pitch ratio = c/s

$$C_L = \frac{2}{\sigma}\sin\alpha_m(\cot\alpha_1 - \cot\alpha_2) - \frac{2\,\Delta p_o \cos\alpha_m \sin^3\alpha_m}{\sigma\rho v_f^2}$$

or $\quad C_L = \dfrac{2}{\sigma}\sin\alpha_m(\cot\alpha_1 - \cot\alpha_2) - C_D\cot\alpha_m$

The cascade efficiency is defined in terms of the static pressures and stagnation pressure drop:

$$\eta = \frac{\Delta p}{\Delta p + \Delta p_o} = \frac{p_2 - p_1}{\frac{1}{2}\rho(v_1^2 - v_2^2)}$$

and substituting gives, after some manipulation,

$$\eta = 1 - \frac{\Delta p_o}{\rho v_f^2 \cot\alpha_m(\cot\alpha_1 - \cot\alpha_2)}$$

Note. The cascade shown is typical of a compressor (axial flow), and the assumption of incompressible flow is a reasonable approxiamtion.

The efficiency can also be expressed in terms of the lift:drag ratio

$$\varepsilon = \frac{C_L}{C_D}, \qquad \eta = 1 - \frac{2}{(\varepsilon + \cot\alpha_m)\sin 2\alpha_m}$$

The circulation Γ can be introduced: it is equal to line (contour) integral of the velocity around the control volume. Hence $\Gamma = s(v_{w1} - v_{w2})$. Using the previous result for *frictionless* flow

$$L = \rho s v_f^2 \frac{\cot\alpha_1 - \cot\alpha_2}{\sin\alpha_m} \qquad \text{and} \qquad v_m = \frac{v_f}{\sin\alpha_m}$$

gives $L = \rho\Gamma v_m$

10.9 Rotor cascade: degree of reaction

An axial flow compressor delivers 18 kg/s of air. Compressor speed = 11500 rev/min. In a particular stage the static conditions at inlet are 1 bar, 300 K. The axial flow velocity is constant and equal to 120 m/s. The air density is constant at 1.16 kg/m^3.

At the mean diameter of 40 cm the degree of reaction = 0.50, and the change in whirl velocity = 0.35u (where u = blade velocity).

Blade pitch = 4 cm, chord = 6 cm.

Friction pressure drop = 1800 N/m^2.

Determine the blade angles and height at the inlet: and the lift and drag coefficients. The following relationships may be used:

$$\sigma C_D = \frac{2\,\Delta p_o \sin^3\theta_m}{\rho v_f^2}$$

$$\sigma C_L = 2\sin\theta_m(\cot\theta_2 - \cot\theta_3) - \sigma C_D \cot\theta_m$$

Solution. In this problem the cascade is moving, and the formulae derived in the previous example are quoted with the 'absolute' angles α replaced by the 'relative' angles θ. The velocity triangles are shown in Fig. 10.18.

The *degree of reaction*, R, is a measure of the way in which the total pressure (or enthalpy) change across a stage is divided between the fixed cascade (stator or guide vanes) and the moving cascade (rotor). It is defined as

$$R = \frac{\Delta p(\text{rotor})}{\Delta p\,(\text{stage})} \quad \text{or} \quad \frac{\Delta h\,(\text{rotor})}{\Delta h\,(\text{stage})}$$

An expression for the reaction can be determined, in terms of the flow coefficient $\phi = v_f/u$ and blade angles as follows: the subscripts 2, 3 refer to the rotor and 3, 4 to the following stator.

$$R = \frac{\Delta h\,(\text{rotor})}{\Delta h\,(\text{rotor}) + \Delta h\,(\text{stator})} = \frac{h_3 - h_2}{h_4 - h_2}$$

Across the rotor the *relative* stagnation enthalpy is constant (since frictional effects produce a reheat effect), and $h_3 - h_2 = \frac{1}{2}(v_{r2}^2 - v_{r3}^2)$. Assuming a *normal* stage, i.e. $v_2 = v_4$, and noting that

$$\Delta h_o = u\,\Delta v_w$$

then $h_4 - h_2 = u(v_{w3} - v_{w2})$

Hence $R = \dfrac{v_{r2}^2 - v_{r3}^2}{2u(v_{w3} - v_{w2})} = \dfrac{v_{w2} + v_{w3}}{2u} = \frac{1}{2}\phi(\cot\theta_2 + \cot\theta_3)$

since $v_r^2 = v_f^2 + (u - v_w)^2$

It should be noted that in Fig. 10.18 the velocity triangles are drawn in three ways: superimposed on the blade, together on a common flow velocity v_f, and together on a common blade velocity u. The choice of style is a matter of preference.

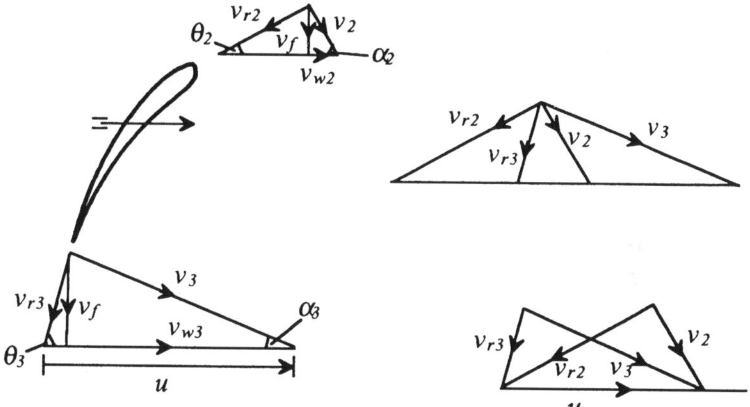

Figure 10.18

In the particular case of 50% reaction, or $R = 0.5$, the velocity triangles are *symmetrical*. Hence

$$\Delta v_w = v_{w3} - v_{w2} = v_f(\cot\theta_2 - \cot\theta_3)$$

Now $u = \pi(0.4)\dfrac{(11500)}{60} = 240.9$ m/s and $\Delta v_w = 0.35u = 84.3$ m/s

Using $v_f = 120$ m/s gives

$$\cot\theta_2 + \cot\theta_3 = \frac{u}{v_f} = 2.0075 \text{ and } \cot\theta_2 - \cot\theta_3 = \frac{84.3}{120} = 0.7025$$

Solving gives

$$\boldsymbol{\theta_2 = 36.4^\circ, \theta_3 = 56.9^\circ}$$

The mass flow rate

$$\dot{m} = 18 \text{ kg/s} = \rho v_f \pi D_m h$$

where D_m = mean blade diameter, h = blade height.

Hence $h = \dfrac{18}{(1.16 \times 120 \times \pi \times 0.4)} = \mathbf{0.103}$ **m**

This gives the blade tip diameter as 0.103 + 0.40 = 0.503 m, and the root diameter as 0.40 – 0.103 = 0.297 m.

The mean relative angle can be determined from the relation

$$\cot\theta_m = \tfrac{1}{2}(\cot\theta_2 + \cot\theta_3)$$

giving $\theta_m = 44.9^o$

The solidity σ = chord/pitch = 1.5.

Hence, substituting into the equations given:

$$C_D = \frac{1}{1.5}\frac{(2 \times 1800 \times \sin^3 44.9)}{(1.16 \times 120^2)} = \mathbf{0.051}$$

$$1.5C_L = 2(0.706)(1.3564 - 0.6519) - 1.5(0.051)(1.0035)$$

$$C_L = \mathbf{0.612}$$

Note. In this problem the cascade efficiency is

$$\eta = 1 - \frac{2C_D}{(C_L + C_D \cot\theta_m)\sin 2\theta_m} = 0.88$$

10.10 Turbine cascade

A turbine rotor cascade consists of blades shown in Fig. 10.19. The axial flow velocity is constant at 120 m/s, and the fluid leaves the rotor in an axial direction.

The static conditions at the blade inlet are 900 K, 5 bar. Blade pitch = 5 cm.

Loss coefficient (in terms of the exit relative velocity) is

$$\zeta = 0.04 + (e/100)^2$$

where e is the deflection across the blade (measured in degrees).

The fluid properties are:

$$C_p = 1.15 \text{ kJ/kg K}, \gamma = C_p/C_v = 4/3.$$

Determine the lift and drag forces on a blade.

Solution

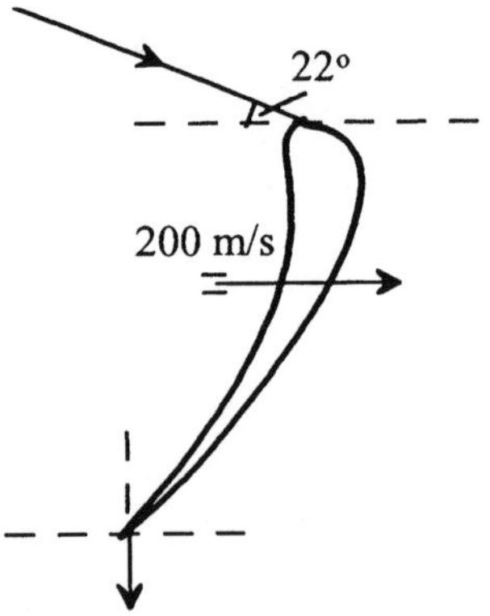

Figure 10.19

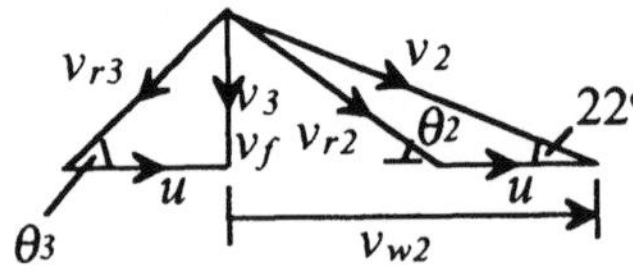

Figure 10.20

The velocity triangles are shown in Fig. 10.20. It should be noted that in this case the whirl velocity at inlet > whirl velocity at exit: energy is *extracted* from the fluid to drive the turbine. In the two previous problems the cascade was one used in a compressor, where there is a pressure rise, exit whirl > inlet and energy is supplied to the machine.

Further, the blade section is no longer an aerofoil so that the fluid deflection is much greater. The tendency for boundary layer separation is however offset by the slower layer thickness growth (due to decreasing pressure across the blade). Finally the change in density is usually appreciable and therefore the *compressible* flow analysis must be used.

Considering the velocity triangles

$$V_{w2} = V_f \cot\alpha_2 = 120\cot 22 = 297 \text{ m/s}$$

$$\tan\theta_2 = \frac{V_f}{V_{w2} - u} = 1.237 \qquad \text{and } \theta_2 = \mathbf{51.05°}$$

$$\tan\theta_3 = \frac{V_f}{u} = 0.60 \qquad \text{and } \theta_3 = \mathbf{30.96°}$$

$$v_{r2}^2 = (120)^2 + (297 - 200)^2 \quad \text{and } v_{r2} = 154 \text{ m/s}$$
$$v_{r3}^2 = (120)^2 + (200)^2 \quad \text{and } v_{r3} = 233 \text{ m/s}$$
$$v_2^2 = (120)^2 + (297)^2 \quad \text{and } v_2 = 320 \text{ m/s}$$

The work done on the rotor /kg fluid is

$$h_{o2} - h_{o3} = u(v_{w2} + v_{w3})$$

(assuming that the flow is *adiabatic*).

The effect of irreversibility is expressed in terms of a loss coefficient

$$\zeta = \frac{h_3 - h_{3s}}{\frac{1}{2}v_{r3}^2}$$

where h_{3s} denotes the enthalpy, at exit, after isentropic expansion. The Soderburg correlation is given in the problem, viz.

$$\zeta = 0.04 + \left(\frac{e}{100}\right)^2$$

In this problem $e = \theta_2 + \theta_3 = 82^o$ giving $\zeta = 0.712$, and

$$\Delta h_o = \zeta(\tfrac{1}{2}v_{r3})^2 = 19330 \text{ J/kg} = h_3 - h_{3s}$$

Now $h_{o2} = h_2 + \frac{1}{2}v_2^2 = 1150(900) + \frac{1}{2}(320)^2 = 1086$ kJ/kg

$$h_{o3} = h_{o2} - u(v_{w2} + v_{w3}) = 1027 \text{ kJ/kg}$$
$$h_3 = h_{o3} - \tfrac{1}{2}v_3^2 = 1013 \text{ kJ/kg}$$

and $T_3 = \dfrac{1013}{1.15} = 881$ K, $\qquad T_{3s} = T_3 - \dfrac{19.33}{1.5} = 868$ K

Hence $\dfrac{p_2}{p_3} = \left(\dfrac{T_2}{T_{35}}\right)^{\frac{\gamma}{\gamma-1}} = 1.156$ and $p_3 = 4.33$ bar

The fluid density can be calculated from the ideal gas law

$$p = \rho RT \qquad \text{where } R = \frac{(\gamma - 1)C_p}{\gamma} = 0.288 \text{ kJ/kg K}$$

At the inlet

$$\rho_2 = \frac{5 \times 10^5}{288 \times 900} = 1.929 \text{ kg/m}^3, \quad \rho_3 = \frac{4.33 \times 10^5}{288 \times 881} = 1.707 \text{ kg/m}^3$$

The mean density is

$$\tfrac{1}{2}(\rho_2 + \rho_3) = 1.818 \text{ kg/m}^3$$

The axial force

$$X = (p_2 - p_3)s \text{ per unit width (span)}$$
$$= (5.0 - 4.33)10^5(0.05) = 3350 \text{ N}$$

The tangential force

$$Y = \rho s v_f(v_{w2} - v_{w3}) = 1.707(0.05)(120)(297 - 0) = 3042 \text{ N}$$

The mean velocity, in magnitude and direction, is required to determine the lift and drag forces.

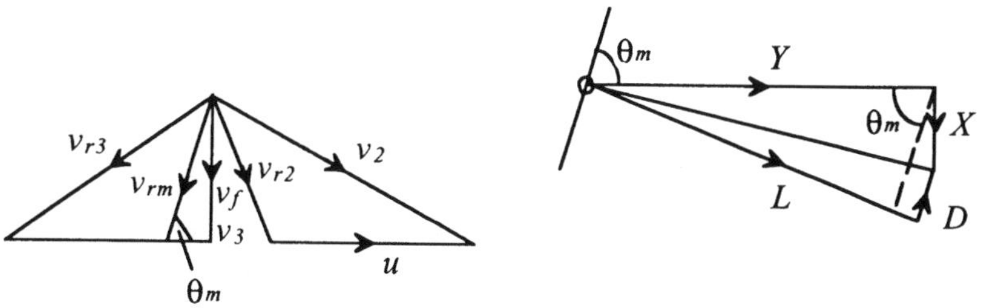

Figure 10.21

Referring to Fig. 10.21,

$$v_{rm}\cos\theta_m = \tfrac{1}{2}(v_{r3}\cos\theta_3 + v_{r2}\cos\theta_2) - v_{r2}\cos\theta_2 = 51 \text{ m/s}$$

$v_{rm}\sin\theta_m = v_f = 120$ m/s giving $v_{rm} = 130$ m/s, $\theta_m = 67.0^o$

Lift force $L = Y\sin\theta_m + X\cos\theta_m =$ **4109** N

Drag force $D = Y\cos\theta_m - X\sin\theta_m =$ **1895** N

10.11 Cascade performance

Discuss the characteristics of a compressor cascade, and how performance data can be correlated. Outline the approach due to Howell, based on the nominal (design) condition.
Indicate how the fluid deviation can be estimated.

Solution. Referring to Fig. 10.6, the convention used so far has been to measure all angles from the *tangential* direction. However the normal practice in cascade performance work is to measure all the angles from the *axial* direction, and this is adopted in the solution (Fig. 10.22).

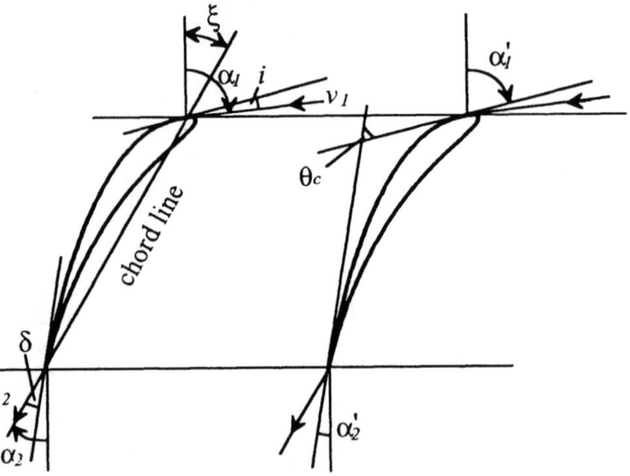

Figure 10.22

The blade angles are denoted by α', and direction of the fluid by α. Thus the fluid *incidence* at inlet, $i = \alpha_1 - \alpha'_1$, and the *deviation* at outlet is

$$\delta = \alpha_2 - \alpha'_2$$

The performance characteristics of a cascade can not be determined by theoretical means alone and experimental data is necessary to estimate cascade performance. The bulk of such data is obtained from cascade wind tunnels, in which the pressure, flow angle and fluid velocity distribution is measured across the cascade entry and exit. From such test results *average* values are obtained. The complete performance of the cascade can be determined by executing similar tests over a range of fluid inlet angles, at the same inlet Mach number and Reynolds number (based on chord length). The testing required is minimised by using low inlet velocities, at a Reynolds number greater than a critical value

$$Re = \frac{\rho v_1 c}{\mu} = 2 \times 10^5 \text{ (approx.)}.$$

At values above this critical value the effect of Reynolds number variation is negligible. Also Mach number effects (compressibility) are small when

$$M_1 < 0.3.$$

The losses incurred are due to the tunnel wall boundary layers interacting with the blades, especially with the end blade (producing stalling); secondary flow produced by the generation of vorticity at blade roots attached to the tunnel walls; and profile loss due to blade surface friction. The total loss is made up of this annulus loss, secondary loss and profile loss.

Low-speed compressor cascade results are of the form shown in Fig.10.23 (Howell, A.R.), where the pressure loss coefficient

$$\zeta = \frac{\Delta p_o}{\frac{1}{2}\rho v_1^2}$$

and fluid deflection

$$\varepsilon = \alpha_2 - \alpha_1$$

are plotted against the incidence.

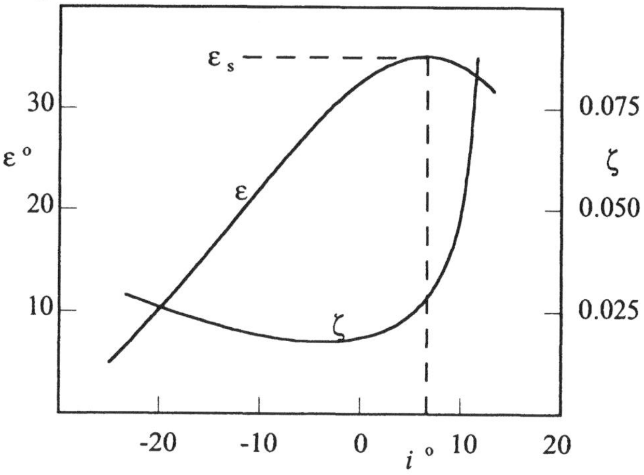

Figure 10.23

The loss increases rapidly as the incidence rises above a certain value and the cascade becomes *stalled*: separation occurring on the suction side of the blade surface. The precise point at which stalling occurs is difficult to define, and therefore a *stall point* is specified at which Δp_o is twice the minimum value.

The correlation of Howell has been widely used and is based on a nominal condition (design) $\varepsilon^* = 0.8\varepsilon_s$. Howell found that

$$\varepsilon^* = f(s/c, \alpha_2^*, Re)$$

and the correlation is almost independent of the blade camber in the range

$$20^o < \theta < 40^o \quad \text{and} \quad Re > 3 \times 10^5$$

The deviation δ depends upon the blade camber, blade shape, pitch/chord ratio (solidity) and stagger angle. The fluid deflection is always reduced by the deviation, and can be of the substantial value. Howell's empirical rule is

$$\delta^* = m\theta_c(s/c)^n$$

where $n = \frac{1}{2}$ for cascades and $n = 1$ for inlet guide vanes

$m = 0.23(2a/c)^2 + \alpha_2^*/500$ for a cascade

$m = 0.19$ for inlet guide vanes

a = distance of maximum camber from the leading edge.

At conditions away from the design point, generalised performance curves of Howell can be used: $\varepsilon/\varepsilon^*$ and C_D are plotted against $(i - i^*)/\varepsilon^*$ for various pitch/chord ratios.

Note. The flow can be taken as two-dimensional and the cascade theory applicable in machines (axial flow) having a high hub/tip ratio. However with lower hub/tip ratios the blades normally twist along their length and 'vortex design' is used (three-dimensional flow). Two-dimensional cascade data is still useful for calculations at discrete blade sections.

10.12 Cascade performance calculation

A cascade has a pitch/chord ratio = 1. The *blade* inlet and outlet angles are 50° and 20° respectively. The blade camber is a maximum at mid-chord.

Determine the fluid deflection, incidence and ideal lift coefficient at the design point. The following equation may be used for the nominal deflection:

$$\varepsilon^* = (15 - 0.2\alpha_2^*)(3 - s/c)^o$$

If the incidence = 40° determine the lift coefficient.

Take $C_D = 0.019$, $\varepsilon/\varepsilon^* = 1.20$.

Solution. $\alpha_1' = 50^o$ and $\alpha_2' = 20^o$: hence the camber $\theta_c = 30^o$. For a cascade

$$m = 0.23(2a/c)^2 + \alpha_2^*/500 = 0.23 + \alpha_2^*/500$$

$$\delta^* = m\theta_c\sqrt{s/c} = m\theta_c$$

Assume $\alpha_2^* = 25^o$: then

$$m = 0.23 + (25/500) = 0.28, \qquad \delta^* = 0.28(30) = 8.4^o$$

$$\alpha_2^* = \alpha_2' + \delta = 28.4^o$$

The difference between the assumed and calculated values of α_2^* is 3.4°. Hence a better agreement is obtained by assuming a higher value, say 28.5°. Then $m = 0.23 + (28.5/500) = 0.287$

$$\delta^* = 0.287(30) = 8.6^o$$

$$\alpha_2^* = 20 + 8.6 = 28.6^o$$

giving reasonable agreement.

Using the relation given

$$\varepsilon^* = (16 - 0.2(28.6))(3 - 1) = \mathbf{20.6^o}$$

Hence $\alpha_1^* = \alpha_2^* + \varepsilon^* = 49.2^o$

$$i^* = \alpha_1^* - \alpha_1 = 49.2 - 50 = \mathbf{-0.8^o}$$

The ideal lift coefficient (i.e. with $C_D = 0$) can be calcualted from the equation derived in W.E.10.8, noting however that in this solution the angles are measured from the *axial* direction, not the tangential direction.

$$C_L = \frac{2}{\sigma}\cos\alpha_m(\tan\alpha_1 - \tan\alpha_2)$$

where $\tan\alpha_m = \frac{1}{2}(\tan\alpha_1 + \tan\alpha_2)$, $\sigma = c/s = 1$

Substituting gives

$$\alpha_m^* = 40.4^o, \qquad C_L = 2(0.762)(0.6133) = \mathbf{0.93}$$

At an incidence of 4° (corresponding to off-design performance)

$$\frac{i - i^*}{\varepsilon^*} = \frac{4 - (-0.8)}{20.6} = 0.233$$

the values of C_D and $\varepsilon/\varepsilon^*$ are given as 0.019 and 1.18 respectively.

Note. These values are read off the Howell generalised performance curves.

Hence $\varepsilon = 1.18(20.6) = 24.3^o$

$$\alpha_1 = \alpha_1' + i = 50 + 4 = 54.0^o$$

$$\alpha_2 = \alpha_1 - \varepsilon = 29.7^o$$

$$\tan\alpha_m = \tfrac{1}{2}(\tan\alpha_1 + \tan\alpha_2) \text{ and } \alpha_m = 44.2^o$$

$$\zeta = \frac{\Delta p_o}{\frac{1}{2}\rho v_f^2} = \frac{\sigma C_D}{\cos^3\alpha_m} = \frac{0.019}{\cos^3 44.2} = 0.051$$

and $$C_L = \frac{2}{\sigma}\cos\alpha_m(\tan\alpha_1 - \tan\alpha_2) - \frac{1}{\sigma}C_D\tan\alpha_m$$
$$= 1.156 - 0.018 = \mathbf{1.138}$$

Problems

1 The characteristics of an aerofoil are as follows:

Angle of attack °	-4	0	4	8	12	16	17	18
C_L	-0.281	0.122	0.523	0.919	1.32	1.67	1.74	1.30
C_D	0.008	0.006	0.007	0.010	0.016	0.032	0.040	0.153

Plot C_L and C_L/C_D against the angle of attack; and hence estimate the stalling angle and maximum value of C_L/C_D.

Determine the slope of the lift curve, and compare it with the theoretical value.

Answer 17°; 92. 6.08 per rad. (theor. 2π)

2 The pressure distribution on a model aerofoil was obtained in a wind tunnel test, giving the following data:

free stream velocity = 40 m/s

air density = 1.2 kg/m^3

	upper surface			lower surface			
x/c	0.0	0.1	1.0	0.0	0.05	0.4	1.0
$p - p_\infty$	0	-1,920	0	0	960	380	0

Estimate the lift coefficient of the aerofoil.

Answer 1.49

3 Obtain an expression for the induced velocity at a point distance x from the centre of an aerofoil, span $2b$; the circulation at the point is Γ.

Calculate the induced velocity, in terms of Γ_o, at the centre of the span, and at the point $x = b/2$, when the circulation follows the law

$$\Gamma = \Gamma_o\left[\frac{2}{3}\left(1 - \frac{x^2}{b^2}\right)^{1/2} + \frac{1}{3}\left(1 - \frac{x^2}{s^2}\right)^{3/2}\right]$$

It may be assumed that

$$\int_0^\pi \frac{\cos n\theta \, d\theta}{\cos\theta - \cos\phi} = \frac{\pi \sin n\phi}{\sin\phi}$$

Answer $0.14\Gamma_o/b$

4 A wing of elliptic plan form has an area of 56 m^2, and an aspect ratio of 6.0. Free stream velocity = 400 km/h. The circulation round the mid-span section is 63 m^2/s. Air density = 0.65 kg/m^3.

Assuming lifting line theory results calculate the lift and induced drag of the aerofoil.

Answer 20830, 104 N

5 Two aerofoils are of the same span but different planforms, and develop the same lift. The distribution of the circulation for one aerofoil is

$$\Gamma = \Gamma_o\left[\left(1 - \frac{x}{b}\right)^2\right]^{1/2} \qquad \text{(i.e. elliptic)}$$

and for the other aerofoil

$$\Gamma = \Gamma_o\left[\left(1 - \frac{x}{b}\right)^2\right]^{3/2} \qquad \text{where } 2b = \text{span}$$

Determine the ratio of the induced drags of the two aerofoils.

The Glauert result (Prob.3) may be used.

Answer 4/9

6 Show that the increase in the lift coefficient due to the deflection δ of a *small* trailing edge flap is approximately

$$8\delta\sqrt{k}$$

where the flap length is k times the chord.

The thin section theory should be used (W.E.10.4).

7 The circulation along an aerofoil, span $2b$, is given by a Fourier series

$$\Delta = 4v_\infty b \sum A_n \sin n\theta$$

where the ordinate $y = -b\cos\theta$.

The lift and induced drag coefficients are given by the expressions

$$C_L = \pi A_1(AR), \qquad C_D = \frac{C_L^2}{\pi(AR)} \sum \frac{nA_n^2}{A_1^2}$$

Show that the most efficient form of untwisted wing is of elliptical plan form; and for this aerofoil the downwash angle is constant.

8 A thin aerofoil is shown in Fig. 10.24. The angle δ is small. Determine the angle of zero lift α_o, and the lift coefficient at incidence α (measured from line AB) in terms of δ, θ_o and e where

$$x = \frac{1}{2}c(1 - \cos\theta), \quad e = \frac{a}{a+b}$$

θ_o = value of θ at point B.

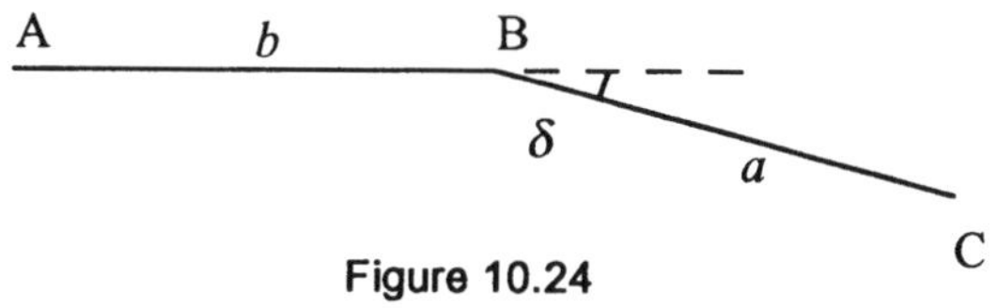

Figure 10.24

Answer $\quad \alpha_o = \frac{\delta}{\pi}(\theta_o - \sin\theta_o) - \delta(1 - e);$

$$C_L = 2\pi\alpha + 2[(\pi - \theta_o) + 2\sin\theta_o]\delta.$$

9 A symmetrical double wedge aerofoil is shown in Fig. 10.25. The incidence = 2° and the free stream Mach number = 1.60. Determine the lift and wave drag coefficients by (a) use of Ackeret's theory, (b) use of Prandtl-Meyer and shock wave tables.

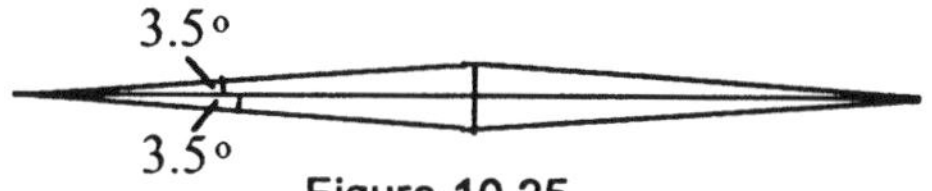

Figure 10.25

Answer (a) 0.112, 0.016. (b) 0.10, 0.012.

10 Repeat Problem 9 for an aerofoil of the shape shown in Fig. 10.26.

Answer (a) 0.112, 0.058. (b) 0.118, 0.040.

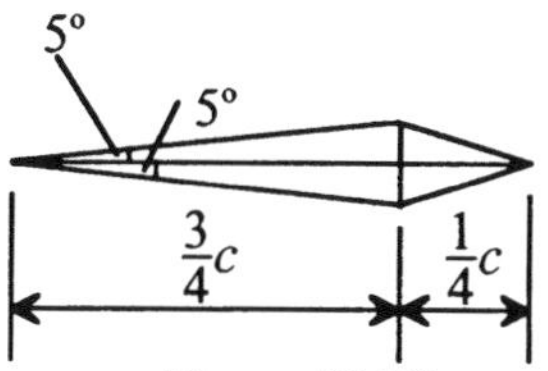

Figure 10.26

11 Using linearised pertubation theory show that the wave drag coefficient for the wedge aerofoil shown in Fig. 10.27 is given by the expression

$$BC_D = 4\alpha^2 + \frac{1}{k(1-k)}\frac{t^2}{c^2}$$

What is the value of k for minimum drag?

Answer 1/2

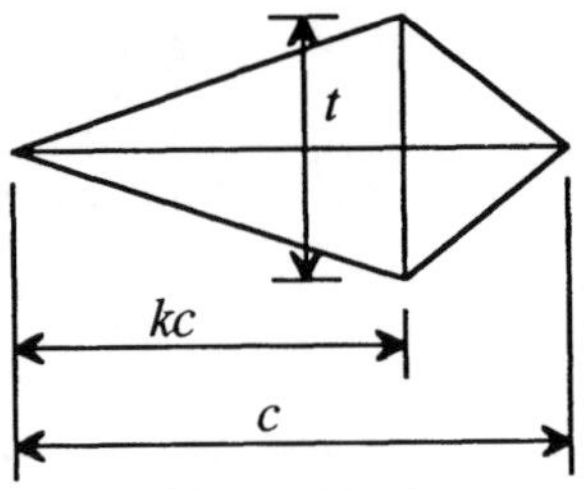

Figure 10.27

12 In a stator cascade of aerofoil blades the pressure drop across the cascade = 850 N/m^2. Blade height = 200 mm. Assuming incompressible flow (fluid density = 1.2 kg/m^3) and neglecting friction calculate the axial and tangential forces on a blade; and the lift coeffcient. Blade chord = 100 mm; pitch = 75 mm. Inlet velocity = 75 m/s in the axial direction. The axial velocity component is constant.

Answer 12.8 N, 50.8 N; 0.73

13 A compressor rotor cascade has blades of pitch 20 mm, height 40 mm, and chord 25 mm. The *blade* angles at inlet and exit are 40° and 20° respectively, measured from the *axial* direction. Blade velocity = 150 m/s. Air density = 1.30 kg/m^3 (constant).

If the incidence = 5° and deviation = 2° determine the angle of deflection of the fluid, change in whirl velocity, the lift and drag coefficients, and cascade efficiency.

The fluid velocity at inlet = 120 m/s (approaching the cascade). Assume incompressible flow. Loss coefficient

$$\frac{\Delta p_o}{\frac{1}{2}\rho v_f^2} = 0.02$$

Answer 23°; 68 m/s; 0.96 and 0.008; 0.97

14 A compressor cascade, of solidity = 1.0, has an outlet fluid angle of 30° (measured from the *axial* direction). C_D = 0.040. The axial flow velocity is constant. Assuming incompressible flow and the lift coefficient at stalling conditions is 0.90 determine the inlet angle.

If the velocity at inlet = 100 m/s, and the fluid density = 1.2 kg/m^3 determine the pressure rise, and circulation around a blade.

Answer Approx. 24°. 4675 N/m^2; 31.7c

15 An axial flow compressor rotor blade is designed to have 40% reaction at the mean blade height. Flow coefficient v_f/u = 0.5. Blade speed, u = 300 m/s. Assuming incompressible flow calculate the static pressure rise across the blade (Fig. 10.28).

Take the air density = 1.2 kg/m^3.

The blade section is on a circular arc camber line and thickness 15%. Chord c = 25 mm, pitch s = 20 mm. $\nu = 1.3 \times 10^{-5}$ m^2/s. Determine the stagger, camber and blade angles.

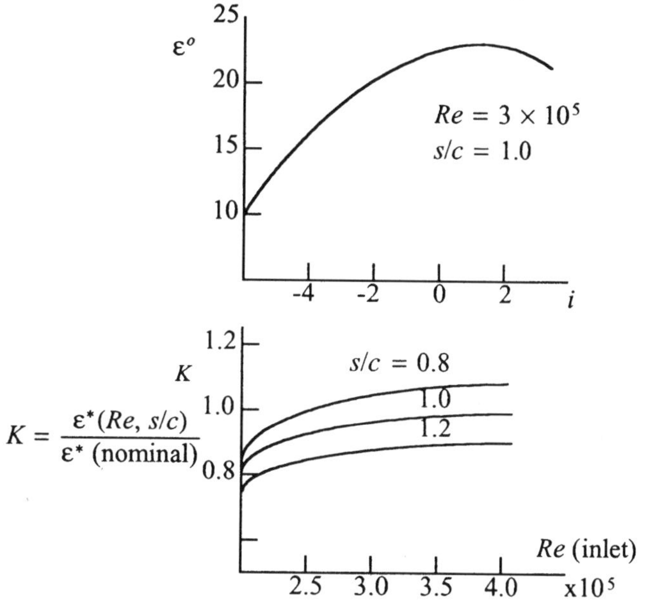

Figure 10.28

Answer 21600 N/m^2. 44° (from axial direction); 35.7°; 37.6 and 73.3° (from tangential direction).

11

Propellers, fans, windmills

Propellers and windmills employ blades having a large pitch, so that the blades can be considered in isolation. The primary object of a screw propeller is the production of thrust from the blade rotation and propellers are widely used in marine vessels, light aircraft, etc. A windmill is essentially a propeller working in reverse: the thrust of the wind generates the rotary motion of the blades. A fan generates a pressure difference from the blade rotation, thereby inducing a flow of the fluid.

Propellers

The *pitch*, s, defined with reference to Fig. 11.1, is one of the important parameters in propeller performance. A point A moves uniformly along the *fixed* axis OZ, while the plane containing OZ and AB rotates uniformly about OZ (β constant). When the plane OAB makes one complete revolution the point A moves a distance s along OZ: this is the *pitch* of the helicoid.

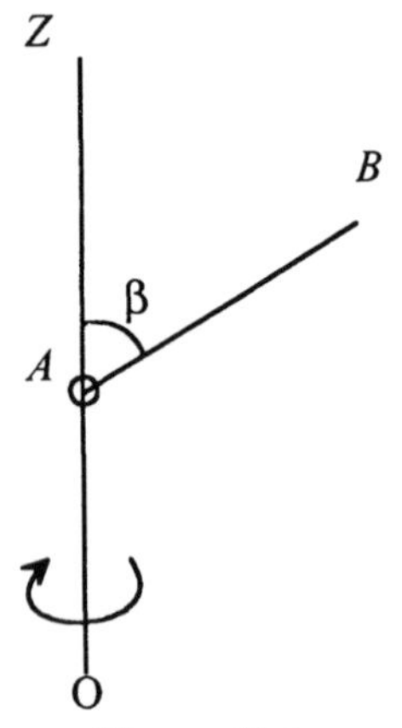

Figure 11.1

Other parameters used include:

slip ratio $= 1 - \dfrac{v}{ns}$

pitch ratio $= \dfrac{s}{D}$

advance ratio $J = \dfrac{v}{nD}$

thrust coefficient $K_F = \dfrac{F}{\rho \Omega^2 D^4}$

torque coefficient $K_T = \dfrac{T}{\rho \Omega^2 D^5}$

efficiency $\eta = \dfrac{Fv}{P} = \dfrac{K_F}{K_T} 2\pi J$

where v = speed of advance relative to undisturbed fluid (m/s)
T = torque (Nm)
D = propeller diameter (m)
n = speed (rev/s) = $\Omega/2\pi$
F = thrust (N)
Ω = rotational speed (rad/s)

A set of typical efficiency curves is shown in Fig. 11.2.

The analysis of a propeller can be approached by *actuator disc* theory or *blade element* theory. The former replaces the propeller by a disc and it is assumed that the thrust/unit area is constant over the disc (Fig. 11.3); there is no rotation in the slip-stream (leaving the disc); and the velocity is continuous throughout the disc. For inviscid, incompressible flow the thrust is given by

$$F = 2a(1 + a)\rho A v^2$$

and efficiency

$$\eta = \frac{1}{1 + a}, \qquad \text{where } a = \text{axial inflow factor} = \frac{v'}{v_\infty}$$

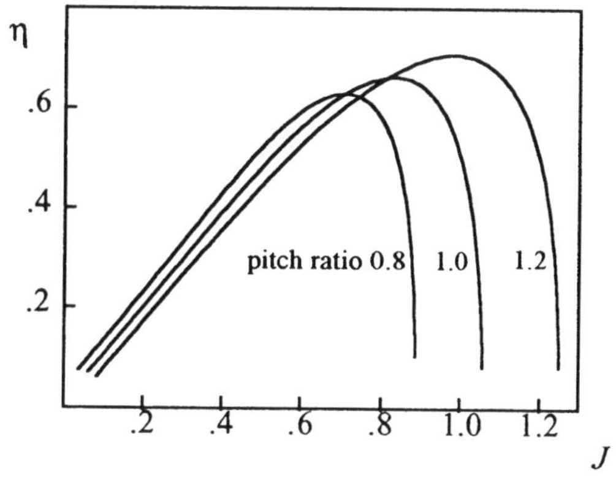

Figure 11.2

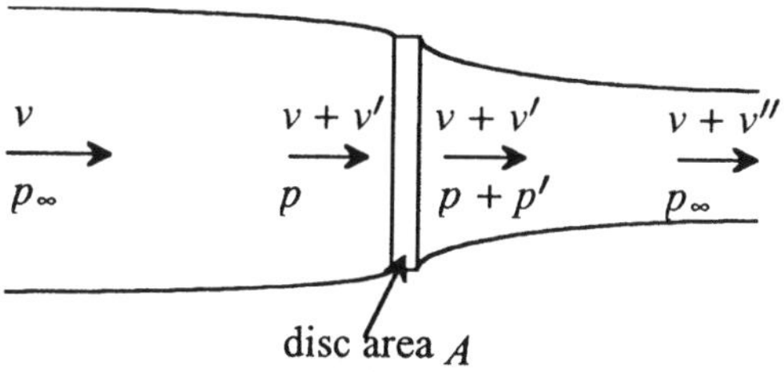

Figure 11.3

The blade element theory uses the forces on a small element of the blade to derive the thrust and torque by integration over the whole blade. For a blade section (Fig. 11.4) at a radius r

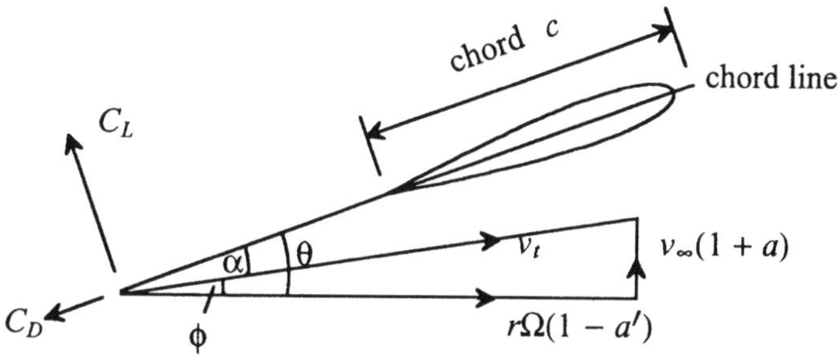

Figure 11.4

$$\frac{dF}{dr} = \rho v_t^2 \pi r\sigma(C_L \cos\phi - C_D \sin\phi) = \rho v_t^2 \pi r\sigma\lambda_1$$

$$\frac{dT}{dr} = \rho v_t^2 \pi r\sigma(C_L \sin\phi + C_D \cos\phi) = \rho v_t^2 \pi r\sigma\lambda_2$$

where σ = solidity.

$$\text{The blade element efficiency} = \frac{1 - a'}{1 + a} \frac{\tan \phi}{\tan(\phi + \varepsilon)}$$

where a, a' = axial and rotational inflow factors

$\varepsilon = \arctan(C_D/C_L)$.

The inflow factors can be determined by the use of *vortex* theory, giving

$$\frac{a}{1 + a} = \frac{\sigma\lambda_1}{2(1 - \cos 2\phi)}, \qquad \frac{a'}{1 - a'} = \frac{\sigma\lambda_2}{2 \sin 2\phi}$$

Windmills

The developing use of renewable energy sources has led to a wide variety of windmills now employed. The earliest types used flat blades (Dutch, farm) and were designed for irrigation (water raising), milling and crushing, rather than power generation. More modern types include the Savonius, Darrieus, giromill, ducted rotor, high speed two-blade and multi-blade (Fig. 11.5, 11.6).

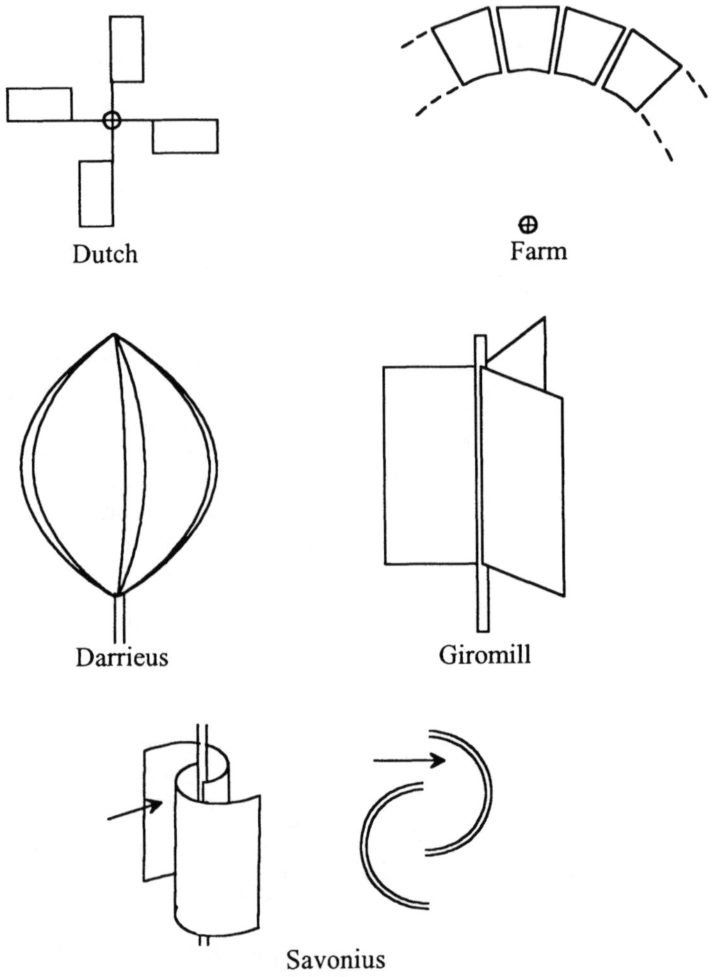

Figure 11.5

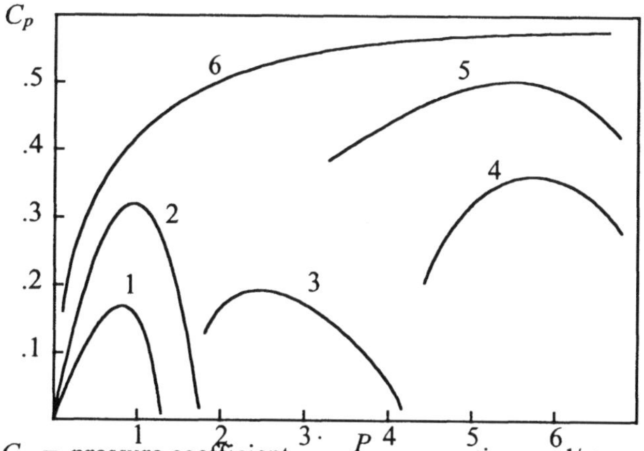

C_p = pressure coefficient = $\frac{P}{\frac{1}{2}\rho A v_\infty^3}$ tip speed/stream speed

1. Multi-blade
2. Savonius
3. Dutch
4. Darrieus
5. High-speed two blade
6. Ideal propeller

Figure 11.6

The earliest analysis (Rankine-Froude) was based on momentum theory (Fig. 11.7):

$$T = \dot{m}(v_\infty - v_1) = \rho A v(v_\infty \; v_1), \qquad F = A\,\Delta p = \tfrac{1}{2}\rho A(v_\infty^2 - v_1^2)$$

hence $v = \frac{1}{2}(v_\infty + v_1)$, $\qquad P = \frac{1}{2}\rho A v(v_\infty^2 - v_1^2)$

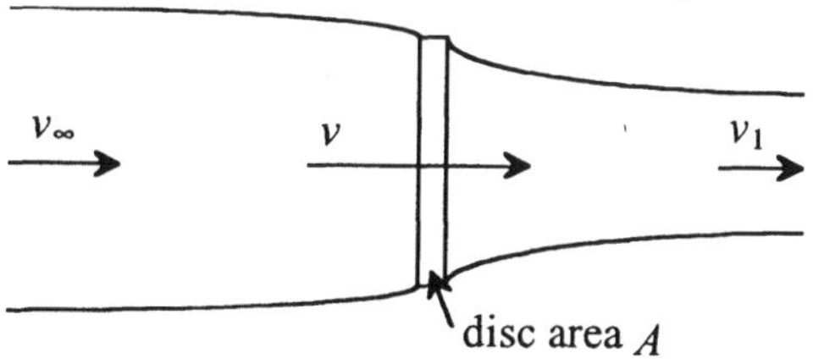

Figure 11.7

or the power coefficient

$$C_p = \frac{P}{\frac{1}{2}\rho A v_\infty^3} = 4a(1-a)^2, \qquad \text{where } a = 1 - \frac{v}{v_\infty}.$$

$$\text{The efficiency} = \frac{P}{\frac{1}{2}\rho A v\, v_\infty^2} = 4a(1-a).$$

11.1 Windmill performance

A windmill has two blades, tip-to-top diameter 10 m. The free stream air velocity = 20 m/s. The air conditions (static) are 20°C, 1.01 bar. The air velocity downstream of the windmill = 18 m/s. Calculate the thrust, power output and overall efficiency using one-dimensional theory.

Solution. Consider a *large* control volume as shown in Fig. 11.8: then $p_1 = p_4$.

Assuming incompressible flow the Bernoulli equation gives

$$p_1 + \tfrac{1}{2}\rho v_1^2 = p_2 + \tfrac{1}{2}\rho v_2^2 \qquad \text{and} \qquad p_3 + \tfrac{1}{2}\rho v_3^2 = p_4 + \tfrac{1}{2}\rho v_4^2$$

Since $v_2 = v_3 = v_m$ then $p_3 - p_2 = \frac{1}{2}\rho(v_4^2 - v_1^2)$

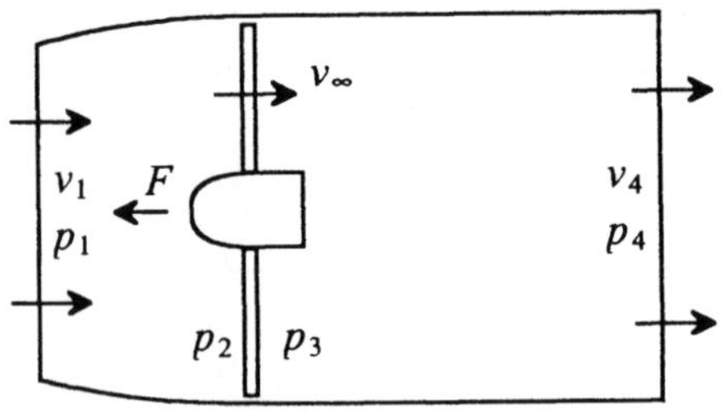

Figure 11.8

The momentum equation gives

$$F = (p_2 - p_3)A = \dot{m}(v_1 - v_4) \text{ and so } (p_3 - p_2) = \rho v_m(v_4 - v_1)$$

since $\dot{m} = \rho A v_m$

Hence $p_3 - p_2 = \rho v_m(v_4 - v_1) = \frac{1}{2}\rho(v_4^2 - v_1^2)$ and $v_m = \frac{1}{2}(v_1 + v_4)$

The power input (or available) is $v_m = \frac{1}{2}(v_1 + v_4)$

$$\dot{m}(\tfrac{1}{2}\rho v_1^2) = \tfrac{1}{2}\rho A v_1^3$$

Hence the efficiency

$$\eta = \frac{\frac{1}{2}\rho A v_m(v_1^2 - v_4^2)}{\frac{1}{2}\rho A v_1^3} = \frac{v_m(v_1^2 - v_4^2)}{v_1^3} = \frac{(v_1 + v_4)(v_1^2 - v_4^2)}{2v_1^3}$$

In this specific problem $v_1 = 20$, $v_4 = 18$ m/s, $v_m = 19$ m/s,

$$\rho = \frac{1.01 \times 10^5}{(287 \times 293)} = 1.20 \text{ kg/m}^3$$

disc area $A = \frac{1}{4}\pi(10)^2 = 78.54$ m^2

Substituting the data gives

thrust $F = \rho A v_m(v_4 - v_1) = 1.20(78.54)(19)(-2) = \mathbf{-3581}$ N

$$\text{efficiency} = \frac{(20 + 18)(400 - 324)}{2(20)^3} = \mathbf{0.18}$$

power output $= \eta \frac{1}{2}\rho A v_1^3$

$= 0.18(\frac{1}{2})(1.20)(78.54)(20)^3$ W $= \mathbf{67.86}$ kW

Note. The efficiency is a function of the ratio v_4/v_1, and it can be shown that it has a maximum value of 16/27.

11.2 Actuator disc theory

Show how the actuator disc theory can be applied to a propeller. Assuming inviscid, incompressible flow show that the efficiency $= 1/(1 + a)$ where a is the axial inflow factor.

Outline how the method can be applied to a windmill, and that the maximum efficiency is 16/27.

Solution

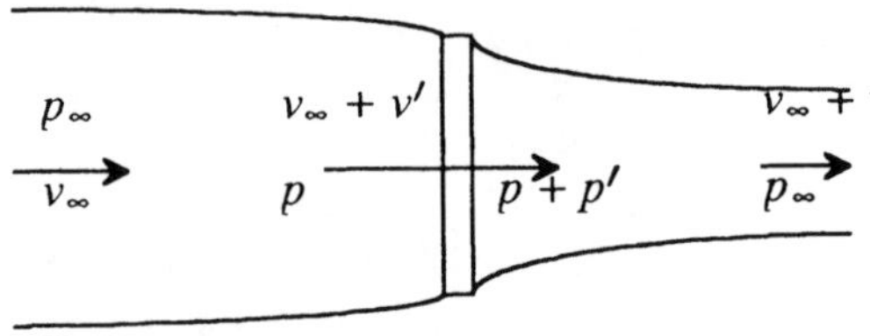

Figure 11.9

The actuator disc is equivalent to the propeller in producing a pressure change (Fig. 11.9). The *simple* theory assumes a constant change (and therefore thrust) /m^2, continuous velocity through the disc, and *no* rotational velocity in the slip-stream. In practice the rotation in the wake is in the direction of rotation of the propeller (and in the opposite direction for a windmill).

The Bernoulli equation gives

$$p + \tfrac{1}{2}\rho(v_\infty + v')^2 = p_\infty + \tfrac{1}{2}\rho v_\infty^2 \qquad \text{upstream of the disc}$$

$$p + p' + \tfrac{1}{2}\rho(v_\infty + v')^2 = p_\infty + \tfrac{1}{2}\rho(v_\infty + v_o)^2 \qquad \text{downstream of the disc}$$

Hence $p' = \tfrac{1}{2}\rho(v_\infty + v_o)^2 - \tfrac{1}{2}\rho v_\infty^2 = \rho v_o(v_\infty + \tfrac{1}{2}v_o)$

The thrust

$$F = p'A = \rho A v_o(v_\infty + \tfrac{1}{2}v_o)$$

The momentum equation, for steady flow, gives

$$F = \rho A v_o(v_\infty + v')$$

Thus $\boldsymbol{v' = \tfrac{1}{2}v_o}$

Introducing the axial inflow factor,

$$a = \frac{v'}{v_\infty}$$

$$F = \rho A v_o(v_\infty + \tfrac{1}{2}v_o) = 2\rho A v'(v_\infty + v') = 2a(1 + a)\rho A v_\infty^2$$

Efficiency

$$\eta = \frac{F v_\infty}{F v_\infty + \tfrac{1}{2}\dot{m} v_o^2} = \frac{2a(1 + a)\rho A v_\infty^3}{2a(1 + a)\rho A v_\infty^3 + \tfrac{1}{2}\rho A(v_\infty + v')v_o^2}$$

which reduces to

$$\eta = \frac{1}{1 + a}$$

For a windmill the efficiency is now

$$\eta = \frac{\text{power output } P}{\tfrac{1}{2}\rho A v_\infty^3} = 2\rho v'(v_\infty - v')A\,\frac{(v_\infty - v')}{\tfrac{1}{2}\rho A v_\infty^3}$$

$$= 4\left(\frac{v'}{v_\infty}\right)\left(1 - \frac{v'}{v_\infty}\right)^2$$

Introducing the inflow factor a

$$\eta = 4a(1 - a)^2$$

The efficiency is a maximum when $d\eta/da = 0$,

$$\boldsymbol{a = \tfrac{1}{3}} \quad \text{and} \quad \eta_{max} = \tfrac{4}{3}(\tfrac{2}{3})^2 = \boldsymbol{\frac{16}{27}}$$

Note. In the previous example

$$a = 1 - \frac{19}{20}\frac{1}{20}, \qquad \eta = 4\left(\frac{1}{20}\right)\left(\frac{19}{20}\right)^2 = 0.17$$

11.3 Vortex theory

Briefly outline the vortex theory of a propeller, and show how the inflow factors can be derived in terms of the blade geometry and lift and drag coefficients.

Show that the advance ratio at a radius r is given by the equation

$$J = \left(\frac{\pi r}{r_t}\right)\left(\frac{1 - a'}{1 + a}\right)\tan\phi \qquad \text{where } r_t = \text{tip radius.}$$

Solution. As the problem infers vortex theory enables the inflow factors to be determined for use in blade element theory. The vortex theory assumes that the induced flow at a radius r depends only on the thrust and torque at that radius; the induced axial inflow is half the free stream axial velocity (as in the simple actuator disc theory); and the induced *rotational* inflow velocity is half the circumferential velocity in the slip-stream.

A further assumption is that the trailing vortices from a blade element are helical, of pitch equal to the screw advance/revolution.

Consider an annulus of the actuator disc at radius r, width dr.

$$\text{mass flow rate} = \rho\, 2\pi r\, dr\, v_\infty(1 + a)$$

$$\text{downstream velocity} = 2av_\infty$$

$$\text{thrust } dF = 4\pi\rho a r\, dr(1 + a)v_\infty^2$$

Referring to Fig.11.4.

$$\text{lift } dL = \tfrac{1}{2}\rho c v_t^2\, C_L\, dr$$

$$\text{drag } dD = \tfrac{1}{2}\rho c v_t^2\, C_D\, dr$$

where $v_t^2 = (1 + a)^2 v_\infty^2 + (1 - a')^2 r^2 \Omega^2$

Also $\dfrac{dF}{dr} = \tfrac{1}{2}\rho c v_t^2 (C_L \cos\phi - C_D \sin\phi) = \tfrac{1}{2}\rho v_t^2 c\lambda_1$

$$dF = \tfrac{1}{2}\rho c\lambda_1\, v_\infty^2 (1 + a)^2 \operatorname{cosec}^2\phi\, dr$$

Comparing with the equation

$$dF = 4\pi\rho a v_\infty^2 (1 + a) r\, dr$$

gives $\tfrac{1}{2}c\lambda_1(1 + a)\operatorname{cosec}^2\phi = 4\pi a r$

$$\frac{c\lambda_1}{8\pi r}\operatorname{cosec}^2\phi = \frac{a}{1 + a} = \frac{1}{4}\sigma\lambda_1 \operatorname{cosec}^2\phi$$

where $\sigma = \text{solidity} = \dfrac{c}{2\pi r}$

Hence $a = \dfrac{\tfrac{1}{4}\sigma\lambda_1 \operatorname{cosec}^2\phi}{1 - \tfrac{1}{4}\sigma\lambda_1 \operatorname{cosec}^2\phi}$

The tangential velocity of inflow is $a' r\Omega$. Now

torque = rate of change of angular momentum

hence $dT = 2\pi\rho r v_\infty(1 + a)\, dr\, 2r\Omega a' r = 4\pi\rho v_\infty \Omega a'(1 + a) r^3\, dr$

but $dT = \tfrac{1}{2}\rho r c v_t^2 \lambda_2\, dr$, where $v_t = r\Omega(1 - a')\sec\phi$

Comparing the equations

$$\frac{a'(1 + a)\cos^2\phi}{(1 - a')^2} = \frac{c\Omega\lambda_2}{8\pi v_\infty}$$

Using the relationship

$$v_t = r\Omega(1 - a')\sec\phi = v_\infty(1 + a)\operatorname{cosec}\phi$$

gives $\dfrac{a'}{1 - a'} = \dfrac{1}{4}\sigma\lambda_2 \sec\phi \operatorname{cosec}\phi$

or $a' = \dfrac{\tfrac{1}{4}\sigma\lambda_2 \sec\phi \operatorname{cosec}\phi}{1 + \tfrac{1}{4}\sigma\lambda_2 \sec\phi \operatorname{cosec}\phi}$

Referring to Fig. 11.4

$$\tan\phi = \frac{(1 + a)v_\infty}{(1 - a')r\Omega} = \frac{1 + a}{1 - a'}\frac{r_t}{\pi r}J$$

where $J = \text{advance ratio} = \dfrac{v_\infty}{2\pi r_t}$

hence $J = \pi\left(\frac{r}{r_t}\right)\left(\frac{1-a'}{1+a}\right)\tan\phi$

11.4 Vortex theory calculation

> An airscrew is 4 m diameter, and has 4 blades. At a radius of 1.5 m the blade chord is 300 mm, and the blade angle 25°. The local angle of incidence is 4°; $C_L = 0.60$, $C_D = 0.03$. The free stream velocity is 60 m/s. The air density is constant at 1.20 kg/m³.
>
> Using vortex theory determine the advance ratio J, the thrust and torque gradients at the section, and the rotational speed of the airscrew.

Solution. Referring to Fig. 11.4 the angles in this problem are $\theta = 25°$, $\alpha = 4°$ hence $\phi = 21°$. Using the equations from the previous example,

$$\lambda_1 = C_L\cos\phi - C_D\sin\phi = 0.6(0.9460) - 0.03(0.3239) = 0.558$$

$$\sigma = \frac{4c}{2\pi r} \quad \text{(since there are 4 blades)} \quad = \frac{4(0.3)}{2\pi(1.5)} = 0.127$$

$$a = \frac{\frac{1}{4}(0.127)(0.558)(9.531)}{1 - \frac{1}{4}(0.127)(0.558)(9.531)} = 0.203$$

$$\lambda_2 = C_L\sin\phi + C_D\cos\phi = 0.223$$

$$a' = \frac{\frac{1}{4}(0.127)(0.223)(1.057)(3.087)}{1 + 0.023} = 0.023$$

The advance ratio

$$J = \pi\left(\frac{r}{r_t}\right)\left(\frac{1-a'}{1+a}\right)\tan\phi = \pi\left(\frac{1.5}{2.0}\right)\left(\frac{0.977}{1.203}\right)0.342 = \mathbf{0.655}$$

The thrust gradient

$$\frac{dF}{dr} = 4\pi\rho a v_\infty^2(1+a)r = 4\pi(1.2)(0.203)(60)^2(1.203)(1.5)$$

$$= \mathbf{19886}\ \text{N/m}$$

The torque gradient

$$\frac{dT}{dr} = 4\pi\rho v_\infty \Omega a'(1+a)r^3 = 84.49\Omega$$

Now $(1-a')r\Omega\tan\phi = v_\infty(1+a)$

giving $$\Omega = \frac{60(1.203)}{0.977(1.5)(0.342)} = 143.8 \text{ rad/s} = \mathbf{22.9} \text{ rev/s}$$

$$\frac{dT}{dr} = \mathbf{12150}\ \text{Nm/m}$$

Note. The blade efficiency at this radius is

$$\frac{v_\infty}{2\pi n}\frac{dF}{dT} = \frac{60}{2\pi(22.9)}\frac{19886}{12150} = \mathbf{0.68}$$

11.5 Axial flow fan

> An axial flow fan has a hub diameter = 44 cm, tip diameter = 76 cm. Rotational speed = 1450 rev/min. Air flow = 5.7 m³/s against a pressure rise of 500 N/m². At the mean radius $C_L = 0.60$, $C_D = 0.027$ and the solidity = 0.80. There are four blades.
>
> Assuming that the air density is constant and equal to 1.2 kg/m³, C_L/C_D is the same for both rotor and stator, and zero incidence and deviation determine the blade angles, and blade chord at the mean radius. The stator is downstream of the rotor.

Solution. The velocity triangles are shown in Fig. 11.10.

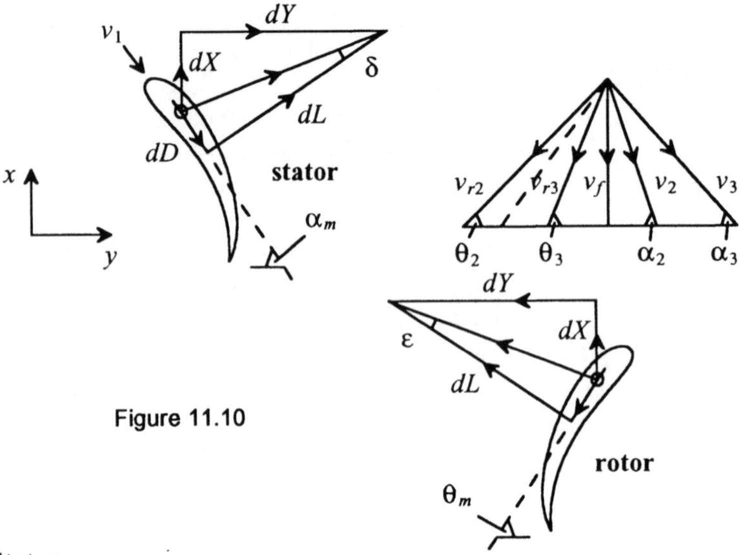

Figure 11.10

Stator

For an element dr, at radius r, the force and momentum equations give

$$dX = (p_2 - p_1)s\,dr$$

$$dY = \rho s v_f(v_{w2} - v_{w1})\,dr \qquad \text{(Chap.10)}$$

where s = pitch between the blades = $2\pi r/4$

Hence $$\frac{dY}{dX} = \frac{\rho v_f(v_{w2} - v_{w1})}{p_2 - p_1} = \tan(\alpha_m + \delta)$$

$$p_2 - p_1 = \rho v_f(v_{w2} - v_{w1})\cot(\alpha_m + \delta)$$

Since δ is small ($0.027/0.6 = 0.045$), $\tan\delta \approx \delta$

$$\tan(\alpha_m + \delta) \approx \frac{\tan\alpha_m + \delta}{1 - \delta\tan\alpha_m} \quad \text{also} \quad \tan\alpha_m = \frac{v_f}{v_{wm}} = \frac{v_f}{\frac{1}{2}(v_{w2} + v_{w3})}$$

Introducing the ratios

$$\phi = \frac{v_f}{u}, \qquad \psi = \frac{v_w}{u}$$

$$p_2 - p_1 = \rho u^2\phi(\psi_3 - \psi_2)\left[\left(1 - \frac{2\delta\phi}{\psi_2 + \psi_3}\right)\Big/\left(\frac{2\phi}{\psi_2 + \psi_3} + \delta\right)\right]$$

Rotor

A similar analysis, with angles θ instead of α, gives

$$\frac{dY}{dX} = \frac{\rho v_f(v_{r2}\cos\theta_2 - v_{r3}\cos\theta_3)}{p_3 - p_2} = \tan(\theta_m + \varepsilon)$$

$$\tan\theta_m = \frac{v_f}{\frac{1}{2}(v_{r2}\cos\theta_2 + v_{r3}\cos\theta_3)} = \frac{2v_f}{(u - v_{w2}) + (u - v_{w3})}$$

$$= \frac{2\phi}{2 - \psi_2 - \psi_3}$$

and $$p_3 - p_2 = \rho u^2\phi(\psi_3 - \psi_2)\frac{2 - \psi_2 - \psi_3 - 2\varepsilon\phi}{2\phi + \varepsilon(2 - \psi_2 - \psi_3)}$$

In this problem

mean radius = $\frac{1}{2}(22 + 38) = 30$ cm

$$\text{blade speed } u = \frac{2\pi(0.3)(1450)}{60} = 45.55 \text{ m/s}$$

$$\text{flow velocity } v_f = \frac{5.7}{\pi(0.38^2 - 0.22^2)} = 18.90 \text{ m/s}$$

$$\phi = \frac{v_f}{u} = 0.415$$

For both rotor and stator $\delta = \varepsilon = 0.045$, and the pressure difference is 500 N/m^2.

Hence $p_3 - p_1 = 500 = (p_2 - p_1) + (p_3 - p_2)$

$$= 1.2(45.55)^2(0.415)\left[(\psi_3 - \psi_2)\frac{\psi_2 + \psi_3 - 2\delta\phi}{2\phi + (\psi_2 + \psi_3)\delta} + (\psi_3 - \psi_2)\frac{2 - \psi_2 - \psi_3 - 2\varepsilon\phi}{2\phi + \varepsilon(2 - \psi_2 - \psi_3)}\right]$$

$$= 1033\left[(\psi_3 - \psi_2)\left(\frac{\psi_2 + \psi_3 - 0.037}{0.045(\psi_2 + \psi_3) + 0.830}\right) + (\psi_3 - \psi_2)\frac{2 - \psi_2 - \psi_3 - 0.037}{0.920 - 0.045(\psi_2 + \psi_3)}\right]$$

The lift coefficient C_L can now be used to obtain another equation for the two unknown values of ψ.

$$dY = dL\frac{\sin(\theta_m + \varepsilon)}{\cos\varepsilon} \approx dL(\sin\theta_m + \varepsilon\cos\theta_m)$$

but $\quad dL = C_L \frac{1}{2}\rho v_{rm}^2 c\, dr \quad$ and $\quad dY = \rho s v_f(v_{w3} - v_{w2})\, dr$

Equating and simplifying gives

$$\sigma C_L = \frac{4(\psi_2 + \psi_3)\phi}{[\phi + \varepsilon(2 - \psi_2 - \psi_3)][4\phi^2 + (2 - \psi_2 - \psi_3)^2]^{1/2}}$$

Substituting the numerical data

$$0.8(0.6) = \frac{1.66(\psi_2 + \psi_3)}{[0.505 - 0.045(\psi_2 + \psi_3)][0.689 + (2 - \psi_2 - \psi_3)^2]^{1/2}}$$

There are now two equations for the two unknowns ψ_2, ψ_3. The solution is somewhat tedious. The equations can be expressed in terms of

$$a = \psi_2 + \psi_3, \qquad b = \psi_3 - \psi_2$$

as

$$\frac{b(a - 0.037)}{0.045a + 0.830} + \frac{b(1.963 - a)}{0.920 - 0.045a} = 0.484$$

and

$$(0.505 - 0.045a)[0.689 + (2 - a)^2]^{1/2} = 3.458a$$

Solving the second equation by trial-and-error (starting with $a = 0.30$) gives, after a few trials, $a = 0.273$.

The first equation then gives $b = 0.226$.

Hence $\psi_2 = 0.024$, $\psi_3 = 0.250$ and $v_{w2} = u\psi_2 = 1.09, v_{w3} = 11.40$ m/s.

The blade angles are:

stator $\quad \alpha_1 = \arctan\frac{v_f}{v_{w2}} = \mathbf{96.3°}, \qquad \alpha_2 = \arctan\frac{v_f}{v_{w3}} = \mathbf{65.4°}$

rotor $\quad \theta_2 = \arctan\frac{v_f}{(u - v_{w2})} = \mathbf{25.6°}, \qquad \theta_3 = \arctan\frac{v_f}{(u - v_{w3})} = \mathbf{35.2°}$

The chord is determined directly from the value of the solidity,

$$\sigma = 0.8 = \frac{c}{s}$$

where $\quad$ pitch, $s = \frac{2\pi r}{4} = 0.471$ m

giving $\quad$ chord, $c =$ **0.377** m

Note. It has been assumed that the flow velocity v_f is constant across the annulus. This is a reasonable assumption, particularly for turbulent flow (with a fairly flat velocity profile) except, of course, near the tips. The edge effect is clearly more pronounced if the fan is ducted.

Problems

1 Show that the thrust /m of an element of a propeller blade at a radius r is given by the equation

$$\frac{dF}{dr} = 4\pi\rho r v_\infty^2 \frac{a(1+a)}{N}$$

where a = axial inflow factor, N = number of blades.

A three-bladed propeller rotates at 1500 rev/min with a forward speed of 60 m/s. The thrust produced is 3000 N/m. The element radius = 1.2 m. Chord = 180 mm. C_D = 0.01. Air density = 1.2 kg/m^3. Calculate the element efficiency and lift coefficient.

Answer 0.67, 2.86.

2 Show that the efficiency of a propeller can be expressed as

$$\frac{K_F}{K_T} 2\pi J$$

where K_F, K_T are the thrust and torque coefficients, and J is the advance ratio.

Test results for a model propeller of unit pitch ratio were as follows:

J	0.5	0.6	0.7	0.8	0.9	1.0	1.112
K_F	0.231	0.198	0.165	0.130	0.093	0.050	0.000
K_T	0.0345	0.0309	0.0270	0.0225	0.0174	0.0117	

Plot a graph of efficiency against slip ratio.

3 A three-bladed propeller, diameter 3.6 m, propels an aeroplane at a velocity of 130 m/s. The advance ratio J = 1.83. The thrust on each blade, at a radius of 1.37 m, is 1770 N/m. At this radius the solidity of the annulus is 0.10, and the blade sections have a zero lift incidence of -1°. Neglecting rotational interference determine the corresponding blade angle.

Answer 36.6°

4 Derive expressions for the thrust and torque gradients at a radius r using
(a) momentum theory
(b) blade element characteristics with vortex theory.

A three-bladed propeller rotates at 1600 rev/min. Forward

speed is 130 m/s. Calculate the blade angle at a radius of 1.4 m if the thrust gradient /blade = 6000 N/m, blade chord = 30 cm.

Neglect rotational inflow, and assume that

$$C_L = 0.1(\alpha + 2), \qquad C_D = 0.01.$$

Answer 15.55°

5 Derive expressions for the thrust and torque gradients of an airscrew blade element in the form

$$\frac{dF}{dr} = \frac{1}{2}\rho C_L v^2 c \cos(\phi + \alpha), \quad \frac{dT}{dr} = \frac{1}{2}\rho C_L v^2 cr \sin(\phi + \alpha)$$

Hence show that the axial and rotational interference factors a, a' can be obtained from the equations

$$\frac{a}{1+a} = \frac{1}{4}\sigma C_L \frac{\cos(\phi + \alpha)}{\sin^2\phi}, \quad \frac{a'}{1-a'} = \frac{1}{4}\sigma C_L \frac{\sin(\phi + \alpha)}{\sin\phi \cos\phi}.$$

Also show that the blade efficiency is given by

$$\eta = \frac{1-a'}{1+a}\frac{\tan\phi}{\tan(\phi + \alpha)}.$$

6 An axial flow fan, with no guide vanes, passes 12.5 m^3/s of air. Rotational speed = 1500 rev/min. Pressure rise = 30 mm water gauge. Air density = 1.2 kg/m^3. Efficiency = 75%. Hub diameter = 300 mm, tip diameter = 1.0 m.

Determine the blade angles and lift coefficient at the hub, mean and tip radii.

Answer 63.0°, 37.5°; 0.87
22.8°, 19.6°; 0.72
13.2°, 12.6°; 0.58.

7 Derive the following results for the *optimum* operation of a propeller type windmill. Neglect interference effects from neighbouring elements and assume that half of the total reduction in the wind velocity is realised at the propeller disc.

$$a = \frac{1}{1 + 2\sec\phi}, \qquad \sigma C_L = 4(1 - \cos\phi)$$

Derive an expression for the local tip speed ratio

$$x = \frac{r\Omega}{V_\infty}$$

in terms of ϕ.

Answer $$x = \frac{(2\cos\phi - 1)(\cos\phi + 1)}{\sin\phi(1 + 2\cos\phi)}$$

8 A windmill has two blades, tip-to-tip diameter 10 m. The free stream air velocity = 20 m/s. Air temperature = 20°C, static pressure = 1.01 bar. The thrust on the blades is 3580 N. Assuming one-dimensional theory calculate the velocity downstream of the windmill, power output and overall

efficiency.

By use of aerofoil theory show that on a blade element at radius r the pressure difference is given by the equation

$$\Delta p = \frac{N\rho c v_{rm}^2}{4\pi r}(C_L \cos\beta + C_D \sin\beta)$$

where N = number of blades, and v_{rn} = mean velocity over the blade at an angle β to the tangential direction.

Answer 18 m/s, 68 kW, 18%.

Appendix: Computer programs for the generation of Flow Tables

The following programs are designed to generate a variety of Flow Tables, in particular:

Table 1: Isentropic flow of dry air with Prandtl-Meyer expansion angles;
Table 2: Frictionless flow of dry air in a constant area duct with heat transfer;
Table 3: Adiabatic flow of dry air in a constant area duct with surface friction;
Table 4: Flow of dry air through a plane normal shock wave.

The program is written using the Microsoft Corporation's QBasic, as provided with many personal computers and those using MS-DOS v5 in particular. Non-standard constructs have been avoided to allow the potential use of any other version of the BASIC language.

Program description

The following documentation applies to all four programs as they have been constructed in an identical manner. Where procedures vary, the relevant table details have been added.

Each program consists of the following sections

1.	main	
2.	file opening	fileopen
3.	file closing	fileclose
4.	variable declaration	vars
5.	title printing	heads
6.	calculated values printing	printval
7.	calculated	calcul

MAIN	This section just calls all the other subroutines
FILEOPEN	This routine opens the relevant files i.e. table1.dat, table2.dat, table3.dat and table4.dat, then returns to the calling procedure (main).
FILECLOSE	This routine closes the files after they have been written to, then returns to the calling procedure (main).
VARS	Table I and IV have all the relevant variables declared, whereas Tables II and III require user input for the variable Cp. The request is in the form of two print statements and one Input statement. It then returns to the calling procedure (main).
HEADS	This procedure prints out the relevant table number and name then returns to the calling procedure (main).

PRINTVAL — This procedure works in the form of a loop with variable M (M1 for table IV) having certain specified values (these values are alterable). The loop consists of a call to the subroutine CALCUL and subsequent printing of results. This is straightforward for Tables III and IV, but Table I will produces no values for mu or nu where m <1 so an additional conditional statement has been used to ensure correctness. Table II will produce no values for m=0 for the variable eqn5 so the solution of infinity has been manually entered.

CALCUL — With all four programs, the calculated values eqn1 thru' eqn5 relate to the values specified in the HEADS routine. i.e. TABLE I eqn1 equates to po/p, Table II eqn2 equates to p/p and so on. As before, Tables III and IV are straightforward, but the anomalies which exist for Tables I and II are repeated. Table I duplicates the values for eqn1, eqn2 and eqn3 to cater for mu and nu. Also, the value of nu is converted from radians to degrees. Table II eliminates the possibility of eqn5 being calculated to produce a "division by zero" error by not calculating it when m=0. On completion of the calculation, the procedure then returns to the calling procedure (printval).

Table 1

```
REM              TABLE I
REM    **************MAIN SECTION*************************
GOSUB fileopen
GOSUB vars
GOSUB heads
GOSUB printval
GOSUB fileclose
PRINT "Output  now produced, check file for results!"
END
REM    **************END OF MAIN SECTION*******************
fileopen:
OPEN "table1.dat" FOR OUTPUT AS #1
RETURN
fileclose:
CLOSE #1
RETURN
vars:
gamma = 1.403
pi = 3.14159
b = ((gamma + 1) / (gamma - 1)) ^ .5
k = (gamma + 1) / (2 * (gamma - 1))
RETURN
heads:
PRINT #1, "                    Table I    "
PRINT #1,
PRINT  #1,  "     ISENTROPIC   FLOW   OF   AIR   (GAMMA=1.403)   WITH
PRANDTL-MEYER ANGLES"
PRINT #1,
PRINT #1,
PRINT #1, "       M     po/p   To/T   A/A*   mu     nu"
PRINT #1,
RETURN
printval:
```

```
FOR m = .45 TO 1.5 STEP .01
GOSUB calcul
PRINT #1, "      ";
PRINT #1, USING "##.## "; m;
PRINT #1, USING "##.### "; eqn1;
PRINT #1, USING "##.### "; eqn2;
PRINT #1, USING "##.### "; eqn3;
IF m < 1! THEN
PRINT #1, "     ";
PRINT #1, "     "
ELSE
PRINT #1, USING "##.## "; eqn4;
PRINT #1, USING "##.## "; eqn5
END IF
NEXT m
RETURN
calcul:
IF m < 1 THEN
eqn1 = (1 + .5 * (gamma - 1) * m ^ 2) ^ (gamma / (gamma - 1))
eqn2 = 1 + .5 * (gamma - 1) * m ^ 2
eqn3 = (1 / m) * ((2 + (gamma - 1) * m ^ 2) / (gamma + 1)) ^ k
RETURN
ELSE
eqn1 = (1 + .5 * (gamma - 1) * m ^ 2) ^ (gamma / (gamma - 1))
eqn2 = 1 + .5 * (gamma - 1) * m ^ 2
eqn3 = (1 / m) * ((2 + (gamma - 1) * m ^ 2) / (gamma + 1)) ^ k
eqn4 = (180 / pi) * ATN((1 / m) / ((1 - (1 / m) ^ 2) ^ .5))
radeqn5 = b * (ATN(((m ^ 2 - 1) ^ .5) / b)) - ATN((m ^ 2 - 1) ^ .5)
eqn5 = radeqn5 * 180 / pi
END IF
RETURN
```

Table 2

```
REM                TABLE II
REM *********************MAIN SECTION**********************
CLS
GOSUB fileopen
GOSUB vars
GOSUB heads
GOSUB printval
GOSUB fileclose
PRINT "Output  now produced, check file for results!"
END
REM    ****************END OF MAIN SECTION*****************
fileopen:
OPEN "table2.dat" FOR OUTPUT AS #1
RETURN
fileclose:
CLOSE #1
RETURN
vars:
PRINT "type in a value for Cp (-2 < Cp < 2)  e.g. .24"
PRINT "then press return"
INPUT Cp
gamma = 1.403
n = gamma / (gamma - 1)
RETURN
heads:
```

```
PRINT #1, "          Table  II    Rayleigh flow "
PRINT #1,
PRINT #1,
PRINT #1, "  M      p/p*     T/T*      To/To*    po/po*   Deltas"
PRINT #1,
RETURN
printval:
FOR m = 0! TO .89 STEP .01
GOSUB calcul
PRINT #1, USING "##.##  "; m;
PRINT #1, USING "##.####  "; eqn1;
PRINT #1, USING "##.#####  "; eqn2;
PRINT #1, USING "##.#####  "; eqn3;
PRINT #1, USING "##.####  "; eqn4;
IF m = 0 THEN
PRINT #1, "  inf"
ELSE
PRINT #1, USING "##.#####  "; eqn5
END IF
NEXT m
RETURN
calcul:
eqn1 = (1 + gamma) / (1 + gamma * m ^ 2)
eqn2 = m ^ 2 * ((1 + gamma) / (1 + gamma * m ^ 2)) ^ 2
eqn3 = ((2 + (gamma - 1) * m ^ 2) / (gamma + 1)) * eqn2
eqn4 = ((2 + ((gamma - 1) * m ^ 2)) / (gamma + 1)) ^ n * eqn1
IF m = 0 THEN
RETURN
ELSE
eqn5 = Cp * (LOG(eqn2) + ((1 / n) * (LOG(1 / eqn1))))
END IF
RETURN
```

Table 3

```
REM                          TABLE III
REM ***************MAIN SECTION***************************
GOSUB fileopen
GOSUB VARS
GOSUB heads
GOSUB printval
GOSUB fileclose
PRINT "Output  now produced, check file for results!"
END
REM**************END OF MAIN SECTION************
fileopen:
OPEN "table3.dat" FOR OUTPUT AS #1
RETURN
fileclose:
CLOSE #1
RETURN
VARS:
PRINT "Type in a value for Cp  (-2 < Cp < 2)  e.g 0.24"
PRINT "then press return"
INPUT Cp
pi = 3.14159
k = (gamma + 1) / (2 * (gamma - 1))
gamma = 1.403
RETURN
```

```
heads:
PRINT #1,
PRINT #1, "            Table III   Fanno flow "
PRINT #1,
PRINT #1, "                                      -  "
PRINT #1, "  M       p/p*     po/po*   T/T*   4f|x-x*|    Deltas "
PRINT #1, "                                 --------"
PRINT #1, "                                     D"
PRINT #1,
RETURN
printval:
FOR m = .45 TO 1.3 STEP .01
GOSUB calcul
PRINT #1, USING "##.##  "; m;
PRINT #1, USING "##.####  "; eqn1;
PRINT #1, USING "##.####  "; eqn2;
PRINT #1, USING "##.####  "; eqn3;
PRINT #1, USING "##.#####  "; eqn4;
PRINT #1, USING "##.#####  "; eqn5
NEXT m
RETURN
calcul:
eqn1 = ((gamma + 1) / (2 + (gamma - 1) * m ^ 2)) ^ .5 / m
eqn2 = (1 / m) * ((2 + (gamma - 1) * m ^ 2) / (gamma + 1)) ^ k
eqn3 = (gamma + 1) / (2 + (gamma - 1) * m ^ 2)
eqn4 = (1 / gamma) * ((1 - m ^ 2) / m ^ 2) + ((gamma + 1) / (2 * gamma)) *
(LOG(((gamma + 1) * m ^
2) / (2 + (gamma - 1) * m ^ 2)))
eqn5 = Cp * (LOG(eqn3) + ((gamma - 1) / gamma) * LOG((1 / eqn1)))
RETURN
```

Table 4

```
REM              TABLE IV
REM*****************MAIN SECTION********************
GOSUB fileopen
GOSUB VARS
GOSUB heads
GOSUB printval
GOSUB fileclose
PRINT "Output  now produced, check file for results!"
END
REM*********END OF MAIN SECTION*************
fileopen:
OPEN "table4.dat" FOR OUTPUT AS #1
RETURN
fileclose:
CLOSE #1
RETURN
VARS:
gamma = 1.403
pi = 3.14159
RETURN
heads:
PRINT #1, " "
PRINT #1, "    Table  IV  Normal Shock Waves "
PRINT #1,
PRINT #1, "  M    p2/p1   T2/T1    M2     p2/p1"
PRINT #1,
```

```
RETURN
printval:
FOR m1 = 1.01 TO 1.9 STEP .01
GOSUB calcul
PRINT #1, USING "#.## "; m1;
PRINT #1, USING "#.#### "; eqn1;
PRINT #1, USING "#.#### "; eqn2;
PRINT #1, USING "#.#### "; eqn3;
PRINT #1, USING "#.#### "; eqn4
NEXT m1
RETURN
calcul:
eqn1 = (2 * gamma * m1 ^ 2 / (gamma + 1)) - (gamma - 1) / (gamma + 1)
eqn2 = ((gamma * (2 * m1 ^ 2 - 1) + 1) / (gamma + 1)) * ((2 + ((gamma - 1) * m1 ^
2)) / ((gamma + 1) *
m1 ^ 2))
eqn3 = (((gamma - 1) * m1 ^ 2 + 2) / (gamma * (2 * m1 ^ 2 - 1) + 1)) ^ .5
eqn4 = ((gamma * (2 * m1 ^ 2 - 1) + 1) / (gamma + 1)) * (((2 + (gamma - 1) * eqn3
^ 2) / 2) ^ (gamma /
(gamma - 1)))
RETURN
```

Index